CRC Handbook of Antibiotic Compounds

Author

János Bérdy
Senior Research Fellow
Institute of Drug Research
Budapest Hungary

Contributors

Adjoran Aszalos
Head of Biochemistry, Chemotherapy
Frederick Cancer Research Center
Frederick, Maryland

Melvin Bostian
Manager of Information Systems Department
Frederick Cancer Research Center
Frederick, Maryland

Karen L. McNitt
Senior Programmer
Frederick Cancer Research Center
Frederick, Maryland

Volume I
Carbohydrate Antibiotics

Volume II
Macrocyclic Lactone (Lactam) Antibiotics

Volume III
Quinone and Similar Antibiotics

Volume IV Part 1
Amino Acid and Peptide Antibiotics

Volume IV Part 2
Peptolide and Macromolecular Antibiotics

Volume V
Heterocyclic Antibiotics

Volume VI
Alicyclic, Aromatic, and Aliphatic Antibiotics

Volume VII
Miscellaneous Antibiotics with Unknown Chemical Structure

Volume VIII Parts 1 and 2
Antibiotics from Higher Forms of Life: Higher Plants

Volume IX
Antibiotics from Higher Forms of Life: Lichens, Algae, and Animal Organisms

Volume X
General Indices

CRC Handbook of Antibiotic Compounds

Volume IV Part 1
Amino Acid and Peptide Antibiotics

Author

János Bérdy
Senior Research Fellow
Institute of Drug Research
Budapest, Hungary

Contributors

Adjoran Aszalos
Head of Biochemistry, Chemotherapy
Frederick Cancer Research Center
Frederick, Maryland

Melvin Bostian
Manager of Information Systems Department
Frederick Cancer Research Center
Frederick, Maryland

Karen L. McNitt
Senior Programmer
Frederick Cancer Research Center
Frederick, Maryland

CRC Press, Inc.
Boca Raton, Florida

Library of Congress Cataloging in Publication Data

Bérdy, János.
Handbook of antibiotic compounds.

Includes bibliographical references and indexes.
CONTENTS: v. 1. Carbohydrate antibiotics.—v. 2. Macrocyclic lactone (lactam) antibiotics.—v. 3. Quinone and similar antibiotics.—v. 4(1). Amino acid and peptide antibiotics.—v. 4(2). Peptolide and macromolecular antibiotics.—v. 5. Heterocyclic antibiotics.—v. 6. Alicyclic, aromatic, and aliphatic antibiotics.—v. 7. Miscellaneous antibiotics with unknown chemical structure.—v. 8. Antibiotics from higher forms of life: higher plants.—v. 9. Antibiotics from higher forms of life: lichens, algae, and animal organisms.—v. 10. General indices.
1. Antibiotics—Handbooks, manuals, etc.
2. Chemistry, Pharmaceutical—Handbooks, manuals, etc.
I. Title. [DNLM: 1. Antibiotics. QV350.3 H236]
RS431.A6B47 615'.329'0202 78-31428
ISBN 0-8493-3450-0 (Complete Set)
ISBN 0-8493-3454-3 (Volume IV part 1)

Direct all inquiries to CRC Press, 2000 N.W. 24th Street, Boca Raton, Florida, 33431.

International Standard Book Number 0-8493-3450-0 (Complete Set)
International Standard Book Number 0-8493-3454-3 (Volume IV Part 1)

Library of Congress Card Number 78-31428
Printed in the United States

FOREWORD

The antibiotics today probably represent the most important field of pharmaceutical specialization, providing the largest bulk of manufactured products, the greatest value in monetary terms, and the greatest single source of profit for the pharmaceutical and related industries. For practical purposes the field of antibiotics was born about 40 years ago with the explosive success of penicillin and, though there have been ups and downs in the assessment of promise and in attention to the field, it appears that it always rebounds from any temporary pessimistic interruption. Today the antibiotic field for research and development is once more firmly established and, of course, it continues to be bed-rock solid in medical application and commercial exploitation.

The growth of the field of antibiotics has been reflected not only in the number of scientists involved and in funding for research, development, and production facilities, but also in the discovery and description of new chemical entities which, in spite of inevitable duplication, accelerates with time and with the addition of increasing numbers of new agents each year. It is estimated that in 1977 about 400 new active agents were described and about 600 corrections or expansions of descriptions of previously announced agents were added to the open literature. Such growth imposes an even more difficult and demanding problem on the practicing scientist who requires reduction of the published descriptive data to tabular, recordable, and recallable form, so that meaningful comparisons may be made.

Early in the development of research and development programs in antibiotics and particularly in programs for the discovery of new agents, it became obvious that early recognition of duplication in a new active agent was essential to economic progress. Large antibiotic research groups have been continuously concerned with devising methods of discovering duplications or with the process of "dereplication" as it has come to be known. In the earliest procedures extensive use of biological activity and resistance patterns served to detect similarities, though such detection may also have led to the rejection of some useful antibiotic analogs. Now however, the great convenience of chemical and physical instrumental methods lays the groundwork for more specific identification and "dereplication".

Clearly, early classification of unknown substances may be of great help in eliminating undesirable duplication. However, another obvious benefit of methods based on chemical and physical comparisons lies in direction of the chemist along the paths of more likely concentration or purification of the unknown substance in his beaker. Early comparisons, if they can conveniently be made, can save the chemist endless hours of effort in his pursuit of a new agent which is usually found in complex mixtures in vanishingly small concentrations.

The author of this work has made the classification and characterization of the antibiotics not only his life work, but his avocation as well. By prodigious effort and endless toil, he has assembled a classification system characterizing more than 6000 substances in such form that exact comparisons may be made. In cooperation with the staff of the Chemotherapy Fermentation Laboratory and the Information Systems Group of the Frederick Cancer Research Center, he has committed his record to computer storage and this record is continually brought up-to-date. Thus comparisons can be made for identification purposes either by using the NCI and NIH computer facilities or by using this most convenient publication.

The antibiotic scientist has good reason to thank János Bérdy for this contribution. It will have real and durable impact on the economy of antibiotic research.

Asger F. Langlykke
Frederick Cancer Research Center
September 19, 1978

PREFACE

The principal objective of this Handbook is to provide in a concise form a readily accessible source of information on the field of antibiotics, specifically information about important physical, chemical, and biological characteristics of these compounds. The data included have been selected from the literature and arranged by computer.

Excluded from the Handbook are the synthetic chemotherapeutics, the chemically modified antibiotic derivatives (semisynthetic antibiotics), and the microbial metabolites, about which we have no information regarding their activity.

Due to the many different general characters and methods of investigation, it was justified to separate the material into two groups. The first one contains the most important group of antibiotic compounds produced by the fermentation of microbes, whereas the second group contains the antimicrobial and antitumor agents of other natural sources such as algae, higher plants, and animals. The latter group will appear in Volumes VIII and IX of this series.

For the most part the work is uncriticized; data and structures have been transcribed just as given in the literature, although attempts have been made to select the recent, more rational data to replace the obsolete. Considerable care has been taken to abstract the literature as deeply and as thoroughly as our resources permitted.

The main body of this work is a set of tables and cross indices, giving the physical, chemical, and biological properties of compounds. In order to make the listing of compounds more coherent, a background has been included, emphasizing general characteristics, structural features, occurrence, and practical importance of the antibiotics in a given group. The compounds are arranged according to families or series on the basis of their chemical structures. In the introduction to the chemical types the structural characterization of the compounds is given.

This book is mainly dedicated to providing a reference for chemists, microbiologists, and pharmacologists working in the research of new antibiotics. Moreover, it is felt that the present format of this book could well stand alone in satisfying particular needs in the entire field of antibiotic research, consisting of data of direct interest not only to scientists, but also to research chemists and biologists who are not experts in the subject and require a brief orientation to the material.

The lack of in vivo and detailed pharmacological, toxicological, or clinical data may appear limiting; however, these data are available in detail in numerous reviews and monographs referred to in our work. The Handbook will not provide a complete reference service, but will give all important and the latest references, as well as other information, thereby serving as a reference in breadth. I think this essentially monoauthored Handbook has certain advantages over the multi-authored reference texts in that it avoids unnecessary duplication as well as in the homogeneity of the format and presentation of the data.

The *Handbook of Antibiotic Compounds* owes its existence to the late Professor D. Perlman, University of Wisconsin, who suggested the usefulness of this type of compilation for wide-range publication; if there is any merit in the realization of this work, it is due to him and to Dr. A. F. Langlykke, Frederick Cancer Research Center, who provided assistance in organizing the computerization of the data. The data were put into a computer-searchable format during my half-year stay at NCI-Frederick Cancer Research Center, Frederick, Maryland, and I am greatly indebted to Drs. J. D. Douros and W. Payne for promoting my work.

I have to pay tribute to the late Dr. K. Magyar, Managing Director of the Antibiotic Division, Research Institute for Pharmaceutical Chemistry, Budapest, who initiated the compilation of data on antibiotics on the card file. I want to express my gratitude to Dr. T. Láng, Director of Research Institute for Pharmaceutical Chemistry, Budapest, for encouraging my work. I am grateful to many colleagues in different parts of the world who have been most helpful by sending me reprints of their papers.

The formidable literature search associated with this compilation could not have been undertaken effectively without the kind assistance of the library staff of the Research Institute for Pharmaceutical Chemistry, Budapest. I am deeply indebted to Mrs. Koczka, Mrs. Kemenes (Budapest), and Dr. C. C. Chiu (Frederick) for their cooperation and technical assistance.

János Bérdy
Budapest
March 1978

INTRODUCTION

Antibiotics are chemical substances produced by metabolism of living organisms which have inhibitory activity against microorganisms and some other animal cells, e.g., tumor cells, or viruses. In the last few decades antibiotics have been increasingly exploited by workers in a number of disciplines. Their usefulness in agriculture as plant protecting agents or for the promotion of animal growth, in the food industry as preservatives, and in basic biochemical research as specific inhibitors claims considerable interest. Their use in the newer field of human and veterinary therapy is also very promising.

Most of these substances are produced by three distinct types of microorganisms, namely actinomycetes, fungi, and bacteria. They are the "classical" antibiotics. Some antibiotically active substances were isolated from other natural sources such as lichens, algae, higher plants, or animal organisms. They are also called, in a wider sense, antibiotics.

Antibiotics have antibacterial, antifungal, antiprotozoal, antitumor, or antiviral activities. Consequently, they can primarily be systematized according to their *origin* or *effectiveness.* It is also possible to classify them on the basis of *biosynthesis* or *mode of action.* Most of the monographs either classify the antibiotics according to the above criteria or list the compounds alphabetically. Nevertheless, today the most rational classification is unambiguously based on the *chemical structures* of the active compounds. However, none of the existing classification systems is universal; each has advantages and disadvantages.

The chemical structures of the antibiotics are one of the most diverse among natural products. They cover almost all types of organic molecules. Besides the common types of natural products (sugars, amino acids, polysaccharides, polypeptides, quinones, phenolics, fatty acids, terpenoids, steroids, flavonoids, alkaloids), numerous specific, unusual chemical structures such as macrolides, aminoglycosides, ansa-lactams, β-lactams, cyclopeptides, etc. which are very rare among other natural and synthetic products were recognized among antibiotics. No other area of the natural product field has confronted such novelty, variety, and complexity of structures.

Antibiotic chemistry has recently undergone explosive growth due to the advancement of various isolation (HPLC, TLC, CCD, ion-exchange) and structural determination (NMR, mass spectroscopic, and X-ray crystallographic) methods. The use of specialized microseparation methods and various instrumental techniques coupled with electron impact, chemical ionization, and field desorption mass spectrometry led to the rapid identification of numerous complicated molecular structures. Applications of computer-assisted X-ray crystallography, circular dichroism spectroscopy, and molecular magnetic resonance using Fourier-transform techniques, as well as the utilization of CMR for structural and conformational studies, resulted in the rapid determination of the stereostructure of compounds. Nowadays, more than half of the new antibiotics are published with complete structures, and more and more of the structures of "old compounds" (previously isolated) are also being determined.

During the last 10 to 15 years "new" antibiotics have been discovered at an ever-increasing rate. However, the efficiency of this research, namely the discovery of medically useful compounds in this field, has unambiguously declined. This is definitely compensated for by the great success of new semisynthetic antibiotics: cephalosporins, penicillins, aminoglycosides, and rifamycins.

Contrary to the above-mentioned declining tendency, antibiotic research all over the world provides more and more new compounds with diverse chemical structures and biological activities. In this decade at least 200 new antibiotics have been described every year (this number in 1976 was more than 300) as a result of wide-spread and more sophisticated screening programs involving the use of automated methods.

Selective methods for the isolation and growth of rarely occurring or fastidious microorganisms, the extensive studies of marine organisms and higher plants, and the use of specific fermentation media, together with the application of new techniques, i.e., multipoint applicator, in the strain isolation processes have resulted in an increase in the number and types of microorganisms investigated. Wider variation in fermentation conditions, use of unique substrates, development of various biotransformations, and cometabolism fermentations are also developing possibilities to produce more new antibiotics. The present screening methods include a larger variety of bacterial, fungal, and viral pathogens, hypersensitive mutants, and tumor cell lines, as well as newer techniques for indicating specific chemical types (β-lactams, polyethers, some N-heterocycles) or specific activities (enzyme inhibition, antimetabolite effects). The animal models permit one to follow the in vivo activities of substances in partially purified preparations for an early indication of the compound's utility. Rapid identification of known compounds has also been improved. The various chromatographic and microphysical and chemical methods, using computerized data-base systems for comparisons of properties determined, have significantly enhanced this process.

On the other hand, a lot of well-known fermentation or other natural products (plant products), without known antimicrobial activity, proved to be effective as antibiotic agents or in other tests, i.e., anticancer, anticoccidial, antiviral, insecticide, ionophoretic, feed efficiency improvement, and enzyme inhibition. In addition, some compounds which were discovered on the basis of the above-mentioned specific effects proved to be active as antimicrobial or antitumor agents. As a result, more than 6000 natural products are known today which have antimicrobial, antitumor, or antiviral activity.

As the numer of antibiotics grew almost exponentially, the literature in this area became less and less perspicuous. It soon became evident that it is impossible to keep abreast with traditional documentation methods in the burgeoning literature. It has become an increasingly difficult task to maintain current awareness, especially in the field of nonmedical compounds with no or minimal practical or theoretical importance. In therapy, agriculture, and other fields about 100 antibiotics are used in practice, about which many excellent monographs and compendia exist. The literature on the other well-known antibiotics which exhibit some theoretically or structurally interesting properties is also extensive in various monographs and reviews. The acquisition of retrospective data on the other, less important antibiotics is particularly difficult and is partly alleviated by some literature reviews or monographs which quickly become outdated; they represent only a part of the whole in time and content. Knowledge about these antibiotics is widely scattered in numerous reviews, original papers, patents, congressional reports, and abstracts, from which it is very difficult to acquire retrospective data.

There is no comprehensive and up-to-date compilation which would include all of the antibiotic compounds. The most satisfactory handbook, Umezawa's *Index of Antibiotics,*[1] which may be up-to-date due to its recent continuous supplementation, unfortunately is limited to Actinomycetales antibiotics. The comprehensive compilations of Korzybsky et al.,[2] Shemyakin et al.,[3] and Miller[4] are excellent textbooks but they are outdated. The newest *Encyclopedia of Antibiotics* by Glasby[5] contains only a limited number of compounds and lacks critical aspects.

In 1960 a compilation of the important chemical, physical, and microbiological data of antibiotics was attempted, initiated by the card index file system at the Research Institute for Pharmaceutical Chemistry, Budapest, Hungary.[6,7] This project was primarily an aid for the early identification of new antibiotics isolated at this Institute by means of comparing the characteristics of isolated unknown compounds with the data of known antibiotics. The scope and content as well as the expectations of the original card file system were changed during the years that passed, but the general principles of compilation remained unchanged. On the basis of this system a comprehensive chemical classification of antibiotics was proposed recently.[8,9]

The satisfactory and effective arrangement of the huge mass of data for wide-ranging application was evidently inconceivable without data processing using computers. The data which have been compiled continuously during the last 15 years at the Research Institute for Pharmaceutical Chemistry were put into computer-searchable form by cooperative efforts at the NCI-Frederick Cancer Research Center, Frederick, Maryland in 1975/76 to assist in the identification of newly isolated antibiotics.[10]

The interest so often expressed by various persons and establishments in this card file and in the computerized data base system led to the reorganization of the data compiled into the format presented here. A certain degree of editing was necessary to correct the chemical classification and clarify the structural correlations. The completion of the data bank with some introductory and explanatory material, structural formulae of compounds, and references was also required. This work has been undertaken and has hopefully removed the ambiguities and duplications, and it will increase the usefulness of this Handbook. To meet the requirements of computer programming, a few compromises were necessary, which we hope will affect neither the accessibility nor the usefulness of the data in any significant way.

This Handbook is not intended to be only a simple data bank. Although no interpretation of data has been included, some critical treatment has been made regarding the selection of certain data from the original literature, and the summarized discussion of general characteristics and structural features has been accomplished. The prime aim during the editing of this work was to unite the advances of textbooks and the comprehensive data books; therefore, a rapid visual retrieval of important information regarding a class of compounds has been emphasized before the mass of various data. Prior to the tabulation of individual compounds, which are arranged according to their chemical types, a short characterization of these compounds, including common physical, chemical, microbiological, and pharmacological properties, will be given. These introductions touch on the problems of biosynthesis, mechanism of action, and clinical or other applications. A short historical survey is sometimes also included.

The listing of data is followed by a set of cross indices designed to permit entry into the main body of the book for any of the several points of view. We sincerely hope this format will meet the needs of the scientific community.

REFERENCES

1. **Umezawa, H., Ed.,** *Index of Antibiotics from Actinomycetes,* University of Tokyo Press, Tokyo, 1967.
2. **Korzybsky, T., Kowszyk-Gindifer, Z., and Kurylowitz, W.,** *Antibiotics: Origin, Nature and Properties,* Pergamon Press, Oxford, 1967.
3. **Shemyakin, M. M., Khokhlov, A. S. et. al.,** *Chemistry of Antibiotics,* 3rd ed., Izdanja Akademii Nauk SSSR, Moscow, 1961.
4. **Miller, M. W.,** *The Pfizer Handbook of Microbial Metabolites,* McGraw-Hill, New York, 1961.
5. **Glasby, J. S.,** *Encyclopedia of Antibiotics,* John Wiley & Sons, London, 1976.
6. **Bérdy, J.,** System for Identification of Antibiotics, Ph.D. thesis, Debrecen, 1961.
7. **Bérdy, J. and Magyar, K.,** Antibiotics: a review, *Proc. Bioch.,* 10, 45, 1968.
8. **Bérdy, J.,** *ICIA,* 10, 1, 1972.
9. **Bérdy, J.,** Recent developments of antibiotic research and classification of antibiotics according to chemical structures, *Adv. Appl. Microb.,* 18, 309, 1974.
10. **Bostian, M., McNitt, K., Aszalos, A., and Bérdy, J.,** *JA,* 30, 633, 1977.

THE AUTHOR

János Bérdy, Ph.D., is a Senior Research Fellow of the Institute of Drug Research (formerly the Research Institute for Pharmaceutical Chemistry), Budapest.

Dr. Bérdy graduated in 1958 from Eötvös Loránd University, Budapest, and received his Ph.D. degree (summa cum laude) in organic chemistry in 1961 from Kossuth Lajos University, Debrecen. He was qualified as a Pharmaceutical Chemistry Engineer in 1969 at the Technical University, Budapest. He is a member of the Hungarian Chemical Society and many other scientific associations.

Dr. Bérdy's research interests include the isolation of new antibiotics, the development of industrial production, and classification and identification problems of antibiotics, as well as the theoretical problems of antibiotics research.

CONTRIBUTORS

Adorjan Aszalos, Ph.D., is Head of Biochemistry, Chemotherapy, Frederick Cancer Research Center, Frederick, Maryland, and is Lecturer in Biochemistry at Hood College, Frederick, Maryland. He recently joined the Bureau of Drugs, Food and Drug Administration, in Washington, D.C. He previously held positions at the Squibb Institute for Medical Research and at Princeton University.

Dr. Aszalos graduated from Technical University of Budapest, Hungary with B.S. and M.S. degrees in chemical engineering and biochemistry. He received his Ph.D. in bioorganic chemistry from Technical University of Vienna, Austria in 1961. Subsequently, he was Post-Doctoral Fellow at Rutgers University.

Dr. Aszalos is a member of the American Chemical Society, Interscience Foundation, and New York Academy of Sciences. In the latter society, he served as Vice Chairman of the Biophysics Section in 1973 to 1975. Dr. Aszalos received, among other awards, the Austrian Industrial Research Award and the Army Post-Doctoral Research Award.

Dr. Aszalos has presented over 30 lectures at National and International meetings and published over 60 research papers and several review articles and chapters. His current major interest is antibiotics and enzymes in chemotherapy.

Melvin S. Bostian is Manager of the Information Systems Department at the Frederick Cancer Research Center, Frederick, Maryland. In his former position as Senior Programmer/Analyst he directed the conversion of the antibiotic compound data base to machine-readable form and designed the data base system used for the conversion.

Mr. Bostian has a degree in mathematics and specializes in the analysis of biomedical data generated by laboratory instruments.

Karen L. McNitt is a Senior Programmer at the Frederick Cancer Research Center, Frederick, Maryland. In this capacity she was responsible for the programming and implementation of the data base system used to collect the information on the antibiotic compounds. She also directed the data entry and validation of the compound information.

Ms. McNitt has a degree in computer science and specializes in the analysis of scientific data.

TABLE OF CONTENTS

Selection of Compounds Included 1

How to Use this Handbook 3
Using the Indices 28
List of Abbreviations 29

Amino Acid and Peptide Antibiotics

Introduction 33

41 Amino Acid Derivatives 39
411 Simple Amino Acids 39
412 Cyclic Amino Acid Derivatives 77
Introduction 77
4121 β-Lactam Antibiotics (Penicillins, Cephalosporins) 78
Newer β-Lactam Antibiotics 78
4122 and 4123 Pyrrothin and Actithiazic Acid Types 133
413 Diketopiperazine Derivatives 147
Introduction 147
4131 Simple Diketopiperazines 149
4132 *Epi*-Oligothiadiketopiperazines 157
4133 Aspergillic Acid Type 187

42 Homopeptide Antibiotics 193
421 Oligopeptides 193
Introduction 193
4211 Pyrrole-Amidino Antibiotics 194
4212 Linear Oligopeptide Antibiotics 209
4213 Cyclic Oligopeptide-Like Antibiotics 232
422 Linear Homopeptides 237
Introduction 237
4221 Gramicidin Type 239
4222 Edein Type 244
4225 Peptaibophol (Alamethicin Type) 251
423 Cyclic Homopeptides 263
Introduction 263
4231 Tyrocidine Type 267
4232 Bacitracin Type 275
4233 Viomycin Type 279
4234, 4235, 423 Other Cyclic Homopeptides 281

43 Heteromer Peptides 311
Introduction 311
431 Lipopeptide Antibiotics 313
Introduction 313
4311 Amphomycin Type 315
4312 Polymyxin Series 323
4313 Echinocandin Type 355
4314 Bacillomycin Type 369
432 Thiapeptides 387

Introduction 387
4321 Thiazolyl Peptides 389
4322 Bottromycin Type 419
4323, 4324, 432 Berninamycin, Leucinamycin, and Less Known Types of Compounds 425
433 Chelate-Forming Peptides 439
4331 Sideromycins 439
4332 Bleomycin Type 459

4 Other Less Known Peptide Antibiotics 499

Indices

Sequence of Alphabetizing 525

Index of Names of Antibiotics 527

Index of Antibiotic Numbers and Names 539

Index of Producing Organisms 551

SELECTION OF COMPOUNDS INCLUDED

The guiding principles in selection of material to include in the Handbook are as follows:

1. The compounds listed in this book are derived from the whole living world, including all types of prokaryotes and eukaryotes, namely microorganisms, lichens, fungi, mosses, algae, higher plants, protozoa, molluscs, sponges, worms, insects, and vertebrates.
2. An essential requirement is the in vitro, or perhaps only in vivo, antimicrobial (at least at a concentration of 500 μg/mℓ) activity or some antitumor, cytotoxic, antiprotozoal, or antiviral (antiphage) effect, regardless that this activity is observable in a specific medium or circumstance only.
3. Every chemical entity, e.g., stereoisomer, forms a separate entry. Components of antibiotic complexes, when they are separated and when some of their properties are determined, are listed individually.
4. The unresolved antibiotic complexes (components are detected by chromatography only) form a single entry. These complexes in many instances differ only by proportions of the same components (e.g., streptothricin or heptaene antibiotic complexes) and are designated by their own name.
5. Crude antibiotic extracts, characterized by some properties such as UV spectra, stability, or others, possessing interesting activity, especially those originating from uncommon sources, also form separate entries.
6. Derivatives of antibiotics made by chemical methods are not listed, unless they are produced by biosynthetic or enzymatic methods also. The products of directed and conversion-type fermentations or mutational biosynthetic processes employing precursor-like compounds incorporated into the active products are included.
7. Alkaloids, stress metabolites, insecticides, anthelminthics with some antimicrobial or antitumor activity, and mycotoxins without significant antimicrobial effect but with high (cyto)toxicity are included. Phytotoxins, enzyme inhibitors, plant growth regulators, animal growth promoters, and other physiologically active metabolites without any antimicrobial, antitumor, antiviral, or cytotoxic activities are excluded from this Handbook.

Consequently this work includes all antibiotically active natural products (antibacterial, antifungal, antiprotozoal, antitumor, antiviral, and occasionally anthelminthic or insecticide agents) discovered, having one or more of the characteristic properties described, although many compounds have not been isolated in pure state and their structures are unknown. After all, the number of entries is not exactly identical with the number of presently existing antibiotic compounds. It is very likely that numerous identities are undetermined and numerous components are unresolved yet.

This Handbook series contains more than 6000 entries, of which about 4500 represent the antibiotics prepared by the fermentation of microorganisms. Approximately 3000 antibiotics are derived from different *Actinomycetales* species, of which about 88 to 90% originate from *Streptomyces* species. It must be noted that in this decade about 20% of *Actinomycetales* antibiotics were derived from non-*Streptomyces* species. Almost 1000 antibiotics come from different fungi, and 500 to 600 come from various bacterial strains (including *Pseudomonales*).

The total number of antibiotics with known chemical structure is about 2500 (nearly 2000 are microbial antibiotics), and about 400 compounds are synthetized. Additionally, there are about 1500 antibiotics about which we have satisfactory knowledge regarding their chemical structure (degradation products, skeleton, principal moieties, etc.). Numerous compounds might be classified on the basis of physical, chemical, and microbiological similarities (e.g., cross-resistance) to the known type compounds. After all, about 85% of the antibiotics have more or less known chemical structural features.

HOW TO USE THIS HANDBOOK

Although this Handbook details vastly different types of compounds, an effort has been made to present the material according to a general format. All compounds (antibiotic entries) have a specific *compound number*, which serves as a title to a group of entries and as a unique numerical identifier. This number consists of two parts. The first element is, in fact, identical to our previously reported[9] *antibiotic code number* (without the separation by commas), which is characteristic of the chemical type of the compound. The second element of the compound number, separated by a hyphen, is a simple *sequence number* assigned individually to any compound according to its addition to the data base. The complete compound number provides access to that compound through the indices for any compound for which no name is listed.

Most of the compounds in this Handbook have been arranged according to our previously reported, continuously revised and completed chemical classification system.[9] This system follows the formal chemical classification but not in the strictest sense. Since this is merely a superficial classification, taking into account some biogenetic and other points of view, it is obvious that the same compound may belong to more than one class. To avoid these duplications, we selected nine basic chemical moieties (principal constituents) most characteristic of the compound, and the primary classification was done accordingly.

Assignment to antibiotic families is performed according to the following principal constituents

1. Sugar
2. Macrocyclic lactone ring (more than eight members)
3. Quinone (or quinone-like) skeleton
4. Amino acid
5. Nitrogen-containing heterocyclic system
6. Oxygen-containing heterocyclic system
7. Alicyclic skeleton
8. Aromatic skeleton
9. Aliphatic chain

The construction of some more or less arbitrary class of compounds seems to be justified. The formation of a family for the macrocyclic lactones and the separation of the quinones and quinone-like compounds from the aromatic (mainly phenolics) compounds was unavoidable. Beyond their frequent occurrence and great importance, their complete new biological properties, different from those of normal aliphatic and aromatic antibiotics, justifies listing them as a separate family of antibiotics. Moreover, the limitation of the carbohydrate (sugar) family of compounds to the mostly sugar-containing structures, excluding most of the glycosides (macrolide-, anthracycline-, peptide-, purine-pyrimidine-, and aromatic-glycosides), which are classified on the basis of their diversified aglycones, surely contributes to the logical classification. In the course of detailed systemization, some further arbitrary decisions became necessary. The grouping of streptothricines among the carbohydrates was permitted because of their properties and activities similar to other water-soluble basic antibiotics. The tetracyclines are grouped together with anthracycline quinones in the family of quinone compounds. Again, all glutarimides were grouped together as alicyclic compounds, rather than grouping them as heterocyclic, aromatic (actiphenol), or aliphatic (streptimidone) compounds. Alkaloids having antimicrobial or antitumor activity (except steroid alkaloids) were grouped as N-heterocyclic compounds. The terpenes were distributed according to their structures into the alicyclic, aromatic, or aliphatic families. The skeleton of this system includes only the families, subfamilies, and groups shown in Table 1.

Table 1

CLASSIFICATION OF ANTIBIOTIC COMPOUNDS

AN	Family, subfamily, group	Important representatives
1	Carbohydrate antibiotics	
11	Pure saccharides	
111	Mono and oligosaccharides	Streptozotocin, nojirimycin
112	Polysaccharides	Glucans, soedomycin
12	Aminoglycoside antibiotics	
121	Streptamine derivatives	Streptomycins, bluensomycin
122	2-Deoxystreptamine derivatives	Neomycin, gentamicin, etc.
123	Inositol-inoseamine derivatives	Kasugamycin, validamycin
124	Other aminocyclitols	Fortimicin
125	Aminohexitols	Sorbistin
13	Other glycosides	
131	Streptothricin group	Streptolin, racemomycin
132	Glycopeptides, C-glycosides	Vancomycin, chromomycin
14	Sugar derivatives	
141	Sugar esters, amides	Everninomicin, lincomycin
142	Sugar lipids	Moenomycin, labilomycin
2	Macrocyclic lactone (lactam) antibiotics	
21	Macrolide antibiotics	
211	Small (12-, 14-membered) macrolide	Erythromycin, picromycin
212	16-membered macrolides	Leucomycin, tylosin
213	Other macrolides	Borrelidin, lankacidin
22	Polyene antibiotics	
221	Trienes	Mycotrienine, proticin
222	Tetraenes	Nystatin, rimocidin
223	Pentaenes	Eurocidin, filipin
224	Hexaenes	Candihexin, mediocidin
225	Heptaenes	Candicidin, amphotericin B
226	Octaenes	Ochramycin
227	Oxo-polyenes	Flavofungin, dermostatin
228	Mixed polyenes	Tetrahexin
23	Macrocyclic lactone antibiotics	
231	Macrolide-like antibiotics	Oligomycin, primycin
232	Simple lactones	Albocyclin, A-26771 B
233	Dilactones	Antimycin, boromycin
234	Polylactones	Nonactin, tetranactin
235	Condensed macrolactones	Chlorothricin, cytochalasin
24	Macrolactam antibiotics	
241	Ansamycin group	Rifamycin, tolypomycin
242	Ansa-lactams (maytanosides)	Ansamitocin, maytansin
243	Lactone-lactams	Viridenomycin
3	Quinone and similar antibiotics	
31	Tetracyclic compounds and anthraquinones	
311	Tetracyclines	Tetracycline, chlorotetracycline
312	Anthracyclines	Adriamycin, rhodomycin
313	Anthraquinone derivatives	Ayamycin, hedamycin
32	Naphtoquinones	
321	Simple naphtoquinones	Javanicin, juglomycin
322	Condensed naphtoquinones	Granaticin, rubromycin
33	Benzoquinones	
331	Simple benzoquinones	Spinulosin, oosporein
332	Condensed benzoquinones	Mitomycin, streptonigrin
34	Quinone-like compounds	
341	Semiquinones	Resistomycin, maytenin
342	Other quinone-like compounds	Epoxidon, aeroplysinin

Table 1 (continued)
CLASSIFICATION OF ANTIBIOTIC COMPOUNDS

AN	Family, subfamily, group	Important representatives
4	Amino acid, peptide antibiotics	
41	Amino acid derivatives	
411	Simple amino acids	Cycloserine, alanosin
412	Amino acid derivatives	Penicillin, aureothricin
413	Diketopiperazine derivatives	Gliotoxin, chaetocin
42	Homopeptides	
421	Oligopeptides	Netropsin, negamycin
422	Linear homopeptides	Gramicidin, alamethicin
423	Cyclic homopeptides	Tyrocidin, bacitracin, viomycin
43	Heteromer peptides	
431	Cyclic lipopeptides	Polymyxin, amphomycin, iturin
432	Thiapeptides	Thiostrepton, althiamycin
433	Chelate-forming peptides	Bleomycin, sideromycins
44	Peptolides	
441	Chromopeptolides	Actinomycin, quinomycin
442	Lipopeptolides	Enduracidin, surfactin
443	Heteropeptolides	Etamycin, ostreogrycin B
444	Simple peptolides	Telomycin, grisellimycin
445	Depsipeptides	Valinomycin, ostreogrycin A
45	Macromolecular peptides	
451	Polypeptides	Nisin, licheniformin
452	Proteins	Neocarzinostatin, pacibilin
453	Proteids (chromo-, gluco-, nucleo-)	Asparaginase, bacteriocins
5	Nitrogen (or S) containing heterocyclic antibiotics	
51	Single heterocycles	
511	Five-membered ring	Pyrrolnitrin, azomycin
512	Six-membered ring	Mocimycin, abikoviromycin
513	Pyrimidine glycosides	Amicetin, polyoxin, blasticidins
52	Condensed heterocycles	
521	Aromatic fused compounds	Albofungin, pyocyanine
522	Fused heterocycles	Anthramycin, fervenulin
523	Purine glycosides	Puromycin, tubercidin
53	Alkaloids	
54	S-containing heterocycles	
6	Oxygen-containing heterocyclic antibiotics	
61	Furan derivatives	
611	Simple furans	Botriodiploidin
612	Condensed furans	Usnic acid, aflatoxins
613	Benzofurans	Furasterin
62	Pyran derivatives	
621	Simple pyrans	Aucubin, plumericin
622	α-Pyrones	Phomalactone, asperline
623	γ-Pyrones	Distacin, kojic acid
63	Benzpyran derivatives	
631	Flavonoids	Chloroflavonin, eupafolin
632	Isoflavonoids	Pisatin, pterocarpan
633	Neoflavones	Dalbergione
634	Other benzopyran derivatives	Radicinin, morellin
64	Small lactones	
641	Simple lactones	Acetomycin, penicillic acid
642	Condensed lactones (coumarins)	Actinobolin, mycophenolic acid

Table 1 (continued) CLASSIFICATION OF ANTIBIOTIC COMPOUNDS

AN	Family, subfamily, group	Important representatives
65	Polyether antibiotics	
651	Saturated polyethers	Monensin, nigericin
652	Unsaturated polyethers	Narasin, salinomycin
653	Aromatic polyethers	Lasalocid
654	Polyether-like antibiotics	A-23187
7	Alicyclic antibiotics	
71	Cycloalkane derivatives	
711	Cyclopentane derivatives	Sarcomycin, pentanenomycin
712	Cyclohexane derivatives	Fumagillin, ketomycin
713	Glutarimide antibiotics	Cycloheximide, streptimidone
72	Small terpenes	
721	Simple mono, sesqui, and diterpenes	Coriolin, cyathin, siccanin
722	Terpene lactones	Vernolepin, enmein, quassin
73	Oligoterpenes	
731	Steroids	Fusidic acid, viridin
732	Triterpenes	Saponins, cardenolides, etc.
733	Terpenoides (Scirpene derivatives)	Trichotecin, verrucarins
8	Aromatic antibiotics	
81	Benzene derivatives	
811	Monocyclic derivatives	Flavipin, versicolin
812	Alkyl-benzene derivatives	Chloramphenicol, ascochlorin
813	Polycyclic benzene derivatives	Xanthocyllin, alternariol
82	Condensed aromatic compounds	
821	Spiro compounds (Grisans)	Griseofulvin, geodin
822	Naphtalene derivatives	Gossypol, carzinophyllin
823	Anthracene-phenantrene derivatives	Thermorubin, orchinol
83	Nonbenzoid aromatic compounds	
831	Tropolones	Puberulic acid
832	Azulene	Lactaroviolin
84	Other aromatic derivatives	
841	Aromatic ethers	Zinninol, bifuhalol
842	Glycosidic antibiotics	Novobiocin, hygromycin A
843	Aromatic esters	Nidulin, phlorizin
9	Aliphatic antibiotics	
91	Alkane derivatives	
911	Saturated alkane derivatives	Elaiomycin, lipoxamycin
912	Polyines	Marasin, mycomycin
92	Carboxylic acid derivatives	
921	Small carboxylic acid derivatives	Enteromycin, cellocidin
922	Fatty acid derivatives	Eulicin, myriocin
93	Sulfur- and phosphor-containing aliphatic compounds	
931	S-containing compounds	Allicin, fluopsin
932	P-containing compounds	Phosphonomycin

The most characteristic feature of this classification system is the utilization of the previously mentioned *antibiotic code number* (AN). This number carries information about the structure or structural type of the compound. The first member of this five-digit number indicates the nine large antibiotic families to which the compound belongs. The second, third, fourth, and occasionally the fifth digits indicate the subfamilies, groups, types, and subtypes, respectively, e.g., 12222 represents the gentamicin subtype among the 4,5-disubstituted (1222) deoxystreptamine (122) derivatives of aminoglycoside antibiotics (12) in the family of carbohydrate antibiotics (1). The less well-known agents receive only the first few figures, indicating the large group to where the compound can surely be ranged. Thus, 12000 indicates an aminoglycoside antibiotic with unknown type. The zero means lack of information; thus the compounds listed throughout the tables without the antibiotic code number (00000) are those for which structural information has not been established as yet. They represent about 600 (10% of all) compounds which are listed in separate volume(s) divided into sections according to type of producing organisms, namely, the compounds produced by Actinomycetales, fungi, and bacteria as well as plants and animals have been arranged alphabetically according to their producing genus and species.

Another identifier, *chemical type,* is a short description of the structural type (aminoglycoside, ansamycin, purine glycoside, etc.) and/or the specification of a peculiar type (neomycin type, oligomycin type, cycloheximide type, etc.) of compound. While the compound always bears one antibiotic code number, sometimes two designations are attached to it. One is characteristic of the larger group, while the other refers to the specific type, e.g., aminoglycoside, neomycin type. Occasionally a compound may bear the antibiotic code number without any chemical type designation. This usually belongs to the newer groups or types of compounds with only a few representatives.

In some cases compounds have been included in the most probable group, even though insufficient data are available to verify the final grouping, hoping that these entries will promote further work in a class of these compounds. Close chemical and microbiological properties will certainly suggest to investigators to do further work on these compounds.

SELECTION OF DATA INCLUDED

The data included in this book were determined by the content of our original card index file system. The selection of data for maintenance in the file system and in the computerized data bank was decided on the basis of their usefulness in screening work searching for new antibiotics. Consequently, the properties which are characteristic for the crude substances or active extracts, isolated in the early phase of research, were emphasized. This is one reason why some properties such as melting points or NMR spectral data are excluded.

The following data, when available, are included for each antibiotic compound:

1. Name, alternate names, and trade name	Name
2. Identical with	Identical
3. Producing organism(s)	PO
4. Chemical type, chemical nature	CT
5. Molecular formula	Formula
6. Elemental analysis	EA
7. Molecular/equivalent weight	MW/EW
8. Color, appearance: Physical characteristics	PC
9. Optical rotation	OR
10. Ultraviolet spectra, solvent(s)	UV
11. Solubility	
Good	SOL-Good
Fair	SOL-Fair
Poor	SOL-Poor
12. Qualitative chemical reactions	Qual

13. Stability	Stab
14. Antimicrobial activity, test organisms	TO
15. Toxicity	LD_{50}
16. Antitumor and/or antiviral activity	TV
17. Isolation methods employed	
Filtration	IS-Fil
Extraction	IS-Ext
Ion exchange	IS-Ion
Absorption	IS-Ab
Chromatography	IS-Chr
Crystallization	IS-Cry
18. Practical application, utility	Utility
19. Structural formula	Structure
20. References	References

The presentation of data involved some compromises to meet the special requirements of computer programming and to maintain the easy usefulness of the cross indices. For example, all letters are capital, and, of course, it would be impossible to use subscript and superscript symbols.

Some data are given slightly differently than they stand in the literature. The molecular weights and elemental analysis values are given in rounded numerals to facilitate the key back to the compounds using the indices. The solubility and stability data are given, sometimes after intelligent transcription of the terminology found in the original papers. All other data reported have been extracted from the literature and presented in their original values. The accuracy of values (±), when available, is indicated by a vertical bar (|). The data presented (solubility, optical rotation) are related to room temperature.

1. Name, Alternate Names, and Trade Name

The *basic name* (title) of any antibiotic compound is generally the trivial, nonproprietary name (underlined). Alternate names (synonyms), such as other chemical and patent names, experimental drug codes (e.g., NSC numbers), and occasionally systematic names, as far as they came to our attention, all have been listed after the basic name, without any differentiation. The trade names (s), if they occur, appear on a separate line. Specific names evidently derived from a related well-known compound, such as 14-hydroxydaunomycin (adriamycin), have also been included. If a compound is not designated specifically, the letter and/or number designations (in most cases the experimental drug codes) were used as the basic name of the compound without the terms "antibiotic" or "number". For example, PA-616 and not Antibiotic PA-616, or 2230-C and not Antibiotic number 2230-C, were used. In a few instances, lacking other identification, exotic names have been used, e.g., "Landy substance" and "bromine-rich marine antibiotics", and are given in quotation marks.

Naturally occurring compounds derived from other trivially named compounds by modifying adjectives such as allo-, methyl-, dihydro-, etc. are listed separately, but in the name index they are listed as the derivatives of the parent compound, sometimes upholding the name in the original format also. Dihydrostreptomycin appears in the index as both Dihydrostreptomycin and Streptomycin, dihyro-. Stereochemical descriptors such as D and L or + and − are incorporated into the names wherever possible, but in the name index these compounds are alphabetized according to the general name.

No attempt has been made to supply systematic names, except when these were obvious or the compound had no trivial or other alternate name. The systematic names sometimes appear slightly modified because of the impossibility of always applying the proper signs, i.e., double parenthesis, commas, or apostrophes, as a consequence of the restrictions of the computer programming. The following symbols are used for Greek letters: A″ = α (alpha), B″ = β (beta), G″ = γ (gamma), D″ = δ (delta), E″ = ε (epsilon), H″ = η (eta), O″ = ω (omega), and X″ = ξ (xi).

Special care has been taken to eliminate duplicates from this Handbook, that is the multiple description of the same compounds referred to by different names by the same authors (quintomycin-lividomycin, marcomycin-hygromycin B, etc.) in patent and the subsequent article.

Compounds unnamed by the discoverers and compounds for which no structures are given or where the structure is too complicated to give a short, meaningful systematic name have been titled simply by their antibiotic code number and/or their sequence number, e.g., 11210-0023 or 00000-4138.

2. Identical With

Very often, a single antibiotic has been isolated independently by several authors from several different sources and thus different names have been given to the same compound. In those cases where the identity has been proved only later, these antibiotics are listed as separate entries, but the identity has been noted under "identical with". In such instances where the first publication is included, the verification of the identity of the newly isolated compound with another formerly known substance — or where this identity has been known for a long time (carbomycin-magnamycin, novobiocin-streptonivicin, etc.) — does not form an individual entry. The specific name (if given) of the newly isolated compound is listed as a synonym of the old compound only, together with its specific data. The possible alternate names of the identical compounds are not listed. All identities are always noted mutually.

When it is not known whether the products are identical, due to the lack of sufficient data, they are treated as separate entries. It is very likely that careful perusal of the data included in the Handbook will indicate that some further compounds reported in one study may be identical to those reported by others. Those questions remain to be solved in the future.

3. Producing Organisms

The genus and species names have been given as stated in the original publications but the obvious faults are corrected and the style is standardized. The unidentified species are indicated by the abbreviation sp. In a few reports the genus name is not given; it is designated by the family or other specification of the type of producing organism given in inverted commas. An attempt has been made to list all organisms which are able to produce the compound in question. In most cases the variants or subspecies are also indicated and separated by a hyphen. *Streptomyces* species are frequently referred as *Actinomyces* according to Krassilnikov's systematization. They are transcribed to *Streptomyces* species, upholding the *Actinomyces* designation.

The + sign after the name of a microorganism followed by a special term signifies the addition of the indicated precursors or other substances to the medium for obtaining the compound desired (directed fermentations, mutational biosynthesis with idiothropes). The + sign between the name of a plant organism and another organism (generally fungi) indicates the production of phytoalexin (stress metabolite) by the host caused by infection.

It is hoped that the classification of compounds through the cross index by taxonomical origin will be of value to the taxonomists and biogeneticists who are able, by means of the data presented, to trace the occurrence of particular structural types through the family of organisms.

4. Chemical Type, Chemical Nature

The identifier chemical type gives a short description of the structural type (aminoglycoside, ansamycin, purine glycoside, etc.) and/or the specification of a peculiar type (neomycin type, oligomycin type, cycloheximide type, etc.) of compound. While the compound always bears one antibiotic code number, sometimes two designations are attached to it. One is characteristic of the larger group, while the other refers to the specific type, e.g., aminoglycoside, neomycin type. Occasionally a compound may bear the antibiotic code number without any chemical type designation. This usually belongs to the newer groups of types of compounds with only a few representatives. The terms used throughout the Handbook to characterize the compounds are listed in Table 2, including the antibiotic code numbers.

The identifier chemical nature indicates the acid-base character of the compounds, distinguising the acidic, basic, amphoteric and neutral characters. In the case of a compound listed as both acidic and amphoteric, an amphoteric compound is meant with a more distinct acidic character. When this information is not given directly in the original paper, but the chemical nature of the compound can evidently be concluded from the properties or structure published, it is stated and listed.

5. Molecular Formula

Chemical formulas are always listed in the sequence of C, H, N, O, S, Hlg, and other elements. When the formulae are uncertain, the most probable average values are given, e.g., $C_{22\text{-}24}H_{44\text{-}46}NO_4$ becomes $C_{23}H_{45}NO_4$ rather than $C_{23\pm1}H_{45\pm1}NO_4$. If in the literature the formula of only some simple salt is provided (e.g., $C_{40}H_{78}O_{11}Na$), the free form is calculated ($C_{40}H_{79}O_{11}$) and the compound listed accordingly. The formulas do not contain subscript symbols. Note that the symbols O (oh) and 0 (zero) are very similar.

6. Elemental Analysis

When the molecular formula is unknown, the elemental analyses have been given in percent to the nearest whole value. For all compounds independent of the known formula or structure, the percentage of nitrogen, sulfur, halogen, phosphor, and other rare elements is given in rounded whole numbers. These values, if given for simple salts or their derivatives only, are calculated for the free form of compounds. The S, Cl, Na, etc. elements occurring in the simple salt-forming radicals (sulfates, hydrochlorides, sodium salts, etc.) are excluded from the coded elemental analysis. When the molecular formula is established and no data about found percentage composition are provided, these values are calculated from the published formula and listed among experimental values.

7. Molecular and/or Equivalent Weight

These are as a rule experimentally found values. Data are given in whole numbers. When these data are not available, they are calculated from the reported molecular formula. All equivalent weights are experimentally found values.

8. Color and Appearance, Physical Characteristics

The colors of substances are given by the author's original description. The different colors listed mean the transitional ones, e.g., white, yellow means a yellowish white. Only the crystalline and solid or liquid state are distinguished by crystalline, powder, oil, liquid, syrup, etc., respectively. No crystal form or other physical properties are given.

9. Optical Rotation

Rotation values in degrees and solvent employed, separated by a comma, are listed. Solvents are abbreviated according to the generally accepted abbreviations (see list of

Table 2
KEY TO THE ANTIBIOTIC TYPES AND SUBTYPES

Volume I: Carbohydrate Antibiotics

AN	Chemical type designations
11111	Sugar, monosaccharide
11112	Sugar, disaccharide
11121	Amino sugar
11122	Aminodisaccharide
11131	Oligosaccharide
11132	Aminooligosaccharide
1114	Sugar derivative
112	Polysaccharide
1121	Polysaccharaide, glucan
1122	Polysaccharaide-protein complex
1123	Lipopolysaccharide
1124	Polysaccharide (hemicellulose)
12	Aminoglycoside
1211	Aminoglycoside, streptomycin-type
1212	Aminoglycoside
1213	Aminoglycoside, spectinomycin-type
12211	Aminoglycoside, neomycin-type
12212	Aminoglycoside, ribostamycin-type
12221	Aminoglycoside, kanamycin-type
12222	Aminoglycoside, gentamicin-type
12223	Aminoglycoside, seldomycin-type
1223	Aminoglycoside, hygromycin B-type
1224	Aminoglycoside, apramycin-type
1225	Aminoglycoside, neamine-type
1231	Aminoglycoside-like, validamycin-type
1232	Aminoglycoside-like, kasugamycin-type
1233	Aminoglycoside-like
1234	Aminoglycoside-like
1241	Aminoglycoside-like, fortimycin-type
1251	Aminoglycoside-like, aminohexitol derivatives
131	Streptothricin-type
1311	Streptothricin-type
1312	Streptothricin-like
1313	Streptothricin-like
132	Glycopeptide
1321	Glycopeptide, ristocetin-type
1322	Glycopeptide, vancomycin-type
1323	Chromomycin-type
1411	Everninomicin-type
1412	Lincomycin-type
1413	
1421	Moenomycin-type
1422	Glycolipid
1423	Sugar derivatives

Volume II: Macrocyclic Lactone (Lactam) Antibiotics

AN	Chemical type designations
21	Macrolide
2111	Macrolide, methymycin-type
21121	Macrolide, picromycin-type
21122	Macrolide, erythromycin-type
21123	Macrolide, megalomycin-type
21124	Macrolide, lankamycin-type
21211	Macrolide, leucomycin-type
21212	Macrolide, spiramycin-type
21221	Macrolide, carbomycin-type
21222	Macrolide, angolamycin-type
21223	Macrolide, cirramycin-type
21231	Macrolide. carbomycin B-type
21232	Macrolide, tylosin-type
21233	Macrolide, juvenimycin B-type
21241	Macrolide, maridomycin-type
21242	Macrolide, cirramycin-type
21251	Macrolide, neutramycin-type
21252	Macrolide, aldgamycin E-type
21311	Macrolide-like, bundlin-type
21312	Macrolide-like
2132	Macrolide-like
22	Polyene
2211	Triene, trienine-type
2212	Triene
222	Tetraene
2221	Tetraene, pimaricin-type
2222	Tetraene, rimocidin-type
2223	Tetraene, nystatin-type
223	Pentaene
2231	Pentaene, methylpentaene
2232	Pentaene, eurocidin-type
2233	Pentaene, capacidin-type
2234	Pentaene
2241	Hexaene, candihexin-type
225	Heptaene
22511	Aromatic heptaene, candicidin-type
22512	Aromatic heptaene
22513	Aromatic heptaene
2252	Nonaromatic heptaene, amphotericin B-type
2261	Octaene
2271	Oxo-pentaene, flavofungin-type
2272	Oxo-hexaene
2281	Polyene, tetra + hexaene
23	(azalomycin F-type)
231	Macrolide-like
2311	Macrolide-like, oligomycin-type
2312	Macrolide-like, venturicidin-type
2313	Macrolide-like
2314	Macrolide-like
2315	Macrolide-like, melanosporin-type
2316	Macrolide-like, humidin-type
2317	Macrolide-like, blasticidin A-type
2321	Simple lactone
2322	Macrolactone
2323	Macrolactone

Table 2 (continued)
KEY TO THE ANTIBIOTIC TYPES AND SUBTYPES

AN	Chemical type designations	AN	Chemical type designations
	Volume II: Macrocyclic Lactone (Lactam) Antibiotics (continued)		
2331	Antimycin-type	2354	Zygosporin-type
2332	Dilactone	2411	Ansamycin, rifamycin-type
2341	Cyclopolylactone, nonactin-type	2412	Ansamycin, streptovaricin-type
2342	Cyclopolylactone-like	2413	Ansamycin
23511	Macrolactone, chlorothricin-type	2414	Ansamycin
23512	Macrolactone, milbemycin-type	2421	Ansa-macrolactam, maytansin-type
2352	Cytochalasin-type	2422	Ansa-macrolactam, rubradirin-type
2353	Brefeldin-type	243	Lactone-lactam
	Volume III: Quinone and Similar Antibiotics		
3	Quinone-type	32222	Naphtoquinone derivatives, rubromycin-type
31111	Tetracycline-type	32223	Naphtoquinone derivates, granaticin-type
31112	Tetracycline-type	32224	Naphtoquinone derivates, naphtazarin
3112	Tetracycline-like	32225	Naphtoquinone derivatives, kalafungin-type
3113	Tetracycline-like	32226	Naphtoquinone derivatives, pyranonaphtoqui none
312	Anthracycline-like	3223	Naphtoquinone derivatives
31211	Anthracycline, rhodomycin-type	3231	Luteomycin-type
31212	Anthracycline, cinerubin-type	3232	Xanthomycin-type
31213	Anthracycline, aklavin-type	3311	Benzoquinone
31214	Anthracyline, daunomycin-type	3312	Benzoquinone derivates
31221	Anthracycline, nogalamycin-type	3313	Benzoquinone derivatives, bibenzoquinones
31222	Anthracycline, steffimycin-type	3314	Benzoquinone derivates
31223	Anthracycline, quinocycline-type	33211	Mitomycin-type
3123	Anthracyclinone	33212	Mitomycin-like
313	Anthraquinone derivatives	3322	Streptonigrin-type
3131	Anthraquinone	3323[a]	Benzoquinone derivates
3132	Dianthraquinone	3324	Benzoquinone derivatives, saframycin-type
3133	Benzanthraquinone, tetrangomycin-type	3411	Semiquinone, quinone-methide
3134	Anthraquinone derivatives	3412[a]	Semiquinone, quinone-methide
3135	Pluramycin-type	34131	Semiquinone, resistomycin-type
3136	Phenanthrenequinone	34132	Semiquinone, herqueinone-type
3137	Anthraquinone derivatives	3421	Quinone-like, epoxydone-type
3211	o-Naphtoquinone	3422[a]	Quinone-like
3212	p-Naphtoquinone	3423[a]	Quinone-like
32211	Naphtoquinone derivatives, cervicarcin-type		
32212	Naphtoquinone derivatives, julimycin-type		
32221	Naphtoquinone derivatives, actinorhodin-type		
	Volume IV Part 1: Amino Acid and Peptide Antibiotics		
4	Peptide/polypeptide	41215	Beta lactam, clavulanic acid-type
41	Amino acid derivatives	4122	Pyrrothine-type
4111	Azaamino acid	4123	Actithiazic acid-type
41121	Amino acid	4131	Diketopiperazine derivatives
41122	Amino acid	41321	Epidiketooligothiapiperazine, gliotoxin-type
41123	Amino acid	41322	Epidiketooligothiapiperazine, chaetocin-type
41124	Amino acid	41323	Epidiketooligothiapiperazine, sporidesmin-type
4113	Amino acid analog	41324	Epidiketooligothiapiperazine, hyalodendrin-type
41211	Beta lactam, penicillin-type		
41212	Beta lactam, cephalosporin-type		
41213	Beta lactam, nocardicin-type		
41214	Beta lactam, thienamycin-type		

Table 2 (continued)
KEY TO THE ANTIBIOTIC TYPES AND SUBTYPES

AN	Chemical type designations	AN	Chemical type designations
	Volume IV Part 1: Amino Acid and Peptide Antibiotics (continued)		
41325	Epidiketooligothiapiperazine, sirodesmin-type	4311	Lipopeptide, amphomycin-type
		43121	Lipopeptide, polymyxin-type
41326	Epidiketooligothiapiperazine	43122	Lipopeptide, octapeptin-type
4133	Aspergillic acid-type	43123	Lipopeptide, polypeptin-type
4211	Oligopeptide, netropsin-like	43124	Lipopeptide, tridecaptin-type
42111	Oligopeptide, netropsin-type	4313	Peptide, echinocandin-type
42112	Oligopeptide, noformicin-type	4314	Peptide, bacillomycin-type
42113	Oligopeptide, kikumycin-type	4315	Peptide
4212	Oligopeptide	432	Peptide
4213	Cyclic oligopeptide-like, diketopiperazine derivatives	43211	Thiazolyl-peptide, thiostrepton-type
		43212	Thiazolyl-peptide, althiomycin-type
4221	Peptide, gramicidin-type	43213	Thiazolyl-peptide
4222	Peptide, edein-type	43214	Thiazolyl-peptide, micrococcin-type
4223	Peptide	4322	Peptide, bottromycin-type
4224	Peptide	4323	Peptide, berninamycin-type
4225	Peptide, peptaibophol-type	4324	Peptide, leucinamycin-type
4226	Peptide, cerexin-type	43311	Sideromycin, albomycin-type
423	Cyclopeptide	43312	Sideromycin, ferrimycin-type
4231	Cyclopeptide, tyrocidine-type	43313	Sideromycin, succinimycin-type
4232	Cyclopeptide, bacitracin-type	43314	Pseudosideromycin
4233	Cyclopeptide, viomycin-type	43315	Sideramine
4234	Cyclopeptide, ilamycin-type	4332	Glycopeptide, bleomycin-type
4235	Cyclopeptide, cyclosporin-type	4333	Peptide-like, chelate-forming
431	Lipopeptide		
	Volume IV Part 2: Peptolide and Macromolecular Antibiotics		
4411	Chromopeptolide, actinomycin-type	4452	Depsipeptide, serratamolide, type
4412	Quinoxaline-peptide, echinomycin-type	4453	Depsipeptide, ostreogrycin-A-type
		4454	Depsipeptide
4413	Peptide like, taitomycin-type	45	Polypeptide, protein, macromolecular
4421	Peptolide, enduracidin-type	4511	Polypeptide
4422	Peptolide, stendomycin-type	4512	Polypeptide
4423	Peptolide, peptidolipid	4513	Polypeptide
4424	Peptolide	4514	Polypeptide, nisin-type
4425	Peptolide	45211	Acidic protein
44311	Peptolide, virginiamycin-type	45212	Basic protein
44312	Peptolide, etamycin-type	45213	Amphoteric protein
44313	Peptolide, pyridomycin-type	4522	Protein
4432	Peptolide, monamycin-type	4523	Lipoprotein
4441	Peptolide, telomycin-type	4531	Chromoproteid
4442	Peptolide, grisellimycin-type	4532	Glycoproteid
4443	Peptolide	4533	Nucleoproteid
4444	Peptolide	4534	Enzyme-like
4451	Depsipeptide, valinomycin-type	4535	Bacteriocin
		4536	
	Volume V: Heterocyclic Antibiotics		
5111	Pyrrole derivatives, pyrrolnitrin-type	5117[a]	Pyrrole derivatives, chlorophyll derivative
5112	Pyrrole derivatives, prodigiosin-type		
51131	Tetramic acid derivatives	5121	Pyridine derivatives
51132	Tetramic acid derivatives, streptolydigin-type	51221	Pyridone derivatives, mocimycin-type
		51222	Pyridone derivatives
51133	Tetramic acid derivatives, oleficin-type	5123	Piperidine derivatives
5114	Pyrrolidine derivatives	5124	Piperidine derivatives
5115	Imidazole derivatives	5125	Pyrimidine derivatives
5116	Pyrrole	5126	Pyrazine derivatives
		51311	Cytosine glycoside, amicetin-type
		51312	Cytosine glycoside, blasticidin-S-type

Table 2 (continued)
KEY TO THE ANTIBIOTIC TYPES AND SUBTYPES

AN	Chemical type designations
Volume V: Heterocyclic Antibiotics (continued)	
51313	Cytosine glycoside, gougerotin-type
51314	Azacytosine glycoside
51315	Pyrimidine glycoside, ezomycin-type
51321	Uracil glycoside, polyoxin-type
51322	Uracil glycoside, mycospocidin-type
51323	Azauracil glycoside
51324	Uracil glycoside
51325	Thymine glycoside
51331	Imidazole glycoside
51341	N-Heterocyclic C-glycoside
51342	N-Heterocyclic C-glycoside
5211	Indole derivatives
5212	Quinoline (quinoxaline) derivatives
5213	Phenazine derivatives
5214	Phenoxazine derivatives
5215	Albofungin-type
5216	N-Heterocyclic derivatives
5217[a]	Alkaloid-like, carbazole derivatives
5221	Benzdiazepine, anthramycin-type
5222	Purine derivatives
5223	Pyrimidotriazine derivatives, fervenulin-type
523	Adenine glycoside-like
52311	Purine glycoside
52312	Adenine glycoside
52313	Adenine derivative
52314	Deazaadenine glycoside
52315	Adenine analog
52316	2-Aminopurine glycoside
52321	Pyrazolopyrimidine C-glycoside, formycin-type
52322	Homopurine glycoside, coformycin-type
5233	Guanine glycoside
5234	Nucleotide
53	Alkaloid
5411	Cyclic polysulfide
5421	Tiophene derivatives
6111	Furan derivatives
6112[a]	Furan derivatives, lignan-like
6121	Aflatoxin-type
6122[a]	Furan derivatives
6131[a]	Dibenzofuran derivatives
6132	Dibenzofuran derivatives, usnic acid-type
6133	Benzofuran derivatives
6134	Benzofuran derivatives
6211	Pyran derivatives
6212[a]	Pyran derivatives
6221	Alpha pyrone, asperline-type
6222	Alpha pyrone
6223[a]	Alpha pyrone derivatives
6224	Alpha pyrone derivatives
6225	Alpha pyrone derivatives
6226	Alpha pyrone derivatives
6231	Gamma pyrone derivatives, aureothin-type
6232	Gamma pyrone derivatives
6233	Gamma pyrone derivatives
6241	Beta pyrone
631[a]	Flavonoid
6311[a]	Flavone-type
6312	Flavonol-type
6313[a]	Flavanone-type
6314	Anthocyanide
6315[a]	Chalcone derivatives
6321[a]	Isoflavone
6322[a]	Pterocarpan-type
6323[a]	Isoflavanone
6324[a]	Isoflavan
6331[a]	Neoflavone-type
6341	Xanthone derivatives
6342[a]	Xanthone derivatives, morellin-type
6343	Condensed gamma pyrone derivatives
63441	Bisnaphtopyran derivatives, viridotoxin-type
63442	Bisnaphtopyran derivatives, cephalochromin-type
6345	Xanthone derivative, ergochrome type
6411	Beta lactone derivatives
6412	Gamma lactone derivatives
6413[a]	Lichesteric acid-type
6414	Tetronic acid
6415	Dilactone derivatives
6416	Dilactone derivatives
64211[a]	Podophyllotoxin-type
64212	Condensed small lactone
6422	Coumarone derivatives
6423	Coumarin derivatives
6424[a]	Coumarin derivatives
6425	Isocoumarin derivatives
65	Polyether
6511	Polyether, monensin-type
65121	Polyether, nigericin-type
65122	Polyether, septamycin-type
6513	Polyether, alborixin-type
6514	Polyether, lysocellin-type
6521	Polyether, narasin-type
6522	Polyether, dianemycin-type
6531	Polyether, lasalocid-type
6532	Polyether
6541	Polyether-like, calcimycin-type
6551	Polyether-like, ambrutycin-type
Volume VI: Alicyclic, Aromatic, and Aliphatic Antibiotics	
7111	Cyclopentane derivatives
7112	Cyclopentane derivatives
7113	Cyclopentane derivatives
7114	Cyclopentane derivatives
7121	Cyclohexane derivatives, fumagillin-type
7122	Cycloohexenone derivatives
7123	Cyclohexene derivatives
7124	Cyclohexanol derivatives

Table 2 (continued)
KEY TO THE ANTIBIOTIC TYPES AND SUBTYPES

Volume VI: Alicyclic, Aromatic, and Aliphatic Antibiotics (continued)

AN	Chemical type designations
713	Glutarimide-like
7131	Glutarimide, cycloheximide-type
7132	Glutarimide, actiphenol-type
7133	Glutarimide, streptimidone-type
7141	Cyclobutane derivatives
72	Terpene-like
7211[a]	Monoterpene
7212	Sesquiterpene
7213	Diterpene
72141	Sesterterpene, ophiobolin-type
72142[a]	Sesterterpene
7215	Terpene glycoside
7221[a]	Sesquiterpene lactone
7222[a]	Diterpene lactone
7223[a]	Terpene lactone derivatives
7224[a]	Glaucarubin-type, terpene derivatives
7225	Nonadrine
7311	Steroid
73111	Fusidic acid-type
73112	Polyporenic acid-type
73113[a]	Cucurbitacin-type
7312[a]	Steroid alkaloid
73131[a]	Cardenolide
73132[a]	Bufadienolide
73133[a]	Withanolide
73134[a]	Sterol glycoside
7314	Viridin-type
7315	Azasteroid
7321[a]	Triterpene
7322[a]	Triterpene glycoside
7323[a]	Saponine
73311	Scirpene derivatives, trichotecin-type
73312	Scirpene derivatives, trichodermin-type.
7332	Scirpene derivatives, macrolactone
8111	Benzene derivatives
8112	Benzene derivatives
8113	Benzene derivatives
8114	Benzene derivatives
81211	Chloramphenicol-type
81212	Benzene derivatives
8122	Aromatic terpene derivatives, ascochlorin-type
8123	Benzene-aliphatic derivatives
8124	Benzene-aliphatic derivatives
8125	Benzene-aliphatic derivatives
8126[a]	Aromatic terpene derivatives
8131	Polycyclic benzene derivatives, xanthocillin-type
8132[a]	Polycyclic benzene derivatives, stilbene-type
8133	Polycyclic benzene derivatives, diphenyl-type
8134	Polycyclic benzene derivatives
8211	Grisan derivatives, griseofulvin-type
8212	Grisan derivatives, geodin-type
8221	Naphtalene derivatives
8222	Naphtalene derivatives, naphtalonone
8223[a]	Naphtalene derivatives, gossypol-type
8224[a]	Naphtalene derivatives
8231	Anthracene derivatives
8232[a]	Phenanthrene derivatives
8232[a]	Phenanthrene derivatives
8241[a]	Indane derivatives, pterosin-type
8311	Tropolone
8312	Tropolone
8321	Azulene
8411	Aromatic ether
8421	Glycosidic antibiotic, hygromycin A-type
8422	Glycosidic antibiotic, chartreusin-type
84231	Glycosidic antibiotic, novobiocin-type
84232	Glyyosidic antibiotic, coumermycin-type
84311	Depsidone, nidulin-type
84312[a]	Depsidone
8432[a]	Depside
8433	Aromatic ester
8434	Aromatic ester
91	Aliphatic
9111	Aliphatic derivatives
9112[a]	Aliphatic derivatives
9113	Aliphatic derivatives, elaiomycin-type
9114	Aliphatic derivatives
9115	Aliphatic derivatives
912	Polyine
9121	Polyine
9122	Polyine
9123	Polyine
92111	Acrylic acid derivatives, enteromycin-type
92112	Acrylic acid derivatives
9212	Acetylene derivatives
9213	Simple carboxylic acid derivatives
922	Fatty acid-like
9221	Fatty acid
9222	Fatty acid
9223	Fatty acid
9224	Fatty acid derivatives
9225	Fatty acid derivatives
9226	Fatty acid derivatives
9311	Thioformine derivatives
9312[a]	Aliphatic sulnoxide
93131[a]	Isothiocyanate derivatives
93132	Isothiocyanate derivatives
9314[a]	Simple aliphatic thio derivatives
932	Phosphonomycin-type

Table 2 (continued)
KEY TO THE ANTIBIOTIC TYPES AND SUBTYPES

Volume VII: Miscellaneous Antibiotics with Unknown Chemical Structure

00000	Unclassified antibiotics (no antibiotic number)

[a] Only plant and animal products exist in this type.

abbreviations). Generally, all the values found in different solvents are listed. No exact temperature and concentration of the compounds is given; the values are regarded to near room temperature. If the magnitude of rotation is unknown, just a + or − sign is coded.

10. Ultraviolet Spectra

The wavelength of all observed maxima (in nanometers) and the corresponding extinction values ($E^{1\%}_{1\,cm}$ and/or molecular extinction) are listed. Values are referred to for any solvents determined. Solvents are abbreviated according to the listed abbreviations. If the spectrum is taken at a particular pH (in water or buffer), the number instead of the solvent indicates these values. Combination solvents are separated by hyphens, e.g., MeOH-HCl means generally 0.1 *N* methanolic hydrochloric acid. UV-MeOH: (235,, 35000) = λ_{max}: 235 nm, ε: 35000 in methanolic solution. UV-8: (240,422,) = λ_{max}: 240 nm, $E^{1\%}_{1\,cm}$: 422 in a pH 8 buffer. UV- : (200,,) means end absorption.

11. Solubility

Data about solubility range from good to fair to poor (insoluble), according to the author's original statement. Solvents are abbreviated according to the general list. The following organic solvents are considered with special emphasis: methanol, ethanol, butanol, acetone, ethyl acetate, chloroform, benzene, ether, and hexane (petrolether). For each compound when two solvents are given which do not appear consecutively in the above list, then include those solvents which are enlisted between these two solvents. For example, the methanol, ether pair in the category solubility-good means that the compound is well soluble in all organic solvents listed before, with the exception of hexane. The acetone, hexane pair in the solubility-poor category means the insolubility of the compound in acetone, ethyl acetate, chloroform, ether, benzene, and hexane.

12. Qualitative Chemical Reactions

The name of the selected eight reactions, listed below with any abbreviations used, and the result (positive, +, and negative, −), separated by a comma, are listed.

Ninhidrine	Ninh.
Sakaguchi	Saka.
Fehling	Fehl.
Ferrichloride	$FeCl_3$
Ehrlich	Ehrl.
2,4-Dinitrophenyl hydrazone	DNPH
Biuret	
Pauly	

13. Stability

The condition (acid, base, heat, light) and the result (stable, +, or unstable, −), separated by a comma, are listed. These data are more or less uncertain because the coding is obviously arbitrary.

14. Antimicrobial Activity

The data, if known, for the following ten test organisms are given for each compound:

Staphylococcus aureus	*S. aureus*
Sarcina lutea	*S. lutea*
Bacillus subtilis	*B. subtilis*
Escherichia coli	*E. coli*
Shigella species	*Shyg.* sp.
Pseudomonas aeruginosa	*Ps. aer.*
Proteus vulgaris	*P. vulg.*
Klebsiella pneumoniae	*K. pneum.*
Saccharomyces cerevisiae	*S. cerev.*
Candida albicans	*C. alb.*

The overall activity on the following microorganism types is also listed, especially when it is outstandingly characteristic of the compound or if specification of the activity is not detailed.

Gram-positive bacteria	G. pos.
Gram-negative bacteria	G. neg.
Mycobacterium species	*Mycob.* sp.
Phytopathogen bacteria (*Xanthomonas oryzae*)	Phyt. bact.
Phytopathogen fungi (*Piricularia oryzae*)	Phyt. fungi
Fungi (excluding yeasts)	
Protozoa	

Other specific test organisms are listed only when the compound is ineffective (or no data about the activity are available) against the formerly listed microorganisms or the activity against these specific test organisms, e.g., *B. mycoides, Corynebacterium* species, *Cryptococcus* species, *Trichophyton* species, *Mycoplasma* species, etc., is very significant.

The microorganisms (abbreviated as before) and the MIC values — if known — (in micrograms per milliliter) are listed and separated by commas. Data of the most sensitive strains (among the identical species or types) are taken into account. If no specific organism is known, the terms antibacterial, antifungal, antimicrobial, etc. are listed. Specific activities are coded as follows: anthelminthic, herbicide, insecticide, nematocide, etc.

15. Toxicity

All data listed are acute LD_{50} values in mice. The abbreviation of the method of administration follows the value, given in milligrams per kilogram, e.g., LD_{50}: (10, i.v.). If no particular dose level is known, the terms toxic or nontoxic are used freely, usually after the author's original statement. The phytotoxicities are also frequently noted.

16. Antitumor and/or Antiviral Activity

The following antitumor (cytotoxic) activities are listed:

Adenocarcinoma 755, mouse	CA-755
Other carcinomas	CA
Croecker sarcoma, mouse	Croecker
Ehrlich ascites or solid carcinoma, mouse	Ehrlich
Guerin carcinoma, rat	Guerin
Lymphoid leukemia L-1210, mouse	L-1210
Lewis lung carcinoma, mouse	Lewis
Human epidermoid carcinomas	H-1, H-2
Other lymphosarcomas	LS
Melanomas (B-16)	Melanoma
Myelosarcomas	Myelo
Novikoff hepatoma, rat	Novikoff
Lymphocytic leukemia P388, mouse	P-388
Leukemia P-815, mouse	P-815
Leukemia P-1534, mouse	P-1534
Sarcoma 37, mouse	S-37
Sarcoma 45, rat	S-45
Sarcoma 180, mouse	S-180
Leukemia SN-36, mouse	SN-36
Walker carcinosarcoma 256, rat	Walker 256
Yoshida sarcoma, rat	Yoshida
Cell lines	
HeLa human carcinoma, cell culture	HeLa
Portio carcinoma, cell culture	Earle
Human epidermoid carcinoma of the nasopharynx	KB
Németh-Kellner lymphoma, cell culture	NK-Ly

The following antiviral activities are listed:

Columbia SK virus	Columbia
Coxsackie virus	Coxsackie
Influenza virus, PR-8	Influenza
Newcastle disease virus	NDV
Poliovirus	Polio
Rhinovirus	Rhino
Herpesvirus	Herpes
Plant viruses	Plant virus

Tobacco mosaic virus	TMV
Vaccinia virus, pox	Vaccinia

For both antitumor and antiviral activity, no data about the specific circumstances or effective doses are provided; only the existence of the effects is listed. If the specific activity is unknown, or the compound is active only in test(s) excluding the above list, the terms antitumor, cytotoxic, antiviral, or antiphage are listed.

17. Isolation Methods Employed

This information is not listed in the case of plant and animal products.

A. Filtration

The value of the pH when the cultural broth has been filtered is listed. The term original pH means the filtration at the original pH of the broth.

B. Extraction

The solvents of with what, at what pH, and from what, separated by commas, are listed. For example: (EtOAc, 3, filtrate) means the extraction of the active compounds from the cultural filtrate at pH 3. The free places mean the unknown data, e.g., (BuOH,,filtrate) means the extraction with butanol from the filtrate at an unknown pH.

C. Ion Exchange

The resins or other ion-exchange materials and the eluting solvents or solvent systems employed (without quantitative composition), separated by comma, are listed. For example, (IRC-50-Na, HCl) means the absorption of the active compound on the Amberlite IRC-50 resin in sodium form, followed by the elution with diluted hydrochloric acid.

D. Absorption

The absorbent and the eluting solvents are listed, as before.

E. Chromatography

The adsorbent and the eluting solvents or solvent systems (the solvents are listed always according to increasing polarity) are listed as before. The components of the eluting system are separated by hyphens and no quantitative composition is given. The ion-exchange chromatographic methods are included here, e.g., (SILG., CHL-MeOH) means silica gel chromatography with chloroform-methanol mixtures.

F. Crystallization

This identifier summarizes the final purification steps of the isolation process, according to the following:

Isolation-crystallization: Crystallized from what solvent or solvent system.

Isolation-precipitation: Precipitated from what and with what. Sometimes it means the first step of the isolation. Examples: (Prec., Acet, Et_2O) means precipitation with ether from acetone; (Prec., Filt., HCl) means that the active compound was precipitated from the cultural filtrate by acidification with hydrochloric acid.

Isolation-dry: Evaporated to dry from what solvent.

Isolation-lyophilization: Lyophilized from water.

Examples

Is-fil: 2
Is-ext: (BuOAc, 8, filt.) (w, 2, BuOAc) (CHL, 7, w) (MeOH,,mic.)
Is-chr: (AL, benz-hex)
Is-cry: (preci., benz, hex) (cryst., acet-benz)

The meaning of this coded information is the following: the cultural broth was filtered at pH 2 and the filtrate was extracted at pH 8 with butyl acetate. Some additional active substance was extracted from the mycelium with methanol. The active substance(s) was transferred at pH 2 to water and, after neutralization to pH 7, this substance(s) was reextracted with chloroform. The crude substance — after evaporation of the final chloroformic extract — was precipitated by hexane, then was chromatographed on an aluminum oxide column with benzene-methanol mixtures. Finally, the active compound(s) — after evaporation of the pooled active fractions — was crystallized from the acetone-benzene mixture.

18. Utility

In this identifier the practical utilization or potential usefulness of the compounds has been summarized. The following areas of utility are listed:

1. Antibacterial drug	Human drugs	Commercialized compounds
2. Antifungal drug	Human drugs	Commercialized compounds
3. Antiprotozoal drug	Human drugs	Commercialized compounds
4. Antitumor drug	Human drugs	Commercialized compounds
5. Antiviral drug	Human drugs	Commercialized compounds
6. Veterinary drug (including anthelminthics, coccidiostatics)		Commercialized compounds
7. Feed additive		Commercialized compounds
8. Food preservative		Commercialized compounds
9. Plant protecting agent		Commercialized compounds
10. Biochemical reagent		Commercialized compounds
11. On clinical trial — potential drug		
12. No longer available as a commercial product (have only some historical importance)		

The human drugs include the so-called "pre-compounds" such as cephalosporin C or rifamycin B which are only practically and historically important.

19. Structural Formula

The chemical structures of compounds or occasionally partial structures appear as a part of or following the introductory material. The related structures always have been given in summarized form as derivatives of a basic skeleton, as far as it enhances understanding the relationship between the compounds. These collective structural formulae are provided within the scope of the introduction to the group, type, or subtype, preceding the listing of compounds. The unique chemical structures generally are given following the introductory material.

An attempt has been made to depict all structures with the most modern stereochemical representations. Spatial drawings are used where appropriate. The standard convention of heavy and dotted lines is used to demonstrate the spatial arrangements of bonds.

20. References

References are given annexed to the introductory material (reviews) and the individual compounds (original papers, patents, etc.) as well. Referencing is not exhaustive, but much attention has been given to selecting the useful references. Our intent is to give a concise but not full reference story of any compound. In general, an attempt has been made to cite the first publications including the important properties of compounds and the recent papers or reviews, to work on the subject which, by its own bibliography, will include the earlier literature. In the references we made an attempt at completeness in the case of newer, less-known but potentially useful or interesting agents. The well-known antibiotics are referred to in reviews and monographs.

Special attention has been given to the patent literature, which is particularly quick in reporting antibiotics. Some antibiotics have only been published in the patent literature. *Chemical Abstracts* references have been used liberally, particularly when the original journal or patent is unlikely to be readily available. On certain topics the literature is vast and it is impossible, and it is not our aim, to cite all publications. If someone wants to know everything about penicillins or tetracyclines, many excellent monographs and reviews are at hand.

The periodicals and patents in this Handbook are abbreviated unlike the usual citation (owing to the requirements of computer programming); moreover, we refer only to the volume (or year), page, and year of publication of the periodicals and to the nationality and number of patents. The books and monographs (from review journals) are referred to by the name of the author(s) and/or editor, title, and year of publication.

The following lists include the most important books, periodicals, and other publications (proceedings, abstracts, reports, etc.) which are devoted exclusively or partly to antibiotics. These listings cover — together with the information obtained from the patent literature — the sources of data listed in this Handbook. The lists of periodicals include the abbreviations used in the reference part of this Handbook.

List 1

HANDBOOKS, TEXTBOOKS, AND PERIODICALS DEVOTED EXCLUSIVELY TO ANTIBIOTICS

A. Most Useful and Complete Handbooks

1. **Umezawa, H., Ed.,** *Index of Antibiotics from Actinomycetes,* University of Tokyo Press, Tokyo, 1967.
2. **Korzybski, T., Kowszyk-Gindifer, Z., and Kurylowicz, W.,** *Antibiotics: Origin, Nature and Properties,* Pergamon Press, Oxford, and Polish Scientific Publishers, Warsaw, 1967.
3. **Gottlieb, D. and Shaw, P. D., Eds.,** *Antibiotics,* Vol. 1 and 2, Springer-Verlag, Berlin, 1967.
4. **Corcoran, J. W. and Hahn, F. E., Eds.,** *Antibiotics,* Vol. 3, Springer-Verlag, Berlin, 1975.
5. **Glasby, J. S.,** *Encyclopedia of Antibiotics,* John Wiley & Sons, London, 1976.
6. **Shemyakin, M. M., Khokhlov, A. S., Kolosov, M. N., Bergelson, L. D., and Antonov, V. K.,** *Chemistry of Antibiotics,* 3rd ed., Izdanja Akademii Nauk SSSR, Moscow, 1961.
7. **Sevcik, V.,** *Antibiotika aus Actinomyceten,* VEB Gustav Fischer Verlag, Jena, 1963.
8. **Brunner, R. and Machek, G.,** *Die Antibiotica,* Hans Carl Verlag, Nurnberg, 1962.
9. **Waksman, S. A. and Lechevalier, H. A.,** *The Actinomycetes,* Vol. 3, Williams & Wilkins, Baltimore, 1962.

B. Outdated Handbooks

1. **Spector, W. S., Porter, J. N., DeMallo, and G. C., Eds.,** *Handbook of Toxicology,* Vol. 2, W. B. Saunders, Philadelphia, 1957.
2. **Florey, H. W., Chain, E., Heatley, N. G., Jennings, M. A., Sanders, A. G., Abraham, E. P., and Florey, M. E.,** *Antibiotics,* Oxford University Press, Oxford, 1949.
3. **Karel, L. and Roach, E. S.,** *A Dictionary of Antibiosis,* Columbia University Press, New York, 1951.
4. **Baron, A. L.,** *Handbook of Antibiotics,* Reinhold, New York, 1950.
5. **Klosa, J.,** *Antibiotika,* Verlag Technik, Berlin, 1952.
6. **Robinson, F. A.,** *Antibiotics,* Pitman & Sons, London, 1953.
7. **Werner, G. E.,** *Antibiotica Codex,* Wissenschaftliche Verlag, Stuttgart, 1963.

C. Textbooks

1. General (Chemistry, Biochemistry)

1. **Umezawa, H.,** *Recent Advances in Chemistry and Biochemistry of Antibiotics,* Microbial Chemistry Research Foundation, Tokyo, 1964.
2. **Hash, J. H., Ed.,** *Methods in Enzymology,* Vol. 43, Academic Press, New York, 1975.
3. **Sammes, P. G., Ed.,** *Topics in Antibiotic Chemistry,* Vol. 1, Ellis Horwood Ltd., Chichester, 1977.
4. **Mitsuhashi, S., Ed.,** *Drug Action and Drug Resistance on Bacteria,* Vol. 1 and 2, University of Tokyo Press, Tokyo, 1975.
5. **Perlman, D., Ed.,** *Structure-Activity Relationships Among the Semisynthetic Antibiotics,* Academic Press, New York, 1977.
6. **Perlman, D.,** *Antibiotics,* Rand McNally, Chicago, 1970.
7. **Evans, R. M.,** *Chemistry of the Antibiotics Used in Medicine,* Pergamon Press, London, 1965.
8. **Goldberg, H. S., Ed.,** *Antibiotics, Their Chemistry and Non-medical Uses,* D. Van Nostrand, Princeton, 1959.
9. **Prescott, S. C. and Dunn, C. G.,** *Antibiotics, Industrial Microbiology,* McGraw-Hill, New York, 1959.
10. **Waksman, S. A. and Lechevalier, H. A.,** *Actinomycetes and Their Antibiotics,* Williams & Wilkins, Baltimore, 1953.
11. **Gause, G. F.,** *The Search for New Antibiotics,* Yale University Press, New Haven, 1960.

2. General (Biosynthesis, Mechanism of Action)

12. **Snell, J. F.,** *Biosynthesis of Antibiotics,* Academic Press, New York, 1966.
13. **Vanek, Z. and Hostalek, Z., Eds.,** *Biogenesis of Antibiotic Substances,* Academic Press, New York, 1966.
14. **Gale, E. F., Cundliffe, E., Reynolds, P. E., Richmond, M. H. and Waring, M. J.,** *The Molecular Basis of Antibiotic Action,* John Wiley & Sons, London, 1972.
15. **Franklin, T. J. and Snow, G. A.,** *Biochemistry of Antimicrobial Action,* Chapman and Hall, London, 1971.
16. **Zähner, H.,** *Biologie der Antibiotica,* Springer-Verlag, Berlin, 1965.
17. **Newton, B. A. and Reynolds, P. E., Eds.,** *Biochemical Studies of Antimicrobial Drugs,* Cambridge University Press, Cambridge 1966.
18. **Mitsuhashi, S.,** *Transferable Drug Resistance Factor R,* University Park Press, Baltimore, 1971.
19. **Barber, M. and Garrod, L. P.,** *Antibiotic and Chemotherapy,* E & S Livingstone, London, 1963.
20. **Garrod, L. P. and O'Grady, F.,** *Antibiotic and Chemotherapy,* 3rd ed., E & S Livingstone, Edinburgh, 1971.

3. Special (Assay, Physical, Applications)

21. **Grove, D. C. and Randall, W. A.,** *Assay Methods of Antibiotics. A Laboratory Manual,* Medical Encyclopedia, New York, 1955.
22. **Kavanagh, F., Ed.,** *Analytical Microbiology,* Academic Press, New York, 1963.
23. **Wagman, G. H. and Weinstein, M. J.,** *Chromatography of Antibiotics,* Elsevier, Amsterdam, 1973.
24. **Blinov, N. O. and Khokhlov, A. S.,** *Paper Chromatography of Antibiotics,* Izdanja Akademii Nauk SSSR, Moscow, 1970.
25. **Abraham, E. P.,** *Biochemistry of Some Peptide and Steroid Antibiotics,* John Wiley & Sons, London, 1957.
26. **Maeda, K.,** *Streptomyces Products Inhibiting Mycobacteria,* John Wiley & Sons, New York, 1965.
27. **Rinehart, K. L., Jr.,** *The Neomycins and Related Antibiotics,* John Wiley & Sons, New York, 1964.
28. **Woodbine, M., Ed.,** *Antibiotics in Agriculture,* Butterworths, London, 1962.
29. **Bücher, T. and Sies, H., Eds.,** *Inhibitors: Tools in Cell Research,* Springer-Verlag, Berlin, 1969.
30. **Jukes, T. H.,** *Antibiotics in Nutrition,* Medical Encyclopedia, New York, 1955.
31. **Bilai, V. I.,** *Antibiotic Producing Microscopic Fungi,* Elsevier, Amsterdam, 1963.
32. **Flynn, E. H., Ed.,** *Cephalosporins and Penicillins; Chemistry and Biology,* Academic Press, New York, 1972.
33. **Barker, B. M. and Prescott, F.,** *Antimicrobial Agents in Medicine,* Blackwell, Oxford, 1973.
34. **Sermonti, G.,** *Genetics of Antibiotic-Producing Microorganisms,* John Wiley & Sons, London, 1969.

D. Journals

	Abbreviation
1. *Journal of Antibiotics* (formerly *Journal of Antibiotics, Series A*)	*JA*
2. *Japanese Journal of Antibiotics* (in Japanese) (formerly *Journal of Antibiotics, Series B*)	*Jap. J. Ant.*
3. *Antimicrobial Agents and Chemotherapy* (1971—)	*AAC*

4.	*Antibiotiki (Moscow)* (in Russian)	*Antib.*
5.	*Hindustan Antibiotic Bulletin*	*HAB*
6.	*Antibiotics & Chemotherapy* (1951—1962)	*Ant. & Chem.*
7.	*Revista Instituto de Antibioticos (Recife)*	*Rev. Inst. Antib.*
8.	*Information Bulletin, International Center of Information on Antibiotics*	*ICIA*

E. Other Periodicals

1.	*Antibiotics Annual* (1953—54 to 1959—60)	*Ant. An.*
2.	*Antimicrobial Agents Annual 1960*	*Ant. A. An.*
3.	*Antimicrobial Agents and Chemotherapy 1961—1970* (Proc. Interscience Conf. Antimicrobial Agents and Chemotherapy)	*AAC year*
4.	*Abstracts Interscience Conf. Antimicrobial Agents and Chemotherapy* (1971—)	*Abst. AAC*
5.	*Antibiotica et Chemotherapia* (S. Karger, Basel) Vol. 1 to 24 (1954—1978)	
6.	*Progress in Antimicrobial and Anticancer Chemotherapy,* Proc. 6th Int. Congr. Chemotherapy, Tokyo, 1969, University of Tokyo Press, Tokyo, 1970)	*Progr. AAC*
7.	*Advances in Antimicrobial and Antineoplastic Chemotherapy,* Proc. 7th Int. Congr. Chemotherapy, Prague, 1971, Urban & Schwarzenberg Verlag, Munich, 1972	*Adv. AAC*
8.	*Progress in Chemotherapy (Antimicrobial, Antiviral, Antineoplastic),* Proc. 8th Int. Congr. Chemotherapy, Athens, 1973, Hellenic Society of Chemotherapy, Athens, 1974	
9.	*Antibiotics. Advances in Research, Production and Clinical Use,* Proc. Congr. Antibiotics, Prague, 1964, Butterworths, London, 1966	
10.	*Biochemistry of Antibiotics,* Proc. 4th Int. Congr. Biochemistry, Vienna, 1958, Pergamon Press, London, 1959	
11.	*Antibiotics and Mould Metabolites,* Symp. Chem. Soc., Nottingham, 1956, Chemical Society, London, 1956	
12.	*Antibiotics. Their Production, Utilization and Mode of Action,* Symp. Hindustan Antibiotics Ltd., Pimpri, 1956, Council of Science and Industrial Research, New Delhi, 1958	
13.	*Symposyum on Antibiotics,* Quebec, 1971, Butterworths, London, 1971	

List 2

HANDBOOKS, TEXTBOOKS, AND PERIODICALS DEVOTED PARTLY TO ANTIBIOTICS

A. General Handbooks

1. **Laskin, A. I. and Lechevalier, H. A., Eds.,** *CRC Handbook of Microbiology,* Vol. 3, CRC Press, Cleveland, 1973.
2. **Miller, M. W.,** *The Pfizer Handbook of Microbial Metabolites,* McGraw-Hill, New York, 1961.
3. **Turner, W. B.,** *Fungal Metabolites,* Academic Press, New York, 1971.
4. **Stecher, P. G., Ed.,** *The Merck Index,* 9th ed., Merck & Company, Rahway, N.J., 1977.
5. **Shibata, S., Natori, S., and Udagawa, S.,** *List of Fungal Products,* Charles C Thomas, Springfield, Ill., 1964.
6. **Devon, T. K. and Scott, A. I.,** *Handbook of Naturally Occurring Compounds,* Academic Press, New York, 1972.
7. **Ciegler, A., Kadis, S., and Ajl, S. J., Eds.,** *Microbial Toxins,* Vol. 1 to 7, Academic Press, New York.
8. **Foster, J. W.,** *Chemical Activities of Fungi,* Academic Press, New York, 1949.
9. **Thompson, R. H.,** *Naturally Occurring Quinones,* Academic Press, New York, 1971.
10. **Dean, F. M.,** *Naturally Occurring Oxygen Ring Compounds,* Butterworths, London, 1963.
11. **Culberson, C. F.,** *Chemical and Botanical Guide to Lichen Products,* University of North Carolina Press, Chapel Hill, 1969.

B. Special Textbooks

1. Chemistry

1. **Nakanishi, K., Goto, T., Ito, S., Natori, S., and Nozoe, S., Eds.,** *Natural Products Chemistry,* Vol. 1 and 2, Kodansha Ltd. and Academic Press, Tokyo-New York, 1975.

2. **Coffey, S., Ed.,** *Rodd's Chemistry of Carbon Compounds,* Elsevier, Amstedam, 1967.
3. **Geissman, T. A. and Crout, D. H. G.,** *Organic Chemistry of Secondary Plant Metabolism,* Freeman, Cooper & Company, San Francisco, 1969.
4. **Ollis, W. D., Ed.,** *Recent Developments in the Chemistry of Natural Phenolic Compounds,* Pergamon Press, Oxford, 1961.
5. **Pigman, W. and Horton, D.,** *The Carbohydrates. Chemistry and Biochemistry,* 2nd ed., Academic Press, New York, 1970.
6. **Jeanloz, R. W., Ed.,** *The Amino Sugars,* Academic Press, New York, 1969.
7. **Asahina, Y. and Shibata, S.,** *Chemistry of Lichen Substances,* Japan Society for Promotion of Science, Tokyo, 1954.

2. Biosynthesis and Microbiology

8. **Bu'Lock, J. D.,** *The Biosynthesis of Natural Products,* McGraw-Hill, London, 1965.
9. **Bu'Lock, J. D.,** *Essays in Biosynthesis and Microbial Development,* John Wiley & Sons, London, 1967.
10. **Bernfeld, P., Ed.,** *Biogenesis of Natural Compounds,* Pergamon Press, Oxford, 1967.
11. **Grisebach, H.,** *Biosynthetic Patterns in Microorganisms and Higher Plants,* John Wiley & Sons, New York, 1967.
12. **Sykes, G. and Skinner, F. A.,** *Actinomycetales: Characteristics and Practical Importance,* Academic Press, New York, 1973.
13. **Rainbow, C. and Rose, A. H.,** *Biochemistry of Industrial Microorganisms,* Academic Press, New York, 1963.

3. Mechanism of Action

14. **Sexton, W. A.,** *Chemical Constitution and Biological Activity,* E & FN Spon Ltd., London, 1963.
15. **Blood, F., Ed.,** *Essays in Toxicology,* Academic Press, New York, 1970.
16. **Hochster, R. M., and Quastel, J. H., Eds.,** *Metabolic Inhibitors,* Academic Press, New York, 1964.
17. **Goodman, L. S. and Gilman, A.,** *The Pharmacological Basis of Therapeutics,* 3rd ed., MacMillan, New York, 1965.
18. **Meynell, G. G.,** *Bacterial Plasmids,* MIT Press, Cambridge, Mass., 1973.

C. Periodicals (Review Journals)

	Abbreviations
1. *Zechmeister's Forschritte der Organische Chemie Naturstoffe* (Herz, W., Grisebach, H., and Kirby, G. W., Eds., Springer-Verlag, Vienna)	*Forschr.*
2. *Advances in Applied Microbiology* (Perlman, D., Ed., Academic Press, New York)	*Adv. Appl. Microb.*
3. *Progress in Industrial Microbiology* (Hockenhull, D. J. D., Ed., Churchil Livingstone, Edinburgh)	*Progr. Ind. Microb.*
4. *Advances in Carbohydrate Chemistry and Biochemistry* (Tipson, R. S. and Horton, D., Eds., Academic Press, New York)	*Adv. Carb. Chem.*
5. *Annual Reviews in Biochemistry*	*An. Rev. Bioch.*
6. *Annual Reviews in Microbiology*	*An. Rev. Microb.*
7. *Progress in Medicinal Chemistry* (Ellis, G. P. and West, G. B., Eds., Elsevier, Amsterdam)	*Progr. Med. Chem.*

D. Journals

1. General

Annales da Academia Brasileira de Ciencias	*An. Acad. Brasil.*
Annals of the New York Academy of Sciences	*An. N.Y. Acad. Sci.*
Canadian Journal of Research, Section E: Medical Science	*Can. J. Res. Sect. E*
Comptes Rendus Hebdomadaires des Seances de l' Academie des Sciences, Serie D: Sciences Naturelles	*CR Ser. D*
Current Science	*Curr. Sci.*
Doklady Akademii Nauk SSSR	*Dokl.*
Experientia	*Exp.*
Izvestiya Akademii Nauk SSSR, Seriya Biologicheskaya	*Izv. Ser. Biol.*
Izvestiya Akademii Nauk SSSR, Seriya Khimicheskaya	*Izv. Ser. Khim.*
Journal of Scientific and Industrial Research, Section C: Biological Sciences	*J. Sci. Ind. Res. Sect. C*

Nature (London)	*Nature*
Naturwissenschaften	*Naturwiss.*
Pakistan Journal of Scientific and Industrial Research	*Pak. J. Sci. Ind. Res.*
Proceedings of the Japan Academy	*Proc. Jap. Acad.*
Proceedings of the National Academy of Sciences of the United States of America	*Proc. Nat. Acad. Sci.*
Science	*Sci.*
Scientia Sinica (Hua Hsueh Pao)	*Sci. Sinica*

2. Chemistry

Acta Chemica Scandinavica	*Acta Chem. Scand.*
Acta Chimca Sinica	*Acta Chim. Sinica*
Analytical Chemistry	*Anal. Chem.*
Angewandte Chemie	*Angew.*
Arkiv fUr Kemi	*Ark. Kemi*
Australian Journal of Chemistry	*Aust. J. Chem.*
Bulletin de la Societe Chimique de Belgique	*Bull. Soc. Chim. Belg.*
Bulletin de la Societe Chimique de France	*Bull. Soc. Chim. Fr.*
Bulletin of the Chemical Society of Japan	*Bull. Ch. Soc. Jap.*
Canadian Journal of Chemistry	*Can. J. Chem.*
Carbohydrate Research	*Carb. Res.*
Chemical Communications — Journal of the Chemical Society, Series D (formerly Proceedings of the Chemical Society, to 1969)	*CC*
Chemical Letters	*Chem. Lett.*
Chemicke Zvesti	*Chem. Zv.*
Chemische Berichte	*Ber.*
Chemistry & Industry (London)	*Chem. & Ind.*
Chimia (Basel)	*Chim. (Basel)*
Collection of Czechoslovak Chemical Communications	*Coll.*
Gazzetta Chimica Italiana	*Gaz.*
Helvetica Chimica Acta	*Helv.*
Heterocycles	*Heterocycl.*
Indian Journal of Chemistry	*Ind. J. Chem.*
Journal of the American Chemical Society	*JACS*
Journal of the Chemical Society (London)	*JCS*
Journal of the Chemical Society, Section C: Organic	*JCSC*
Journal of the Chemical Society, Perkin Transactions I: Organic and Bio-Organic Chemistry	*JCS Perkin I*
Journal of Chromatography	*J. Chrom.*
Journal of Heterocyclic Chemistry	*J. Heterocycl. Chem.*
Journal of the Indian Chemical Society	*J. Ind. Ch. Soc.*
Journal of Organic Chemistry	*JOC*
Liebig's Annalen der Chemie	*Liebigs Ann.*
Monatshefte fUr Chemie	*Monatsh.*
Recueil des Travaux Chimiques des Pays-Bas	*Rec.*
Suomen Kemistilehti	*Suomen Kem.*
Svensk Kemisk Tidskrift	*Svensk Kem. Tid.*
Tetrahedron	*Tetr.*
Tetrahedron Letters	*TL*
Zeitschrift fUr Chemie	*Z. Chem.*

3. Microbiology, Bacteriology, Pathology, Fermentation

Acta Microbiologica Hungarica	*Acta Micr. Hung.*
Acta Microbiologica Polonica	*Acta Micr. Pol.*
Acta Microbiologica Sinica (Wei Sheng Wu Hsueh Pao)	*Acta Micr. Sinica*
Biotechnology and Bioengineering	*Biotech. Bioeng.*
Annales de l'Institute Pasteur (Paris)	*Ann. Pasteur*
Annali di Microbiologia et Enzymologia	*Ann. Micr. Enzym.*
Antoine van Leeuwenhoek, Journal of Microbiology and Serology	*J. Leeuwenhoek*
Applied and Environmental Microbiology (formerly Applied Microbiology)	*Appl. Micr.*
Archiv fUr Mikrobiologie	*Arch. Mikr.*
Bacteriological Proceedings	*Bact. Proc.*

Bacteriological Reviews	*Bact. Rev.*
British Journal of Experimental Pathology	*Brit. J. Exp. Path.*
Canadian Journal of Microbiology	*Can. J. Micr.*
Developments in Industrial Microbiology	*Dev. Ind. Micr.*
European Journal of Applied Microbiology	*Eur. J. Appl. Micr.*
Folia Microbiologica	*Folia Micr.*
Giornale di Microbiologia	*Giorn. Micr.*
Japanese Journal of Bacteriology (Nippon Saikug. Zashi)	*Jap. J. Bact.*
Japanese Journal of Microbiology	*Jap. J. Micr.*
Journal of Applied Bacteriology	*J. Appl. Bact.*
Journal of Bacteriology	*J. Bact.*
Journal of Fermentation Technology (Hakko Kagaku Kaishi)	*J. Ferm. Techn.*
Journal of General Microbiology	*J. Gen. Micr.*
Medical Microbiology and Immunology	*Med. Microb.*
Mikrobiologichnii Zhurnal (Kiev)	*Mikrob. Zh.*
Mikrobiologiya (Moscow)	*Mikrob.*
Mycologia	*Mycol.*
Mycopathologia & Mycologia Applicata	*Mycopath.*
Postepy Higieny i Medycyny Doswiadczalnej	*Med. Dosw.*
Prikladnaya Biokhimiya i Mikrobiologiya	*Prikl. Biokh. Mikr.*
Transactions of the British Mycological Society	*Trans. Brit. Mycol. Soc.*
Zentralblatt für Bakteriologie, Parasitenkunde, Infectionkrankheiten und Hygiene, Abteilung: Originale	*Zbl. Bakt. Parasit.*
Zertschrift für Allgemeine Mikrobiologie	*Z. Allg. Mikr.*
Zhurnal Microbiologii, Epidemiologii i Immunbiologii	*Zh. Micr. Epid. Imm.*

4. Pharmaceutical Chemistry, Pharmacology, and Natural Products

Annales Pharmaceutiques Francoises	*Ann. Farm. Franc.*
Archiv für Pharmazei	*Arch. Pharm.*
Arzneimittelforschung	*Arzn. Forsch.*
Bioorganic Chemistry	*Bioorg. Chem.*
Bioorganicheskaya Khimiya	*Bioorg. Khim.*
Chemical Pharmaceutical Bulletin	*Chem. Ph. Bull.*
Dissertation Pharmacy	*Diss. Pharm.*
Il Farmaco, Edizione Scientifica (Pavia)	*Farmaco, Sci.*
Il Farmaco, Edizione Practica (Pavia)	*Farmaco, Pract.*
Indian Journal of Pharmacy	*Ind. J. Pharm.*
Journal of Medicinal Chemistry	*J. Med. Chem.*
Journal of Pharmaceutical Sciences	*J. Pharm. Sci.*
Journal of Pharmaceutical Society Japan (Yakugaku Zasshi)	*J. Ph. Soc. Jap.*
Journal of Pharmacy and Pharmacology	*J. Pharm. Pharmacol.*
Khimicheskaya Promyslennost, Khimiko-Farmatsevticheskii Zhurnal	*Khim. Prom.*
Khimiya Prirodnykh Soedinenii	*Khim. Prir. Soed.*
Lloydia (Journal of Natural Products)	*Lloydia*
Phytochemistry	*Phytoch.*
Polish Journal Pharmacy and Pharmacology	*Pol. J. Pharm. Pharmacol.*
(Die) Pharmazie	*Pharm.*
Zeitschrift für Naturforschung Teil B: Inorganic and Organic Chemistry	*Z. Naturforsch. Ser. B*
Zeitschrift für Naturforschung Teil C: Biosciences	*Z. Naturforsch. Ser. C*

5. Biochemistry, Physiology, Biology

Agricultural and Biological Chemistry	*Agr. Biol. Ch.*
Anais do Sociedade de Biologia da Pernambuco	*Anais Biol. Pernambuco*
Annals of Applied Biology	*Ann. Appl. Biol.*
Archives of Biochemistry and Biophysics	*ABB*
Biochimica and Biophysica Acta	*BBA*
Biochemical and Biophysical Research Communications	*BBRC*
Biochemical Journal (London)	*Bioch. J.*
Biochemical Pharmacology	*Bioch. Pharm.*
Biochemical Society Transactions	*Bioch. Soc. Trans.*

Biochemistry	*Biochem.*
Biochemische Zeitschrift	*Bioch. Z.*
Biologica (Bratislava)	*Biol. (Bratislava)*
Biologicheskie Nauki (Moscow)	*Biol. Nauk.*
Bolletino della Societa Italiane di Biologica Sperimentale	*Boll. Soc. Ital. Biol.*
Bulletin de la Societe de Chimie Biologique	*Bull. Soc. Chim. Biol.*
Comptes Rendus des Seances de la Societe de Biologie et de Ses Filiales	*CR Soc. Biol.*
European Journal of Biochemistry	*Eur. J. Bioch.*
Federation Proceedings	*Fed. Proc.*
FEBS Letters	*FEBS Lett.*
Hoppe Seyler's Zeitschrift für Physiologische Chemie	*Hoppe Seyler*
Indian Journal of Biochemistry	*Ind. J. Bioch.*
Indian Journal of Experimental Biology	*Ind. J. Exp. Biol.*
Journal of Biochemistry (Tokyo)	*J. Bioch. (Tokyo)*
Journal of Biological Chemistry	*J. Biol. Chem.*
Journal of Cell Physiology	*J. Cell Physiol.*
Life Sciences	*Life Sci.*
Marine Biology	*Marine Biol.*
Molecular Biology	*Mol. Biol.*
Molecular Pharmacology	*Mol. Pharm.*
Process Biochemistry	*Proc. Bioch.*
Rivista de Biologia	*Riv. Biol.*

6. Chemotherapy, Clinical

American Review of Tuberculosis	*Am. Rev. Tub.*
Archivum Immunologie et Therapiae Experimentalis (Wroclaw)	*Arch. Immun.*
Cancer Chemotherapy Reports from 1976	*Canc. Chemoth. Rep.*
Cancer Treatment Reports	*Canc. Tmt. Rep.*
Cancer Research	*Cancer Res.*
Chemotherapy (Basel)	*Chemother.*
Chemotherapy (Tokyo)	*Chemother. (Tokyo)*
Gann	*Gann*
Indian Journal of Medical Research	*Ind. J. Med. Res.*
Japanese Journal of Experimental Medicine	*Jap. J. Exp. Med.*
Japanese Journal of Medical Science & Biology	*Jap. J. Med. Sci. Biol.*
Japan Medical Gazetta	*Jap. Med. Gaz.*
Japanese Medical Journal	*Jap. Med. J.*
Journal of the American Medical Association	*JAMA*
Journal of Clinical Investigations	*J. Clin. Invest.*
Journal of Experimental Medicine	*J. Exp. Med.*
Journal of Infectious Diseases	*J. Inf. Dis.*
Presse Medica	*Presse Med.*
Proceedings of the Society for Experimental Biology & Medicine	*Proc. Soc. Exp. B. M.*
Rassagne Medica	*Rass. Med.*
Revue Internationale d'Oceanographie Medicale	*Rev. Int. Oceanogr.*

7. Botanical, Agriculture

Annales Phytopathological Society Japan	*Ann. Phytop. Soc. Jap.*
Botanical Gazetta	*Bot. Gaz.*
Canadian Journal of Botany	*Can. J. Bot.*
Indian Journal of Phytopathology	*Ind. J. Phyt.*
Japanese Journal of Botany	*Jap. J. Bot.*
Journal of Agricultural Chemical Society of Japan	*J. Agr. Chem. Soc. Jap.*
Journal of Agricultural and Food Chemistry	*J. Agr. Food Chem.*
Physiologica Plantarum	*Physiol. Plant.*
Physiological Plant Pathology	*Physiol. Plant Path.*
Phytopathologische Zeitschrift	*Phytopath. Z.*
Phytopathology	*Phytopath.*
Plant Disease Reporter	*Plant Dis. Rep.*
Plant Physiology	*Plant Phys.*
Plant Science Letters	*Plant Sci. Lett.*
Planta Medica	*Planta Med.*

Rastitel'nye Resursy	*Rast. Res.*
Science & Culture	*Sci. & Cult.*
South African Journal of Agricultural Sciences	*S. Afr. J. Agr. Sci.*

8. Report Journals

Annual Report Takeda Research Laboratories (Takeda Kenkyusho Ho)	*An. Rep. Takeda*
Annual Reports Sankyo Co. (Sankyo Kenkyusho Nempo)	*An. Rep. Sankyo*
Annual Reports Shionogi Co. (Shionogi Kenkyusho Nempo)	*An. Rep. Shionogi*
Annual Reports, Institute of Food Microbiology, Chiba University (Chiba)	*An. Rep. Chiba Univ.*
Bulletin Faculty Meiji University	*Bull. Fac. Meiji*
Journal of the National Cancer Institute	*J. Nat. Cancer Inst.*
Kitasato Archives of Experimental Medicine	*Kitasato Arch.*
Scientific Reports, Meiji Pharmaceutical Co. (Meiji Seika Kenkyusho Nempo)	*Sci. Rep. Meiji*
Tanabe Seiyaku Kenkyu Nempo	*Tanabe Seiyaku*
Tohoku Journal of Experimental Medicine	*Tohoku J. Exp. Med.*

9. Abstract Journals

Biological Abstracts	*BA*
Chemical Abstracts	*CA*
Dissertation Abstracts, International Section B	*Diss. Abst.*
Microbiological Abstracts	*Micr. Abst.*

E. Patents

Belgian patent	*Belg. P*
British patent	*BP*
Canadian patent	*Can. P*
Czechoslovakian patent	*Cz. P*
Dutch (Holland) patent	*Holl. P (year/number)*
East German patent	*DDR P*
European patent	*EP*
French patent	*Fr. P*
German patent	*DT*
Hungarian patent	*Hung. P*
Indian patent	*Ind. P*
Japanese Patent (kokai)	*JP (year/number)*
Polish patent	*Pol. P*
Soviet (USSR) patent	*SU P*
Swiss patent	*Swiss P*
USA patent	*USP*

USING THE INDICES

Each volume will contain a general name index, including "identical with" and trade names, and an index of producing organisms. A separate index volume (Volume X) covering name, formula, producing organisms, molecular weight, elemental analysis, optical rotation, chemical type, antitumor/antiviral activity and the utility of the compounds will also be published.

Each listing in the indices directs the reader to the *compound number.* The compound number covers the antibiotic code number and the sequence number, separated by a hyphen, and this numerical identifier refers to the volumes in which the compounds are arranged according to this number, except the plant and animal products, which are listed separately in Volumes VIII and IX. The sequence number is assigned individually to any compound according to the addition of a new entry to the data base. Compounds with the same antibiotic code number are listed in numerical order by sequence number.

Similar types of compounds are listed in the same volume. If someone knows the chemical type of a compound, he will find it accordingly among its relatives on the basis of the chemical type key (Table 2) or code number index. When only the trivial, patent, trade, or chemical name is known, or when the name is restricted in common local use (in a particular region of the world), then it may easily be located in the alphabetical cross index. In this index almost 7000 names are listed.

If someone is interested in the active metabolic products of a given organism (species or genus), he only has to turn to the index of the producing organisms, which contains the full reference.

If a "new" compound was isolated and there are sufficient data known about this compound, e.g., mass spectrometric molecular weight, UV spectra, rotation, some activities, etc., on the basis of these indices it is relatively easy to recognize the similar or perhaps identical compounds.

This Handbook, as is evident from the preceding explanation, has a strong chemical character. It seemed to be very complicated, in contrast to the exact physical and chemical data, to formulate the special microbiological, taxonomic, chemotherapeutic, pharmacological, and clinical data in a standardized and computer-searchable format.

During the compilation and the editing of this work great care has been taken to assure the accuracy of the information; however there is a possibility that some mistakes do exist in the values. The Editor and the Publisher cannot be responsible for errors in the original publications.

It is recognized, however, that all data are the subject of continuous revision; therefore special care has been taken to collect and carefully select all new information related to any known compounds and add or occasionally replace them in the existing data.

The work of editing was finished at the end of 1977, but some important new data have been included recently (1979).

LIST OF ABBREVIATIONS

General

Simple chemicals are abbreviated by the formula (NaCl, HCl, NaOH, NH_4OH, NH_4Cl, HCOOH, CH_2Cl_2, etc.). Generally the *Chemical Abstracts* abbreviations are used.

Solvents

W	Water	Acet	Acetone
Pyr	Pyridine	Benz	Benzene
		Tol	Toluene
MeOH	Methanol	Et_2O	Diethyl ether
EtOH	Ethanol	Hex	Hexane, petroleter
PrOH	n-Propanol	AcOH	Acetic acid (glacial)
BuOH	n-Butanol	AcCN	Acetonitrile
AmOH	Amyl alcohol	DMSO	Dimethylsulfoxide
EtOAc	Ethyl acetate	DMF	Dimethylformamide
CHL	Chloroform	THF	Tetrahydrofurane

Other Chemicals

i-	iso-	Me-	Methyl-
i-PrOH	Isopropanol	Et-	Ethyl-
t-	tertier	Bu-	Butyl- as in Me-Et-Ketone, di-Bu-ether
t-BuOH	tertier-Butanol		
c-	cyclo-	NH_4	Ammonium
Ac	Acetyl, acetate	PTSA	*p*-Toluene sulfonic acid
NH_4OAc	Ammonium acetate		

Absorbents

Cel	Cellulose
Pap.	Paper
SILG	Silica gel, SiO_2-xH_2O
AL	Aluminum oxide Al_2O_3
Carbon	Carbon (Norit A)
Diatom	Kieselguhr, etc.
XAD-2	Amberlite XAD-2

IRC-50-H	Amberlite IRC-50 resin in hydrogene form
IR-120-Na	Amberlite IR-120 resin in sodium form
CG-50-NH_4	Amberlite CG-50 resin in ammonium form
XE-	Amberlite XE resins
Dowex-1-OH	Dowex-1 resin in hyroxyl form
| (vertical bar)	±
+ (in producing organism)	Addition of precursors or other compounds to the medium (directed fermentations, mutational biosynthesis with idiothrops)

Special

Some abbreviations are listed in "How to Use This Handbook" (qualitative reactions, antimicrobial activity and antitumor, antiviral activity)

Producing Organisms

S.	*Streptomyces*
Act.	*Actinomyces*
Noc.	*Nocardia*
Mic.	*Micromonospora*
Stv.	*Streptoverticillium*
B.	*Bacillus*
Ps.	*Pseudomonas*
P.	*Penicillium*
Asp.	*Aspergillus*
Fus.	*Fusarium*
Cep.	*Cephalosporium*
sp.	*species*
PL	*Plant products*
AN	*Animal products*

Chemical Type

Deriv.	Derivative
t.	Type
l.	like

Color and Appearance

Powder	Powder, amorphous substance
Wh.	White
Cryst.	Crystalline

Toxicity

IV	Intravenous
IP	Intraperitoneal
SC	Subcutaneous
IM	Intramuscular
PEROS	Per os

Isolation Methods

Filt.	Filtered fermentation broth
Orig.	Original pH
Mic.	Mycelium
WB.	Whole broth
Evap.	Evaporated
Cryst.	Crystallization
Prec.	Precipitation
Liof.	Lyophilization

Amino Acid and Peptide Antibiotics

INTRODUCTION

Amino acids are unambiguously the most common building stones (along with sugars) of natural products. They also occur very frequently in various microbial metabolites.

The family of microbial antibiotics derived from amino acids represents the largest group of antibiotic compounds containing more than 1000 individual members. However, this number includes numerous macromolecular antibiotics (bacteriocins, proteins, enzyme-like inhibitors), and the actual number of relatively simple, lower molecular weight (less than 3000) peptide antibiotics is about 800.

This family covers all of the amino acid-, peptide-, and protein-type compounds and those heterocyclic compounds in which the existing heterocyclic structure or structures is actually derived from amino acids by a simple cyclization reaction, e.g., β-lactams, diketopiperazines, aspergillic acid, and thiostrepton-type compounds. Excluded are, however, some simple aromatic amino acid derivatives such as chloramphenicol, and compounds containing one or more usual amino acids in which the other principal constituents are dominant (e.g., actinobolin).

Streptothricins, containing β-lysine and an unusual heterocyclic amino acid, due to their amino sugar content and their physical and microbiological properties, are listed among the carbohydrate antibiotics (131). Some simple heterocyclic amino acid derivatives — tenuazonic acid, indolyl derivatives — are listed among heterocyclic antibiotics, while others, especially long-chain amino acids or fatty amino acids, are considered aliphatic compounds (eulicin, thermozimocidin).

Only a relatively small number (about 50) of the free natural amino acid type compounds are known to have antimicrobial properties, usually with uncommon structures. They are all very likely antimetabolites of common amino acids. The great majority of the antibiotics in this family are cyclic or linear oligo- or polypeptides, substituted peptides, and protein-type compounds.

The first subfamily, the ***amino acid derivatives,*** covers the aforementioned simple amino acids, the diketopiperazine derivatives, and the compounds derived biogenetically from a few amino acids by "hypercyclization". The subfamily of ***homopeptides*** includes the oligopeptide-type compounds containing two to four amino acid residues (or sometimes amino acid-like residues) linked by a normal peptide bond and higher linear peptides containing at least one other simple constituent on the N-terminal end of the peptide chain, as well as homocyclopeptides without other constituents. In the ***heteromer peptide*** subfamily mainly cyclic peptides are enlisted in which various constituents other than amino acids (fatty acids, sulfur-containing heterocycles, sugars, etc.) occur. These compounds as a rule are built up only by peptide linkages, while the great and important subfamily of ***peptolides*** consists of peptide-type compounds in which the cyclic skeleton is formed — besides the peptide linkages — with the participation of lactone linkages. In this subfamily heterocyclic chromophore or fatty acid-containing peptolides, simple peptolides, and depsipeptides containing aliphatic hydroxy acids are covered. The ***macromolecular peptide*** subfamily contains various high molecular weight polypeptide-type compounds from nisin and subtilin to bacteriocins or enzyme-like macromolecules.

Over and above the essential importance of β-lactam antibiotics, a great number of other peptide antibiotics are used in the various fields of human and veterinary medicine, agriculture, and biochemical research. The significance of β-lactam antibiotics (penicillins, cephalosporins) will be discussed separately. The practical utility of various peptide antibiotics is summarized in the following table:

Antitumor antibiotics	Actinomycin D (dactinomycin)
	Actinomycin C (sanamycin)[a]
	Asparaginase
	Azaserine[a]
	Azotomycin (duazomycin)[a]
	Bleomycin
	DON (6-diazo-5-oxo-L norleucine)[a]
	Neocarzinostatin
	Pacibanil (OK-432)
	Piperazinedione (593-A)[a]
	U-42126[a]
Antibacterial antibiotics	β-Lactams
Antimycobacterial agents	Capreomycin
	Cycloserin
	Tuberactinomycin
	Viomycin
Narrow-spectrum systemic agents	Polymyxin B
	Colistin
	Enduracidin
	Pristinamycin
	Ostreogrycin
	Polymyxin M
	Bicyclomycin[a]
	Negamycin[a]
Narrow-spectrum topical agents	Amphomycin
	Gramicidins
	Tyrothrycin
	(Bacitracin)
Antifungal antibiotic	Saramycetin[a]
Antiviral antibiotics	Alanosin[a]
	Distamycin
Veterinary drugs	Mikamycin
	Netropsin[a]
	Thiostrepton
Feed additives	Bacitracin
	Mikamycin
	Siomycin
	Nosiheptid
	Thiopeptin
	Virginiamycin
	Parvulin[a]
Food preservatives	Nisin
Research tools	Actinomycins
	Valinomycin

[a] These compounds are on clinical trial or their commericalization has been stopped.

Whereas, apart from the β-lactams, more than 30 peptide antibiotics have been used (or had been used) in the world, the general medical importance of these compounds is much less than that of either aminoglycosides or tetracyclines, mainly because of their undesirable side reactions, particularly renal toxicity. Presently in medical practice only polymyxins and some antitumor and antitubercular compounds (actinomycin, bleomycin, cycloserin, capreomycin) are in wide-range use. However, in recent years polymyxins in Gram-negative therapy were replaced by aminoglycosides and semisynthetic β-lactams and the antitubercular peptides were replaced by rifampicin.

The importance of peptide antibiotics as animal feed additives will very likely increase. Several types of less toxic antibacterial peptides with insufficient activity for therapeutic purposes in many countries gradually replaced penicillins, tetracyclines, and other medical antibiotics in animal feeding.

Simultaneously with the wide spreading of peptides and proteins in nature, a great variety of microorganisms are able to produce peptide antibiotics. They are produced by numerous different species of actinomycetes, bacteria, and fungi. It is remarkable that *Bacillus* species produce almost exclusively peptide antibiotics. The very frequent occurrence of modified amino acids (β-lactams, diketopiperazines, etc.) among the metabolites of fungi is also noticeable. The higher forms of life (plants, animals) produce only macromolecular protein-like compounds (and some free amino acids) which arise by a different mechanism.

Chemically the peptide antibiotics have many characteristic features which distinguish them from the normal natural polypeptides (degradation products of proteins) and proteins. The unique features which arise from the specific formation mechanism of these compounds will be discussed later. The most remarkable characteristic of peptide antibiotics (excluded are the simple amino acid and macromolecular compounds) are

1. Frequent occurrence of unusual (both structurally and stereochemically) amino acids and simultaneously the very rare occurrence of some common amino acids (arginine, histidine, methionine). Among the unusual amino acids are sulfur-containing, complicated heterocyclic, unsaturated, N-methylated, imino or β-amino acids as well as specific proline derivatives. The presence of D amino acids, sometimes with both the configurations of an amino acid in the same molecule, is one of the most characteristic features of these antibiotics. The D amino acid residues which occur in peptide antibiotics arise from the corresponding L acids by C-2 epimerization involving D amino acid racemases, only after incorporation of the L residues into the peptide chain. The bacterial peptides do not contain N-methylamino acids and they frequently contain only D and L normal acids. Several streptomycetal and fungal peptides, on the other hand, consist almost exclusively of uncommon constituents.
2. Frequent occurrence of other constituents besides the amino acids. They are mostly fatty acids, aliphatic amines, or hydroxy acids, sugars, heterocyclic chromophores or other specific heterocyclic moieties (in fact they are derived mainly from amino acids by biosynthetic modifications), metals, etc. These unusual amino acids and the other constituents will be discussed later on with special emphasis in the introduction to each antibiotic type.
3. The presence of unusual structural elements, rarely found in the common peptides. These are primarily various cyclic structures.
   A. A great number of peptide antibiotics have macrocyclic structure without free amino or carboxylic functions. These macrocycles usually contain 4 to 16 amino acids.
   B. The great tendency to cyclization is observable between the proper amino acid radicals, which leads to additional small cyclic areas by intramolecular condensation within a peptide chain in the macro ring. This "hypercyclization", held by proximity, frequently gives off thiazoline, oxazoline, or other small heterocyclic rings.

4. The molecular size of peptide antibiotics is much smaller than that of proteins. Their average molecular weight is about 1000, ranging between 300 and 3000. The macromolecular antibiotics are obviously comprehensible exceptions.
5. They are produced as a rule in the form of mixtures of closely related compounds differing from each other by one or a few amino acid residues or minor differences in the other constituents. These replacements are observable with biologically acceptable similar constituents.
6. As a consequence of the above features, the peptide antibiotics are resistant to enzymatic attack.

These specific features become obvious considering that the biosynthesis of the peptide antibiotics, by all means, runs differently from the normal route of protein synthesis. Inhibitors of protein biosynthesis such as chloramphenicol, tetracyclines, or puromycin are generally ineffective on the biosynthesis of peptide antibiotics. Antibiotic production continues, or increases, when protein synthesis is inhibited in the antibiotic-producing microorganisms. Additionally, the great variety of specific structures (more than 200 unusual amino acids and a similar number of other amino acid-like constituents) would be impossible to construct by the general mechanism which is operative in normal protein synthesis. In this ''normal'' way only the macromolecular peptide antibiotics are synthesized, which, of course, contain only common amino acids.

Regarding the biosynthesis of these microbial peptides, which include not only antibiotics, many hypotheses and speculations were revealed. It is a fact that these compounds are not biosynthesized with the strict fidelity of the ribosome-RNA system; consequently they cannot be regarded as small proteins. Most probably the amino acid building stones or its specific precursors are assembled on the limited surface of a multienzyme system. This novel mechanism which is designated as protein template mechanism may be considered at the biosynthesis of bacterial peptides in which a proven multienzyme thiotemplate directs the biosynthetic process. A similar mechanism may be involved in the biosynthesis of all microbial peptides. During this mechanism amino acids are activated by ATP to form enzyme-bound aminoacyl adenylates and they are transferred to specific SH groups of an enzyme, serving as secondary acceptors. Initiation, elongation, and termination are inherent properties of this enzyme system. Antibiotic biosynthesis is generally initiated from the N-terminal and cyclization is usually the final step.

The other natural peptides, (e.g., several hormones) with the same molecular size as microbial peptides are degradation products of proteins. The importance of the peptide antibiotics in the life of the producing organisms is disputed.

The peptide antibiotics are generally toxic, narrow spectrum compounds with a wide variety of other biological effects such as antimetabolite, membrane-active, immunosupressive, neurotoxic, enzyme-inhibiting, hypotensive, etc. effects.

Nearly all of the early discovered antibiotics (up to 1946) were some kind of peptide-type compound (penicillin, gramicidins, tyrocidin, gliotoxin, actinomycin, bacitracin, etc.). Most of these antibiotics and the other peptide antibiotics — except penicillins — after their early success were surpassed by other agents in medical practice. Disregarding the theoretical importance, peptide antibiotics other than β-lactams have subsidiary importance. Their large-volume application is limited to animal feeding and food preservation. The production of bacitracin and virginiamycin amounts to about 1000 tons yearly, but only 0.1 to 10 tons of the other peptide antibiotics is produced.

The largest and still rapidly expanding group of microbial peptide antibiotics has been derived from *Actinomycetales* species. In contrast to the relatively simple bacterial peptides, they exceed in the great variety of unusual constituents. Recently progress in the area of bacterial polypeptides has again been noticeable.

REFERENCES

1. *Nature*, 204, 840, 1964; 224, 595, 1969.
2. *AAC 1965*, 122; *AAC 1967*, 464.
3. *Progr. Med. Chem.*, 5, 1, 1967.
4. *Lloydia*, 31, 364, 1968.
5. *Exp.*, 24, 1068, 1968.
6. *Sci.*, 163, 352, 1969; 173, 875, 1971.
7. *Pure Appl. Chem.*, 28, 551, 1971.
8. *An. Rev. Bioch.*, 43, 445, 1974; 40, 449, 1971.
9. *Pharm.*, 27, 491, 1972.
10. *Adv. Appl. Microb.*, 12, 189, 1970; 17, 19, 1974.
11. *Progr. Org. Chem.*, 8, 129, 1973.
12. *Adv. Enzymol.*, 35, 1, 1971.
13. *Acc. Chem. Res.*, 6, 361, 1973.
14. *Bact. Rev.*, 41, 449, 1977.
15. *Tetr.*, 31, 2177, 1975.
16. **Schröder, E. and Lübke, K.**, *The Peptides*, Vols. 1 and 2, Academic Press, New York, 1965—1966.
17. **Abraham, E. P.**, *Biochemistry of Some Peptide and Steroid Antibiotics*, John Wiley & Sons, New York, 1957.
18. **Ovchinnikov, Yu. A., Ivanov, V. T., and Shkrob, A. M.**, *Membrane Active Complexones*, Elsevier, Amsterdam, 1974.
19. Specialist Periodical Reports, Amino Acids, Peptides and Proteins, Vols. 1—6, The Chemical Society, London, 1969—1975.

41
AMINO ACID DERIVATIVES

411
Simple Amino Acids

In contrast with the huge distribution and importance of peptides and polypeptides in nature, up to now only about 150 to 200 relatively simple amino and imino acids have been isolated in free form from natural sources (microorganisms, plants, animals). The great majority of these "unusual" amino acids have very limited distribution. Among the hydrolysis products of specific natural peptides, primarily in antibiotics, a further 200 to 300 "unusual" amino acids have been found. They may arise in a variety of different ways, e.g., by modification of usual biosynthetic pathways (biological methylation or deamination of the common amino acids, etc.) or by novel, unexpected pathways.

Different microorganism species are able to produce these types of compounds (along with common amino acids) which have some antimicrobial, antitumor, or antiviral activity. Most of the amino acid antibiotics are isolated from *Streptomyces* species. These compounds are close chemical analogs of the common amino acids; therefore they are able to antagonize the metabolism of a corresponding normal substrate during the biosynthesis of the macromolecules, and it is not surprising to find that most of these compounds act as antimetabolites. Their role in the life of the organisms which produce them is not quite clear; they might function as general protective agents.

Microbial amino acid-type antibiotics are distributed into those containing a diazo or nitroso group (azaamino acid type), the so-called simple amino acid-type compounds including aliphatic, ether, alicyclic, and heterocyclic subtypes (from 41121 to 41124), and the amino acid analog-type (4113) derived by modification of simple amino acids.

In the azaamino acid type (4111) some antitumor diazoketoamino acids and their dipeptide derivatives are included. They are extremely acid-labile, toxic compounds with characteristic UV absorption spectra (two maxima at 245 to 250 and 274 to 276 nm). Their antimicrobial spectrum is broad, but the observed in vitro activities are weak.

Azaserine (O-diazoacetyl-L-serine), DON (6-diazo-5-oxo-L-norleucine), and azotomycin (duazomycin B) are clinically effective antitumor agents. They are active against some kinds of melanomas, lymphomas, and leukemias. Azaserine (NSC-742) was one of the first compounds whose discovery was the direct result of a systematic search for antitumor antibiotics in 1954. Azotomycin shows clinical effect against gastrointestinal carcinomas and soft-tissue sarcomas. However, azotomycin is significantly less toxic than either azaserine or DON, and none of these compounds has proved to be a widespread practical drug.

Azaamino acids function as glutamine and purine antagonists. They inhibit purine biosynthesis, alkylating the enzymes which are repsonsible for conversion of formylglycinamide ribonucleotide to formylglycinamidine ribonucleotide, which is the initial step of *de novo* purine synthesis.

A somewhat different structural type is represented by alanosine, which was the first naturally occurring nitrosohydroxyamino group containing substance. Alanosin has interesting antitumor and antiviral activity.

All of the discovered simple amino acid-type (4112) antibiotics are a kind of antimetabolite of the common natural amino acids. In consequence of their antimetabolite nature, most of these compounds are active only in vitro and only on a synthetic medium, because the usual medium (e.g., nutrient agar) provides all the common biochemicals; therefore they reverse the activity of the antimetabolite-type compounds.

These antibiotics generally show weak antibacterial and/or antifungal activity and very frequently possess antitumor, antiviral, and enzyme-inhibiting activity. Antitubercular (cycloserine, HON), plant growth inhibiting, phytotoxic activities, and vitamin B_{12} antagonistic effects are also frequently occurring properties of these compounds. Their mechanism of action in most cases is a simple isosteric competitive inhibition of an enzyme system.

Among the amino acid antibiotics only cycloserine (produced by chemical synthesis rather than fermentation) is applied clinically. Although cycloserine is a broad-spectrum antibiotic, its use is limited to the treatment of tuberculosis in cases caused by resistant mycobacteria and in the intolerability of other antimycobacterial agents. Cycloserine is absorbed orally and shows neurotoxic side effects. Cycloserine is a competitive antagonist of D-alanine in cell wall synthesis. It inhibits bacterial peptidoglycan synthesis by inhibition of the alanine racemase and D-ala-D-ala synthetase which incorporate the D-ala-D-ala residue into the uridine nucleotide precursor of bacterial cell wall peptidoglycan.

A 3-chloro-isooxazole-containing amino acid antibiotic (U-42126) and the amino acid analog hadacidin are presently on clinical trial as antitumor (antileukemic) agents.

All azaamino acids and the majority of simple amino acid antibiotics are produced by *Streptomyces* species. Some compounds in this type and the amino acid analogs are fungal metabolites.

Structures

41110

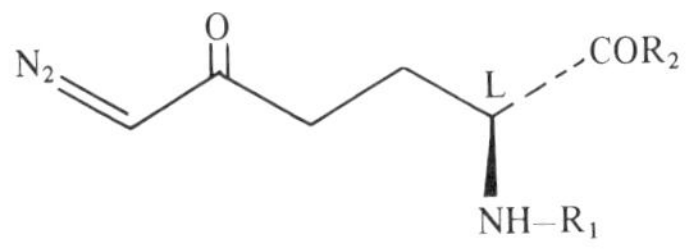

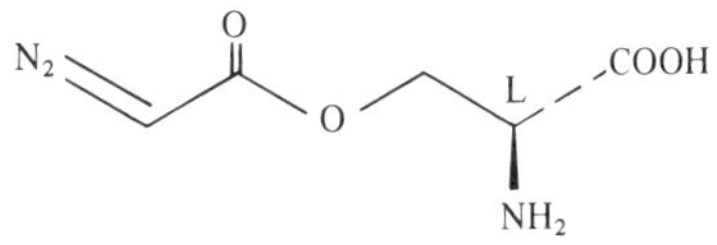

azaserine

Antibiotic	R_1	R_2
DON	H	OH
Duazomycin A	$-COCH_3$	OH
Duazomycin B	$-CO-CH(CH_2)_2-CO=N_2$ with $NHCO(CH_2)_2-CH(COOH)(NH_2)$ on the CH	OH
Duazomycin C	$-CO-CH(NH_2)(CH_2)_2-CO=N_2$	$-NH-\overset{L}{C}H(CH_3)(COOH)$

41121

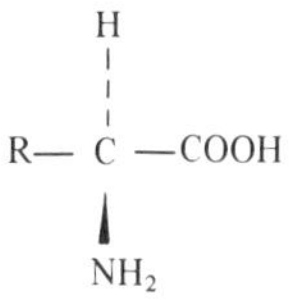

Antibiotic	R
Alanosine	$-CH_2-N(NO)(OH)$
Armentomycin (2-amino-4,4-dichlorobutyric acid)	$-CH_2-CH(Cl)(Cl)$
L-4-Azaleucine(2-amino-3-dimethylamino-propionic acid)	$-CH_2-N(CH_3)(CH_3)$
Dehydroleucine (2-amino-4-methyl-5-hexenoic acid)	$-CH_2-CH(CH_3)(CH=CH_2)$
HON (L-δ-hydroxy-γ-oxo-norvaline)	$-CH_2-CO-CH_2OH$
Propargylglycine (L-2-amino-4-pentynoic acid)	$-CH_2-C \equiv CH$
O- Carbamyl-D-serine[a]	$-CH_2-O-CONH_2$
SF-1293B [L-β(3-hydroxyureido) alanine]	$-CH_2-NH-CO-NHOH$
439 A (4-keto-isoleucine)	$-CH(CH_3)-COCH_3$
L-*threo*-β-Hydroxyaspartic acid	$-CH(COOH)-OH$
L-*threo*-α-Amino-β,γ-dihydroxybutyric acid (2-amino-3,4-dihydroxy-butyric acid)	$-CH(CH_2OH)-OH$
L-2-Amino-4-methoxy-*trans*-3-butenoic acid	$-CH=CH-OCH_3$ (trans)

[a] Opposite configuration.

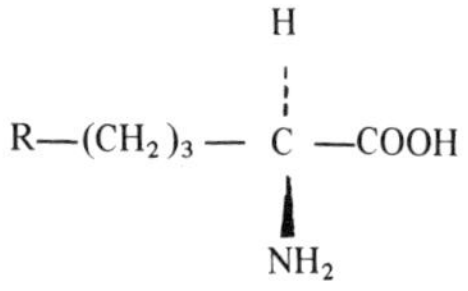

Antibiotic	R
L-N^5-(1-Iminoethyl)ornithine	−NH−C(=NH)−CH_3
L-N^5-Hydroxyarginine (δ-N-hydroxy-L-arginine)	−N(OH)−C(=NH)−NH_2
O-(L-Norvalyl-5)-isourea	−O−C(=NH)−NH_2

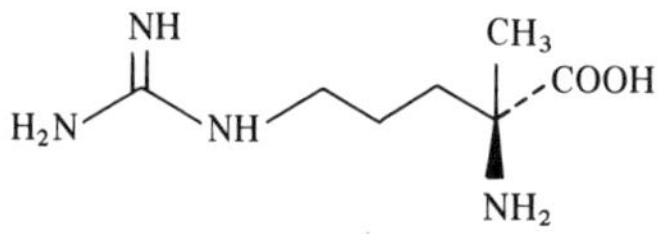

2-methyl-L-arginine

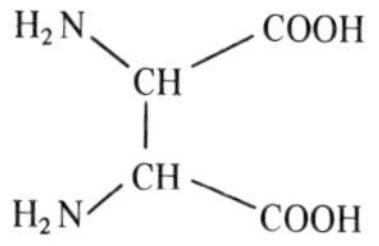

2,3-diaminosuccinic acid

41122

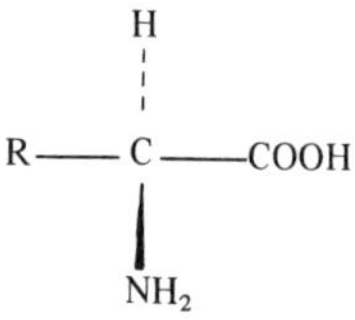

Antibiotic	R
L-4-Oxalysine (L-2-amino-3-(2-aminoethoxy)-propionic acid)	−CH_2−O−CH_2NH_2
L-*trans*-2-Amino-4(2-aminoethoxy)-3-butenoic acid	−CH=CH−O−$(CH_2)_2NH_2$ (t)
Rhizobitoxin (L-2-amino-4(2-amino-3-hydroxy-propoxy)but-3-enoic acid)	−CH=CH−O−CH_2−C(H)(NH_2)−CH_2OH (t)
Dihydrorhizobitoxin	−$(CH_2)_2$−O−CH_2−CH(NH_2)−CH_2OH

41123

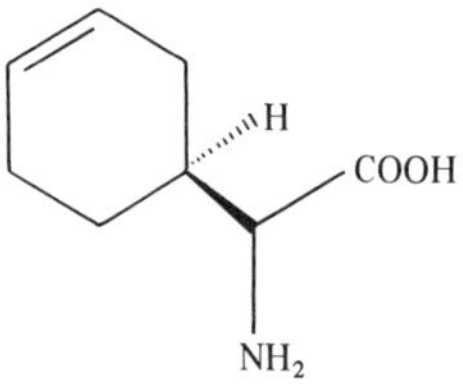

3-cyclohexenyl-l-glicine

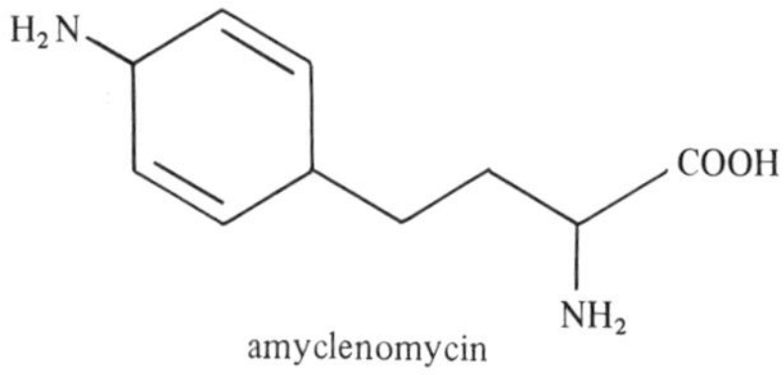

amyclenomycin

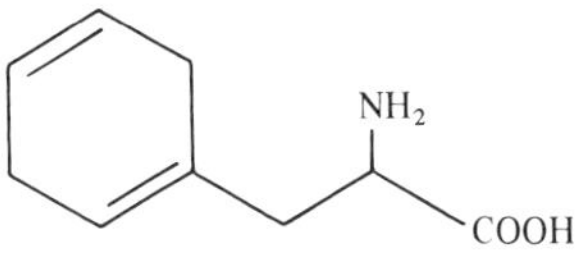

L-3-(2,5-dihydrophenyl)alanine

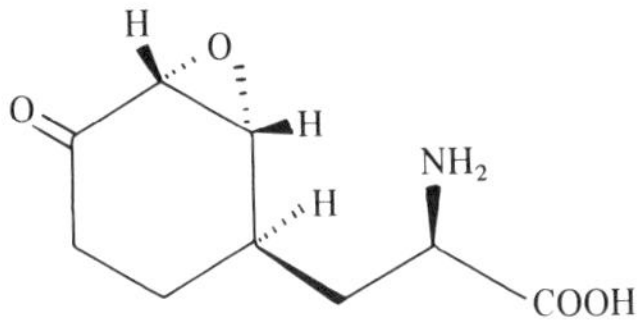

anticapsin

L-2,3-epoxy-4-oxo-hexahydro-phenylalanine

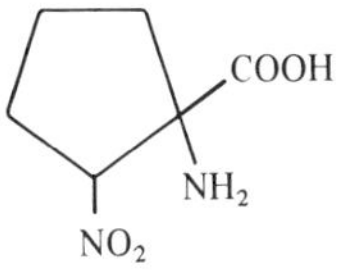

MM-27

1-amino-2-nitro-cyclopentane 1-carboxylic acid

41124

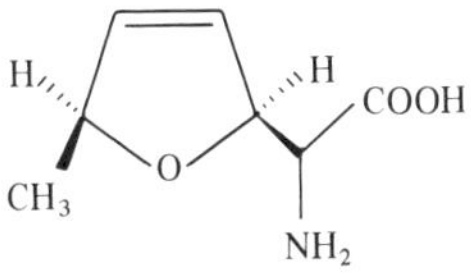

threomycin
(furanomycin)

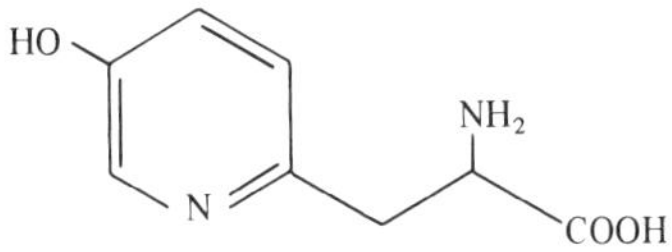

SF-1346

L-β-(5-hydroxy-2-pyridyl)alanine

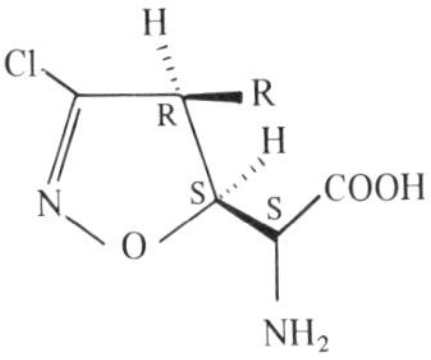

U-42126 R=H

(αS,5S)-α-amino-3-chloro-4,5-dihydroisooxazolinyl-5-acetic acid

U-43795 R=OH

(αS,4S,5R)-α-amino-3-chloro-4-hydroxy-4,5-dihydroisooxazole-5-acetic acid

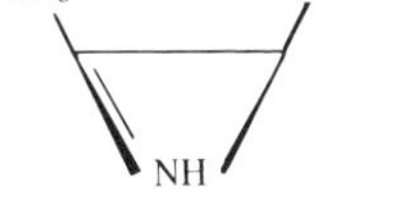

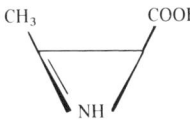

azirinomycin

3-methyl-[2H] azirinecarboxylic acid

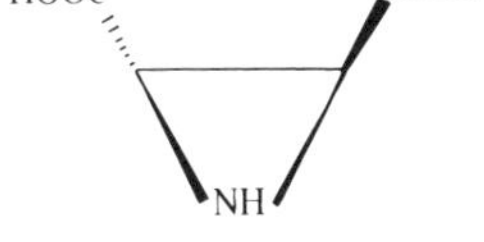

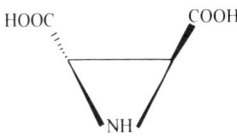

S-2,3-dicarboxyaziridine

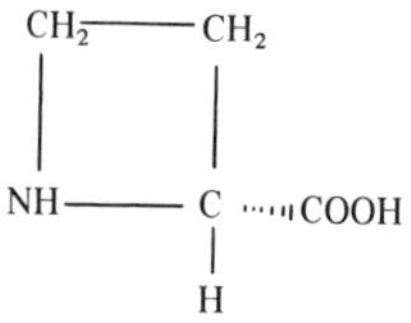

L-azetidine-2-carboxylic acid

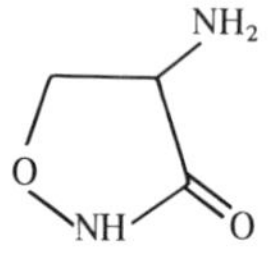

cycloserine

(D-4-amino-3-isooxazolidone)

41125

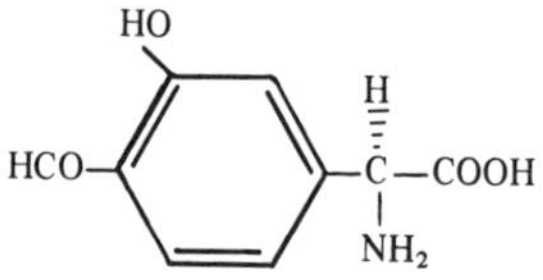

forphenicine

41130

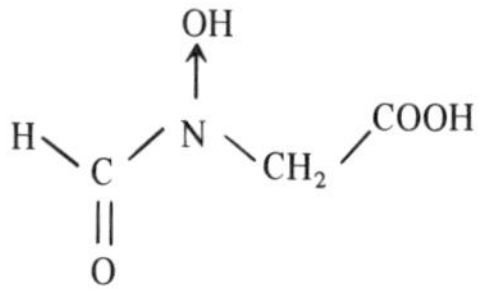

hadacidin

(N-formylhydroxyaminoacetic acid)

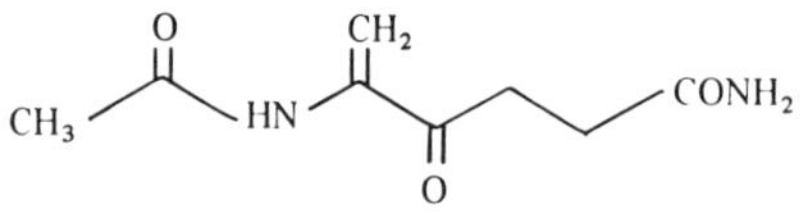

primocarcin

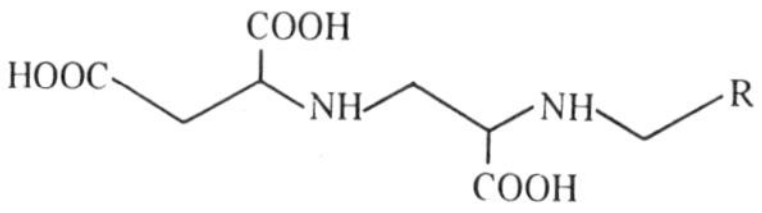

aspergillomyrasmine A $R = CH(NH_2)COOH$

lycomarasmine $R = CONH_2$

41110-1454

NAME:	AZASERIN, NSC-742, O-DIAZOACETYL-L-SERINE
PO:	S.FRAGILIS
CT:	AZAAMINO ACID, AMPHOTER
FORMULA:	C5H7N3O4
EA:	(N, 24)
MW:	173
EW:	175
PC:	YELLOW, GREEN, CRYST.
OR:	(-.5, PH5.18 PUFF) (+9.7, HCL)
UV:	7: (250.5, 1140,)
UV:	NAOH: (252, 1230,)
SOL-GOOD:	W
SOL-FAIR:	MEOH, ETOH, ACET
SOL-POOR:	ETOAC, HEX
QUAL:	(NINH., +) (PAULY, -)
STAB:	(ACID, -) (BASE, -) (HEAT, -)
TO:	(E.COLI, 100) (SHYG., 50) (MYCOB.SP.,) (C.ALB., 250) (G.POS., 100)
LD50:	(50, SC) (93|31, IV)
TV:	EHRLICH, S-180, CA-755, HELA, NK-LY, WALKER-256, ANTIVIRAL
IS-EXT:	(ETOH, 7, EVAP.FILT.)
IS-ABS:	(AL, ETOH)
IS-CRY:	(CRYST., ETOH)
UTILITY:	ANTITUMOR DRUG

REFERENCES:

Sci., 120, 270, 1954; 121, 213, 1954; *JACS*, 76, 2878, 1954; 77, 501, 1955; 80, 3941, 1958; *Nature*, 173, 71, 1954; 178, 1119, 1955; *Ant. & Chem.*, 4, 775, 948, 1958; 6, 100, 1956; *AAC 1961*, 245; *JA*, 8, 120, 1955; *Cancer Res.*, 16, 154, 1956; *BBA*, 30, 195, 1958; 51, 597, 1961; *J. Biol. Chem.*, 235, 443, 1960

41110-1455

NAME:	DON, 6-DIAZO-5-OXO-L-NORLEUCIN, NSC-7365
PO:	S.AMBOFACIENS, S.SP., S.PHAEOCHROMOGENES
CT:	AZAAMINO ACID, AMPHOTER
FORMULA:	C6H9N3O3
EA:	(N, 24)
MW:	171
PC:	YELLOW, GREEN, CRYST.
OR:	(+21, W)
UV:	7: (244, 376,) (274, 683,)
UV:	HCL: (200, ,)
UV:	NAOH: (200, ,)
SOL-GOOD:	W
SOL-FAIR:	MEOH, ETOH
SOL-POOR:	BUOH, HEX
QUAL:	(NINH., +)
STAB:	(ACID, -) (HEAT, -) (BASE, -)
TO:	(E.COLI, 100) (B.SUBT., 100) (TORULOPSIS SP.,) (C.ALB.,)
LD50:	(76|14, IV)
TV:	ANTITUMOR, ANTIVIRAL
IS-FIL:	6.8
IS-ABS:	(AL, ETOH)
IS-CHR:	(CARBON, ACET-W)
IS-CRY:	(CRYST., MEOH-W)
UTILITY:	ANTITUMOR DRUG

REFERENCES:

Ant. & Chem., 7, 81, 653, 1957; 6, 487, 1956; *JACS*, 78, 3075, 1956; 80, 3941, 1958; *Proc. Soc. Exp. B.M.*, 93, 314, 1957; *Proc. Am. Assoc. Cancer Res.*, 2, 97—151, 1956; *An. N.Y. Acad. Sci.*, 76, 630, 825, 1968; *J. Nat. Cancer Inst.*, 18, 413, 1957; 22, 433, 1959; *Ant. An.*, 943, 1959—60; USP 29655471, 2965634; JP 61/3648

41110-1456

NAME: DUAZOMYCIN-A, DIAZOMYCIN-A, N-ACETYL-DON, BA-8509-A, NSC-51097
PO: S.AMBOFACIENS
CT: AZAAMINO ACID, AMPHOTER, ACIDIC
FORMULA: C8H11N3O4
EA: (N, 17)
MW: 213
EW: 220|10
PC: YELLOW, POW.
UV: 7: (245, 315,) (275, 530,)
UV: MEOH: (245, 228,) (275, 440,)
SOL-GOOD: W, MEOH, BUOH
SOL-POOR: ACET, HEX
QUAL: (NINH., +) (BIURET, -) (DNPH, -)
STAB: (ACID, -) (BASE, -) (HEAT, -)
TO: (B.SUBT., 1) (S.CEREV., 12)
TV: S-180, CA-755, L-1210
IS-FIL: 7.5
IS-ION: (DX-1-AC, PH7.7 PUFF)
IS-ABS: (CARBON, ACET-W)
IS-CHR: (SILG, BUOH-I.PROH)
REFERENCES:

AAC, 1961, 178; *AAC 1962*, 179; *Ant. An.*, 943, 1959—60; USP 3148119; Belg. P 583346; BP 935327

41110-1457

NAME: DUAZOMYCIN-B, DIAZOMYCIN-B, 1719, BA-8509-B, NSC-5664
TRADE NAMES: AZOTOMYCIN
PO: S.AMBOFACIENS, ACT.SP.
CT: AZAAMINO ACID, AMPHOTER, ACIDIC
FORMULA: C17H23N7O8
EA: (N, 18) (N, 21)
MW: 453
PC: YELLOW, POW.
UV: 7: (245, 340,) (275, 550,)
SOL-GOOD: W
SOL-FAIR: MEOH
SOL-POOR: BUOH, HEX
QUAL: (NINH., +) (DNPH, +)
STAB: (ACID, -)
TO: (B.SUBT., .05) (S.CEREV., 1)
TV: S-180, CA-755, L-1210
IS-ION: (DX-1-AC, PH7 PUFF)
UTILITY: ANTITUMOR DRUG
REFERENCES:

AAC, 1962, 179; *Ant. An.*, 943, 1959—60; *Fed. Proc.*, 21, 176, 1962; *Canc. Chemoth Rep.*, 31, 207, 1969; *Bioch. Pharm.*, 23, 3467, 1974; BP 935327; USP 3148119

41110-1458

NAME:	DUAZOMYCIN-C, DIAZOMYCIN-C, BA-8509-C, NSC-10270
TRADE NAMES:	AMBOMYCIN
IDENTICAL:	ALAZOPEPTIN
PO:	S.AMBOFACIENS, S.CANDIDUS-AZOTICUS
CT:	AZAAMINO ACID, AMPHOTER
FORMULA:	C15H21N7O6
EA:	(N, 24)
PC:	YELLOW, CRYST.
UV:	7: (245, 210,) (275, 340,)
SOL-GOOD:	W, MEOH
SOL-POOR:	ETOH, HEX
QUAL:	(NINH., +)
STAB:	(ACID, -)
TO:	(B.SUBT., 100) (S.CEREV., 500)
TV:	S-180, CA-755, L-1210
IS-FIL:	7.5
IS-ABS:	(CARBON, ACET-W)
IS-CHR:	(SILG, BUOH-I.PROH)
IS-CRY:	(CRYST., ETOH-ACET)

REFERENCES:

Ant. An., 943, 1959—60; BP 935321

41110-1459

NAME: ALAZOPEPTIN
TRADE NAMES: AMBOMYCIN
IDENTICAL: DUAZOMYCIN-C
PO: S.GRISEOPLANUS, S.CANDIDUS-AZOTICUS
CT: AZAAMINO ACID, AMPHOTER
FORMULA: C15H21N7O6.H2O
EA: (N, 24)
EW: 402
PC: WH., CRYST.
OR: (+9.5, W)
SOL-GOOD: W
SOL-FAIR: ACOH, FA, DMSO, MEOH, ACET
SOL-POOR: ETOH, HEX
QUAL: (NINH., +) (BIURET, +)
STAB: (ACID, -) (BASE, +)
TO: (CORYNEBACT.SP.,) (SALMONELLA SP.,)
LD50: (150, IP-RATS)
TV: S-180, EHRLICH
IS-FIL: ORIG.
IS-EXT: (BUOH, 9, W)
IS-ABS: (CARBON, MEOH-W)
IS-CHR: (AL, MEOH-W)
IS-CRY: (CRYST., ACET-W)
REFERENCES:

Ant. An., 730, 1956—57; *Ant. & Chem.*, 7, 532, 1957; *J. Bact.*, 89, 212, 1964; *Proc. Soc. Exp. B.M.*, 97, 888, 1960; *An. N.Y. Acad. Sci.*, 76, 575, 1958; *AAC 1965*, 115; JP 79/50193; *CA*, 77, 62308

41110-1461

NAME: OS-3256-B
PO: S.CANDIDUS-AZOTICUS
CT: AZAAMINO ACID, AMPHOTER
EA: (C, 47) (H, 6) (N, 18)
PC: WH., POW.
UV: W: (226, 394,) (276, 310,)
SOL-GOOD: W
SOL-FAIR: MEOH-W
SOL-POOR: BUOH, HEX
QUAL: (NINH., +)
TO: (S.AUREUS, 25) (S.LUTEA, 25) (B.SUBT., 1.56) (E.COLI, 3.12) (S.CEREV., 100)
TV: L-1210, S-180, HELA
IS-FIL: ORIG.
IS-ABS: (CARBON, ACET-W)
IS-CHR: (SILG, W) (AVICEL, ETOH-NH4OH-W)
IS-CRY: (PREC., MEOH, ACET)
REFERENCES:

JA, 26, 181, 1973; 27, 620, 1974; JP 75/107190; USP 3995078; *CA*, 84, 3288; 87, 20605

41121-1460

NAME: ALANOSINE, NSC-143647
PO: S.ALANOSINICUS
CT: AMINO ACID, AMPHOTER
FORMULA: C3H7O34
EA: (N, 28)
MW: 145
EW: 155, 152
PC: WH., CRYST.
OR: (-37.8, W) (+8, HCL) (-46, NAOH)
UV: HCL: (228, 505,)
UV: NAOH: (250, 630,)
UV: W: (250, 630,)
SOL-GOOD: ACID, BASE
SOL-POOR: MEOH, HEX
QUAL: (NINH., +)
STAB: (HEAT, -) (ACID, +)
TO: (C.ALB., 10) (S.CEREV., 2)
LD50: (600, IP) (300, IV)
TV: S-180, ANTIVIRAL
IS-CRY: (CRYST., W)
REFERENCES:
Nature, 211, 1198, 1966; *TL*, 1769, 1966; *Farmaco, Sci.*, 21, 269, 1966; *Bull. Ch. Soc. Jap.*, 46, 1847, 1973; BP 1115041

41121-1464

NAME: ARMENTOMYCIN, U-10923, 2-AMINO-4.4-DICHLORO-BUTYRIC ACID
PO: S.ARMENTOSUS
CT: AMINO ACID, AMPHOTER
FORMULA: C4H7NO2CL2
EA: (N, 9) (CL, 41)
MW: 172
EW: 168, 174
PC: WH., CRYST.
OR: (+6.7, W) (+26.2, HCL)
UV: W: (200, ,)
SOL-GOOD: W, MEOH, BUOH
SOL-POOR: ACET, HEX
QUAL: (NINH., +)
TO: (E.COLI,) (P.VULG.,) (PS.AER.,)
LD50: (25, SC)
IS-EXT: (MEOH, , EVAP.FILT.)
IS-CRY: (CRYST., MEOH-W)
REFERENCES:
Biochem., 6, 165, 1967; USP 3342681; *CA*, 66, 74947

41121-1465

NAME: L-4-AZALEUCIN, 2-AMINO-3-DIMETHYLAMINO-PROPIONIC ACID
PO: S.NEOCALIBERIS
CT: AMINO ACID, AMPHOTER
FORMULA: C5H12N2O2
EA: (N, 20)
MW: 144
EW: 185
PC: WH., CRYST.
OR: (-17.8, W) (+18.8, W-HCL)
UV: W: (200, ,)
SOL-GOOD: W
SOL-FAIR: MEOH
SOL-POOR: BUOH, HEX
QUAL: (NINH., +)
STAB: (BASE, +)
TO: (S.LUTEA,) (E.COLI,) (K.PNEUM.,) (P.VULG.,)
LD50: (100|20, SC)
IS-FIL: ORIG.
IS-ION: (DX-50-H, NH4OH)
IS-CHR: (DX-50-H, NH4OH)
IS-CRY: (DRY, NH4OH) (CRYST., ETOH-ACET-W)
REFERENCES:

J. Med. Chem. , 10, 353, 1967; *Biochem.*, 6, 165, 1967; *AAC,* 1967; *ABB,* 102, 313, 1963; *J. Bact.*, 108, 95, 1971; Holl. P 66/9508

41121-1467

NAME: DEHYDROLEUCIN, 2-AMINO-4-METHYL-5-HEXENOIC ACID, U-30116
PO: S.SP., BOLETUS IXOCAMUS-NUDI
CT: AMINO ACID, AMPHOTER
FORMULA: C7H13NO2
EA: (N, 10)
MW: 143
PC: WH., CRYST.
UV: W: (200, ,)
SOL-GOOD: W
SOL-FAIR: MEOH
SOL-POOR: BUOH, HEX
QUAL: (NINH., +)
STAB: (BASE, +)
TO: (S.AUREUS,) (B.SUBT.,) (S.LUTEA,)
IS-FIL: ORIG.
IS-ION: (DX-50-H, NH4OH)
IS-ABS: (CARBON, ACET-W)
IS-CRY: (CRYST., ETOH-W)
REFERENCES:

Can. J. Chem., 47, 2504, 1969; *BBRC,* 47, 290, 1972

41121-1468

NAME:	HON, L-D"-HYDROXY-G"-OXO-NORVALINE, H-899
PO:	S.AKIYOSHIENSIS
CT:	AMINO ACID, AMPHOTER
FORMULA:	C5H9NO4
EA:	(N, 10)
MW:	147, 175, 168
EW:	147|3
PC:	WH., CRYST.
OR:	(-8.2, W)
UV:	W: (271, 24,)
SOL-GOOD:	W
SOL-FAIR:	BUOH-W
SOL-POOR:	BUOH, HEX
QUAL:	(NINH., +) (FEHL., +)
STAB:	(ACID, -) (BASE, +)
TO:	(MYCOB.TUB., .10)
LD50:	(5200, IV) (8000, SC) (7600, PEROS)
TV:	ANTITUMOR
IS-FIL:	3
IS-EXT:	(BUOH, 3.5, W)
IS-ION:	(IR-120-H, NH4OH)
IS-CRY:	(CRYST., ACET-W) (PREC., BUOH, ACET)

REFERENCES:

JA, 14, 39, 1961; *Chem. Ph. Bull.*, 8, 1071, 1079, 1960; *An. Rep. Takeda*, 22, 148, 167, 1963; *Am. Rev. Resp. Dis.*, 81, 924, 1960; BP 873893; DT 1124045

41121-1469

NAME:	L-2-AMINO-PENTYNOIC ACID, PROPARGYLGLYCINE
PO:	S.SP.
CT:	AMINO ACID, AMPHOTER
FORMULA:	C5H8NO2
EA:	(N, 12)
MW:	173
PC:	WH., CRYST.
OR:	(-31.1, W) (-5.5, HCL)
SOL-GOOD:	W
SOL-POOR:	BUOH, HEX
QUAL:	(NINH., +)
STAB:	(ACID, +) (BASE, +)
TO:	(B.SUBT.,) (S.CEREV.,)
IS-ION:	(DX-50-H, PYR-W)
IS-CHR:	(AG-50W-H, HCL)
IS-CRY:	(CRYST., ETOH-W)

REFERENCES:

JA, 24, 239, 1971; *J. Bact.*, 82, 640, 1961; *JACS*, 71, 3573, 1949

41121-1470

NAME:	<u>L-2-AMINO-3.4-DIHYDROXYBUTYRIC ACID</u>
PO:	S.SP.
CT:	AMINO ACID, AMPHOTER
FORMULA:	C4H9NO4
EA:	(N, 11)
MW:	135
PC:	WH., CRYST.
OR:	(-13.3, W)
UV:	W: (200, ,)
SOL-GOOD:	ETOH
SOL-FAIR:	W
SOL-POOR:	BUOH, HEX
QUAL:	(NINH., +)
TO:	(E.COLI,)
IS-FIL:	ORIG.
IS-ION:	(DX-50-H, PYR-W)
IS-CHR:	(FLORISIL, ETOH-W)
IS-CRY:	(CRYST., ETOH-W)

REFERENCES:

JA, 24, 330, 1971

41121-1471

NAME:	<u>L-N5-1-IMINOETHYLORNITHINE</u>
PO:	S.SP.
CT:	AMINO ACID, AMPHOTER, BASIC
FORMULA:	C7H15N3O2.HCL
EA:	(N, 20)
MW:	173
PC:	WH., CRYST.
OR:	(+20.6, HCL)
UV:	W: (200, ,)
SOL-GOOD:	W
SOL-POOR:	BUOH, HEX
TO:	(E.COLI,)
IS-ION:	(DX-50-H, NH4OH)

REFERENCES:

JA, 25, 179, 1972

41121-1472

NAME:	<u>L-N5-HYDROXYARGININE</u>
IDENTICAL:	D"-N-HYDROXY-L-ARGININE
PO:	B.CEREUS, B.SP.
CT:	AMINO ACID, AMPHOTER, BASIC
FORMULA:	C6H14N4O3
EA:	(N, 29)
MW:	190
PC:	WH., CRYST.
OR:	(+21, HCL)
UV:	W: (200, ,)
SOL-GOOD:	W
SOL-POOR:	BUOH, HEX
QUAL:	(NINH., +)
STAB:	(ACID, +) (BASE, +) (HEAT, +)
TO:	(E.COLI,) (PS.AER.,) (K.PNEUM.,)
TV:	KB
IS-FIL:	2
IS-ION:	(DX-50-H, NAOH) (AG-1-NA, PH9.4 PUFF)
IS-CRY:	(CRYST., ETOH-W-HCL)

REFERENCES:

JA, 26, 284, 1973; 27, 826, 1974

41121-1473

NAME:	<u>D"-N-HYDROXY-L-ARGININE</u>
IDENTICAL:	L-N5-HYDROXYARGININE
PO:	NANIZZIA GYPSEA, DERMATOPHYTA
CT:	AMINO ACID, AMPHOTER, BASIC
FORMULA:	C6H14N4O3
EA:	(N, 29)
MW:	190
PC:	WH., CRYST.
OR:	(+10.1, W) (+32.25, HCL) (+21, HCL)
UV:	W: (200, ,)
SOL-GOOD:	W
SOL-POOR:	BUOH, HEX
QUAL:	(NINH., +)
STAB:	(ACID, +)
TO:	(B.SUBT., 200) (E.COLI, 200) (S.CEREV., 3000)
IS-ION:	(DX-50-NH4, NH4OH)
IS-CHR:	(SILG, PROH-W)
IS-CRY:	(CRYST., MEOH-W)

REFERENCES:

Arch. Mikr., 91, 203, 1973; Ph.D. thesis, Univ. Tubingen, 1970; *JA*, 26, 282, 1973

41121-1474

NAME: L-2-AMINO-4-METHOXY-TRANS-3-BUTENOIC ACID, AMB
PO: PS.AERUGINOSA
CT: AMINO ACID, AMPHOTER
FORMULA: C5H9NO3
EA: (N, 11)
MW: 131
PC: WH., CRYST.
OR: (+115, W)
UV: W: (200, ,)
SOL-GOOD: W
SOL-POOR: BUOH, HEX
QUAL: (NINH., +)
STAB: (ACID, +) (BASE, +) (HEAT, +)
TO: (B.SUBT.,) (TRICHOMONAS SP.,)
IS-CHR: (AG-1-HCO3, TRIMETILAMIN)
IS-CRY: (CRYST., ETOH-W)
REFERENCES:
JA, 25, 122, 1972; 26, 389, 1973; *Sci.*, 185, 322, 1974; USP 3739022, 3859171

41121-1475

NAME: O-L-NORVALYL-5-ISOUREA
PO: B.SP.
CT: AMINO ACID, AMPHOTER
FORMULA: C6H13N3O3
EA: (N, 24)
MW: 175
PC: WH., POW., HYGROSCOPIC
UV: W: (200, ,)
SOL-GOOD: W
SOL-POOR: BUOH, HEX
QUAL: (NINH., +) (SAKA., -)
STAB: (ACID, -) (BASE, -)
TO: (B.SUBT., 5) (E.COLI, 20)
IS-FIL: ORIG.
IS-ABS: (CARBON, MEOH-W)
IS-CHR: (DX-50-H, NACL) (SEPHADEX G-10, W) (BIOGEL P-2, ACOH-W)
IS-CRY: (DRY, ACOH-W)
REFERENCES:
JA, 26, 44, 1973

41121-1490

NAME:	<u>O-CARBAMYL-D-SERINE</u>
IDENTICAL:	E-733-B
PO:	S.POLYCHROMOGENES, S.FRADIAE, PS.SP.
CT:	AMINO ACID, AMPHOTER
FORMULA:	C4H8N2O4
EA:	(N, 19)
MW:	144, 167
EW:	149, 153
PC:	WH., CRYST.
OR:	(+2, W) (+7.5, W) (-18.5, HCL) (-19.6, HCL)
UV:	W: (200, ,)
SOL-GOOD:	W
SOL-FAIR:	MEOH, ETOH
SOL-POOR:	BUOH, HEX
QUAL:	(NINH., +) (BIURET, +) (SAKA., -) (PAULY, -) (FECL3, -)
STAB:	(BASE, -)
TO:	(B.SUBT., 100) (SHYG., 50)
LD50:	(1500, IV)
TV:	ANTIVIRAL
IS-ION:	(IR-120-H, NH4OH) (XE-98-OH, ACOH-W)
IS-CRY:	(CRYST., ETOH-W)

REFERENCES:

JA, 15, 147, 1962; 16, 217, 1963; 17, 8, 1964; *JACS,* 78, 2412, 1956; *JA,* 21, 170, 1968; *BBRC,* 12, 68, 1963; BP 775946

41121-3728

NAME:	<u>N-NITROGLICIN</u>, NITRAMINOACETIC ACID
PO:	S.NOURSEI
CT:	AMINO ACID DERIV., ACIDIC
FORMULA:	C2H4N2O4
EA:	(N, 23)
MW:	120
EW:	122
PC:	WH., CRYST.
OR:	(0,)
UV:	HCL: (228, , 5640)
UV:	NAOH: (204, , 14100) (236, , 8160)
UV:	W: (235, , 5520)
SOL-GOOD:	W, MEOH, ETOH, ACET
SOL-FAIR:	ETOAC, ET2O
SOL-POOR:	CHL, CCL4, BENZ, HEX
QUAL:	(FECL3, +) (NINH., -) (FEHL., -)
STAB:	(ACID, +) (LIGHT, -)
TO:	(E.COLI, .18) (PHYT.BACT., 1)
LD50:	(32, IV) (43, IP) (40, PEROS)

REFERENCES:

JA, 21, 279, 1968

41121-4781

NAME: HYDROXYASPARTIC ACID, L-THREO-B"-HYDROXYASPARTIC ACID
PO: S.SP., ARTHRINIUM PHAEOSPERMUM
CT: AMINO ACID, ACIDIC, AMPHOTER
FORMULA: C4H7NO5
EA: (N, 9)
EW: 149
PC: WH., CRYST.
OR: (+46, HCL)
UV: W: (200, ,)
SOL-GOOD: ACID
SOL-FAIR: W
SOL-POOR: MEOH, HEX
QUAL: (NINH., +) (FECL3, -) (DNPH, -) (FEHL., -) (BIURET, -) (SAKA., -)
TO: (B.SUBT., 62) (BOTRYTIS SP., 10)
LD50: NONTOXIC
IS-FIL: 2
IS-ION: (DX-1-OH, HCL)
IS-CHR: (XAD-2, W)
IS-CRY: (PREC., W, ETOH) (CRYST., ETOH-W)
REFERENCES:
JA, 28, 821, 1975

41121-5004

NAME: SF-1293-B, L-B"-3-HYDROXYUREIDOALANINE
PO: S.HYGROSCOPICUS
CT: AMINO ACID, BASIC, AMPHOTER
FORMULA: C4H9N3O4
EA: (N, 26)
MW: 163
EW: 174
PC: WH., CRYST.
OR: (-12, HCL) (-2, NAOH) (-11.5, W)
UV: W: (200, ,)
SOL-GOOD: ACID, BASE
SOL-FAIR: W
SOL-POOR: MEOH, HEX
QUAL: (NINH., +) (BIURET, +) (FECL3, +) (FEHL., -)
TO: (B.SUBT.,) (E.COLI,) (PS.AER.,)
IS-FIL: 3
IS-ION: (DX-50-H, NH4OH)
IS-CRY: (CRYST., W)
REFERENCES:
Chem. Ph. Bull., 23, 2669, 1975; JP 75/13592, 13332; *CA*, 83, 41552, 59267

41121-5053

NAME:	2-METHYLARGININE, X-11837
PO:	S.SP.
CT:	BASIC, AMPHOTER, AMINO ACID
FORMULA:	C7H16N4O2
EA:	(N, 24)
MW:	224
PC:	WH., POW.
OR:	(+21, HCL)
UV:	W: (200, ,)
SOL-GOOD:	W
SOL-POOR:	MEOH, HEX
QUAL:	(NINH., +) (SAKA., +)
TO:	(B.SUBT., 200) (E.COLI, 2) (B.SP., 2)
IS-FIL:	2
IS-ION:	(DX-50-H, NH4OH) (DX-50-NA, PH6.1 PUFF)
IS-CHR:	(SILG, CHL-MEOH-NH4OH-W) (CEL, CHL-MEOH-NH4OH)

REFERENCES:

JA, 29, 213, 1976; USP 4061542

41121-5297

NAME:	439-A, 4-KETO-ISOLEUCIN, 2-AMINO-4-KETO-3-METHYLPENTANOIC ACID
PO:	B.CEREUS
CT:	AMINO ACID, AMPHOTER
FORMULA:	C6H11NO3
EA:	(N, 10)
MW:	146
PC:	WH., POW.
UV:	(200, ,)
SOL-GOOD:	W
TO:	(E.COLI, 15) (PS.AER., 80) (B.SUBT., 5) (S.LUTEA, 10) (S.AUREUS, 5)
IS-FIL:	2
IS-ION:	(DX-50X4-H, PYR-W)
IS-CHR:	(AVICEL, ACET-MEOH-W)

REFERENCES:

Bioorg. Chem., 6, 263, 1977

41121-5981

NAME:	KT-151
PO:	S.LUTEOGRISEUS
CT:	AMPHOTER, AMINO ACID
FORMULA:	C5H12N2O2
EA:	(N, 21)
MW:	132
PC:	WH., CRYST.
OR:	(-0.21, W) (+0.32, PH3 PUFF)
UV:	W: (200, ,)
SOL-GOOD:	W
SOL-FAIR:	MEOH, ETOH
SOL-POOR:	BUOH, HEX
QUAL:	(NINH., +) (SAKA., -) (BIURET, -) (FECL3, -)
TO:	(B.SUBT., .1) (PS.AER., 2) (E.COLI, 5)
IS-FIL:	3
IS-ION:	(IR-120 B-NH4, NH4OH) (CG-120-AC, NH4OH)
IS-CRY:	(CRYST., ETOH)

REFERENCES:

Agr. Biol. Ch. 41, 1767, 1977

41122-1466

NAME: <u>L-2-AMINO-4-2-AMINOETHOXY-3-BUTENOIC ACID</u>, X-11085
PO: S.SP.
CT: AMINO ACID, AMPHOTER
FORMULA: C6H12N2O3.HCL
EA: (N, 14)
MW: 160
PC: WH., CRYST.
OR: (+85.6, W) (+89.2, PH7 PUFF)
UV: W: (200, ,)
SOL-GOOD: W
SOL-POOR: MEOH, HEX
QUAL: (NINH., +)
STAB: (BASE, -)
TO: (B.SUBT., 300) (S.AUREUS,) (ANTHELMINTHIC,)
LD50: (500, PEROS)
REFERENCES:

JA, 27, 229, 1974; USP 3751459, 3775255, 3865694; Swiss P 579866; *CA*, 86, 38601

41122-1476

NAME: <u>RHIZOBITOXIN</u>
PO: RHIZOBIUM JAPONICUM
CT: AMINO ACID, AMPHOTER
FORMULA: C7H14N2O4
EA: (N, 15)
MW: 191
PC: WH., CRYST.
OR: (+78.85, W)
SOL-GOOD: W
SOL-POOR: BUOH, HEX
QUAL: (NINH., +)
TO: (SALMONELLA TYPHI,)
LD50: PHYTOTOXIC
IS-CHR: (CG-50-H, NH4OH)
REFERENCES:

Bact. Proc., 19, 1967; *Plant Phys.*, 40, 931, 1965; 48, 1, 1971; *BBA*, 158, 219, 1968; 227, 671, 1971; *Tetr.* 31, 2629, 1975; *CC*, 714, 715, 1972; *Sci.*, 185, 322, 1974; *Tetr.*, 31, 2629, 2633, 1975; USP 3672862

41122-1477

NAME: L-4-OXALYSINE
PO: S.CHARTREUSIS, S.ERYTHROCHROMOGENES
CT: AMINO ACID, AMPHOTER
FORMULA: C5H12N2O3.HCL
EA: (N, 16)
MW: 148
PC: WH., CRYST.
OR: (+1.655,)
UV: W: (225, ,)
SOL-GOOD: W
SOL-POOR: ETOH, HEX
QUAL: (NINH., +)
TO: (S.LUTEA,) (E.COLI,)
LD50: (2500, IP)
IS-FIL: 3
IS-ION: (DX-50-NA, NH4OH)
IS-CHR: (CEL, BUOH-ACOH-W)
IS-CRY: (CRYST., ETOH-W)
REFERENCES:

AAC, 1967, 401; *JACS,* 79, 5693, 1957; *Rec.,* 78, 404, 1959; 81, 713, 1962; *An. Inst. Farmacol. Espanol.,* 185, 1970, 1966—67

41123-1479

NAME:	<u>MM-27</u>, 1-AMINO-2-NITROCYCLOPENTANE CARBOXYLIC ACID
PO:	ASP.WENTII
CT:	AMINO ACID, AMPHOTER
FORMULA:	C6H10N2O4
EA:	(N, 16)
PC:	WH., CRYST.
SOL-GOOD:	W
QUAL:	(NINH., +) (FECL3, +) (SAKA., -) (BIURET, -)
TO:	(PHYT.FUNGI,)
LD50:	PHYTOTOXIC
IS-ION:	(IR-120-H, NH4OH)

REFERENCES:

Nature, 207, 998, 1965; *JCSC*, 255, 1966; BP 1038722; *CA*, 65, 14394

41123-1480

NAME:	<u>CYCLOHEXENYL-1-GLYCINE</u>, NIKKOMYCIN
PO:	S.ANTIBIOTICUS
CT:	AMINO ACID, AMPHOTER, ACIDIC
FORMULA:	C8H13NO2
EA:	(N, 9)
MW:	155
PC:	WH., CRYST.
OR:	(+100, H3PO4) (+110,)
SOL-GOOD:	ACID, BASE
SOL-FAIR:	W
SOL-POOR:	MEOH, HEX
QUAL:	(NINH., +)
TO:	(S.AUREUS, 250) (E.COLI, .9) (P.VULG., 7.8)
LD50:	(1000, SC)

REFERENCES:

Naturwiss., 58, 603, 1971; *JACS*, 80, 2698, 1958; DT 1230525; Belg. P 644682

41123-1481

NAME:	AMYCLENOMYCIN
PO:	S.LAVENDULAE
CT:	AMINO ACID, AMPHOTER
FORMULA:	C10H16N2O2
EA:	(N, 14)
MW:	294, 196
EW:	210
PC:	WH., YELLOW, POW.
OR:	(+10.9, W)
UV:	W: (200, ,)
SOL-GOOD:	W, MEOH
SOL-POOR:	BUOH, HEX
QUAL:	(NINH., +) (BIURET, -) (FECL3, -) (SAKA., -)
STAB:	(HEAT, +) (ACID, -) (BASE, -)
TO:	(MYCOB.TUB., 3.1)
LD50:	(1500, IV)
IS-FIL:	ORIG.
IS-ION:	(CG-50-NH4, NH4OH)
IS-ABS:	(CARBON, ACET-W)

REFERENCES:

JA, 27, 656, 1979; 28, 215, 222, 1975; JP 75/94189

41123-1483

NAME: L-2.5-DIHYDRO-PHENYLALANINE, L-1.4-CYCLOHEXADIEN-1-ALANINE, L-DIHYDROPHENYLALANINE, DIHYDROPHENYLALANINE
IDENTICAL: FN-1636, X-13185, U-15738, U-51738
PO: S.DIASTATOCHROMOGENES, S.ARENAE, S.SP., S.LEMENSIS, S.LUTEOGRISEUS
CT: AMINO ACID, AMPHOTER
FORMULA: C9H13NO2
EA: (N, 8)
MW: 167, 174
PC: WH., CRYST.
OR: (-54, W) (-60.3, W)
UV: W: (200, ,)
SOL-GOOD: W, MEOH
SOL-POOR: ETOH, HEX
QUAL: (NINH., +)
STAB: (HEAT, -)
TO: (PS.AER., 5) (E.COLI, 8.5) (FUNGI, 6)
LD50: (600, IV)
TV: S-180
IS-FIL: 4
IS-ION: (IR-45-OH, CHL-ACET)
IS-ABS: (CARBON, MEOH-HCOOH)
IS-CHR: (SILG, ETOH)
IS-CRY: (CRYST., ETOH-W)
REFERENCES:

JA, 23, 537, 618, 1970; 30, 675, 1977; *Arch. Mikr.*, 75, 346, 1971; 76, 28, 1971; *Can. J. Micr.*, 16, 545, 1970; *JOC*, 33, 1774, 1968; 37, 2933, 1972; JP 70/26712; USP 4019548

41123-1484

NAME: ANTICAPSIN, A-19427
IDENTICAL: AA-1
PO: S.GRISEOPLANUS, B.SUBTILIS
CT: AMINO ACID, AMPHOTER
FORMULA: C9H13NO4
EA: (N, 7)
MW: 210, 199
PC: WH., CRYST.
OR: (-125, W)
UV: W: (200, ,)
SOL-GOOD: W, DMFA
SOL-FAIR: MEOH, ETOH
SOL-POOR: BUOH, HEX
QUAL: (NINH., +) (FEHL., -) (SAKA., -) (BIURET, -) (FECL3, -)
STAB: (ACID, -) (BASE, -)
TO: (B.SUBT., 25) (S.LUTEA, 25) (S.AUREUS,) (S.PYOGENES, 3)
IS-ABS: (CARBON, MEOH)
IS-CHR: (SILG, W) (SILG, ACET-W) (SEPHADEX G-25, W)
REFERENCES:
Bioch. J., 118, 557, 563, 1970; *Appl. Micr.*, 24, 907, 1972; 21, 1075, 1969; *JA*, 23, 613, 1970; *CC*, 849, 1977; USP 3794564

41123-5055

NAME: 3-CYCLOHEXENYLGLICIN, NIKKOMYCIN
PO: S.TENDAE
CT: AMINO ACID, AMPHOTER
FORMULA: C8H13NO2
EA: (N, 9)
MW: 145
PC: WH., POW.
SOL-GOOD: W
QUAL: (NINH., +)
TO: (MUCOR HIRMALIS,)
IS-ION: (DX-50, PH5.8 PUFF)
IS-ABS: (CARBON, ACET-HCOOH)
IS-CHR: (BIOGEL P-2, W) (CEL, PROH-W)
IS-CRY: (DRY,)
REFERENCES:
Z. Naturforsch. Ser. B, 30, 626, 1975

41124-1487

NAME: <u>AZIRINOMYCIN</u>
PO: S.AUREUS
CT: AMINO ACID, AMPHOTER, ACIDIC
FORMULA: C4H5NO2
EA: (N, 14)
MW: 99
PC: WH., POW.
SOL-GOOD: W
SOL-FAIR: ETOAC
STAB: (ACID, -) (BASE, -) (HEAT, -)
TO: (P.VULG., .1) (S.AUREUS, .1) (B.SUBT., 1)
(S.LUTEA,) (E.COLI,) (PS.AER.,)
LD50: (150, IP)
IS-FIL: ORIG.
IS-EXT: (ETOAC, , W)
IS-ION: (DX-1-CL, NACL)
REFERENCES:
JA, 24, 42, 48, 1971; *JOC*, 31, 3907, 1966; *Chem. Lett.*, 1063, 1976

41124-1488

NAME: <u>U-42126</u>, AT-125, NSC-163501, A"-S-5-S-A"-AMINO-3-CHLORO-2-ISOOXAZOLYNYL-5-ACETIC ACID
PO: S.SCIVEUS
CT: AMINO ACID, AMPHOTER
FORMULA: C5H7N2O3CL
EA: (N, 16) (CL, 20)
MW: 178.6
PC: WH., CRYST.
UV: W: (200, ,)
SOL-GOOD: W
SOL-FAIR: MEOH
SOL-POOR: BUOH, HEX
QUAL: (NINH., +)
TO: (B.SUBT., .31) (E.COLI,) (S.CEREV.,)
LD50: NONTOXIC
TV: L-1210, P-388
IS-FIL: ORIG.
IS-ION: (DX-50-H, NH4OH)
IS-CHR: (CEL, BUOH-BENZ-MEOH-W)
IS-CRY: (CRYST., MEOH-W)
UTILITY: ANTITUMOR DRUG, ON CLINICAL TRIAL
REFERENCES:
AAC, 3, 425, 1973; 7, 807, 1975; *TL*, 2549, 1973; *Canc. Chemoth. Rep.*, 57, 141, 1973; 58, 793, 1974; DT 2311655

41124-1489

NAME: N-ACETYL-TYRAMINE
PO: S.GRISEUS, MYCOBACTERIUM TUBERCULOSIS
CT: AMINO ACID, AMPHOTER, NEUTRAL
FORMULA: C10H13NO2
PC: WH., POW.
OR: (0,)
REFERENCES:
Helv., 42, 1730, 1959; *CA*, 50, 5839

41124-1491

NAME: CYCLOSERINE, D-4-AMINO-ISOOXAZOLIDONE, RO-1-9213, I-1431, 106-7, 8217, NJ-21, 5915
TRADE NAMES: CYCLOMYCIN, ORIENTMYCIN
IDENTICAL: OXYMYCIN, SEROMYCIN, PA-94, K-300, E-733-A, 17452, OXAMYCIN
PO: S.GARYPHALUS, S.LAVENDULAE, S.NAGASAKIENSIS, S.ORCHIDACEUS, S.ROSEOCHROMOGENES, S.SP., PS.FLUORESCENS
CT: AMINO ACID, AMPHOTER
FORMULA: C3H6N2O2
EA: (N, 27)
MW: 102
EW: 102
OR: (+121, W) (+64, MEOH) (+112, NAOH)
UV: W: (226, 402,)
SOL-GOOD: W
SOL-FAIR: MEOH, ACET, FA, PYR
SOL-POOR: BUOH, HEX
QUAL: (NINH., +) (FECL3, +)
STAB: (BASE, +) (HEAT, +)
TO: (S.AUREUS, 10) (B.SUBT., 20) (E.COLI, 40) (SHYG., 50) (PS.AER., 80) (MYCOB.TUB., 2.5)
LD50: (1810, IV) (2800, SC) (5290, PEROS)
TV: ANTIVIRAL
IS-ION: (IR-120-H, NH4OH)
UTILITY: ANTIBACTERIAL DRUG
REFERENCES:
Ant. & Chem., 5, 183, 204, 398, 582, 1955; 6, 360, 708, 1956; *JACS*, 77, 2344, 1955; 79, 3236, 1957; *JA*, 4, 327, 1951; 9, 164, 1956; *Ant. A.*, 136-169, 1955—56; *Kitasato Arch.*, 36, 61, 1964; *AAC 1968*, 268

41124-1492

NAME:	<u>THREOMYCIN</u>, FURANOMYCIN, NSC-116328
PO:	S.SP.
CT:	AMINO ACID, AMPHOTER
FORMULA:	C7H11NO3
EA:	(N, 9)
MW:	164
EW:	163
PC:	WH., CRYST.
OR:	(+136.1, W)
UV:	W: (196, , 6300)
SOL-GOOD:	W
SOL-FAIR:	MEOH, BUOH
SOL-POOR:	ACET, HEX
QUAL:	(NINH., +) (BIURET, -) (SAKA., -)
TO:	(B.SUBT., 1) (SHYG., 2) (E.COLI, 5) (K.PNEUM.,) (MYCOB.TUB.,)
LD50:	(710, IV)
TV:	ANTIPHAGE, HELA
IS-FIL:	ORIG.
IS-ION:	(IR-120-H, NH4OH)
IS-CRY:	(CRYST., W)

REFERENCES:

J. Med. Chem., 10, 1149, 1967; *Chem. Lett.*, 1975; JP 67/3076

41124-3893

NAME:	<u>U-43795</u>, NSC-176324, A"-S-4-S-5-R-A"-AMINO-3-CHLORO-4-HYDROXY-4.5-DIHYDRO-5-ISOOXAZOLE ACETIC ACID
PO:	S.SCIVEUS
CT:	AMINO ACID, AMPHOTER
FORMULA:	C5H7N2O4CL
EA:	(N, 15) (CL, 18)
MW:	194, 212
PC:	WH., CRYST.
OR:	(+,)
UV:	W: (200, ,)
SOL-GOOD:	W
SOL-POOR:	ACET, HEX
QUAL:	(NINH., +)
TO:	(B.SUBT.,) (S.LUTEA,)
LD50:	NONTOXIC
TV:	L-1210, P-388
IS-FIL:	ORIG.
IS-ION:	(DX-50-H, NH4OH)
IS-CHR:	(CEL, BUOH-BENZ-MEOH-W)
UTILITY:	ON CLINICAL TRIAL

REFERENCES:

JA, 28, 91, 1975; *Canc. Chemoth. Rep.*, 58, 793, 935, 1974; 59, 481, 1975; *AAC*, 7, 807, 1975; DT 2514984; USP 3944562

41124-4057

NAME: SF-1346, L-B"-5-HYDROXY-2-PYRIDILALANINE
PO: S.CHIBAENSIS
CT: BASIC, AMPHOTER, AMINO ACID
FORMULA: C8H10N2O3
EA: (N, 15)
MW: 182
PC: WH., CRYST.
OR: (+30, W)
UV: HCL: (228, 175,) (289, 235,)
UV: NAOH: (241, 445,) (302, 165,)
UV: W: (219, 330,) (280, 140,) (320, 15,)
SOL-GOOD: W, MEOH, BUOH-W, BASE
SOL-FAIR: ETOH
SOL-POOR: ACET, HEX
QUAL: (NINH., +) (FECL3, +)
TO: (B.SUBT., 1) (E.COLI, 10) (PIRICULARIA ORYZAE, .1)
IS-FIL: 3
IS-ION: (DX-50-H, NH4OH)
IS-ABS: (CARBON, ACET-W)
IS-CRY: (CRYST., ACET-W)
REFERENCES:
Chem. Ph. Bull., 23, 2669, 1975; *Sci. Rep. Meiji*, 15, 1, 1976; JP 74/41595; *CA*, 81, 134623; 86, 70027

41124-4782

NAME: S-2.3-DICARBOXY-AZIRIDINE
PO: S.SP.
CT: AMINO ACID, ACIDIC, AMPHOTER
FORMULA: C4H5NO4
EA: (N, 10)
EW: 131
PC: WH., CRYST.
OR: (+54, W)
UV: W: (200, ,)
SOL-GOOD: W, DMSO
SOL-POOR: MEOH, HEX
QUAL: (NINH., +)
TO: (AEROMONAS SALMONECIDA, 25) (PHYT.FUNGI,)
LD50: (300|100, IV)
IS-CHR: (DX-50-H, W)
IS-CRY: (PREC., EVAP.FILT., MEOH) (CRYST., W)
REFERENCES:
JA, 28, 828, 1975; JP 77/38091; *CA*, 87, 51625

41124-6221

NAME:	SF-1836
PO:	S.ZAOMYCELICUS
CT:	AMPHOTER, AMINO ACID DERIV.
FORMULA:	C5H7NO2
EA:	(N, 12)
MW:	113
PC:	WH., CRYST.
OR:	(-140, W)
UV:	W: (200, ,)
SOL-GOOD:	W
SOL-FAIR:	MEOH, ETOH, BUOH
SOL-POOR:	ETOAC, HEX
QUAL:	(NINH., +)
TO:	(PHYT.BACT.,)
REFERENCES:	

41125-6119

NAME:	FORPHENICINE, 4-FORMYL-3-HYDROXYPHENYLGLYCINE
PO:	ACT.FULVOVIRIDIS-ACARBADICUS
CT:	AMPHOTER, AMINO ACID
FORMULA:	C9H9NO4
EA:	(N, 7)
MW:	195
EW:	195
PC:	YELLOW, CRYST.
OR:	(+140, HCL)
UV:	7: (258, 780,) (324, 200,)
UV:	HCL: (212, , 23790) (255, , 15600) (322, , 4100)
UV:	NAOH: (271, , 11120) (377, , 7610)
SOL-GOOD:	W, ACID, BASE
SOL-POOR:	MEOH, BENZ, HEX, PYR, DMSO
QUAL:	(NINH., +) (FECL3, +) (FEHL., +) (DNPH, +) (SAKA., -)
LD50:	(125, IV)
TV:	LS, CA
IS-FIL:	3
IS-ABS:	(CARBON, ETOH-W)
IS-CHR:	(SP-SEPHADEX C-25-H, W)
IS-CRY:	(CRYST., W)

REFERENCES:

JA, 31, 244, 483, 1978; *Jap. J. Ant.*, 30, 153, 1977

41130-1462

NAME: HADACIDIN, NFHAA, NSC-521778
PO: P.FREQUENTANS, P.PURPURESCENS, P.OMANTIV-VIOLACEUM
CT: AMINO ACID ANALOG, ACIDIC
FORMULA: C3H5NO4
EA: (N, 12)
EW: 111, 123
PC: WH., CRYST.
OR: (0,)
UV: W: (200, ,)
SOL-GOOD: W, MEOH, ETOH, ACET, ET2O
QUAL: (FECL3, +) (NINH., +)
STAB: (HEAT, -)
TV: ANTITUMOR, H-2
IS-EXT: (MEOH, , EVAP.FILT.)
IS-CRY: (CRYST., ETOH)
UTILITY: ON CLINICAL TRIAL
REFERENCES:

Proc. Soc. Exp. B.M., 109, 852, 1960; 112, 57, 1963; *Cancer Res.*, 22, 1356, 1962; *Biochem.*, 1, 340, 1962; 5, 1174, 1966; *Nature*, 212, 93, 1966; *Mycol.*, 54, 476, 1962

41130-1463

NAME: PRIMOCARCIN
PO: NOC.FUKAYAE
CT: AMINO ACID ANALOG, NEUTRAL
FORMULA: C8H12N2O3
EA: (N, 15)
MW: 189
PC: WH., CRYST.
OR: (0,)
UV: HCL: (253, 190,)
UV: NAOH: (200, ,) (215, ,) (347, ,)
UV: W: (253, 190,)
SOL-GOOD: W, MEOH, ETOH, BUOH, PYR, ACET
SOL-FAIR: ETOAC
SOL-POOR: BENZ, ET2O, HEX
QUAL: (PAULY, +) (FEHL., +) (DNPH, +) (FECL3, -) (NINH., -) (BIURET, -) (SAKA., -)
STAB: (ACID, -) (BASE, -)
TO: (S.AUREUS, 50) (E.COLI, 50) (B.SUBT., 100) (S.LUTEA, 100)
LD50: (50, IP)
TV: EHRLICH
IS-ION: (C-1-H, ACET-W)
IS-CRY: (CRYST., MEOH)
REFERENCES:

JCS, 470, 1965; *TL*, 1897, 1964; *JA*, 13, 416, 1960; 14, 160, 1961; 15, 75, 77, 80, 1962; 20, 167, 1967; JP 63/2798

41130-1493

NAME: ASPERGILLOMARASMIN-A
PO: ASP.FLAVUS-ORYZAE
CT: AMINO ACID ANALOG, AMPHOTER
FORMULA: C10H17N3O8
EA: (N, 14)
PC: WH., CRYST.
OR: (-48, PH7 PUFF)
SOL-GOOD: ACID, BASE
SOL-POOR: W, BUOH, HEX
QUAL: (NINH., +)
TV: PLANT V
REFERENCES:
Bull. Soc. Chim. Fr., 187, 1962; 2778, 1964; 832, 1965; *Liebigs Ann.*, 668, 132, 1963; *Helv.*, 48, 729, 1965; *CR Ser. D*, 276, 1903, 1973

41130-1494

NAME: LYCOMARASMIN
IDENTICAL: ASPERGILLOMARASMIN-B
PO: FUS.LYCOPERSICI
CT: AMINO ACID ANALOG, AMPHOTER
FORMULA: C9H14N2O8
EA: (N, 15)
MW: 366.7
PC: WH., CRYST.
OR: (-45|3, PH7 PUFF)
SOL-FAIR: W
SOL-POOR: ACID, BASE
QUAL: (NINH., +) (BIURET, +) (FECL3, -)
TV: PLANT V
REFERENCES:
Helv., 48, 729, 1965; 46, 60, 1963; *JCS*, 4555, 1957; *Exp.*, 1, 195, 1945; 3, 70, 202, 1947; *CR Ser. D*, 260, 5924, 1964; 263, 710, 1965

41130-1496

NAME: 2.3-DIAMINOSUCCINATE
PO: S.RIMOSUS
CT: AMINO ACID ANALOG
FORMULA: C4H8N2O4
EA: (N, 19)
MW: 148
TO: (E.COLI,)
REFERENCES:
JOC, 24, 679, 1959; *J. Biol. Chem.*, 162, 451, 1946

41000-1495

NAME:	FWH-775
PO:	ASP.NIGER
CT:	AMINO ACID DERIV.
SOL-GOOD:	W
SOL-POOR:	ETOAC, CHL, BENZ, ET2O
STAB:	(HEAT, +) (ACID, -)
TV:	VACCINIA

REFERENCES:

USP 3819832

41000-4005

NAME:	O-2867-B"
PO:	S.SP.
CT:	AMPHOTER
FORMULA:	C10H17N3O7, C11H19N3O7
EA:	(N, 14)
MW:	313
PC:	WH., CRYST.
OR:	(-16, W)
UV:	W: (200, ,)
SOL-GOOD:	W, MEOH
SOL-FAIR:	ETOH, ACET
SOL-POOR:	ETOAC, HEX
QUAL:	(NINH., +) (EHRL., +) (FECL3, -)
TO:	(PIRICULARIA ORYZAE, 3.1)
IS-CRY:	(CRYST., W)

REFERENCES:

JA, 24, 774, 1971

41000-4006

NAME:	<u>0-2867-A"</u>
PO:	S.SP.
CT:	AMPHOTER, ACIDIC
FORMULA:	C14H25N3O9
EA:	(N, 12)
MW:	380
PC:	WH., POW.
OR:	(-43, W)
UV:	W: (200, ,)
SOL-GOOD:	W, MEOH
SOL-FAIR:	ETOH, ACET
SOL-POOR:	ETOAC, HEX
QUAL:	(NINH., +) (EHRL., +) (FECL3, -)
STAB:	(BASE, +)
TO:	(PIRICULARIA ORYZAE, 6) (PHYT.FUNGI, 6)
IS-FIL:	7
IS-ION:	(IR-120-H, NH4OH) (IR-4B-OH, HCL)
IS-ABS:	(CARBON, ACET-W)
IS-CHR:	(CARBON, ACET-W) (CEL, BUOH-ACOH-W)
IS-CRY:	(LIOF.,)

REFERENCES:

JA, 24, 774, 1971

412
Cyclic Amino Acid Derivatives

Introduction

Compounds belonging to this group may be classified as a whole as heterocyclic compounds, but their evident and close biogenetic and chemical relationship with amino acids justifies their classification in the peptide family of antibiotics. This group is subdivided into the outstandingly important β-lactam antibiotics (4121) as well as into the chemically related pyrrothine-type compounds (4122) and the biotin analog actithiazic acid type (4123). All compounds in this group are nitrogen- and sulfur-containing, relatively small molecular antibiotics (pseudodi- or pseudotripeptides) containing fused heterocyclic rings.

Pyrrothine and actithiazic acid type of compounds are produced exclusively by *Streptomyces* species, while β-lactams were isolated from fungi and actinomycetes alike.

4121
β-Lactam Antibiotics (Penicillins, Cephalosporins)

Since the discovery of penicillin by Fleming in 1928, β-lactam antibiotics have been considered to be the most important chemotherapeutic agents. The almost complete lack of toxicity and wide range of antibacterial activity, together with excellent pharmaceutical properties, made these natural and semisynthetic antibiotics a "miracle drug".

Because a great number of comprehensive and up-to-date reviews have been published in this field, the present introduction is limited only to the most important facts and a comparative treatment of the topic.

Until 1975 only two types of β-lactam antibiotics (penicillins and cephalosporins) were known. In the very recent years, however, three entirely new types of β-lactams (nocardicin, thienamycin, and clavulanic acid types) were discovered, promising a new fruitful development in this area.

The term "β-lactam antibiotics" refers to the family of nontoxic compounds of biosynthetic origin and to their semisynthetic derivatives, containing a fused or unfused β-lactam (azetidinone) ring. Excluded are the bacterial toxins (tabtoxin) and plant sterol agents (pachystermines) containing a β-lactam ring. This latter type of compound shows quite different biochemical and microbiological activities.

The β-lactam antibiotics may be organized into penicillin (41211), cephalosporin (41212), nocardicin (41213), thienamycin (41214), and clavulanic acid (41215) subtypes. Molecular fragments characteristic to each of the above subtypes are illustrated below:

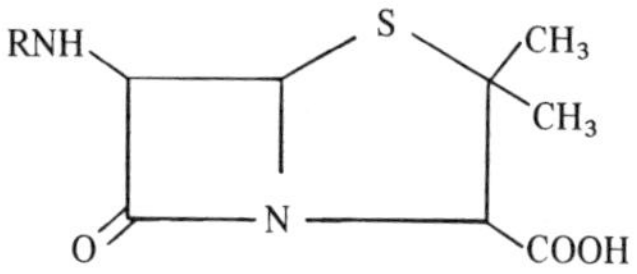

41211

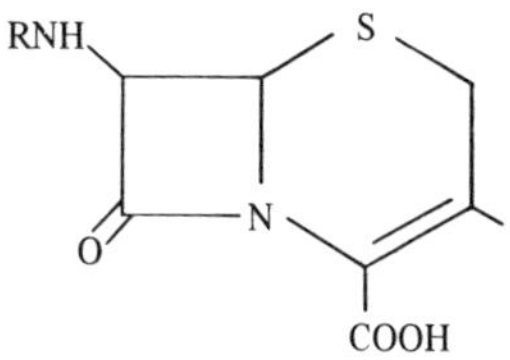

41212

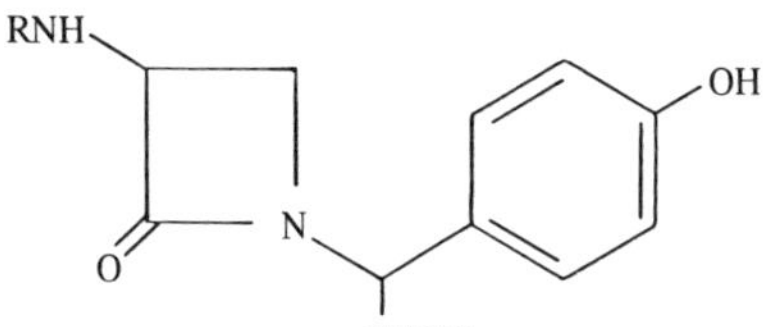

41213

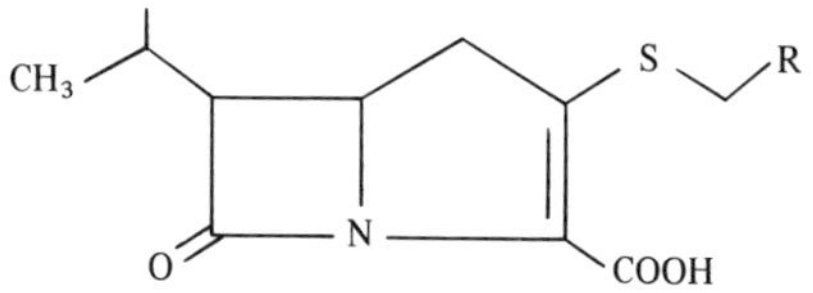

41214

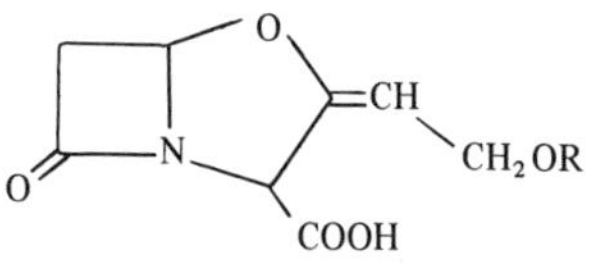

41215

All of these compounds contain — besides the β-lactam ring — a free carboxyl function and, except nocardicins, a five- or six-membered heterocyclic ring condensed with the β-lactam fragment, as well as, except clavulanic acids, an acylamino or alkyl side chain on the β-lactam ring. In the following discussion, first the most important penicillin and cephalosporin type compounds will be considered.

Penicillins have a β-lactam-thiazolidine structure. The terms "penam" **(1)**, penicillanic acid **(2)**, and "penicillin nucleus" or 6β-aminopenicillanic acid **(3)** mean the basic, commonly encountered structures in this type.

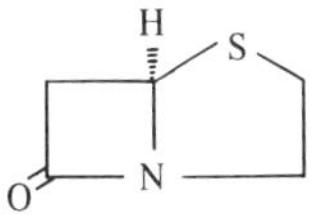

(1)

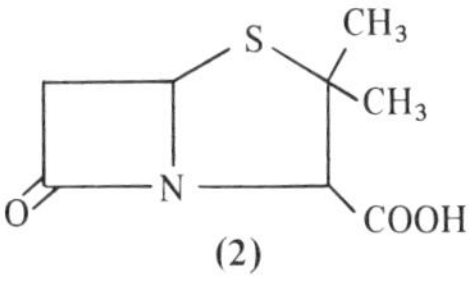

(2)

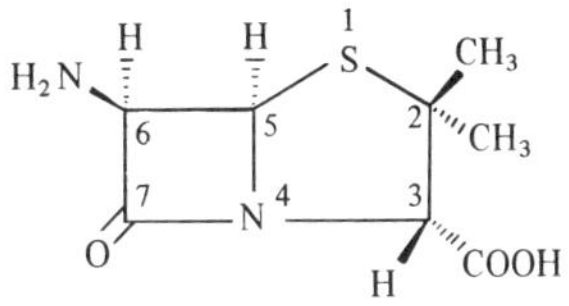

(3)

Penicillins contain three asymmetric centers; therefore eight stereoisomeric forms are possible. X-ray crystallographic studies have established that the natural penicillins (and all of the bioactive synthetic derivatives) possess 3S, 5R(β), 6R(β) configuration as shown on **(3)**. The favored conformation of penicillins is shown on **(4)**. The β-lactam ring is planar and the chirality around this ring is the same in both the penicillins and cephalosporins.

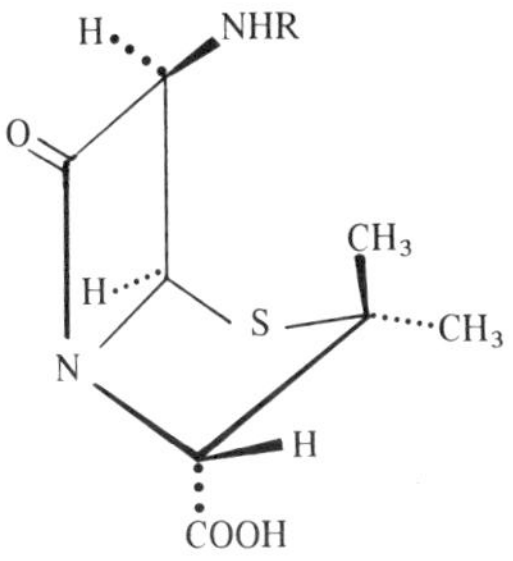

(4)

Cephalosporins differ from penicillins in that they contain the dihydro-1,3-thiazine ring instead of the thiazolidine ring. The bicyclic unit is called "cepham" (1-aza-5-thia-6R-bicyclo[4,2,0]octan-8-one)**(5)**. Cephalosporanic acid **(6)** contains a ceph-3-em system and the "cephalosporin nucleus" or 7β-aminocephalosporanic acid **(7)** are the basic units of cephalosporin-type compounds.

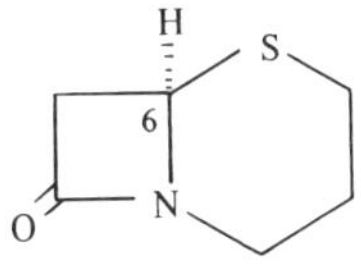

(5)

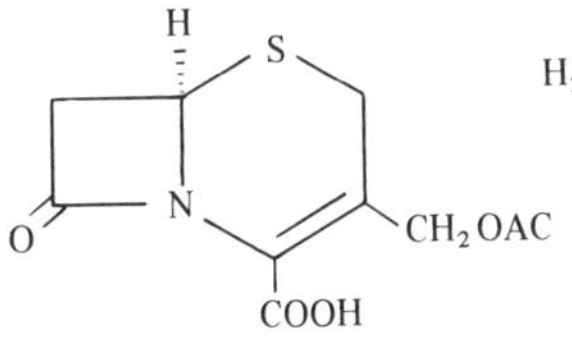

(6)

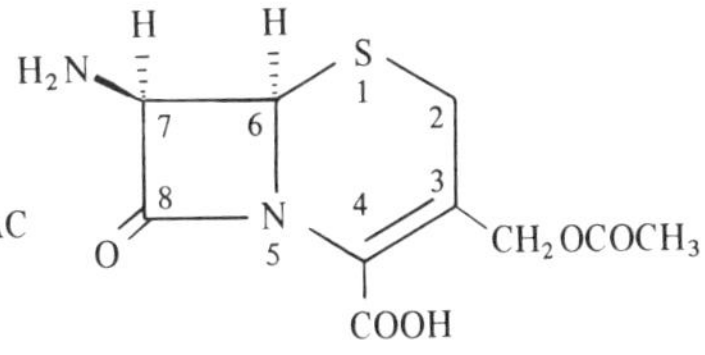

(7)

The stereostructure of the cephalosporins — the *cis* orientation of the hydrogen atoms on the β-lactam ring — is identical and the absolute configuration also conforms with that of the penicillins.

The various penicillins differ only in the nature of the 6-acylamido side chain, while cephalosporins, besides the differences in the corresponding 7-acylamido substituent, vary in the nature of the C-3 substituents (methyl, oxymethyl, acetoxymethyl) and the substitution on the 7α position (hydrogen or methoxy). The N-acyl side chain in the penicillins is usually an apolar residue, but it could be a polar α-aminoadipyl fragment or its derivatives (glutaryl or δ-hydroxyvaleryl) in cephalosporins and in penicillin N.

All natural penicillins, except the hydrophilic penicillin N, were exclusively isolated from a wide variety of fungal species. Cephalosporins and penicillin N are produced by fungal and *Streptomyces* species also. The chemical structures of streptomycetal cephalosporins are more variable than the fungal ones. They are usually 7α-methoxy derivatives containing various substituents (carbamoyl, cinnamic acid, sulfonyl, etc.) on the C-3 methyl group. The fungi which produce penicillins or cephalosporins are apparently unable to produce 7-methoxy derivatives.

The production of penicillins may be influenced by the addition of various precursors to fermentation. In this way enhanced production and discovery of some new penicillins (penicillin V, penicillin O) was possible. The attempt to obtain new cephalosporins in this way was unsuccessful.

The natural penicillins are acidic and the cephalosporins as well as penicillin N are amphoteric compounds. Penicillins having an apolar side chain are more soluble in organic solvents than cephalosporins, which are soluble in water and methanol only.

Penicillins have end absorption on the UV region, but the cephalosporins show absorption maxima at 260 to 266 nm (normal cephalosporins) or at 240 to 243 and 264 to 266 nm (7-methoxy cephalosporins). Methoxy cephalosporins containing cinnamic acid-like fragment show strong absorption around 300 nm (between 287 and 318 nm).

The optical rotation values of penicillins are between + 250 and + 300°, while the found α_D values of cephalosporins lie between + 100 and + 150°.

The β-lactam antibiotics, especially penicillins, are less stable compounds. Their sensitivity against acids is markedly pronounced. The isolation of cephalosporins and penicillins from cultural broths is rather difficult. Extraction or precipitation methods (penicillins) as well as ion-exchange or chromatographic processes are usually applied for their isolation.

Most of the new cephalosporins isolated in recent years were obtained as impure amorphous products. Because of their less characteristic physical and chemical properties these new natural compounds can only be identified by their chemical structures.

The antimicrobial spectra of penicillins cover all kinds of Gram-positive bacteria and some kinds of Gram-negative pathogens (*Neisseria* sp.), as well as *Trepanoma* species. Cephalosporins isolated from natural sources have a broader but weaker spectrum of activity, inhibiting Gram-negative bacteria also.

β-Lactam antibiotics are almost atoxic compounds. Their specific activity on the bacterial cell wall, lacking in animal cells, provides a guarantee of their very low human toxicity. The only severe untoward effect is their allergenic property, which sometimes causes anaphylactoid reactions. The incidence of hypersensitive individuals in the normal population is about 1 to 5%. It has been shown that the presence of penicilloylated protein impurity in the natural penicillins may be responsible for the induction of hypersensitivity.

β-Lactams are rapidly distributed to most body tissues and fluids (except cerebrospyral liquor) when administered via an appropriate route.

The greatest problem in penicillin therapy is the fast development of bacterial resistance against these drugs. The serious consequence of this fact and the tremendous research efforts which were directed in the last decades to solve these problems are well known. These intensive efforts have resulted in the introduction of semisynthetic β-lactam antibiotics in human therapy. These semisynthetic drugs almost completely displaced the natural penicillins from medical practice. Presently only penicillins G and V are in limited therapeutic use.

Cephalosporin C, although possessing only a relatively low order of antimicrobial activity, has two promising properties. It is effective against penicillin-resistant bacteria and its activity is extended to Gram-negative species. While the conversion of natural cephalosporins to 7-aminocephalosporanic acid was relatively easy and the preparation of 7-aminodesacetoxycephalosporanic acid derivatives from the cheap penicillins was industrially acceptable, the preparation of very effective broad-spectrum semisynthetic cephalosporins, not available by fermentation, resulted in the most useful and popular new antibacterial drugs. At present the semisynthetic β-lactams are the most important antibacterial drugs, uniting the advantages of the penicillins, tetracyclines, macrolides, and partly aminoglycosides.

The route of biosynthesis of β-lactams is not fully established in all details. The units from which these compounds are built up are L-cysteine, L-valine, and the appropriate side chain precursor. The presumable common precursor for penicillins and cephalosporins is (L-α-aminoadipyl)-L-cysteinyl-D-valine **(8)**

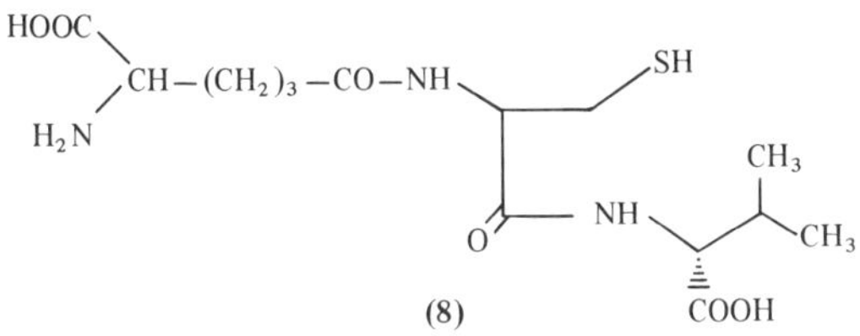

(8)

The mechanism of cyclization of the tripeptide **(8)** to penicillin N (the precursor of deacetoxycephalosporins) or isopenicillin N (the precursor of 6-aminopenicillanic acid and penicillins) is not clarified yet. The methyl group in methoxycephalosporins is supplied by methionine.

β-Lactams interfere with the final step of the bacterial cell wall synthesis. The rigid cell wall is essential for all microorganism's welfare. In the last stage of the synthesis of the rigid bacterial capsule, a cross-linking between two linear peptidoglycan chains occurs, constructing a three-dimensional network of the cell wall. This bridging reaction is catalyzed by a transpeptidase which reacts with the D-ala-D-ala end of the terminal pentapeptide of the peptidoglycan. The activated (thioester) acylenzyme then reacts with the glycine end of a second chain forming the cross-linking.

Penicillins, and with small differences cephalosporins also, are structurally similar to D-ala-D-ala and they irreversibly acylate the transpeptidase which is responsible for cross-linking, forming a penicyllanoyl derivative, thereby inactivating it. This reaction results in the inhibition of cell wall synthesis in dividing cells, causing the rupture of the weakened cell wall by osmotic pressure. The close analogy between N-acyl-D-ala-D-ala and the penicillins is formulated in the following figure:

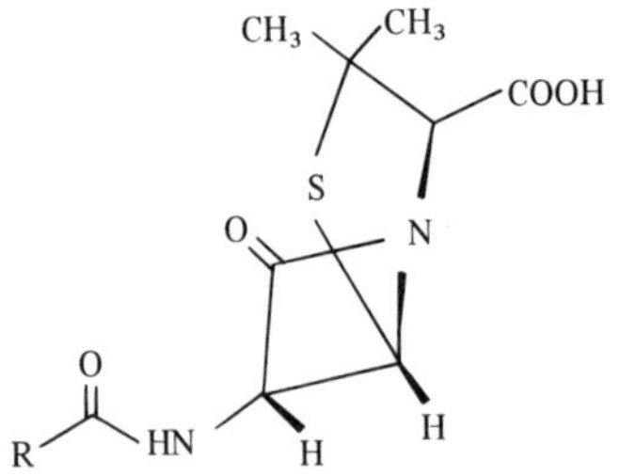

penicillin

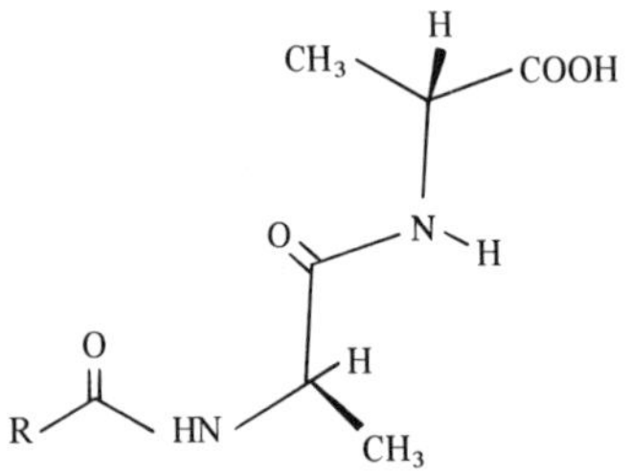

D-ala-D-ala

Instead of a detailed historical survey, the main milestones of β-lactam research are listed in the following table.

1928	Fleming recognizes the penicillin production of *Penicillium notatum*
1940	Isolation of pure penicillin in Oxford
1941—1944	Anglo-American cooperation; structure and industrial production of penicillin
1945—1948	Brotzu isolates *Cephalosporium acremonium* and sends the culture to Oxford
1948	Biosynthetic penicillins, precursor technique
1950, 1953	Sakaguchi and Kato make early observations about penicillin nucleus
1953—1955	Isolation of penicillin N (cephalosporin N, synnematin B)
1954	Penicillin V, acid-stable penicillin
1955	Isolation of cephalosporin C
1959—1962	Total synthesis of 6-APA and penicillin V by Sheehan
1959	Isolation of 6-APA by the Beecham group
1960	Penicillin-amidase
1960—1967	Semisynthetic penicillins (pheneticillin, methicillin, oxacillin, ampicillin, carbenicillin)
1961	Structure of cephalosporin C
1963	Penicillin → cephalosporin conversion
1964—1967	Semisynthetic cephalosporins (cephalothin, cefazolin, cefamandol, cefoxitin)
1966	Total synthesis of cephalosporin C
1971	Isolation of cephalosporins from Streptomycetes by Lilly and Merck groups
	Enzymatic synthesis of penicillins
1974—1975	β-Lactamase inhibitors (clavulanic and olivanic acids)
1976	New β-lactam types (nocardicin, thienamycin)

Even the shortest discussion of the structural modifications performed on the penicillin and cephalosporin molecules would be an extremely difficult task and outside the scope of this introduction. Up to now at least 20,000 to 25,000 semisynthetic derivatives have been prepared both from penicillanic and cephalosporanic acids.

The modifications in the penicillin series have been centered on the acylation of the amino group of 6-APA. The various side chains influence the solubility, acid stability, adsorption properties, resistance to penicillinase (methicillin), spectrum of activity (ampicillin, carbenicillin), and systemic action after oral use. Recently other modifications have been favored, namely modifications of the penam ring system by total synthetic routes.

The modifications of the cephalosporin nucleus in the last years have been made at nearly every possible position. These changes have had a profound effect on both the potency and antimicrobial spectrum of these compounds and may also affect transport properties. The most successful modifications are those directed to the N-acyl side chain and C3 methyl (oxymethyl) group. In this field numerous other ring alterations, e.g., replacing the sulfur in the ring with oxygen or sp^3 carbon, have also been undertaken.

In general, the various modifications and the recent total synthetic investigations revealed that the thiazolidine ring of penicillin and the dihydrothiazine ring of cephalosporins are not obligatory for biological functions of β-lactam antibiotics. Consequently, in many laboratories discovery of newer methods for synthesis of entirely new types of β-lactam antibiotics is encouraged, as well as development of newer screening methods to recognize new β-lactam structures among microbial metabolites.

Penicillins and cephalosporins act as analoges of N-acyl derivatives of D-ala-D-ala, and they function as acylating agents. Coinciding with the results obtained from the analysis of semisynthetic modifications, the amido side chain, the β-lactam ring, and the free 3-carboxyl group are essential structural requirements for biological activity.

The minimal structural requirements may be depicted as:

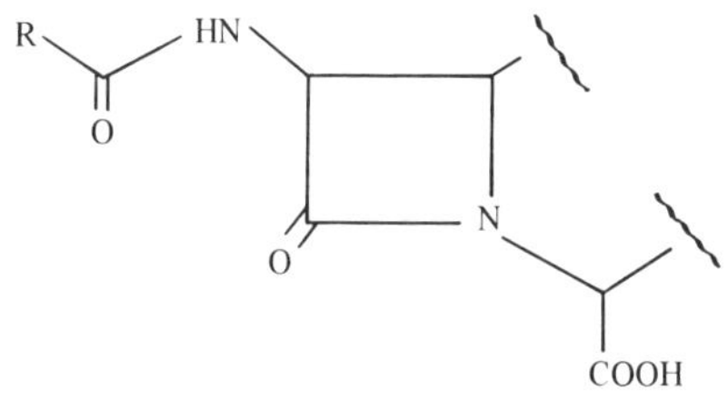

The hetero-rings fused with the β-lactam system may be important only because they sustain β-lactam reactivity and they specifically orientate the 3-carboxyl group. The somewhat different action of cephalosporins may partly be derived from the different orientation of the 3-carboxyl group. Generally, the changes which increase the stability of the β-lactam system (e.g., the isolated β-lactam ring in nocardicins) reduce the intrinsic activity of compounds. The sulfur atom and the C-2 geminal methyl substituents do not play a direct role in biological activity.

Modern fermentation methods have enabled penicillin production to reach a level of about 10,000 tons annually. Recently penicillins obtained by fermentation can be regarded as a raw material for transformation into other more useful drugs, because the current highlighting of β-lactams came with the revelation that modified cephalosporin derivatives surely have more advantageous properties than the penicillins.

Newer β-Lactam Antibiotics

In recent years several new types of β-lactam antibiotics were discovered on the basis of using specific hypersensitive mutants for screening of microbial metabolites or indicating the β-lactamase-inhibiting activity of the microbial cultures. By the former method a lot of new penicillins and cephalosporins were also discovered. A hypersensitive mutant was used for the discovery of nocardicins (41213). The *Nocardia*-produced nocardicins contain an unfused β-lactam ring and a new type of N-acyl side chain containing the unusual oxime function. The acid-stable nocardicins have moderate in vitro antibacterial activity against Gram-negative bacteria, but their in vivo activity against these pathogens including *Pseudomonas* and *Proteus* species is more remarkable. They are resistant against β-lactamases. The molecule of nocardicin A is apparently formed from two molecules of L-p-hydroxyphenylglicine, L-homoserine, and L-serine. The very recently obtained "nocardicin nucleus", 3-aminonocardicinic acid, allows the preparation of new and potentially more useful derivatives. Nocardicins are the first example of monocyclic β-lactams possessing relatively high potency. The p-hydroxyphenylglycine unit is rarely found in nature.

Detection of β-lactamase inhibitors during the screening of various microorganisms led to the isolation of a series of olivanic acid **(9)** derivatives (41214). These β-lactam antibiotics contain a 1-hydroxyethyl side chain on the β-lactam ring instead of the aminoacyl function and a 2-aminoethyl or 2-aminoethylene substituent on the sulfur-free five-membered ring. They are effective against both Gram-positive and Gram-negative bacteria. The best known member of this group, thienamycin **(10)**, is an extremely active broad-spectrum agent, but its lability prevents its clinical application for the time being. These compounds contain a 1-carba-penem system **(11)**.

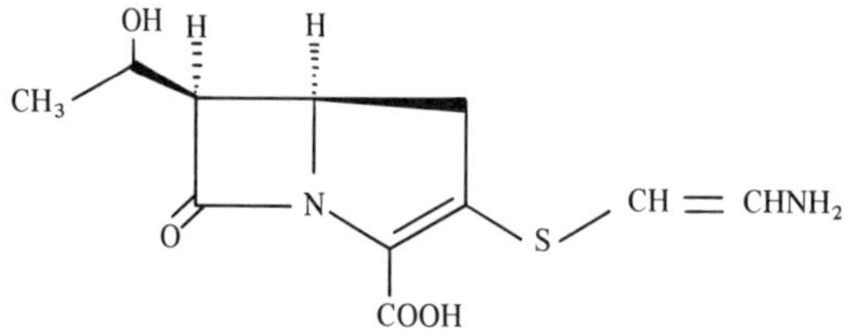

(9)

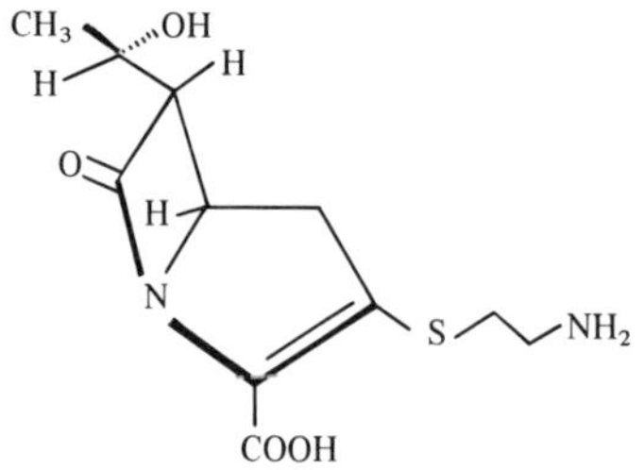

(10)

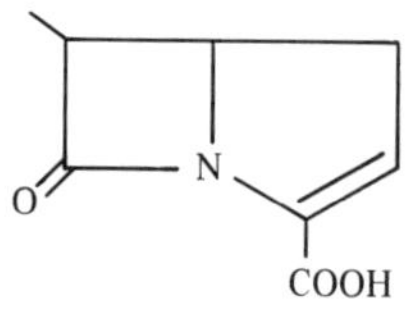

(11)

Clavulanic acid and its derivatives represent another type of potent β-lactamase inhibitors (41215). Clavulanic acid has a β-lactame fused oxazolidine structure without N-acyl or another side chain on the lactame ring. It was obtained from *Streptomyces* species, which produces a number of cephalosporins and penicillin N. The synergistic action of clavulanic acid and other β-lactams, e.g., ampicillin, gave excellent results in clinical trials.

The absolute stereochemistry of these compounds is the same as in the penams and cephems, except thienamycin where the hydrogens of the β-lactam ring are *trans*. Very recently a tremendous development was achieved in this field, resulting in numerous new stereochemically variable compounds.

REFERENCES

1. *Pharm. Rev.*, 14, 473, 1962.
2. *Quart. Rev.*, 21, 231, 1967.
3. *AAC 1967*, 670.
4. *J. Pharm. Pharmacol.*, 21, 337, 1969.
5. *Adv. Appl. Microb.*, 2, 17, 1969; 13, 163, 1970.
6. *Adv. Pharm. Sci.*, 1, 1, 1967.
7. *Adv. Drug. Res.*, 1, 1, 1964; 4, 1, 1967; 7, 1, 1973.
8. *J. Pharm. Sci.*, 60, 503, 1971.
9. *Forschr.*, 28, 343, 1970; 31, 1, 1974.
10. *Bull. Soc. Chim. Fr.*, 2733, 1971.
11. *Progr. Org. Chem.*, 8, 102, 1972.

12. *Pure Appl. Chem.*, 33, 1, 1973.
13. *Acc. Chem. Res.*, 6, 32, 1973.
14. *Int. Rev. Sci. Biochem. Ser. I*, 6, 247, 1973.
15. *Progr. Med. Chem.*, 12, 395, 1975; 14, 181, 1977.
16. *Org. Comp. Sulphur, Selenium, Tellurium*, 3, 190, 1975.
17. *Chem. Rev.*, 76, 113, 1976.
18. *Chim. (Basel)*, 30, 13, 1976.
19. *Postepy Microbiol.*, 15, 15, 1976.
20. *Hakko Kagaku Zasshi*, 54, 171, 1976.
21. *Lloydia*, 40, 519, 1977.
22. *Heterocycl.*, 8, 719, 1977.
23. *An. Rep. Ferm. Proc.*, 1, 327, 1977.
24. *Jap. J. Ant.*, 30 (Suppl.) S-1, S-207, S-218, S-230, S-239, 1977.
25. *Tetr.*, 34, 1731, 1978.
26. **Flynn, E. H.**, Ed., *Cephalosporins and Penicillins*, Academic Press, New York, 1972.
27. **Manhas, M. S. and Bose, A. K.**, *Beta-Lactams, Natural and Synthetic*, John Wiley & Sons, New York, 1969.
28. **Clarke, H. T., Johnson, J. R., and Robinson, R.**, Eds., *The Chemistry of Penicillin*, Princeton University Press, Princeton, N. J., 1949.

Structures

41211

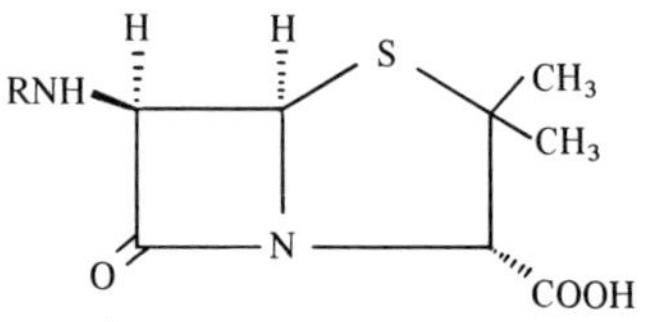

Antibiotic	R
6-Aminopenicillanic acid	H
Penicillin G	$COCH_2C_6H_5$
Penicillin V	$COCH_2-O-C_6H_5$
Penicillin F	$COCH_2CH=CHCH_2CH_3$
Penicillin X	$COCH_2-pOHC_6H_4$
Penicillin K	$CO(CH_2)_6CH_3$
Dihydropenicillin F	$CO(CH_2)_4CH_3$
Penicillin O	$COCH_2SCH=CH-CH=CH_2$
Penicillin N	$CO(CH_2)_3\overset{5'}{C}H<^{NH_2}_{COOH}$
Isopenicillin N[a]	$CO(CH_2)_3\overset{5'}{C}H<^{NH_2}_{COOH}$
RIT-D-2214	$COCH_2-S-CH_2CH$
KPN	$CO(CH_2)_3CH_2OH$

[a] Isomer at C-5′.

41212

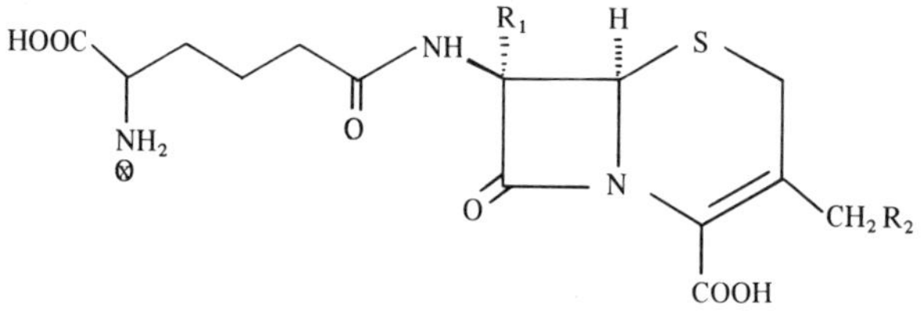

Antibiotic	R_1	R_2
Cephalosporin C	H	$OCOCH_3$
Desacetoxycephalosporin C	H	H
Desacetylcephalosporin C	H	OH
F_1	H	SCH_3
C-43-219	H	$SC(CH_3)_2CH<^{NH_2}_{COOH}$
N-Acetyldesacetoxycephalosporin C⊗	H	H
Cephamycin A	OCH_3	[a]
Cephamycin B	OCH_3	[b]
C-2801 X	OCH_3	[c]
Cephamycin C (A-16886-I)	OCH_3	$OCONH_2$
A-16886-II (WS-3442-B)	H	$OCONH_2$
A-16884 (7-methoxycephalosporin C)	OCH_3	$OCOCH_3$
WS-3442-D	OCH_3	H
Y-G19Z-D3(7-methoxydesacetoxycephalosporin C)	OCH_3	OH
SF-1623	OCH_3	$S-SO_3H$

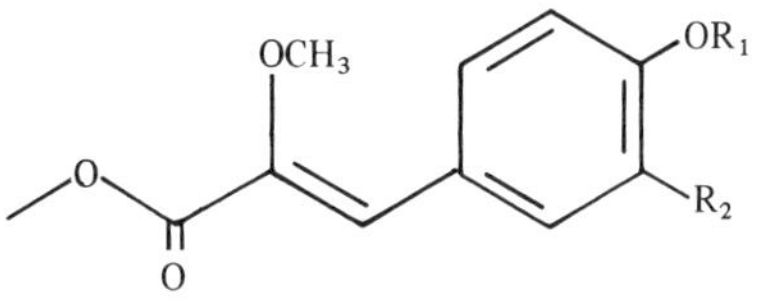

[a] $R_1 = SO_3H$; $R_2 = H$
[b] $R_1 = H$; $R_2 = H$
[c] $R_1 = H$; $R_2 = OH$

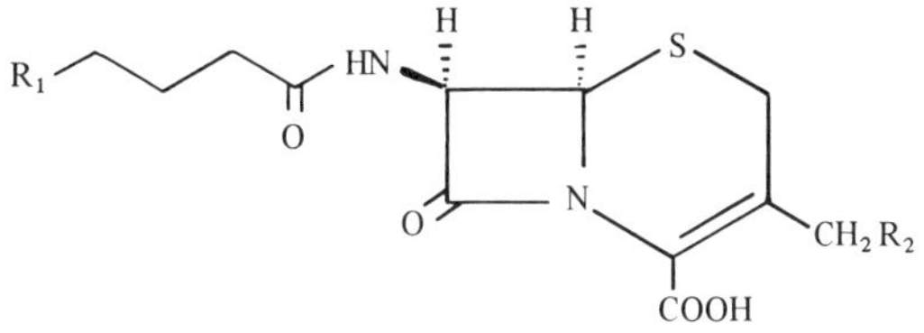

Antibiotic	R_1	R_2
C-1778 A	COOH	$OCOCH_3$
C-1778 B	COOH	H
C-1778 C	COOH	OH
C_2	COCOOH	OH
C_4	COCOOH	$OCOCH_3$
C_6	COCOOH	H
GK-340	$CH_2CH(NH_2)COOH$	$OCOCH_3$

41213

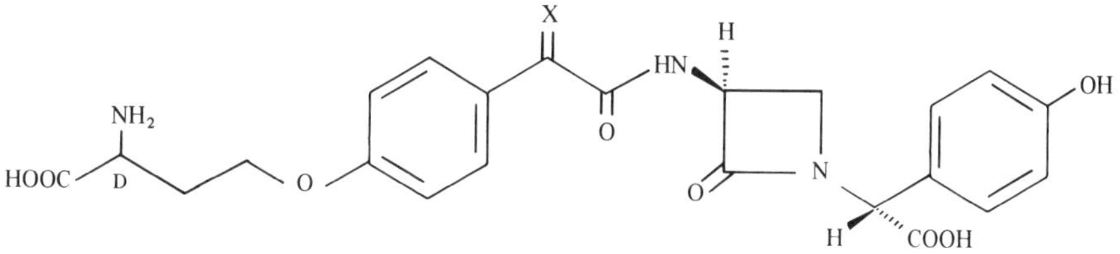

Nocardicin A X = $\underset{\|}{N}{-}OH$

Nocardicin B X = $HO{-}\underset{\|}{N}$

Nocardicin C X = NH_2, H
Nocardicin D X = O=

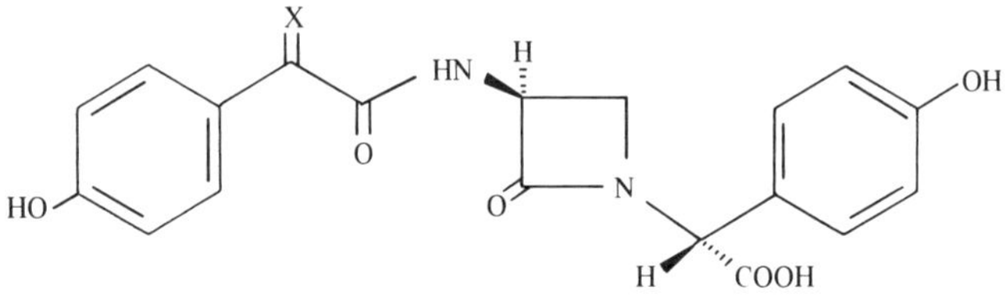

Nocardicin E X = $\underset{\|}{N}{-}OH$

Nocardicin F X = $OH{-}\underset{\|}{N}$

Nocardicin G X = NH_2, H

41214

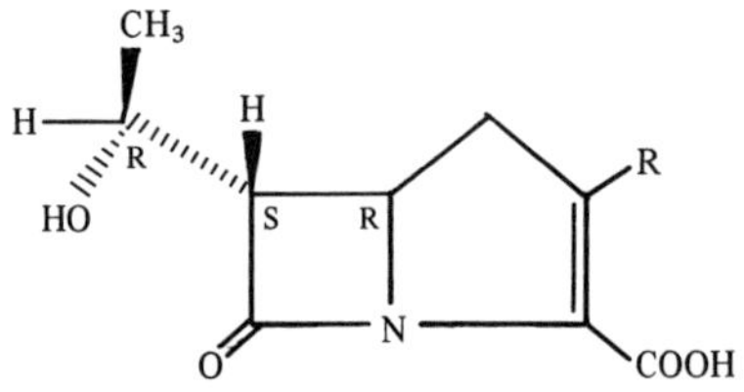

Thienamycin	$R = SCH_2CH_2NH_2$
N-Acetylthienamycin	$R = SCH_2CH_2NHCOOH_3$
N-Acetyldehydrothienamycin	$R = SCH{=}CH{-}NH{-}COCH_3$

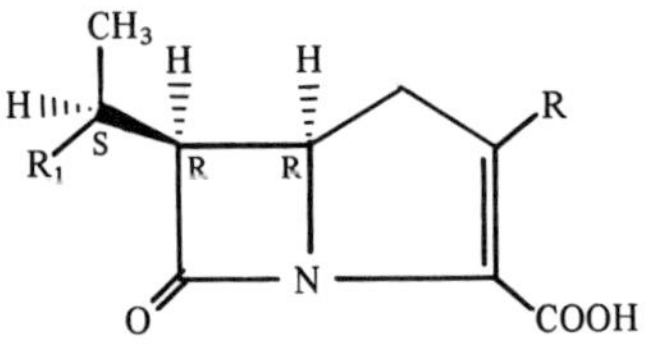

	R_1	R_2
MM-5500 (MC 696-SY2-A)	OSO_3H	$S(O){-}CH{=}CH{-}NHCOCH_3$
MM-13902 (890-A_9)	OSO_3H	$S{-}CH{=}CH{-}NHCOCH_3$
MM-17880 (890-A_{10})	OSO_3H	$S{-}CH_2CH_2NHCOCH_3$
MM-22380 (890-A_1)	OH	$S{-}CH_2CH_2NHCOCH_3$
MM-22382 (890-A_2)	OH	$S{-}CH{=}CH{-}NHCOCH_3$

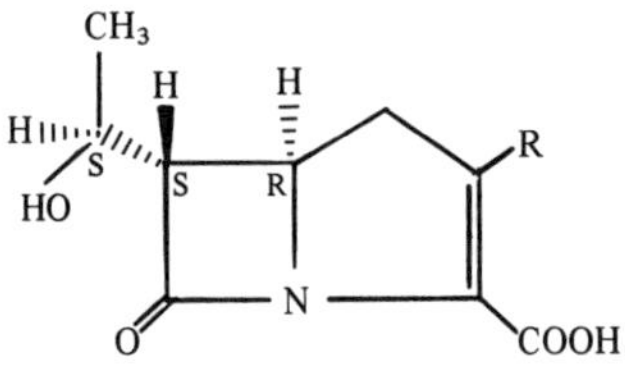

MM-22381 (890-A_3)	$R = S{-}CH_2CH_2{-}NHCOCH_3$
MM-22383 (890-A_5)	$R = S{-}CH{=}CH{-}NHCOCH_3$

PS-5:

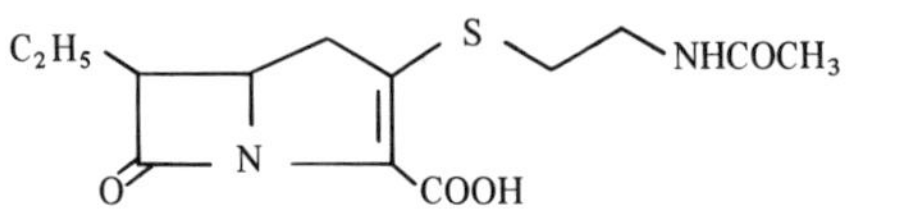

41215

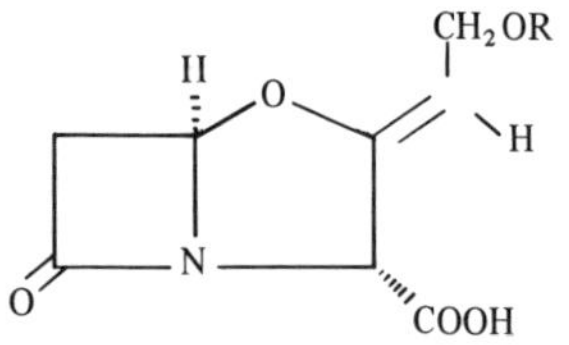

Antibiotic	R
Clavulanic acid (MM-14151, 3008B)	H
1β-Hydroxypropylclavulanic acid	$COCH_2CH_2OH$

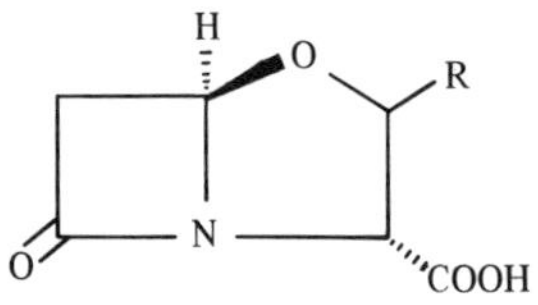

Antibiotic	R
2-Hydroxymethylclavam	CH_2OH
2-Formyloxymethylclavam	CH_2OCHO

41211-1497

NAME:	6-AMINOPENICILLANIC ACID, 6-APA
IDENTICAL:	PENICILLIN NUCLEUS
PO:	P.CHRYSOGENUM, MALBRANCHELLA SP., GYMNOASAUS SP., POLYPAECILIUM SP.
CT:	PENICILLIN T., AMPHOTER, B"-LACTAM
FORMULA:	C8H12N2O3S
EA:	(N, 13) (S, 14)
MW:	216
PC:	WH., CRYST.
OR:	(+216, HCL)
UV:	MEOH: (200, ,)
SOL-GOOD:	ACID, BASE
SOL-POOR:	W, BUOH, HEX
QUAL:	(NINH., +)
STAB:	(ACID, +) (BASE, -)
TO:	(G.POS., 10)
IS-CRY:	(PREC., FILT., 4.5)

REFERENCES:

See also General References; *JA*, 6, 130, 184, 1953; *J. Agr. Chem. Soc. Jap.*, 23, 411, 1950; *Nature*, 187, 236, 1960; *Naturwiss.*, 47, 474, 1960; *Proc. R. Soc. London*, 179, 321, 1971; *J. Ferm. Techn.*, 53, 339, 1975

41211-1498

NAME: PENICILLIN-G, BENZYLPENICILLIN, PENICILLIN-II
IDENTICAL: PARASTICIN
PO: P.SP., ASP.SP., TRICHOPHYTON SP., P.NOTATUM, P.CHRYSOGENUM
CT: PENICILLIN T., ACIDIC, B"-LACTAM
FORMULA: C16H18N2O4S
EA: (N,) (S, 10)
MW: 334, 331
PC: WH., HYGROSCOPIC, CRYST.
OR: (+522, PH7 PUFF) (+305, W)
UV: W: (252, , 295) (275.5, , 242) (264, , 178)
SOL-GOOD: MEOH, ET2O
SOL-FAIR: W
SOL-POOR: TOL, HEX
QUAL: (FEHL., +) (PAULY, +)
STAB: (ACID, -) (BASE, -) (HEAT, -)
TO: (G.POS., .001)
LD50: (2000, IV)
IS-FIL: 5
IS-EXT: (ETOAC, 3, FILT.)
UTILITY: ANTIBACTERIAL DRUG
REFERENCES:

See also General References; *JA*, 6, 130, 184, 1953; *J. Agr. Chem. Soc. Jap.*, 23, 411, 1950; *Nature*, 187, 236, 1960; *Naturwiss.*, 47, 474, 1960; *Proc. R. Soc. London*, 179, 321, 1971; *J. Ferm. Techn.*, 53, 339, 1975

41211-1499

NAME: PENICILLIN-V, PHENOXYMETHYLPENICILLIN
PO: P.SP.+PHENOXYACETIC ACID
CT: PENICILLIN T., ACIDIC, B"-LACTAM
FORMULA: C16H18N2O5S
EA: (N, 8) (S, 9)
MW: 350
PC: WH., CRYST.
UV: CHL: (270, ,) (276, ,)
UV: W: (268, ,) (274, ,)
SOL-GOOD: MEOH, ET2O
SOL-FAIR: HEX, CCL4
SOL-POOR: W
STAB: (ACID, +) (BASE, -) (HEAT, -)
TO: (G.POS., .001)
LD50: (2000, IV)
UTILITY: ANTIBACTERIAL DRUG
REFERENCES:

See also General References; *JA*, 6, 130, 184, 1953; *J. Agr. Chem. Soc. Jap.*, 23, 411, 1950; *Nature*, 187, 236, 1960; *Naturwiss.*, 47, 474, 1960; *Proc. R. Soc. London*, 179, 321, 1971; *J. Ferm. Techn.*, 53, 339, 1975

41211-1500

NAME:	PENICILLIN-F, 2-PENTENYLPENICILLIN, PENICILLIN-I, FLAVICIDIN
PO:	P.SP., ASP.SP.
CT:	PENICILLIN T., ACIDIC, B"-LACTAM
FORMULA:	C14H20N2O4S
EA:	(N, 9) (S, 10)
MW:	312
PC:	WH., CRYST.
OR:	(+305, W)
UV:	W: (200, ,)
SOL-GOOD:	MEOH, ET2O
SOL-FAIR:	HEX, CCL4
SOL-POOR:	W
STAB:	(ACID, -) (BASE, -) (HEAT, -)
TO:	(G.POS., .005)
LD50:	(2000, IV)

REFERENCES:

See also General References; *JA*, 60, 130, 184, 1953; *J. Agr. Chem. Soc. Jap.*, 23, 411, 1950; *Nature*, 187, 236, 1960; *Naturwiss.*, 47, 474, 1960; *Proc. R. Soc. London*, 179, 321, 1971; *J. Ferm. Techn.*, 53, 339, 1975

41211-1501

NAME:	PENICILLIN-X, HYDROXYBENXYLPENICILLIN, PENICILLIN-III
PO:	P.SP
CT:	PENICILLIN T., ACIDIC, B"-LACTAM
FORMULA:	C16H18N2O5S
EA:	(N, 5) (S, 9)
MW:	530
PC:	WH., CRYST.
OR:	(+267, W)
UV:	ETOH-W: (278, , 17000)
SOL-GOOD:	MEOH, ET2O
SOL-FAIR:	HEX, CCL4
SOL-POOR:	W
STAB:	(ACID, +) (HEAT, -) (BASE, -)
TO:	(G.POS., .01)
LD50:	(2000, IV)

REFERENCES:

See also General References; *JA*, 6, 130, 184, 1953; *J. Agr. Chem. Soc. Jap.*, 23, 411, 1950; *Nature*, 187, 236, 1960; *Naturwiss.*, 47, 474, 1960; *Proc. R. Soc. London*, 179, 321, 1971; *J. Ferm. Techn.*, 53, 339, 1975

41211-1502

NAME:	PENICILLIN-K, HEPTYLPENICILLIN, PENICILLIN-IV
PO:	P.SP.
CT:	PENICILLIN T., ACIDIC, B"-LACTAM
FORMULA:	C16H26N2O4S
EA:	(N, 8) (S, 9)
MW:	342
PC:	WH., CRYST.
OR:	(+258, W)
UV:	W: (200, ,)
SOL-GOOD:	MEOH, ET2O
SOL-FAIR:	HEX, CCL4
SOL-POOR:	W
STAB:	(HEAT, -) (ACID, -) (BASE, -)
TO:	(G.POS., .01)
LD50:	(2000, IV)

REFERENCES:

See also General References; *JA*, 6, 130, 184, 1953; *J. Agr. Chem. Soc. Jap.*, 23, 411, 1950; *Nature*, 187, 236, 1960; *Naturwiss.*, 47, 474, 1960; *Proc. R. Soc. London*, 179, 321, 1971; *J. Ferm. Techn.*, 53, 339, 1975

41211-1503

NAME:	DIHYDROPENICILLIN-F, AMYLPENICILLIN
IDENTICAL:	GIGANTIC ACID
PO:	ASP.GIGANTEUS, P.SP.
CT:	PENICILLIN T., ACIDIC, B"-LACTAM
FORMULA:	C14H22N2O4S
EA:	(N, 8) (S, 9)
MW:	314
PC:	WH., CRYST.
OR:	(+319, W)
UV:	W: (265, , 340)
SOL-GOOD:	MEOH, ET2O
SOL-FAIR:	HEX
SOL-POOR:	W
STAB:	(HEAT, -) (ACID, -) (BASE, -)
TO:	(G.POS., .01)
LD50:	(2000, IV)

REFERENCES:

See also General References; *JA*, 6, 130, 184, 1953; *J. Agr. Chem. Soc. Jap.*, 23, 411, 1950; *Nature*, 187, 236, 1960; *Naturwiss.*, 47, 474, 1960; *Proc. R. Soc. London*, 179, 321, 1971; *J. Ferm. Techn.*, 53, 339, 1975

41211-1504

NAME:	<u>FLAVICIN</u>, FLAVACIN
IDENTICAL:	FLAVACIDIN, PENICILLIN F+DIHYDROPENICILLIN
PO:	ASP.SP., P.SP.
CT:	PENICILLIN T., ACIDIC, B"-LACTAM

REFERENCES:

J. Pharmacol., 84, 262, 1945

41211-1505

NAME:	<u>PENICILLIN-O</u>, ALLYLMERCAPTOMETILPENICILLIN
PO:	P.SP.+ALLYMERCAPTOACETIC ACID
CT:	PENICILLIN T., ACIDIC, B"-LACTAM
EA:	(N, 6) (S, 18)
PC:	WH.
STAB:	(ACID, +)
TO:	(G.POS., .01)
UTILITY:	ANTIBACTERIAL DRUG

REFERENCES:

Ant. & Chem., 3, 1149, 1953; USP 2528175, 2623876, 2647894

41211-1506

NAME:	<u>PENICILLIN-N</u>, CEPHALOSPORIN-N, CEPHALOSPORIN-R
TRADE NAMES:	SALMOTIN
IDENTICAL:	SYNNEMATIN-B
PO:	S.SP., ACT.CINEREORECTUS, CEP.SALMOSYNNEMATUM, CEP.SP., CEP.ACREMONIUM, TILACLADIUM SP.
CT:	PENICILLIN T., ACIDIC, AMPHOTER, B"-LACTAM
FORMULA:	C14H21N3O6S
EA:	(N, 11) (S, 9)
MW:	359
PC:	WH., POW.
OR:	(+187, W)
UV:	W: (200, ,)
SOL-GOOD:	W, MEOH
SOL-POOR:	ETOH, HEX
QUAL:	(NINH., +)
STAB:	(ACID, -) (BASE, -)
TO:	(S.AUREUS, 10) (B.SUBT., 5) (S.LUTEA, 5) (SHYG., 5) (K.PNEUM., 10) (P.VULG., 10)
LD50:	(2000, IV) (5000, IP)
IS-FIL:	6
IS-ABS:	(CARBON, ACET-W) (AL, ACET-W)

REFERENCES:

Proc. Soc. Exp. B.M., 76, 307, 1951; *Nature*, 171, 343, 1953; 176, 551, 1955; *Ant. A. An.*, 48, 1960; *JACS*, 84, 4594, 1962; *Biochem. J.*, 58, 94, 103, 1954; 50, 168, 1952; *Antib.*, 195, 1974; *JA*, 27, 169, 1974; USP 2831797, 2899425

41211-1507

NAME: ISOPENICILLIN-N, ISOCEPHALOSPORIN-N
PO: P.CHRYSOGENUM
CT: PENICILLIN T., ACIDIC, AMPHOTER, B"-LACTAM
FORMULA: C14H21N3O6S
EA: (N, 11) (S, 8)
MW: 359
PC: WH., POW.
OR: (+212, W)
QUAL: (NINH., +)
STAB: (ACID, -)
TO: (S.AUREUS,) (G.POS.,)
REFERENCES:
JACS, 84, 4594, 1962; *JA*, 27, 169, 1974; *Bioch. J.*, 151, 729, 1975; *Antib.*, 195, 1979

41211-5330

NAME: KPN
PO: PAECYLOMYCES CARNEUS, PAECYLOMYCES PERSICINUS
CT: PENICILLIN T., ACIDIC, B"-LACTAM
FORMULA: C13H20N2O5S
EA: (N, 8) (S, 10)
PC: WH., POW.
OR: (+255.8, W)
UV: MEOH: (200, ,)
SOL-GOOD: MEOH, ETOH, W
SOL-POOR: ACET, ETOAC, BENZ, HEX
QUAL: (NINH., -)
TO: (S.AUREUS, .07) (S.LUTEA, .05)
IS-ION: (IRA-900-OAC, NH4OH) (XAD-4, BUOH-W)
IS-ABS: (CARBON, BUOH-W)
IS-CHR: (SILG, ACET-W) (SILG, MEOH-ACET)
IS-CRY: (PREC., MEOH, ACET)
REFERENCES:
J. Ferm. Techn., 54, 705, 1976; JP 76/70883; *CA*, 85, 157967

41211-5418

NAME:	RIT-D-2214
PO:	ACREMONIUM CHRYSOGENUM+CARBOXYMETHYLEYSTEIN
CT:	ACIDIC, AMPHOTER, PENICILLIN T., B"-LACTAM
FORMULA:	C13H19N3O6S2
EA:	(N, 11) (S, 16)
MW:	377
PC:	WH., POW.
SOL-GOOD:	W
SOL-FAIR:	MEOH
SOL-POOR:	BUOH, HEX
QUAL:	(NINH., +)
STAB:	(ACID, -)
TO:	(S.AUREUS, 1.2) (B.SUBT., .3) (E.COLI, 1.25) (SHYG., 20) (K.PNEUM., 80) (PS.AER., 80)
LD50:	(750|250, IV)
IS-ION:	(IRA-68-HCOOH, AMMONIUMFORMIAT) (XAD-4, W)
IS-ABS:	(CARBON, ACET-W)
IS-CHR:	(SILG, I.PROH-W)

REFERENCES:

JA, 29, 1258, 1976; USP 4002530

41212-1508

NAME:	CEPHALOSPORIN-C, F2, C2
PO:	CEP.SP., CEP.ACREMONIUM, PAECYLOMYCES CARNEUS, EMERICELLOPSIS SP.
CT:	CEPHALOSPORIN T., ACIDIC, AMPHOTER, B"-LACTAM
FORMULA:	C16H20N308SNA
EA:	(N, 10) (S, 7)
MW:	470
EW:	480
PC:	WH., CRYST.
OR:	(+103, W) (+108, W)
UV:	W: (260, , 9500)
SOL-GOOD:	W
SOL-POOR:	ETOH, HEX
QUAL:	(NINH., +)
STAB:	(ACID, +) (BASE, -)
TO:	(S.AUREUS, 13.3) (B.SUBT., 2.9) (S.LUTEA, 50) (P.VULG., 5) (K.PNEUM., 10) (PS.AER., .05)
LD50:	(5000, IV)
IS-ION:	(XE-59,) (XAD-2, I.PROH) (IRA-68-OH, PYR-ACOH-W)
UTILITY:	ANTIBACTERIAL DRUG

REFERENCES:

Bioch. J., 62, 651, 1956; 79, 377, 393, 1961; 103, 877, 1967; 162, 681, 1977; *J. Med. Chem.*, 7, 689, 1964; *JA*, 29, 902, 1976; *J. Ferm. Techn.*, 54, 683, 1976; *JACS*, 88, 852, 1966; *AAC*, 6, 447, 1974; DT 2157693, 2239321, 2445615; JP 75/69295, 69293

	41212-1509
NAME:	<u>DESACETOXYCEPHALOSPORIN-C</u>
IDENTICAL:	WS-3442-A, C3, F3
PO:	CEP.SP., S.LACTAMDURANS, EMERICELLOPSIS SP., PAECYLOMYCES SP., DIHETEROSPORA SP., ARACHNOMYCES SP., ANIXIOPSIS SP., SPIRIDONIUM SP., CEP.ACREMONIUM, CEP.CHRYSOGENUM, S.WADAYAMENSIS, PAECYLOMYCES CARNEUS, PAECYLOMYCES PERSICINUS
CT:	CEPHALOSPORIN T., ACIDIC, AMPHOTER, B"-LACTAM
FORMULA:	C14H18N3O6SNA
EA:	(N, 10) (S, 8)
MW:	357
PC:	WH., CRYST.
OR:	(+144.1, W)
UV:	W: (260, 189,)
SOL-GOOD:	W
SOL-POOR:	ETOH, HEX
QUAL:	(NINH., +)
TO:	(B.SUBT., 28) (K.PNEUM., 50) (PS.AER., .05) (SALMONELLA SP., 10)
LD50:	(5000, IV)
IS-FIL:	6
IS-ION:	(IRA-68-AC, NAOAC)
IS-ABS:	(CARBON, ACET-W)
IS-CRY:	(PREC., I.PROH, ET2O)

REFERENCES:

Bioch. J., 103, 877, 891, 902, 1967; *Appl. Micr.*, 16, 1021, 1968; *Agr. Biol. Ch.*, 38, 1761, 1974; *J. Ferm. Techn.*, 52, 785, 1974; 54, 696, 1976; *CC*, 321, 1974; *AAC*, 6, 334, 1974; *JA*, 27, 298, 1974; *JACS*, 85, 1896, 1963; USP 3862008, 3847742; DT 2320696

	41212-1510
NAME:	<u>DESACETYLCEPHALOSPORIN-C</u>
IDENTICAL:	F1
PO:	CEP.ACREMONIUM, CEP.SP., ANIXIOPSIS SP., PAECYLOMYCES CARNEUS, PAECYLOMYCES PERSICINUS
CT:	CEPHALOSPORIN T., ACIDIC, AMPHOTER, B"-LACTAM
FORMULA:	C14H18N3O7SNA
EA:	(N, 10) (S, 9)
MW:	400|20
PC:	WH., CRYST.
UV:	W: (260, ,)
TO:	(B.SUBT., 6.7) (S.AUREUS, 50) (S.LUTEA, 50) (P.VULG., 50) (K.PNEUM., 100) (PS.AER., .05)
IS-CRY:	(CRYST., ETOH)

REFERENCES:

Appl. Micr., 16, 1011, 1965; *Nature*, 246, 154, 1973; *Agr. Biol. Ch.*, 38, 1761, 1974; 39, 1295, 1975; *J. Ferm. Techn.*, 52, 785, 1974; *JA*, 30, 775, 1977; *J. Med. Chem.*, 7, 117, 1964; DT 2318650

41212-1511

NAME: CEPHAMYCIN-A, 810-A
PO: S.GRISEUS, S.VIRIDOCHROMOGENES, S.FIMBRIATUS, S.HALSTEDII, S.HETEROMORPHUS, S.PANAYENSIS
CT: CEPHALOSPORIN T., ACIDIC, AMPHOTER, B"-LACTAM
FORMULA: C25H28N3O14S2NA
EA: (N, 7) (S, 9)
MW: 681
PC: WH., POW.
OR: (+141.4, W)
UV: HCL: (287, 437,)
UV: NAOH: (280, 432,)
UV: W: (220, 223,) (285, 430,)
SOL-GOOD: W, MEOH, ETOH
SOL-POOR: ACET, HEX
QUAL: (NINH., +) (FECL3, -)
STAB: (ACID, -) (BASE, -)
TO: (P.VULG., 6.25) (S.AUREUS, 50) (B.SUBT., 25) (S.LUTEA,) (E.COLI,) (K.PNEUM., 100)
LD50: (2000, IV)
IS-FIL: 3
IS-EXT: (W, 9.5, CHL) (CHL, 2, W)
IS-ION: (XAD-2, MEOH-W)
IS-CHR: (DEAE-SEPHADEX A-25,)
IS-CRY: (DRY,)
REFERENCES:

AAC, 2, 122, 132, 281, 287, 1972; 3, 254, 1973; *TL*, 2911, 1972; *JA*, 29, 113, 1976; *Antib.*, 1059, 1976; 22, 1977; DT 2109854, 2132357, 2210155; USP 3719563, 3718644, 3770590, 3902968, 3985742, 4036696; JP 75/64489

41212-1512

NAME:	CEPHAMYCIN-B, 810-B
PO:	S.GRISEUS, S.VIRIDOCHROMOGENES, S.FIMBRIATUS, S.HALSTEDII, S.HETEROMORPHUS, S.PANAYENSIS
CT:	CEPHALOSPORIN T., ACIDIC, AMPHOTER, B"-LACTAM
FORMULA:	C25H28N3O11SNA
EA:	(N, 6) (S, 4)
MW:	601
PC:	WH., POW.
OR:	(+137, W)
UV:	HCL: (305, 524,)
UV:	NAOH: (328, 564,)
UV:	W: (226, 300,) (305, 520,)
SOL-GOOD:	W, MEOH, ETOH
SOL-POOR:	ACET, HEX
QUAL:	(NINH., +)
STAB:	(ACID, -) (BASE, -)
TO:	(B.SUBT., 25) (S.AUREUS, 50) (S.LUTEA, 1) (P.VULG., 50) (PS.AER., 100) (E.COLI, 100) (K.PNEUM., 25)
LD50:	(2000, IV)
IS-EXT:	(W, 9.5, CHL) (CHL, 2, W)

REFERENCES:

AAC, 2, 122, 132, 281, 1972; 3, 254, 1973; *TL*, 2911, 1972; *JA*, 29, 113, 1976; *Antib.*, 1059, 1976; 22, 1977; DT 2109854, 2132357, 2210155; USP 3719563, 3718644, 3770590, 3902968, 3985742, 4036696; JP 75/64489

41212-1513

NAME:	CEPHAMYCIN-C, 842-A
IDENTICAL:	CEPHEMIMYCIN, A-16886-I, WS-3442-C, 3016, P-6621
PO:	S.LACTAMDURANS, S.SP., S.GRISEUS, S.FIMBRIATUS, S.HALSTEDII, S.WADAYAMENSIS, S.ALBOGRISEOLUS, S.FILIPINENSIS-CEPHAMICINI, ACREMONIUM CHRYSOGENUM
CT:	CEPHALOSPORIN T., ACIDIC, AMPHOTER, B"-LACTAM
FORMULA:	C16H21N4O9SNA
EA:	(N, 11) (S, 6)
MW:	446
PC:	WH., POW.
OR:	(+148, W)
UV:	W: (240, 135,) (266, 160,) (242, ,) (264, ,)
SOL-GOOD:	W
QUAL:	(NINH., +)
STAB:	(ACID, +) (BASE, -)
TO:	(S.AUREUS, 10) (S.LUTEA, 10) (P.VULG., 1) (PS.AER., 10) (K.PNEUM., 1) (B.SUBT., 50) (PS.AER., 100) (S.LUTEA, 220) (S.AUREUS, 90) (E.COLI, 25) (S.CEREV., 250)
LD50:	(2000, IV)
IS-FIL:	4
IS-EXT:	(W, 9.5, CHL) (CHL, 2, W)
IS-ION:	(DX-1-CL, NACL) (DX-50-H, PYR-W)
IS-CRY:	(DRY,)
UTILITY:	ANTIBACTERIAL

REFERENCES:

AAC, 2, 122, 132, 281, 1972; 3, 254, 1973; *TL*, 2911, 1972; *JA*, 29, 113, 1976; *Antib.*, 1059, 1976; 22, 1977; DT 2109854, 2132357, 2210155; USP 3719563, 3718644, 3770590, 3902968, 3985742, 4036696; JP 75/64489

41212-1514

NAME:	A-16884, 7-MEHOXYCEPHALOSPORIN-C
PO:	S.LIPMANII
CT:	CEPHALOSPORIN T., ACIDIC, AMPHOTER, B"-LACTAM
FORMULA:	C17H23N3O9S
EA:	(N, 10) (S, 7)
EW:	435, 480
PC:	WH., POW.
OR:	(+140.9, W)
UV:	W: (242, 126,) (265, 158,)
SOL-GOOD:	W, DMSO
SOL-FAIR:	MEOH, BUOH
SOL-POOR:	ACET, HEX
QUAL:	(NINH., +) (FEHL., -) (FECL3, -) (BIURET, -) (SAKA., -)
STAB:	(ACID, +) (BASE, -) (HEAT, +)
TO:	(S.AUREUS, 50) (B.SUBT., 3) (S.LUTEA, 6) (E.COLI, 6.2) (P.VULG., 1) (SHYG., 6) (K.PNEUM., 1)
LD50:	(2000, IV)
IS-EXT:	(W, 9.5, CHL) (CHL, 2, W)
IS-ION:	(IRA-68,)
IS-ABS:	(CARBON, ACET-W)
IS-CRY:	(DRY,)

REFERENCES:

JACS, 93, 2308, 1971; *AAC*, 1, 242, 247, 1972; Belg. P 754424; USP 3973015, 3801464

41212-1515

NAME:	A-16886-I
IDENTICAL:	CEPHAMYCIN-C
PO:	S.CLAVULIGERUS, S.LACTAMDURANS
CT:	CEPHALOSPORIN T., ACIDIC, AMPHOTER, B"-LACTAM
FORMULA:	C16H22N4O9S
EA:	(N, 12) (S, 8)
EW:	450, 530
PC:	WH., POW.
OR:	(+153, W)
UV:	W: (242, 132,) (264, 165,)
SOL-GOOD:	W, MEOH
SOL-POOR:	ACET, HEX
QUAL:	(NINH., +) (FEHL., +) (BIURET, -) (SAKA., -)
STAB:	(ACID, +) (BASE, -)
TO:	(S.AUREUS, 25) (B.SUBT., 1.5) (E.COLI, .39) (P.VULG., 39) (K.PNEUM., 1.56)
LD50:	(5000, PEROS)
IS-FIL:	ORIG.
IS-ION:	(DX-1-OH, NH4-FORMIAT)
IS-ABS:	(CARBON, ACET-W)
IS-CHR:	(CEL, ACOH-W)
IS-CRY:	(DRY,)

REFERENCES:

JACS, 93, 2308, 1971; *AAC*, 1, 242, 247, 1972; Belg. P 754424; USP 3973015, 3801464

41212-1516

NAME:	A-16886-II, A-8
IDENTICAL:	WS-3442-B
PO:	S.CLAVULIGERUS
CT:	CEPHALOSPORIN T., ACIDIC, AMPHOTER, B"-LACTAM
FORMULA:	C17H24N4O9S
EA:	(N, 16) (S, 7)
EW:	528
PC:	WH., POW.
OR:	(+86.2, W)
UV:	W: (260, 148,)
SOL-GOOD:	W, MEOH
SOL-POOR:	ACET, HEX
QUAL:	(NINH., +)
TO:	(B.SUBT., 50) (S.AUREUS, 20) (P.VULG., 2) (E.COLI, 50) (SHYG., 10)
IS-ABS:	(CARBON, ACET-W)
IS-CRY:	(DRY,)

REFERENCES:

JACS, 93, 2308, 1971; *AAC*, 1, 242, 247, 1972; Belg. P 754424; USP 3973015, 3801464

41212-1517

NAME: WS-3442-A, 7-5-AMINO-5-CARBOXYVALERAMIDO-3-METHYL-3-CEPHEM-4-CARBOXYLIC ACID
IDENTICAL: DESACETOXYCEPHALOSPORIN-C
PO: S.WADAYAMENSIS
CT: CEPHALOSPORIN T., ACIDIC, AMPHOTER, B"-LACTAM
FORMULA: C14H19N3O6S
EA: (N, 12) (S, 9)
MW: 357
PC: WH., POW.
UV: 6.5: (262, 143,)
SOL-GOOD: W
TO: (B.SUBT.,) (S.AUREUS,) (E.COLI,) (P.VULG.,)
IS-FIL: 4.5
IS-ION: (DUOLIT-A-6-AC, PYR-ACOH-W)
IS-ABS: (CARBON, ACET-W)
IS-CHR: (CEL, BUOH-ACOH-W)
IS-CRY: (DRY,)
REFERENCES:
DT 2332065; JP 71/32861, 74/26488, 25199, 30593, 102889; BP 957543

41212-1518

NAME: WS-3442-D
PO: S.WADAYAMENSIS
CT: CEPHALOSPORIN T., ACIDIC, AMPHOTER, B"-LACTAM
FORMULA: C15H21N3O7S
EA: (N, 11) (S, 8)
MW: 487
PC: YELLOW, POW.
UV: 6.5: (263, 106,)
TO: (G.POS.,) (G.NEG.,)
REFERENCES:
DT 2332065; JP 71/32861, 74/26488, 25199, 30593, 102889; BP 957543

41212-1519

NAME: WS-3442-E
PO: S.WADAYAMENSIS
CT: CEPHALOSPORIN T., ACIDIC, AMPHOTER, B"-LACTAM
FORMULA: C14H19N3O7S
EA: (N, 12) (S, 9)
MW: 473
PC: YELLOW, POW.
UV: PYR: (260, 141,)
TO: (G.POS.,) (G.NEG.,)
IS-CRY: (DRY,)
REFERENCES:
DT 2332065; JP 71/32861, 74/26488, 25199, 30593, 102889; BP 957543

41212-1520

NAME: CEPHEMIMYCIN
IDENTICAL: CEPHAMYCIN-C
PO: S.JUMONJINENSIS
CT: CEPHALOSPORIN T., ACIDIC, AMPHOTER, B"-LACTAM
FORMULA: C16H22N4O9S
EA: (N, 15) (S, 7)
PC: YELLOW, WH., POW.
OR: (+135, W) (+102, W)
UV: HCL: (245, 117,) (263, 133,)
UV: NAOH: (230, 102,)
UV: W: (242, 132,) (263, 187,)
SOL-GOOD: W, MEOH
SOL-FAIR: ETOH
SOL-POOR: ACET, HEX
QUAL: (NINH., +) (FECL3, -) (BIURET, -)
STAB: (ACID, +) (BASE, -)
TO: (B.SUBT., 12.5) (S.LUTEA, 25) (S.AUREUS, 200) (E.COLI, .78) (K.PNEUM., 3.12) (PS.AER., 12) (P.VULG., .1)
LD50: (1000, IV)
IS-FIL: ORIG.
IS-ION: (DUOLIT-A-2-CL, HCL)
IS-ABS: (CARBON, ACET-W)
IS-CHR: (SILG, CHL-MEOH-W)
IS-CRY: (DRY,)
REFERENCES:
Belg. P 804341; USP 3865693

41212-1521

NAME: F-1, 7-5-AMINO-5-CARBOXYPENTAMIDO-3-METHYLTHIOMETHYL-3-CEPHEM-4-CARBOXYLIC ACID
PO: CEP.SP.
CT: CEPHALOSPORIN T., ACIDIC, AMPHOTER, B"-LACTAM
FORMULA: C15H21N3O6S2
EA: (N, 7) (S, 18)
PC: WH., POW.
UV: W: (264, ,)
SOL-GOOD: W
QUAL: (NINH., +)
TO: (S.AUREUS, 40) (S.LUTEA, 40) (B.SUBT., 10) (E.COLI, 80) (P.VULG., 20) (PS.AER., 60)
IS-CHR: (ELFO, ACOH-W) (CEL,)
REFERENCES:
JA, 27, 361, 1974; USP 3647788

41212-1522

NAME: EMERICELLOPSINS
PO: EMERICELLOPSIS MINIMA
CT: CEPHALOSPORIN T., ACIDIC, AMPHOTER, B"-LACTAM
PC: YELLOW, POW.
STAB: (ACID, -)
TO: (B.SUBT.,)
IS-CHR: (CEL, ACET-I.PROH-W)
REFERENCES:
Proc. R. Soc. London, 159, 490, 1961

41212-3894

NAME: C-2801-X
PO: S.HETEROMORPHUS, S.PANAYENSIS
CT: CEPHALOSPORIN T., AMPHOTER, B"-LACTAM
FORMULA: C25H29N3O12S
EA: (N, 7) (S, 5)
PC: WH., POW.
OR: (+124.4, W)
UV: W: (234, , 12800) (318, , 16900)
SOL-GOOD: W, MEOH, ETOH
SOL-POOR: ETOAC, HEX
QUAL: (NINH., +)
STAB: (ACID, -) (BASE, -)
TO: (S.AUREUS, 50) (B.SUBT., 12) (E.COLI, 25) (P.VULG., 3) (K.PNEUM., 6.2)
LD50: NONTOXIC
IS-ION: (XAD-2, PH6.5 PUFF-MEOH)
IS-CRY: (DRY,)
REFERENCES:
JA, 29, 113, 1976; *Bull. Ch. Soc. Jap.*, 49, 767, 1976; DT 2444110

41212-4783

NAME:	SF-1623
PO:	S.CHARTREUSIS, S.VIRIDOCHROMOGENES
CT:	CEPHALOSPORIN T., ACIDIC, B"-LACTAM
FORMULA:	C15H21N3O10S3
EA:	(N, 8) (S, 19)
MW:	550
EW:	525
PC:	WH., POW.
OR:	(+45, W) (+36, HCL)
UV:	HCL: (272, 165,)
UV:	NAOH: (266, 165,)
UV:	W: (271, 220,)
SOL-GOOD:	W
SOL-POOR:	ETOH, HEX
QUAL:	(NINH., +)
STAB:	(ACID, +) (BASE, -) (HEAT, -)
TO:	(P.VULG., 25) (E.COLI, 100) (SHYG., 3.17) (XANTHAMONAS SP., 30)
LD50:	NONTOXIC
IS-ION:	(IRA-68-CL, NACL)
IS-ABS:	(CARBON, W)
IS-CHR:	(DEAE-SEPHADEX A-25-CL, NACL) (SEPHADEX G-10, W)
IS-CRY:	(LIOF.,)

REFERENCES:

DT 2455992; JP 75/155696, 70/76487; *CA*, 84, 162893; 85, 190725; USP 4010155

41212-4784

NAME:	N-ACETYLDEACETOXYCEPHALOSPORIN-C
PO:	CEP.ACREMONIUM
CT:	CEPHALOSPORIN T., ACIDIC, B"-LACTAM
FORMULA:	C16H21N3O7S
EA:	(N, 10) (S, 8)
MW:	400
UV:	W: (264, ,)
TO:	(P.VULG.,)
IS-EXT:	(BUOH, 2, FILT.)

REFERENCES:

JA, 28, 605, 1975

41212-5054

NAME: 7-METHOXYDEACETYLCEPHALOSPORIN-C
IDENTICAL: Y-G19Z-D3
PO: S.OGANOENSIS
CT: ACIDIC, AMPHOTER, CEPHALOSPORIN T., B"-LACTAM
FORMULA: C15H20N3O8S
EA: (N, 10) (S, 7)
PC: WH., POW.
OR: (+42, W) (+168, W)
UV: 6.5: (272, 176,)
UV: W: (243, ,) (272, ,) (241, 124,) (264, 154,)
SOL-GOOD: W
SOL-FAIR: MEOH, ETOH
SOL-POOR: ACET, HEX
QUAL: (NINH., +)
TO: (K.PNEUM., 6.25) (P.VULG., 3.13) (E.COLI, 50) (SHYG., 50)
IS-FIL: 3
IS-ABS: (XAD-2, W) (CARBON, ACET-W)
IS-CHR: (DEAE-SEPHADEX A-25, NH4BR-ACOH-W)
IS-CRY: (DRY,)
REFERENCES:
USP 3974035; JP 76/44694

41212-5278

NAME: Y-G19Z-D3, 7-5-AMINO-5-CARBOXYVALERAMIDO-7-METHOXY-3-HYDROXYMETHYL-3-CEPHEM-4-CARBOXYLIC ACID
PO: S.CHARTREUSIS
CT: ACIDIC, CEPHALOSPORIN T., B"-LACTAM
FORMULA: C15H21N3O8S
EA: (N, 10) (S, 7)
PC: WH., POW.
OR: (+168, W)
UV: W: (241, 124,) (264, 154,)
SOL-GOOD: W
SOL-FAIR: MEOH, ETOH
SOL-POOR: ACET, HEX
QUAL: (NINH., +)
TO: (P.VULG., 1.25)
IS-FIL: 7.6
IS-ION: (DX-1X2-CL, NACL)
IS-ABS: (CARBON, W)
IS-CHR: (DEAE-SEPHADEX A-25-CL, NACL)
IS-CRY: (LIOF.,)
REFERENCES:
DT 2541198; JP 75/121488, 77/83702, 76/44694; *CA*, 85, 3878; 87, 182606

41212-5331

NAME: C-43-219
PO: CEP.ACREMONIUM
CT: AMPHOTER, CEPHALOSPORIN T., B"-LACTAM
FORMULA: C19H28N4O8S2
EA: (N, 11) (S, 12)
PC: WH., YELLOW, POW.
OR: (+50.2, W)
UV: W: (265, 150,)
SOL-GOOD: W
SOL-POOR: MEOH, HEX
QUAL: (NINH., +)
TO: (B.SUBT., 13) (S.AUREUS, 100) (P.VULG., 100)
REFERENCES:
J. Ferm. Techn., 54, 720, 1976; JP 76/76488; *CA*, 85, 190726

41212-5332

NAME: C-17781A, 7-B"-4-CARBOXYBUTANAMIDO-3-METHYL-3-CEPHEM-4-CARBOXYLIC ACID
PO: CEP.CHRYSOGENUM, CEP.POLYALEURUM, CEP.ACREMONIUM
CT: CEPHALOSPORIN T., ACIDIC, B"-LACTAM, CYCLOPOLYLACTONE L.
FORMULA: C13H16N2O6S
EA: (N, 8) (S, 10)
MW: 328
PC: WH., POW.
OR: (+157, W)
UV: W: (260, ,)
SOL-GOOD: W, MEOH
SOL-POOR: BUOH, HEX
QUAL: (NINH., -)
TO: (S.AUREUS, 100)
IS-ION: (IRA-93-CL, NACL)
IS-ABS: (CARBON, ACET-W)
IS-CHR: (CEL, PROH-W)
REFERENCES:
J. Ferm. Techn., 54, 712, 1976; JP 76/70885; *CA*, 85, 175577

41212-5333

NAME: C-1778B, 7-B"-4-CARBOXYBUTANAMIDO-3-HYDROXY-METHYL-3-CEPHEM-4-CARBOXYLIC ACID
PO: CEP.CHRYSOGENUM, CEP.POLYALEURUM, CEP.ACREMONIUM
CT: CEPHALOSPORIN T., ACIDIC, B"-LACTAM
FORMULA: C13H16N2O7
EA: (N, 8) (S, 10)
MW: 344
PC: WH., POW.
OR: (+131, W)
UV: W: (260, ,)
SOL-GOOD: W, MEOH
SOL-POOR: BUOH, HEX
QUAL: (NINH., -)
TO: (S.AUREUS, 50) (S.LUTEA, 50) (B.SUBT., 100)
IS-CHR: (SEPHADEX G-15, W)
REFERENCES:
J. Ferm. Techn., 54, 712, 1976; JP 76/70885; *CA*, 85, 175577

41212-5334

NAME: C-1778C, 7-B"-4-CARBOXYBUTANAMIDO-3-ACETOXY-METHYL-3-CEPHEM-4-CARBOXYLIC ACID
PO: CEP.CHRYSOGENUM, CEP.POLYALEURUM, CEP.ACREMONIUM
CT: CEPHALOSPORIN T., ACIDIC, B"-LACTAM
FORMULA: C15H18N2O8S
EA: (N, 8) (S, 8)
MW: 386
PC: WH., POW.
OR: (+126, W)
UV: W: (260, ,)
SOL-GOOD: W, MEOH
SOL-POOR: BUOH, HEX
QUAL: (NINH., -)
TO: (S.AUREUS, 20) (B.SUBT., 20) (S.LUTEA, 35) (P.VULG., 100)
REFERENCES:
J. Ferm. Techn., 54, 712, 1976; JP 76/70885; *CA*, 85, 175577

41212-5531

NAME: C2
PO: CEP.ACREMONIUM
CT: CEPHALOSPORIN T., ACIDIC, B"-LACTAM
FORMULA: C16H18N209S
EA: (N, 7) (S, 8)
MW: 414
PC: WH., POW.
SOL-GOOD: W
QUAL: (NINH., -)
TO: (S.AUREUS,) (B.SUBT.,) (PS.AER.,)
IS-FIL: ORIG.
IS-EXT: (ETOAC, 2, W+AMMONIUM SULPHATE)
IS-ION: (IRA-93-CL, NACL)
IS-ABS: (CARBON, ACET-W)
IS-CHR: (CEL, BUOH-W)
REFERENCES:
JP 76/70885; *CA*, 85, 175577

41212-5532

NAME: C4
PO: CEP.ACREMONIUM
CT: CEPHALOSPORIN T., ACIDIC, B"-LACTAM
FORMULA: C14H16N207S
EA: (N, 8) (S, 9)
MW: 356
PC: WH., POW.
SOL-GOOD: W
QUAL: (NINH., -)
TO: (B.SUBT.,) (S.AUREUS,) (PS.AER.,)
REFERENCES:
JP 76/70885; *CA*, 85, 175577

41212-5533

NAME: C6
PO: CEP.ACREMONIUM
CT: CEPHALOSPORIN T., ACIDIC, B"-LACTAM
FORMULA: C14H16N208S
EA: (N, 7) (S, 9)
MW: 372
PC: WH., POW.
SOL-GOOD: W
QUAL: (NINH., -)
TO: (B.SUBT.,) (S.AUREUS,) (PS.AER.,)
REFERENCES:
JP 76/70885; *CA*, 85, 175577

41212-5671

PO: S.OGANOENSIS+5-MERCAPTO-1.3.4-THIADIAZOL-2-ACETYC ACID
CT: CEPHALOSPORIN T., ACIDIC, AMPHOTER, B"-LACTAM
FORMULA: C19H23N5O9S3
EA: (N, 11) (S, 18)
MW: 561
PC: WH., POW.
UV: 6.5: (287, ,)
SOL-GOOD: W
SOL-FAIR: MEOH
SOL-POOR: BUOH, HEX
QUAL: (NINH., +)
TO: (E.COLI,) (K.PNEUM.,) (P.VULG.,)
IS-FIL: 2
IS-ION: (XAD-2, ACET-W) (IRA-68-CL, PH7.2 PUFF-NANO3)
IS-CHR: (DEAE-SEPHADEX A-25-AC, ACOH-NH4BR) (AVICEL, I.PROH-W)
IS-CRY: (LIOF.,)
REFERENCES:
Belg. P 849763

41212-5672

PO: S.OGANOENSIS+MERCAPTO-5-METHYL-1-1H-TETRAZOLE
CT: CEPHALOSPORIN T., ACIDIC, AMPHOTER, B"-LACTAM
FORMULA: C17H23N7O7S2
EA: (N, 17) (S, 20)
MW: 486
PC: WH., POW.
UV: 6.5: (273, ,)
SOL-GOOD: W
SOL-FAIR: MEOH
SOL-POOR: BUOH, HEX
QUAL: (NINH., +)
TO: (E.COLI,) (K.PNEUM.,) (P.VULG.,)
REFERENCES:
Belg. P 849763

41212-5673

PO: S.OGANOENSIS+5-MERCAPTO-2-METHYL-1.3.4-THIADIAZOLE
CT: CEPHALOSPORIN T., ACIDIC, AMPHOTER, B"-LACTAM
FORMULA: C18H23N5O7S3
EA: (N, 13) (S, 15)
MW: 517
PC: WH., POW.
UV: 6.5: (272, ,)
SOL-GOOD: W
SOL-FAIR: MEOH
SOL-POOR: BUOH, HEX
QUAL: (NINH., +)
TO: (E.COLI,) (K.PNEUM.,) (P.VULG.,)
REFERENCES:
Belg. P 849763

41212-5674

PO: S.OGANOENSIS+5-MERCAPTO-1.3.4-THIADIAZOLE
CT: CEPHALOSPORIN T., ACIDIC, AMPHOTER, B"-LACTAM
FORMULA: C17H21N5O7S3
EA: (N, 13) (S, 16)
MW: 503
PC: WH., POW.
UV: 6.5: (274, ,)
SOL-GOOD: W
SOL-FAIR: MEOH
SOL-POOR: BUOH, HEX
QUAL: (NINH., +)
TO: (E.COLI,) (K.PNEUM.,) (P.VULG.,)
REFERENCES:
Belg. P 849763

41212-5874

NAME: YG-19Z-D2
PO: S.OGANAENSIS+NA2S2O3
CT: B"-LACTAM, CEPHALOSPORIN T., AMPHOTER
EA: (C, 33) (H, 4) (N,) (S, 17)
PC: WH., POW.
UV: W: (275, 160,)
SOL-GOOD: W
SOL-FAIR: MEOH, ETOH
SOL-POOR: BUOH, HEX
QUAL: (NINH., +)
TO: (G.NEG.,)
IS-ION: (DX-1X2-CL, NACL)
IS-ABS: (CARBON, ACET-W)
IS-CHR: (SEPHADEX G-10,)
REFERENCES:
JP 77/83701, 77/70087; *CA*, 87, 199149, 199153; Belg. P 849763

41212-6070

NAME: GK-340, 7-GLUTARYLAMIDO-CEPHALOSPORANIC ACID
PO: GLIOCLADIUM SP.+CEPHALOSPORIN
CT: B"-LACTAM, CEPHALOSPORIN T., AMPHOTER
FORMULA: C15H18N2O8S
EA: (N, 7) (S, 8)
REFERENCES:
JP 77/72886; *CA*, 87, 199148

41213-4025

NAME:	NOCARDICIN-COMPLEX, FR-1923
PO:	NOC.UNIFORMIS-TSUYAMANENSIS
CT:	B"-LACTAM, ACIDIC, AMPHOTER, NOCARDICIN T.
FORMULA:	C16H17N3O3
EA:	(N, 11)
PC:	WH., CRYST.
OR:	(-135, W)
UV:	8: (272, 310, 15500)
SOL-GOOD:	BASE, PYR, DMSO
SOL-FAIR:	W, MEOH
SOL-POOR:	ACET, HEX
QUAL:	(NINH., +) (FECL3, +) (EHRL., -) (FEHL., -)
STAB:	(ACID, -) (BASE, -)
TO:	(B.SUBT., 50) (S.LUTEA, 6.1) (S.AUREUS, 800) (P.VULG., .3) (PS.AER., 200) (SHYG., 3.3) (E.COLI, 200) (K.PNEUM., 200)
LD50:	(2300|100, IV) (2500, IP) (10000, PEROS)
IS-ION:	(XAD-4, MEOH-W)
IS-CRY:	(CRYST., ETOH-W)

REFERENCES:

DT 2242699, 2512396, 2529941; USP 3923977; *CA*, 78, 134496; *Abst. AAC*, 15, 98, 99, 1975

41213-5186

NAME: <u>NOCARDICIN-A</u>, FR-2458, FR-1923-C
PO: NOC.UNIFORMIS-TSUYAMANENSIS
CT: B"-LACTAM, ACIDIC, NOCARDICIN T.
FORMULA: C23H24N4O9
EA: (N, 11)
MW: 500
PC: WH., POW.
OR: (-135, W)
UV: ETOH: (270, , 14900)
UV: ETOH-NAOH: (245, , 23500) (285, , 11300)
UV: ETOH-W: (220, , 21000) (272, , 16000)
UV: NAOH: (244, 460,) (283, 270, 9500)
SOL-GOOD: W, BASE, DMSO
SOL-FAIR: MEOH
SOL-POOR: CHL, ETOAC, ET2O
QUAL: (NINH., +) (FECL3, +) (EHRL., -) (FEHL., -)
TO: (S.AUREUS, 800) (PS.AER., 12.5) (B.SUBT., 50) (S.LUTEA, 6.25) (E.COLI, 100) (K.PNEUM., 200) (P.VULG., 3.13) (SHYG., 3.13)
LD50: (2400, IV) (2500, IP) (3000, SC)
IS-ION: (DUOLIT-A-6-AC, W-PYR-ACOH)
IS-ABS: (CARBON, ACET-W-NH4OH)
IS-CHR: (DEAE-SEPHADEX A-25-CL, NH4OH)
IS-CRY: (PREC., W, HCL) (CRYST., ACID-W)
UTILITY: ON CLINICAL TRIAL, ANTIBACTERIAL
REFERENCES:

JACS, 98, 3023, 1976; 100, 3933, 1978; *JA*, 29, 492, 890, 1976; 30, 917—938, 1977; *Agr. Biol. Ch.*, 41, 2007, 2013, 1977; JP 76/54985; Belg. P 848430

41213-5187

NAME:	<u>NOCARDICIN-B</u>, FR-2458
PO:	NOC.UNIFORMIS-TSUYAMANENSIS
CT:	B"-LACTAM, ACIDIC, AMPHOTER, NOCARDICIN T.
FORMULA:	C23H24N4O9
EA:	(N, 11)
MW:	500
PC:	CRYST.
OR:	(-162, W)
UV:	8: (223, 507,) (271, 181,)
UV:	ETOH: (224, , 24600) (270, , 9700)
UV:	ETOH-NAOH: (275, , 9400)
UV:	ETOH-W: (267, , 8900)
UV:	NAOH: (245, , 26000) (280, , 11100)
SOL-GOOD:	W, BASE, DMSO
SOL-FAIR:	MEOH
SOL-POOR:	CHL, ETOAC, ET2O, ACID
QUAL:	(NINH., +)
TO:	(B.SUBT., 50) (E.COLI, 100) (P.VULG., 400) (PS.AER., 200)
LD50:	(1000|250, IV) (3000|1000, PEROS)
IS-FIL:	4
IS-ION:	(DIAION HP-20, MEOH-W)

REFERENCES:

JACS, 98, 3023, 1976; *JA*, 29, 890, 1243, 1976

41213-5675

NAME:	<u>NOCARDICIN-E</u>
PO:	NOC.UNIFORMIS
CT:	B"-LACTAM, ACIDIC, NOCARDICIN T.
FORMULA:	C19H17N3O7
EA:	(N, 10)
MW:	383
PC:	WH., CRYST.
OR:	(-192, W)
UV:	MEOH: (272, 396,)
UV:	MEOH-NAOH: (248, 719,) (298, 324,)
SOL-GOOD:	BASE, PYR, DMSO
SOL-FAIR:	MEOH, ETOH
SOL-POOR:	ETOAC, CHL, HEX
TO:	(PS.AER., 12.5)
LD50:	NONTOXIC
IS-FIL:	ORIG.
IS-ABS:	(CARBON, ACET-W) (DIATOM., CHL-ETOAC)
IS-CHR:	(SILG, ETOAC-CHL-MEOH)
IS-CRY:	(CRYST., MEOH-CHL)

REFERENCES:

JA, 30, 917, 1977; DT 2651655; Belg. P 848366

41213-5676

NAME: NOCARDICIN-F
PO: NOC.UNIFORMIS-TSUYAMANENSIS
CT: B"-LACTAM, ACIDIC, NOCARDICIN T.
FORMULA: C19H17N3O7
EA: (N, 10)
MW: 383
PC: WH., CRYST.
OR: (-181, W)
UV: MEOH: (224, 516,) (270, 248,)
UV: MEOH-NAOH: (247, 720,) (295, 253,)
SOL-GOOD: BASE, PYR, DMSO
SOL-FAIR: MEOH, ETOH
SOL-POOR: ETOAC, CHL, HEX
QUAL: (EHRL., -) (NINH., -)
TO: (PS.AER., 100)
LD50: (1000|500, IV)
IS-FIL: ORIG.
IS-EXT: (ACET, ,)
IS-ION: (DIAION HP-20, ETOH-W)
IS-ABS: (CARBON, MEOH-W)
IS-CHR: (SILG, CHL-MEOH) (SILG, ETOAC-CHL)
IS-CRY: (CRYST., MEOH-W)
REFERENCES:
JA, 30, 917, 1977; DT 2651655

41213-5875

NAME: NOCARDICIN-C, FR-29038
PO: NOC.UNIFORMIS-TSUYAMANENSIS
CT: B"-LACTAM, NOCARDICIN T., AMPHOTER
FORMULA: C23H26N3O8
EA: (N, 9)
MW: 472
PC: WH., CRYST.
SOL-GOOD: W
SOL-POOR: ACET, HEX
TO: (B.SUBT.,) (E.COLI,) (P.VULG.,) (PS.AER.,)
LD50: (2000|1000, IV)
IS-EXT: (ETOH-W, 7, MIC.)
IS-ABS: (CARBON, MEOH-W)
IS-CHR: (CEL,)
IS-CRY: (CRYST., ACET)
REFERENCES:
Agr. Biol. Ch., 41, 2013, 1977; JP 77/44291; *CA*, 87, 199144

41213-5876

NAME:	NOCARDICIN-D, FR-29055
PO:	NOC.UNIFORMIS-TSUYAMANENSIS
CT:	B"-LACTAM, NOCARDICIN T., ACIDIC, AMPHOTER
FORMULA:	C23H23N2O9
EA:	(N, 6)
MW:	473
PC:	WH., CRYST.
SOL-GOOD:	W
SOL-POOR:	ACET, HEX
TO:	(B.SUBT.,) (E.COLI,) (K.PNEUM.,) (SHYG.,)
LD50:	(1000|500, IM)
IS-ION:	(DIAION HP-20, MEOH-W)
IS-ABS:	(CARBON, MEOH-W)
IS-CRY:	(CRYST., W)

REFERENCES:

Agr. Biol. Ch., 41, 2013, 1977; JP 77/44292; *CA*, 87, 199143; Belg. P 848366

41213-5980

NAME:	NOCARDICIN-G, FR-29644
PO:	NOC.UNIFORMIS-TSUYAMAENSIS
CT:	B"-LACTAM, NOCARDICIN T., AMPHOTER
FORMULA:	C19H19N3O6
EA:	(N, 10)
MW:	385
PC:	WH., CRYST.
OR:	(-205, NAHCO3)
UV:	HCL: (228, 454,) (273, 52,)
UV:	NAOH: (248, 562,) (292, 107,)
SOL-GOOD:	W
SOL-POOR:	BUOH, HEX
QUAL:	(FECL3, +) (NINH., +)
STAB:	(ACID, -) (BASE, -) (HEAT, -)
TO:	(PS.AER., 400)
LD50:	NONTOXIC
IS-EXT:	(BUOH, 2, W) (W, 7, BUOH-HEX)
IS-ABS:	(DIAION HP-20, W) (CARBON, MEOH-W)
IS-CHR:	(CEL, BUOH-W)
IS-CRY:	(PREC., W, ACET) (CRYST., W)

REFERENCES:

Agr. Biol. Ch., 41, 2013; JP 77/94496; *CA*, 88, 49016

41214-2262

NAME: MM-4550
IDENTICAL: MC696-SY2-A
PO: S.OLIVACEUS
CT: B"-LACTAM, AMPHOTER, ACIDIC, THIENAMYCIN T.
FORMULA: C13H14N2O9S2
EA: (N, 8) (S, 17)
MW: 364, 408
PC: WH., POW.
OR: (-137, W)
UV: W: (240, , 13560) (287, , 12110)
SOL-GOOD: W
QUAL: (EHRL., +)
TO: (K.PNEUM.,) (PENICILLINASE INHIBITOR,) (S.AUREUS,) (G.POS., 5) (G.NEG., 5)
LD50: NONTOXIC
IS-ION: (IRC-50-NA, PH8 PUFF)
REFERENCES:
JA, 29, 668, 1976; *CC*, 523, 1977; Belg. P 772636; BP 1363075, 1483142, 1467413; DT 2146400, 2513855; *CA*, 77, 32682

41214-4253

NAME: MC696-SY2-A
IDENTICAL: MM-4550
PO: S.FULVOVIRIDUS
CT: ACIDIC, B"-LACTAM, THIENAMYCIN T.
FORMULA: C13H16N2O9S2
EA: (N, 6) (S, 15)
MW: 400
PC: WH., POW.
OR: (-110, W)
UV: W: (240, , 15400) (280, , 11100)
SOL-GOOD: W
TO: (PENICILLINASE INHIBITOR,) (E.COLI, 250)
IS-ION: (IRA-401-SO4, NH4CL)
IS-ABS: (CARBON, PROH-W)
IS-CHR: (DEAE-CEL, NACL)
IS-CRY: (LIOF.,)
REFERENCES:
JA, 26, 51, 1973; 30, 770, 1977; DT 2340005

41214-4800

NAME:	MM-13902
IDENTICAL:	890-A9
PO:	S.OLIVACEUS, ALTEROMONAS LUTEO-VIOLACEUS
CT:	B"-LACTAM, ACIDIC, THIENAMYCIN T.
FORMULA:	C13H16N2O8S2
EA:	(S,) (N,)
PC:	WH., YELLOW, POW.
OR:	(-81, W)
UV:	W: (225, 330,) (308, 343,) (227, , 14560) (307, , 15520)
SOL-GOOD:	W
SOL-FAIR:	MEOH
SOL-POOR:	BUOH, HEX, CHL, ET2O, BENZ
STAB:	(ACID, -) (BASE, -)
TO:	(S.AUREUS, .3) (B.SUBT., .15) (PS.AER., 50) (P.VULG., .6) (SHYG., .6) (K.PNEUM., .03) (E.COLI, .15)
IS-ABS:	(CARBON, ACET-W)
IS-CHR:	(CEL, PROH-W)

REFERENCES:

JA, 29, 668, 1976; *CC*, 1976, 523, 1977; DT 2513854; Belg. P 827332; BP 1483142

41214-4902

NAME:	890-A1, N-ACETYL-EPI-THIENAMYCIN-A
PO:	S.FLAVOGRISEUS
CT:	B"-LACTAM, THIENAMYCIN T., ACIDIC
FORMULA:	C13H18N2O5S
EA:	(N, 9) (S, 10)
MW:	314
PC:	WH., POW.
UV:	W: (299.5, ,) (300, 208,)
SOL-GOOD:	W
TO:	(G.POS.,) (G.NEG.,)
LD50:	NONTOXIC

REFERENCES:

DT 2652677, 2652678, 2652681

41214-5056

NAME:	THIENAMYCIN
PO:	S.CATTLEYA
CT:	AMPHOTER, B"-LACTAM, NOCARDICIN T.
FORMULA:	C11H16N2O4S
EA:	(N, 10) (S, 12)
MW:	272, 290
PC:	WH., POW.
OR:	(+82.7, PH7 PUFF)
UV:	12: (300.5, ,)
UV:	2: (309, ,)
UV:	W: (296.5, 290, 7900)
SOL-GOOD:	W
SOL-FAIR:	MEOH
SOL-POOR:	BUOH, HEX
QUAL:	(NINH., +) (SAKA., -)
STAB:	(ACID, -) (BASE, -)
TO:	(S.AUREUS, .02) (B.SUBT., .01) (E.COLI, .15) (K.PNEUM., .3) (PS.AER., .6) (P.VULG.,)
LD50:	(3500, IV)
IS-CHR:	(BIOGEL P-2, W-BUOH)
UTILITY:	ON CLINICAL TRIAL, ANTIBACTERIAL

REFERENCES:

JACS, 100, 313, 1978; *AAC,* 12, 406, 1977; *Abst. AAC,* 16, 227, 1976; DT 2652677, 2652674, 2652675, 2652676, 2672680; USP 3950357, 4006060; Belg. P 848545; JP 76/73191

41214-5370

NAME:	MM-17880
IDENTICAL:	890-A10
PO:	S.OLIVACEUS
CT:	B"-LACTAM, ACIDIC, THIENAMYCIN T.
FORMULA:	C13H18N2O8S2
EA:	(N, 6) (S, 13)
MW:	394
PC:	WH., POW.
UV:	7: (297, 150,)
SOL-GOOD:	W
STAB:	(HEAT, +)
TO:	(B.SUBT., .2) (S.AUREUS, .4) (E.COLI, .1) (K.PNEUM., .8) (P.VULG., .2) (PS.AER., 50)
IS-EXT:	(CH2CL2, , WB.)
IS-CHR:	(QAE-SEPHADEX, PH7 PUFF) (BIOGEL P-2, BUOH-W)
IS-CRY:	(LIOF.,)

REFERENCES:

JA, 29, 668, 1976; *CC,* 953, 1977; DT 2609766; Belg. P 839324; BP 1483142

41214-5677

NAME:	N-ACETYL-THIENAMYCIN
IDENTICAL:	924-A1
PO:	S.CATTLEYA, S.FUNGICIDICUS
CT:	B"-LACTAM, ACIDIC, THIENAMYCIN T.
FORMULA:	C13H18N2O5S
EA:	(N, 9) (S, 10)
MW:	314
PC:	WH., POW.
UV:	W: (290, 301,)
TO:	(S.AUREUS,) (B.SUBT.,) (E.COLI,) (K.PNEUM.,) (PS.AER.,)

REFERENCES:

Belg. P 848346, 848349; DT 2652677

41214-5982

NAME:	890-A2
IDENTICAL:	N-ACETYL-EPI-THIENAMYCIN-B
PO:	S.FLAVOGRISEUS
CT:	B"-LACTAM, THIENAMYCIN T., ACIDIC
FORMULA:	C13H16N2O5S
EA:	(N, 9) (S, 10)
MW:	312
PC:	WH., POW.
UV:	HCL: (228, ,) (308, ,)
UV:	W: (228, 475,) (308, 490,)
SOL-GOOD:	W
TO:	(B.SUBT.,) (S.AUREUS,) (S.LUTEA,) (E.COLI,) (K.PNEUM.,) (P.VULG.,) (PS.AER.,)
LD50:	NONTOXIC
IS-ION:	(DX-1X2-CL, NACL-PH7 PUFF) (XAD-2, W)
IS-CHR:	(SEPHADEX G-10, W) (DX-1X4, MEOH-W)
IS-CRY:	(LIOF.,)

REFERENCES:

DT 2718782; Holl. P 77/4040

41214-5983

NAME:	890-A5
IDENTICAL:	N-ACETYL-EPI-THIENAMYCIN-D
PO:	S.FLAVOGRISEUS
CT:	B"-LACTAM, THIENAMYCIN T., ACIDIC
FORMULA:	C13H16N2O5S
EA:	(N, 9) (S, 10)
MW:	312
PC:	WH., POW.
UV:	HCL: (228, ,) (308.5, ,)
UV:	W: (228, 470,) (308.5, 490,)
SOL-GOOD:	W
TO:	(S.AUREUS,) (S.LUTEA,) (B.SUBT.,) (E.COLI,) (K.PNEUM.,) (P.VULG.,)
LD50:	NONTOXIC
IS-ION:	(DX-1X2-CL, NACL-PH7 PUFF) (XAD-2, W)
IS-CHR:	(DX-1X4-CL, NACL-MEOH-W) (SEPHADEX G-10, MEOH-NH4OH) (DX-50X2-NA, W)

REFERENCES:

DT 2718782; Holl. P 77/4040

41214-6080

NAME:	PS-5
PO:	S.SP.
CT:	B"-LACTAM, THIENAMYCIN T., ACIDIC
FORMULA:	C13H18N2O4S
EA:	(N, 9) (S, 10)
MW:	318
PC:	WH., POW.
OR:	(+1.23, PH8 PUFF)
UV:	W: (301, 267,)
SOL-GOOD:	W
SOL-POOR:	ETOAC, BENZ, ACET
QUAL:	(EHRL, +) (NINH, -)
TO:	(S.AUREUS, .10) (K.PNEUM., 3.13) (S.LUTEA, .1) (B.SUBT., .16) (E.COLI, 2.5) (P.VULG., 12.5)
LD50:	NONTOXIC
IS-FIL:	ORIG.
IS-ION:	(DIAION HP-20, MEOH-W)
IS-ABS:	(CARBON, ACET-W)

REFERENCES:

JA, 31, 480, 1978; Belg. P 865578

41214-6120

NAME:	<u>890-A9</u>
IDENTICAL:	MM-13902
PO:	S.FLAVOGRISEUS
CT:	B"-LACTAM, THIENAMYCIN T., ACIDIC
FORMULA:	C13H16N20852
EA:	(N,) (S,)
MW:	456
PC:	WH., POW.
UV:	W: (228, ,) (308, ,)
SOL-GOOD:	W
STAB:	(ACID, -) (BASE, -) (HEAT, -)
TO:	(B.SUBT.,) (S.AUREUS,) (S.LUTEA,) (E.COLI,) (P.VULG.,) (K.PNEUM.,)
IS-ION:	(DX-1X2-CL, NACL-PH7 PUFF) (XAD-2, W)
IS-CHR:	(BIOGEL P-2, W)

REFERENCES:

DT 2751260

41214-6121

NAME:	<u>890-A10</u>
IDENTICAL:	MM-17880
PO:	S.FLAVOGRISEUS
CT:	B"-LACTAM, THIENAMYCIN T., ACIDIC
FORMULA:	C13H18N208S2
EA:	(N,) (S,)
MW:	458
PC:	WH., POW.
UV:	W: (299, 214,)
SOL-GOOD:	W
STAB:	(ACID, -) (BASE, -) (HEAT, -)
TO:	(B.SUBT.,) (S.AUREUS,) (S.LUTEA,) (E.COLI,) (P.VULG.,) (K.PNEUM.,)

REFERENCES:

DT 2751303, 2805701

41214-6223

NAME:	N-ACETYL-EPI-THIENAMYCIN-A, "COMP.IA", M-22380
IDENTICAL:	890-A1
PO:	S.OLIVACEUS
CT:	B"-LACTAM, THIENAMYCIN T., ACIDIC
FORMULA:	C13H18N2O5S
EA:	(N, 9) (S, 10)
MW:	314
PC:	WH.
UV:	W: (298, , 8131)
SOL-GOOD:	W
TO:	(B.SUBT., .16) (S.AUREUS, .6) (E.COLI, .3) (K.PNEUM., 2.5) (P.VULG., 5)
IS-ION:	(CELL.DE-52, PH7 PUFF)
IS-ABS:	(CARBON, ACET-W)
IS-CHR:	(XAD-4, W-PROH) (QAE-SEPHADEX, NACL) (BIOGEL P-2, BUOH-W) (IRA-U58, PH7 PUFF)

REFERENCES:

DT 2808563

41214-6224

NAME:	N-ACETYL-8-EPI-THIENAMYCIN-C, "COMP.IB", M-22381
IDENTICAL:	890-A3
PO:	S.OLIVACEUS
CT:	B"-LACTAM, THIENAMYCIN T., ACIDIC
FORMULA:	C13H18N2O5S
EA:	(N, 9) (S, 10)
MW:	314
PC:	WH.
UV:	W: (301, , 7930)
SOL-GOOD:	W
TO:	(B.SUBT., 1.2) (S.AUREUS, 1.2) (E.COLI, 2.5) (K.PNEUM., 5) (P.VULG., 10)

REFERENCES:

DT 2808563

41214-6225

NAME:	N-ACETYL-EPI-THIENAMYCIN-B, "COMP.IIA", M-22382
IDENTICAL:	890-A2
PO:	S.OLIVACEUS
CT:	B"-LACTAM, THIENAMYCIN T., ACIDIC
FORMULA:	C13H16N2O5S
EA:	(N, 9) (S, 10)
MW:	312
PC:	WH.
UV:	W: (228, ,) (308, , 13000)
SOL-GOOD:	W
TO:	(B.SUBT., .08) (S.AUREUS, .3) (E.COLI, .3) (K.PNEUM., 1.2) (P.VULG., 10)
IS-ION:	(IRA-458, PH7 PUFF)
IS-CHR:	(XAD-4, W-PROH)

REFERENCES:
DT 2808563

41214-6226

NAME:	N-ACETYL-EPI-THIENAMYCIN-D, "COMP.II B", M-22383
IDENTICAL:	890-A5
PO:	S.OLIVACEUS
CT:	B"-LACTAM, THIENAMYCIN T., ACIDIC
FORMULA:	C13H16N2O5S
EA:	(N, 9) (S, 10)
MW:	312
PC:	WH.
UV:	W: (229, ,) (309|1, , 13933)
SOL-GOOD:	W
TO:	(B.SUBT., 2.5) (S.AUREUS, 2.5) (E.COLI, 5) (K.PNEUM., 5) (P.VULG., 20)

REFERENCES:
DT 2802563

41214-6227

NAME:	<u>17927-A1</u>
PO:	S.FULVOVIRIDIS, S.OLIVACEUS
CT:	B"-LACTAM, THIENAMYCIN T., ACIDIC
EA:	(C, 50) (H, 6) (N, 10) (S, 8)
MW:	425|175
PC:	WH., YELLOW, POW.
UV:	HCL: (282, 160,)
UV:	W: (298, 192,)
SOL-GOOD:	W
SOL-FAIR:	MEOH
SOL-POOR:	ETOAC, CHL, BENZ
QUAL:	(NINH., -)
STAB:	(ACID, -) (BASE, -)
TO:	(S.AUREUS, .39) (B.SUBT., .05) (E.COLI, .2) (K.PNEUM., .39) (P.VULG., 1.56) (PS.AER., .6.25)
IS-ION:	(DIAION HP-20, ACET-W) (XAD-2, W)
IS-CHR:	(CARBON, ACET-W) (DEAE-SEPHADEX A-25, PH7 PUFF) (AVICEL, ACCN-W)
IS-CRY:	(LIOF.,)

REFERENCES:

DT 2809235

41214-6228

NAME:	<u>17927-A2</u>
PO:	S.FULVOVIRIDIS, S.OLIVACEUS
CT:	B"-LACTAM, THIENAMYCIN T., ACIDIC
EA:	(C, 50) (H, 6) (N, 9) (S, 9)
MW:	425|175
PC:	WH., YELLOW, POW.
UV:	HCL: (260, 512,)
UV:	W: (306, 490,)
SOL-GOOD:	W
SOL-FAIR:	MEOH
SOL-POOR:	ETOAC, CHL, BENZ
QUAL:	(NINH., -)
STAB:	(ACID, -) (BASE, -)
TO:	(S.AUREUS, .39) (B.SUBT., .05) (E.COLI, .2) (K.PNEUM., .39) (P.VULG., 25) (PS.AER., 25)

REFERENCES:

DT 2809235

41214-6265

NAME: 890-A3
IDENTICAL: N-ACETYL-8-EPI-THIENAMYCIN-C
PO: S.CATTLEYA, S.FUNGICIDICUS, S.FLAVOGRISEUS
CT: B"-LACTAM, THIENAMYCIN T.
FORMULA: C13H18N2O5S
EA: (N,) (S,)
MW: 314
UV: W: (301, 290,)
TO: (B.SUBT.,) (S.AUREUS,) (E.COLI,) (P.VULG.,) (K.PNEUM.,)
REFERENCES:
Abst. AAC, 17, 80, 81, 1977; DT 2652677, 2652678, 2652681

41214-6568

NAME: N-ACETYL-DEHYDROTHIENAMYCIN
PO: S.CATTLEYA
CT: B"-LACTAM, THIENAMYCIN T., ACIDIC
FORMULA: C13H16N2O5S
EA: (N, 9) (S, 10)
TO: (S.AUREUS,) (E.COLI,)
IS-EXT: (ETOAC, 5, FILT.)
REFERENCES:
DT 2816608

41215-5057

NAME:	CLAVULANIC ACID, MM-14151, BRL-14151
IDENTICAL:	3008-B
PO:	S.CLAVULIGERUS, S.JUMONJINENSIS
CT:	ACIDIC, B"-LACTAM, CLAVULANIC ACID T.
FORMULA:	C8H9NO5
EA:	(N, 6)
MW:	199
PC:	WH., POW.
OR:	(+54, DMSO)
UV:	NAOH: (259, 590,)
UV:	W: (200, ,)
SOL-GOOD:	W
QUAL:	(EHRL., +)
TO:	(S.AUREUS, 7.5) (B.SUBT., 62) (E.COLI, 31) (K.PNEUM., 31) (SHYG., 62) (PS.AER., 500)
LD50:	(4000, IV) (4500, SC)
IS-FIL:	2
IS-EXT:	(BUOH, 2, FILT.) (W, 6.8, BUOH)
IS-CHR:	(PERMUTIT-ZEOLIT FE-CL, NACL) (BIOGEL P-2, BUOH-W) (CEL, BUOH-ETOH-W)
IS-CRY:	(LIOF.,)
UTILITY:	ON CLINICAL TRIAL

REFERENCES:

CC, 266, 1976; 248, 1977; *AAC*, 11, 852, 1977; 12, 406, 1977; *JA*, 29, 668, 1976; DT 2517316, 2559410, 2559611; Belg. P 827926, 846933, 851872, 855483

41215-5081

NAME:	1-B"-HYDROXYPROPIONYLCLAVULAVIC ACID
PO:	S.CLAVULIGERUS
CT:	B"-LACTAM, CLAVULANIC ACID T., ACIDIC
FORMULA:	C11H13NO7
EA:	(N,)
PC:	WH.
TO:	(PS.AER., .14) (E.COLI, .01) (S.AUREUS, .34)

REFERENCES:

DT 2708047; Belg. P 827926; *CA*, 88, 4767

41215-5369

NAME: 3008-B
IDENTICAL: CLAVULANIC ACID
PO: S.JUMONJINENSIS
CT: B"-LACTAM, ACIDIC, CLAVULANIC ACID T.
FORMULA: C8H9NO5
EA: (N, 7)
MW: 199
PC: WH., OIL
UV: MEOH: (200, ,)
SOL-GOOD: W, MEOH, ETOH, DIOXAN, THF
SOL-FAIR: ETOAC
SOL-POOR: CHL, BENZ, CCL4, ET2O, HEX
QUAL: (NINH., -) (DNPH, +)
STAB: (HEAT, -)
TO: (S.AUREUS, 6.25) (B.SUBT., 12.5) (S.LUTEA, 50) (E.COLI, 25) (P.VULG., 25) (PS.AER., 3.12) (K.PNEUM., 6.25)
LD50: (1000|400, IV)
IS-FIL: 4
IS-EXT: (ETOAC, 3, W)
IS-ABS: (CARBON, W)
IS-CHR: (SEPHADEX LH-20, ETOAC) (SILG, BENZ-ETOAC)
IS-CRY: (DRY,)
REFERENCES:

JP 76/118890; Holl. P 76/3818

41215-6213

NAME: 2-HYDROXYMETHYLCLAVAM
PO: S.CLAVULIGERUS
CT: NEUTRAL, B"-LACTAM, CLAVULANIC ACID T.
FORMULA: C6H9NO3
EA: (N, 9)
MW: 143
PC: YELLOW, OIL
OR: (-166, DMSO)
UV: MEOH-NAOH: (270, ,)
TO: ANTIFUNGAL
REFERENCES:

DT 2725690

41215-6610

NAME: FORMYLOXYMETHYLCLAVAM
PO: S.CLAVULIGERUS
CT: NEUTRAL, B"-LACTAM, CLAVULANIC ACID T.
FORMULA: C7H9NO4
EA: (N, 8)
MW: 171
PC: YELLOW, OIL
OR: (-352, DM50)
UV: NAOH: (259, , 646)
SOL-GOOD: W
TO: (PHYT.FUNGI,)
IS-EXT: (ETOAC, 6.8, W) (BUOH, 7, W)
IS-ION: (XAD-4, ACET-W)
IS-CHR: (SILG, TOL-ETOAC) (SILG, HEX-ETOAC)
REFERENCES:
DT 2725690; *CC*, 282, 1979

41215-6611

NAME: CLAVAM-2-CARBOXYLIC ACID
PO: S.CLAVULIGERUS
CT: ACIDIC, B"-LACTAM, CLAVULANIC ACID T.
FORMULA: C6H7NO4
EA: (N, 8)
MW: 157
PC: WH., POW.
UV: NAOH: (258, , 415)
SOL-GOOD: W
TO: (PHYT.FUNGI,)
REFERENCES:
DT 2725690; *CC*, 282, 1979

4122 and 4123
Pyrrothin and Actithiazic Acid Types

The antibiotics belonging to the pyrrothin type (4122) are biogenetically and structurally related to penicillins. In their molecules an unsaturated γ-lactam ring (lactem) is fused with a sulfur-containing five-membered heterocycle (diethiene-3) forming a pyrrolinodithiole nucleus — 1,2-dithio[4,3-b] pyrrole **(1)**.

The generic name of their nucleus is pyrrothine **(2)**; however its N-demethyl derivative, holothin **(3)**, would rather represent the real nucleus of these antibiotics.

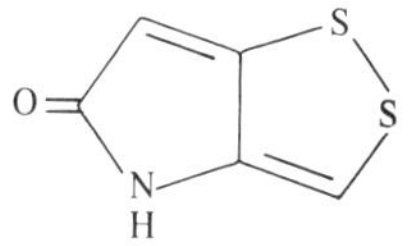

(1)

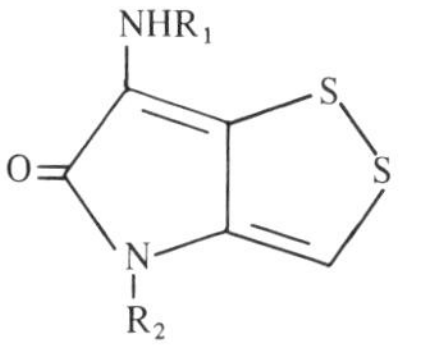

(2) R_1 = H; R_2 = CH_3
(3) R_1 = H; R_2 = H
(4) R_1 = $COCH_3$; R_2 = H

The individual antibiotics differ only in the nature of the N-acyl side chain and in the substituent (methyl or hydrogen) attached to the lactem nitrogen.

These antibiotics are neutral, yellow, optically inactive, crystalline compounds. One of the most characteristic property is their UV absorption spectra, showing strong absorption around 380 to 390 nm and two weaker peaks at 245 to 250 and 305 to 310 nm. They exhibit high in vitro activity against Gram-positive, Gram-negative, and mycobacteria, as well as yeasts, fungi, and ameboid parasites. Unfortunately these compounds are strongly toxic substances with a local irritating effect. Holomycin **(4)** is evidently derived from cystine and acetate, as shown in the following figure:

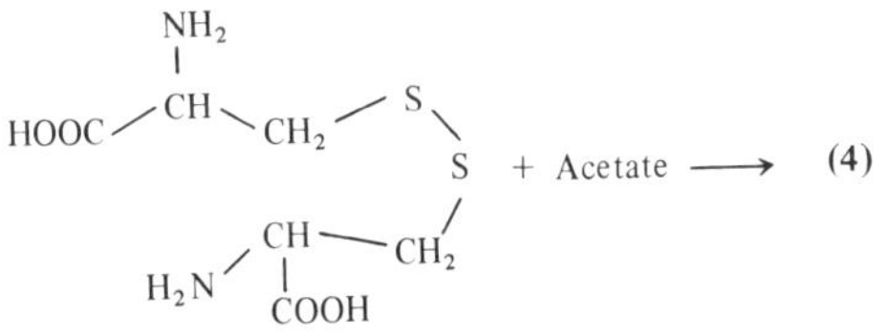

The type of actithiazic acid (4123) consists of several biotin antimetabolites, structurally related to biotin. The in vitro antimicrobial activity of these less toxic compounds is limited to *Mycobacteria* species. These compounds are inactive in vivo because the biotin which is present in the tissue of the host reverses their inhibitory effect. These compounds are metabolites rather than precursors of biotin in the producing organisms. They show affinity for avidin.

Structures

41220

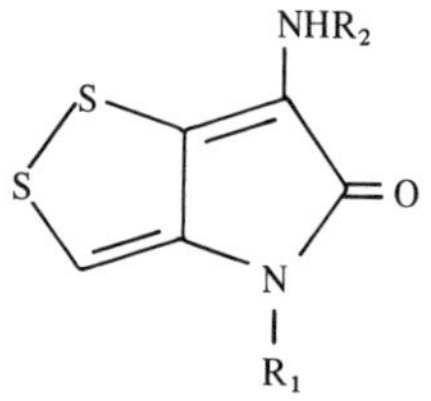

Antibiotic	R_1	R_2
Holothin	H	II
VD-846 B	H	CHO
Holomycin	H	$COCH_3$
n-Propionyl-holothin	H	COC_2H_5
Thioaurin	CH_3	CHO
VD-844	CH_3	CHO ?
Thiolutin	CH_3	$COCH_3$
Aureothricin	CH_3	COC_2H_5
Isobutyropyrrothin	CH_3	$CH(CH_3)_2$
WS-1921 ?	C_3H_7	H

41230

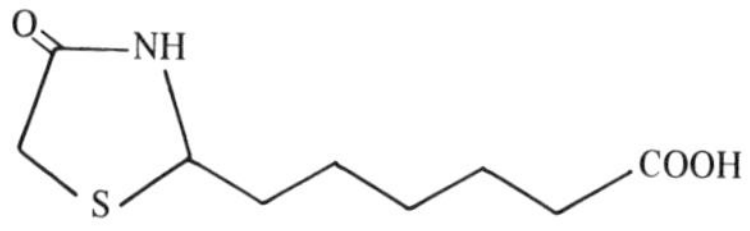

actithiazic acid

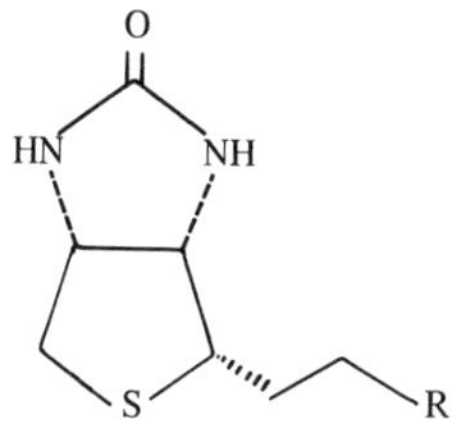

lydimycin $R = CH\overset{t}{=}CH—COOH$

α-methylbiotin $R = —CH_2—CH(CH_3)—COOH$

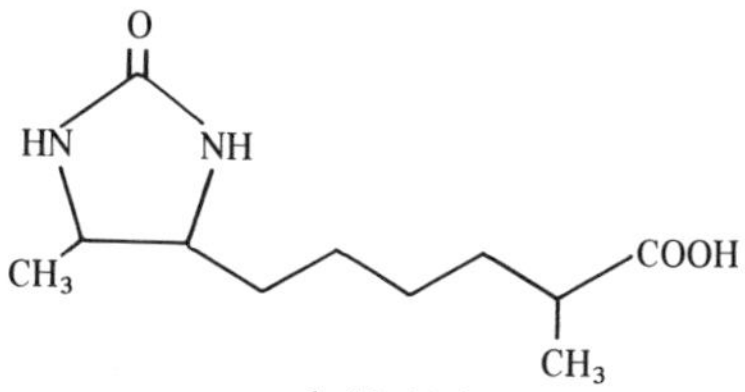

α-methyldethiobiotin

41220-1523

NAME:	AUREOTHRICIN, PROPYONYLPYRROTHIN
TRADE NAMES:	FARCINICIN
IDENTICAL:	4738-A, M-6-62A
PO:	S.THIOLUTEUS, S.FARCINICUS, S.CELLULOFLAVUS, S.CYANOFLAVUS
CT:	PYRROTHINE T., NEUTRAL
FORMULA:	C9H10N2O2S2
EA:	(N, 12) (S, 26)
MW:	242
PC:	GOLDEN, YELLOW, CRYST.
OR:	(0,)
UV:	ETOH: (246, , 6500) (313, , 4000) (390, , 11100)
UV:	MEOH: (248, 245, 6100) (312, 168, 3900) (388, 449, 11000)
SOL-GOOD:	MEOH, CHL
SOL-FAIR:	BENZ
SOL-POOR:	ET2O, W, HEX
STAB:	(ACID, +) (HEAT, +) (BASE, -)
TO:	(B.SUBT., 7.5) (S.AUREUS, 5) (S.LUTEA, 5) (E.COLI, 7.5) (SHYG., 50) (S.CEREV., 7) (C.ALB., 10) (PHYT.FUNGI, 1)
LD50:	(10, SC)
TV:	ANTITUMOR, ANTIVIRAL
IS-FIL:	ORIG.
IS-EXT:	(ETOAC, 6, WB.)
IS-CHR:	(AL, ETOAC-ET2O)
IS-CRY:	(CRYST., ETOAC)

REFERENCES:

JA, 2, 105, 107, 1949; 4, 137, 1951; 6, 57, 1953; 11, 143, 1958; 8, 120, 1955; *JACS*, 77, 2861, 1955; *Ant. An.*, 622, 1953—54; *Bull. Ch. Soc. Jap.*, 47, 1484, 1974; *Jap. Med. J.*, 2, 85, 1949; 1, 512, 1948; *J. Ph. Soc. Jap.*, 95, 347, 1975; *Angew.*, 74, 328, 1962

41220-1524

NAME:	HOLOMYCIN, DES-N-METHYLTHIOLUTIN
PO:	S.GRISEUS
CT:	PYRROTHINE T., NEUTRAL
FORMULA:	C7H6N2O2S2
EA:	(N, 13) (S, 30)
MW:	214
PC:	ORANGE, CRYST., YELLOW
OR:	(0,)
UV:	ETOH: (245, , 6310) (302, , 3310) (390, , 11750)
SOL-GOOD:	MEOH, CHL
SOL-POOR:	W, HEX
TO:	(S.AUREUS, 10) (E.COLI, 10) (K.PNEUM., 10) (PS.AER., 100) (C.ALB., 100)
IS-EXT:	(ETOAC, 7, FILT.)
IS-CHR:	(AL, CHL-MEOH)
IS-CRY:	(CRYST., MEOH-ETOAC)

REFERENCES:

Helv., 42, 563, 1959; *JACS*, 86, 5654, 1964; 85, 647, 1963; *JA*, 30, 334, 1977; *Angew.*, 74, 328, 1962; *Bull. Ch. Soc. Jap.*, 47, 1484, 1974; DT 1085297

41220-1525

NAME:	THIOLUTIN, ACETOPYRROTHIN
PO:	S.ALBUS, S.CELLULOFLAVUS, S.THIOLUTEUS, S.PIMPRINA, S.LUTEORETICULI
CT:	PYRROTHINE T., NEUTRAL
FORMULA:	C8H8N2O2S2
EA:	(N, 12) (S, 28)
MW:	228
EW:	239
PC:	GOLDEN, YELLOW, CRYST.
OR:	(0,)
UV:	(245, ,) (315, ,) (365, ,)
UV:	MEOH: (245, 275,) (312, 180,) (388, 472,)
SOL-GOOD:	MEOH, CHL
SOL-POOR:	W, HEX, ET2O, BENZ
STAB:	(ACID, +) (HEAT, +) (BASE, -)
TO:	(B.SUBT., 1) (S.AUREUS, 5) (SHYG., 5) (E.COLI, 2) (K.PNEUM., 2) (P.VULG., 5) (C.ALB., 1) (PHYT.FUNGI, 1)
LD50:	(25, SC)
TV:	ANTIVIRAL
IS-EXT:	(BUOH, 2, FILT.)
IS-CRY:	(CRYST., BUOH)

REFERENCES:

JACS, 74, 6304, 1952; 77, 2861, 1955; *Ant. & Chem.*, 2, 357, 1952; 5, 737, 1955; *Ant. An.*, 622, 1953—54; *JA*, 2, 105, 795, 1949; *Phytopath.*, 42, 338, 1952; 43, 463, 1953; *Proc. Ind. Acad. Sci.*, 61, 97, 1952; *Bull. Ch. Soc. Jap.*, 47, 1459, 1974; *Angew.*, 74, 328, 1962

41220-1526

NAME: THIOMYCIN
PO: S.PHAEOCHROMOGENES
CT: PYRROTHINE T., NEUTRAL
EA: (C, 49) (H, 5) (N, 9) (S, 16)
PC: GOLDEN, YELLOW, CRYST.
OR: (0,)
UV: HCL: (370, 690,)
UV: MEOH: (223, 140,) (370, 375,) (305|10, ,)
UV: NAOH: (300, 555,)
SOL-GOOD: MEOH, BENZ
SOL-FAIR: W
SOL-POOR: ET2O, HEX
QUAL: (NINH., -) (FECL3, -) (FEHL., -)
STAB: (ACID, +) (BASE, -)
TO: (S.AUREUS, 10) (B.SUBT., 12) (E.COLI, 12) (SHYG., 3) (P.VULG., 3)
LD50: (10, SC)
IS-FIL: 2
IS-EXT: (ETOAC, 4, W)
IS-ION: (IONEX-C, ACET-W)
IS-CHR: (SILG, CHL)
IS-CRY: (CRYST., ETOAC)
REFERENCES:
JA, 8, 118, 1955

41220-1527

NAME: THIOAURIN, HA-9
IDENTICAL: VD-844, B-870, OROSOMYCIN
PO: S.LIPMANII
CT: PYRROTHINE T., NEUTRAL
FORMULA: C7H6N2O2S2
EA: (N, 13) (S, 30)
MW: 226
PC: YELLOW, CRYST.
OR: (0,)
UV: HCL: (233, ,) (368, ,)
UV: MEOH: (232, 199,) (370, 520,)
UV: NAOH: (300, ,)
SOL-GOOD: MEOH, ACET
SOL-FAIR: ETOAC, BENZ, CHL
SOL-POOR: W, ET2O, HEX
QUAL: (FECL3, -)
TO: (S.AUREUS, 4.5) (B.SUBT., 10) (E.COLI, 1.1) (SHYG., 5) (P.VULG., 8) (PS.AER., 72) (K.PNEUM., 8)
LD50: (16, IV) (20, SC)
IS-CRY: (CRYST., ETOAC)
REFERENCES:
Ant. & Chem., 3, 382, 385, 1953; *Ant. An.*, 622, 1953—54 USP 2749273

41220-1528

NAME: ISOBUTYROPYRROTHIN
PO: S.PIMPRINA, S.SP.
CT: PYRROTHINE T., NEUTRAL
FORMULA: C10H12N2O2S2
EA: (N, 11) (S, 24)
MW: 256
PC: ORANGE, CRYST.
OR: (0,)
SOL-GOOD: CHL, ACET, ETOAC
SOL-FAIR: BENZ
SOL-POOR: W, HEX
TO: (S.LUTEA, .45) (B.SUBT., 1.25) (S.AUREUS, 1)
IS-EXT: (CHL, , FILT.)
REFERENCES:
Exp., 16, 504, 1960; *HAB*, 6, 153, 1964

41220-1529

NAME: VD-846-B
PO: S.SP.
CT: PYRROTHINE T., NEUTRAL
FORMULA: C6H4N2O2S2
EA: (N, 14) (S, 32)
MW: 200
PC: ORANGE, CRYST.
OR: (0,)
UV: MEOH: (247, , 5800) (301, , 3350) (387, , 11000)
SOL-GOOD: ETOAC, MEOH, CHL
SOL-FAIR: W
SOL-POOR: HEX
TO: (S.AUREUS, 1.6) (B.SUBT., 1.6) (E.COLI, 3.2) (K.PNEUM., .5) (P.VULG., .2) (SHYG., 1.3) (PS.AER., 25)
LD50: (7.5|2.5, IV)
IS-EXT: (ETOAC, , FILT.)
IS-CRY: (CRYST., ACET)
REFERENCES:
JA, 22, 233, 1969

41220-1530

NAME:	VD-844
IDENTICAL:	THIOAURIN
PO:	S.SP.
CT:	PYRROTHINE T., NEUTRAL
FORMULA:	C7H6N2O2S2
EA:	(N, 13) (S, 30)
MW:	214
PC:	YELLOW, CRYST.
OR:	(0,)
UV:	MEOH: (231, , 6600) (367, , 15800)
SOL-GOOD:	ETOAC, CHL, ACET
SOL-POOR:	W, HEX
TO:	(S.AUREUS, .5) (B.SUBT., 13) (E.COLI, 16) (K.PNEUM., 10) (P.VULG., 5) (PS.AER., 16) (SHYG., 10)
LD50:	(7.5|2.5, IV)
IS-EXT:	(ETOAC, 2, FILT.)
IS-CRY:	(CRYST., ETOAC)

REFERENCES:

JA, 22, 233, 1969

41220-1531

NAME:	WS-1921
PO:	S.GRISEOLUS-SULFOANTIBIOTICUS
CT:	PYRROTHINE T., NEUTRAL
FORMULA:	C8H10N2OS2
EA:	(N, 13) (S, 29)
MW:	214
PC:	ORANGE, YELLOW, CRYST.
OR:	(0,)
UV:	MEOH: (230, 450,) (370, 1150,)
SOL-GOOD:	MEOH, CHL
SOL-FAIR:	BENZ
SOL-POOR:	HEX, W
QUAL:	(FEHL., +) (EHRL., +) (FECL3, +) (SAKA., -) (NINH., -)
TO:	(S.AUREUS, 3) (B.SUBT., 4.4) (S.LUTEA, .056) (E.COLI, 2.2) (PS.AER., 250) (S.CEREV., 100) (C.ALB., 560)

REFERENCES:

JP 72/679

41220-1532

NAME:	F-10-C
PO:	S.LUTEORETICULI
CT:	PYRROTHINE T., NEUTRAL
PC:	ORANGE, CRYST.
UV:	MEOH: (245, ,) (310, ,) (340, ,)
SOL-GOOD:	ETOAC
TO:	(G.POS.,) (G.NEG.,) (FUNGI,) (C.ALB.,)
IS-EXT:	(ETOAC, , FILT.)

REFERENCES:

Fukui Kenkyu Ho., 10, 52, 1957

41220-5419

NAME:	N-PROPIONYLHOLOTHIN
PO:	S.SP.
CT:	NEUTRAL, PYRROTHINE T.
FORMULA:	C8H8N2O2S2
EA:	(N, 12) (S, 28)
MW:	228
PC:	ORANGE, YELLOW, CRYST.
UV:	MEOH: (246, , 7800) (302, , 4250) (388, , 14400)
SOL-GOOD:	MEOH
TO:	(SERRATIA MARCESCENS,) (B.SUBT.,)
IS-FIL:	ORIG.
IS-EXT:	(BUOH, , FILT.)
IS-CHR:	(SEPHADEX LH-20, MEOH)

REFERENCES:

JA, 30, 335, 1977; *Helv.*, 42, 563, 1959

41220-6222

NAME:	AK-PS
PO:	S.FLAVOCHROMOGENES-IMAYAENSIS
CT:	NEUTRAL, PYRROTHINE T.
FORMULA:	C7H6N2O2S2
EA:	(N, 12) (S, 30)
MW:	214
PC:	YELLOW, CRYST.
OR:	(0, CHL)
UV:	ETOH: (236, , 7200) (300, , 3800) (375, , 11000)
SOL-GOOD:	MEOH, ETOAC
SOL-POOR:	W
QUAL:	(EHRL., +) (NINH., +)
STAB:	(HEAT, +)
TO:	(S.AUREUS, 1) (B.SUBT., 1) (S.LUTEA, .05) (E.COLI, 1) (SHYG., 1) (PS.AER., 5) (K.PNEUM., 5)
LD50:	(5, IV)
IS-EXT:	(ETOAC, 2.5, FILT.)
IS-CHR:	(SILG,)

REFERENCES:

JP 78/47589; *CA*, 89, 105898

41230-1533

NAME:	ACTITHIAZIC ACID, THIAZOLIDONE ANTIBIOTIC, THIAZOLIDOMYCIN
IDENTICAL:	ACIDOMYCIN, CINNAMONIN, MYCOBACIDIN, PA-95, 6604-4
PO:	S.CINNAMONENSIS, S.ACIDOMYCETICUS, S.LYDICUS, S.VIRGINIAE, S.LAVENDULAE, S.ROSEOCHROMOGENES
CT:	ACTITHIAZIC ACID T., ACIDIC
FORMULA:	C9H15N3OS
EA:	(N, 6) (S, 15)
MW:	217
EW:	213|2
PC:	WH., CRYST.
OR:	(-62.5, MEOH) (-60.5, ETOH)
UV:	MEOH: (200, ,) (245, ,)
SOL-GOOD:	MEOH, CHL, BASE
SOL-FAIR:	CH2CL2
SOL-POOR:	W, ACID, BENZ, HEX
QUAL:	(NINH., -) (DNPH, -)
STAB:	(ACID, +) (BASE, +)
TO:	(MYCOB.TUB., 1) (MYCOB.SP., .6) (S.AUREUS, 100) (E.COLI, 100) (C.ALB., 50)
LD50:	(1500, IV) (2500, IP) (20000, SC)
IS-EXT:	(BUOH, 2, FILT.) (W, 9, BUOH) (BUOAC, 4.5, W)
IS-ABS:	(CARBON, ETOH-HCL)
IS-CHR:	(AL,)
IS-CRY:	(CRYST., MEOH)

REFERENCES:

ABB, 40, 263, 270, 1952; *Ant. & Chem.*, 2, 399, 400, 453, 1952; 3, 332, 1953; *JACS*, 74, 2946, 1952; 75, 105, 109, 1953; *Ant. An.*, 886, 1955—56; *Chem. Ph. Bull.*, 1, 84, 89, 93, 1953; *JA*, 5, 572, 1952; 6, 159, 1953; *Jap. J. Med. Sci.*, 6, 143, 395, 1953; BP 729208; USP 2678929; *Antib.*, 14, 1970

41230-1534

NAME:	LYDIMYCIN, U-15965, A"-DEHYDROBIOTIN
PO:	S.LYDICUS
CT:	ACTITHIAZIC ACID T., ACIDIC
FORMULA:	C10H14N2O3S
EA:	(N, 11) (S, 13)
MW:	243
EW:	244
PC:	WH., CRYST.
OR:	(+92, PH7 PUFF)
UV:	ETOH: (203, , 15000)
SOL-GOOD:	MEOH, ET2O
SOL-FAIR:	W
TO:	(S.AUREUS, 1) (S.LUTEA, 1) (B.SUBT., 10) (E.COLI, 1) (P.VULG., 1) (SHYG., 1) (S.CEREV., 100)
IS-FIL:	4
IS-ABS:	(CARBON, ACET-W)
IS-CHR:	(DIATOM., ETOAC-C.HEX-PH3 PUFF)
IS-CRY:	(CRYST., MEOH)

REFERENCES:

Sci., 154, 1667, 1967; *AAC*, 1, 135, 1972; *JAMA*, 204, 386, 1968; *J. Bact.*, 100, 42, 1969; USP 3395220

41230-1535

NAME: <u>A"-METHYLBIOTIN</u>, A"-MB
PO: S.LYDICUS
CT: ACTITHIAZIC ACID T., ACIDIC
FORMULA: C11H18N2O5S
EA: (N, 11) (S, 12)
MW: 258
PC: WH., CRYST.
SOL-GOOD: W
SOL-FAIR: ACET
TO: (B.SUBT., 500) (MYCOB.SP., 1.2) (S.CEREV.,)
IS-ABS: (CARBON, ACET-W)
REFERENCES:
TL, 3791, 1971; *AAC,* 1, 135, 1972; DT 2023047

41230-1536

NAME: <u>A"-METHYL-DETHIOBIOTIN</u>, A"-MDB
PO: S.LYDICUS, S.LAVENDULAE-AMYCLENOMYCINT
CT: ACTITHIAZIC ACID T., ACIDIC
FORMULA: C11H20N2O3
EA: (N, 12)
MW: 228
PC: WH., CRYST.
SOL-GOOD: W
SOL-FAIR: ACET
TO: (MYCOB.SP., .2) (B.SUBT., .5) (E.COLI, 8)
(P.VULG., 1000)
IS-ABS: (CARBON, ACET-W)
IS-CRY: (CRYST., ACET)
REFERENCES:
TL, 3791, 1971; *AAC,* 1, 135, 1972; DT 2023047

413
Diketopiperazine Derivatives

Introduction

The diketopiperazines are frequently occurring compounds in nature. They are considered with growing a tendency to be important metabolic intermediates, rather than protein artefacts. Among the microbial metabolites, various diketopiperazine derivatives with antimicrobial and/or antiviral properties are recognized frequently, so this type of antibiotic currently numbers nearly 60.

The diketopiperazines are actually anhydro dimers of amino acids forming a piperazine ring. All of the natural diketopiperazine antibiotics are 2,5-diketopiperazine **(1)** derivatives.

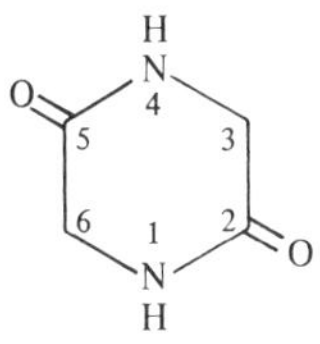

(1)

They differ in their properties from ordinary peptides. The simple members are neutral compounds, sparingly soluble in water, and giving a negative ninhydrine test. Included in this group are the simple (monocyclic) diketopiperazine derivatives (4131), the sulfur-bridged oligothiapiperazine derivatives (4132), and the aspergillic acid type compounds (4133) with cyclic hydroxamic acid structures. The characteristic structural moieties of these compounds are as follows:

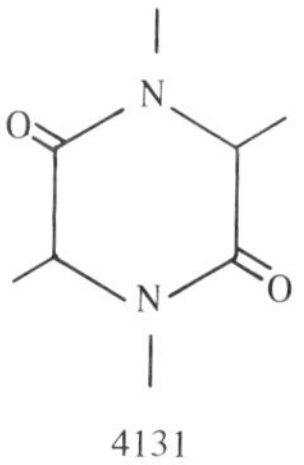

4131

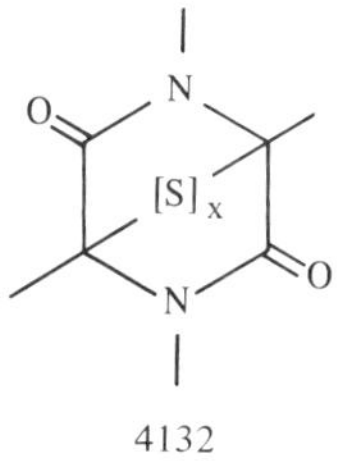

4132

X = 2,3,4

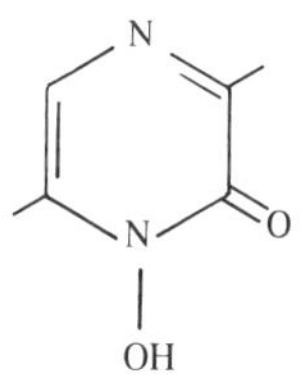

4133

Excluded from this group are the more complicated diketopiperazine-containing compounds such as bicyclomycin or amphomycin.

The majority of these derivatives belong to the second type. These compounds and the aspergillic acid type of antibiotics are produced exclusively by fungi. Several simple diketopiperazine derivatives are produced by *Streptomyces* species. No bacterial metabolite is known in this group.

REFERENCES

1. *Forschr.*, 32, 51, 1975.
2. Mateles, R. and Wogan, G. N., *Eds., Biochemistry of Some Foodborne Microbial Toxins*, MIT Press, Cambridge, Mass., 1967.

4131
Simple Diketopiperazines

Among these compounds, the most interesting antibiotic is piperazinedione, which was isolated from *Streptomyces* species. It is a symmetrically substituted bis-5-chloro-2-piperidyl derivative of diketopiperazine. The 2-chloroethylamine function which occurs in this compound is typical of nitrogen mustard. Piperazinedione represents the first natural occurrence of this fragment. It is not surprising that piperazinedione exhibits excellent antitumor activity. Clinical trials show that it is active against certain human lymphomas.

Gancidin W (cyclo-L-pro-L-leu) with a recently recognized diketopiperazine structure also has antitumor activity. Mycellianamid, a fungal antibiotic, has an aromatic-terpene side chain and shows butiryl-cholinesterase-inhibiting activity.

41310-1537

NAME:	ALBONOURSIN, P-42-2, B-73
IDENTICAL:	2ND COMP.PHALAMYCIN
PO:	S.ALBULUS, S.ALBUS-FUNGATUS, S.NOURSEI, S.TUMEMACERANS
CT:	DIKETOPIPERAZINE DERIV., ACIDIC
FORMULA:	C15H16N2O2
EA:	(N, 10)
MW:	256
PC:	WH., CRYST.
OR:	(+3.43, DMFA)
UV:	(236, ,) (316, ,)
UV:	MEOH: (234, 357,) (318, 1140,)
SOL-GOOD:	BASE, PYR, DMFA
SOL-FAIR:	MEOH, CHL
SOL-POOR:	W
TO:	(B.SUBT., 100) (K.PNEUM., 25)
LD50:	(100, IV)
TV:	EHRLICH
IS-EXT:	(ETOAC, , FILT.)
IS-CHR:	(SILG, MEOH-I.PR.ETER)

REFERENCES:

Antib., 201, 1963; *TL*, 1881, 1963; *JOC*, 25, 661, 1960; 30, 277, 1965; *Chem. & Ind.*, 1686, 1964; *Bull. Ch. Soc. Jap.*, 42, 191, 1969; *JA*, 26, 175, 1973; *An. Rep. N.Y. State Dept. Health*, 10, 1957; 47, 1958; 52, 1959; *JACS*, 82, 1127, 1960

41310-1538

NAME: MYCELIANAMIDE
PO: P.NIGRICANS, P.PATULUM, P.GRISEOFULVUM
CT: DIKETOPIPERAZINE DERIV., ACIDIC, NEUTRAL
FORMULA: C22H28N2O5
EA: (N, 7)
MW: 400
EW: 228
PC: WH., CRYST.
OR: (-217, CHL) (-160, CHL) (-133, DIOXAN)
UV: ETOH: (234, ,) (324, ,)
UV: MEOH: (234, , 12000) (325, , 23500)
SOL-GOOD: MEOH, CHL, DIOXAN, PYR, BASE, ACET
SOL-FAIR: CHL, BENZ, ETOAC, ACOH, ET2O, W
SOL-POOR: ACID, HEX
QUAL: (FECL3, +) (BIURET, -) (EHRL., -)
STAB: (BASE, -) (HEAT, +)
TO: (S.AUREUS, 50) (P.SP.,)
IS-EXT: (ET2O, , MIC.) (CHL-ETOH, , MIC.)
IS-CHR: (SILG, CHL-MEOH)
IS-CRY: (CRYST., BENZ)
REFERENCES:

Bioch. J., 25, 31, 39, 1931; 29, 1002, 1935; 33, 240, 1939; 42, 323, 1948; *Chem. & Ind.*, 1599, 1955; 1300, 1966; *JCS*, 3717, 1956; *Gazz.*, 94, 1301, 1964; *TL*, 1683, 1963; *JA*, 29, 526, 1976; *Aust. J. Chem.*, 21, 1581, 1968

41310-1539

NAME:	DCS, 2.5-BIS-AMINOOXYMETHYL-3.6-DIKETOPIPERAZINE
PO:	S.NAGASAKIENSIS
CT:	DIKETOPIPERAZINE DERIV., BASIC
FORMULA:	C6H10N2O2
EA:	(N, 19)
MW:	138
EW:	117
PC:	WH., MICROCRYST., HYGROSCOPIC
OR:	(+7.2, W)
UV:	NAOH: (286, ,)
SOL-GOOD:	W
SOL-FAIR:	MEOH
SOL-POOR:	ETOH, HEX
QUAL:	(FEHL., +) (NINH., -) (FECL3, -) (BIURET, -)
STAB:	(ACID, -)
LD50:	(1000, IP)
TV:	ANTITUMOR
IS-FIL:	3
IS-ION:	(DX-50-H, NH4OH) (IRA-400-OH, ACOH-W)
IS-CHR:	(CEL, ETOH-W)
IS-CRY:	(CRYST., ETOH)

REFERENCES:

JP 61/11297; *CA*, 56, 3927; *Osaka Shiritsu Daigaku Zasshi*, 8, 1837, 1959

41310-1540

NAME:	PIPERAZINEDIONE, 593-A, NSC-135758
TRADE NAMES:	PIPERAZIDONE
PO:	S.GRISEOLUTEUS
CT:	DIKETOPIPERAZINE DERIV., BASIC
FORMULA:	C14H22N4O2CL2
EA:	(N, 15) (CL, 20)
MW:	349
EW:	215
PC:	WH., CRYST.
OR:	(+11, W)
UV:	(200, ,)
SOL-GOOD:	W, MEOH, CHL
SOL-POOR:	HEX, ET2O
STAB:	(ACID, +) (HEAT, -)
TO:	(S.AUREUS, 100) (P.VULG., 1000) (E.COLI,)
LD50:	(5, IP)
TV:	H-1, WALKER-256, RIDGWAY, ANTITUMOR, KB, L-1210
IS-EXT:	(ETOH, , EVAP.FILT.) (BUOH, 10, FILT.) (ETOAC, 8, W)
IS-ION:	(XAD-2, ACET-HCL)
IS-CRY:	(CRYST., MEOH) (PREC., ETOAC, ET2O)
UTILITY:	ON CLINICAL TRIAL, ANTITUMOR DRUG

REFERENCES:

JA, 23, 305, 1970; *Chem. Eng. News*, 4, 17, 24, 1972; *Cancer Chemoth. Rep.*, 5, 37, 1974; *Tetr.*, 29, 2743, 1973; *JACS*, 98, 6742, 1976; USP 3718651, 3987046; DT 2029708

41310-1541

NAME:	3.6-DIBENZYL-2.5-DIOXOPIPERAZINE
PO:	EPICOCCUM NIGRUM
CT:	DIKETOPIPERAZINE DERIV., NEUTRAL
FORMULA:	C18H18N2O2
EA:	(N, 10)
MW:	294
PC:	WH., CRYST.
SOL-GOOD:	CHL
SOL-POOR:	W
TO:	(G.POS.,)
IS-EXT:	(CHL, , MIC.) (CHL, , FILT.)
IS-CRY:	(CRYST., CHL)

REFERENCES:

Bull. Soc. Pharm. Bordeaux, 112, 169, 1973; *CA*, 81, 60867; *Bioch. J.*, 85, 523, 1962

41310-1542

NAME:	ARGLECIN
PO:	S.TOXYTHRICINI, S.SP.
CT:	DIKETOPIPERAZINE DERIV., BASIC
FORMULA:	C12H21N5O
EA:	(N,)
MW:	251
PC:	WH., CRYST.
OR:	(0,)
UV:	HCL: (226, , 8703) (338, , 9400)
UV:	NH4OH: (258, , 8200) (321, , 9100)
UV:	W: (226, , 8000) (322, , 9600)
SOL-GOOD:	W, MEOH, PYR, DMSO
SOL-POOR:	BUOH, HEX
QUAL:	(SAKA., +) (NINH., -) (EHRL., -)
STAB:	(ACID, +) (BASE, -)
TO:	ENZYME INHIBITOR

REFERENCES:

JA, 24, 735, 1971; 25, 674, 1972; *TL*, 259, 1971

41310-4049

NAME:	GANCIDIN-W, CYCLO-L-LEU-L-PRO
PO:	S.SP., S.GANCIDICUS
CT:	NEUTRAL, DIKETOPIPERAZINE DERIV.
FORMULA:	C11H18N2O2
EA:	(N, 14)
MW:	210
PC:	WH., CRYST.
OR:	(-149.8, ETOH)
UV:	ETOH: (206, 296,)
UV:	HCL: (200, ,)
SOL-GOOD:	MEOH, ETOH, ACET, CHL
SOL-FAIR:	ETOAC, CCL4, ET2O, W
SOL-POOR:	HEX
QUAL:	(BIURET, -) (NINH., -) (EHRL., -) (FEHL., -) (DNPH, -) (FECL3, -)
TO:	(S.AUREUS, 8) (E.COLI, 63) (K.PNEUM., 16)
LD50:	(80, IV)
TV:	EHRLICH
IS-EXT:	(CHL, 6, W)
IS-ABS:	(CARBON, ACET-HCL)
IS-CRY:	(CRYST., CCL4)

REFERENCES:

JA, 11, 150, 1958; *Heterocycl.*, 7, 341, 1977

41310-5097

NAME:	CYCLO-VAL-PRO, 3-ISOPROPYL-2.5-DIOXO-1.4-DIAZABICYCLO-4.3.0-NONANE, K-73
PO:	S.TANASHIENSIS
CT:	DIKETOPIPERAZINE DERIV.
FORMULA:	C10H16N2O2
EA:	(N, 14)
MW:	196
PC:	WH., CRYST.
OR:	(-146, CHL) (-150, MEOH)
UV:	MEOH: (200, ,)

REFERENCES:

JP 75/116689; *CA*, 84, 57411

4132
Epi-Oligothiadiketopiperazines

This largest group of diketopiperazine antibiotics covers compounds containing an oligosulfide (usually disulfide) bridge across the 3 and 6 carbon atom of the piperazine ring and at least one of the two amino acid constituents of the ring is a heterocyclic derivative. These compounds are called *epi*-dithiaketopiperazine, *epi*-dithiodioxopiperazine, *epi*-dithiopiperazinedione, or *epi*-dithiadiketopiperazine antibiotics. For the generic name of these antibiotics the designation *epi*-oligothiadiketopiperazine antibiotics is proposed, because their sulfur bridge usually contains two to four sulfur atoms.

According to the occurring specific chemical fragments in their molecules (consequently, the number and nature of the rings fused to the diketopiperazine nucleus), this type is subdivided into several subtypes. The simplest gliotoxin subtype (41321), including the aranotin-like compounds, contains antibiotics having three or five fused hetero- or carbocyclic rings, respectively. The chaetocin subtype (41322) includes generally symmetrical dimeric compounds, formed from two identical units, each containing four fused rings. Sporidesmins (41323) are monomeric chaetocin-like compounds with chlorine content. Hyalodendrins (41324) are relatively simple nonfused benzyldiketopiperazine derivatives. Sirodesmins (41325) and antibiotic A-30641 (41326) contain spiro and ether linkages, respectively.

The general properties of some types of these antibiotics are summarized in the following table:

	Antibiotic subtypes				
Properties	Gliotoxin	Aranotin	Chaetocin	Sporidesmin	Hyalodendrin
UV absorption (nm) maximum	265—270 (weak)	End absorption	300—305 (strong)	250—300 (weak)	End absorption
Optical rotation (about)	−300°	−500°	+ 700°	−20 to −70°	−80°
Biological activity against					
Gram-positives	+ +	−	+ +	±	+
Gram negatives	+ +	−	+	−	±
Fungi or yeasts	+	±	−	−	±
Viruses	+	+ +	±	±	±
Cytotoxicity	±	−	+ +	+ +	−

Note: + + : strongly active; + : active; ±: weak or uncertain activity; −: inactive.

As can be seen from the above table, these compounds exhibit wide ranging and variable biological activities, and some types have extremely high optical rotation values.

The unusual chemical structures coupled with diverse physiological and microbiological activities attracted a specific interest towards this group. The presence of dihydrobenzene and the seven-membered dihydroxepin rings in gliotoxins and aranotins, respectively, or the sulfur-bridged diketopiperazine ring itself are unique features in organic chemistry.

The determination of the absolute conformation of these compounds by X-ray crystallographic analysis revealed the boat conformation of the diketopiperazine ring which is flattened or skewed and more or less twisted in the different compounds. The highly strained sulfide bridge does retain the twisted conformation. The -S-S- dihedral angle in these compounds is not the usual value of about 100°, but rather ~10 to 20°. The sulfur atoms are spatially nearer to the adjacent carbonyl groups than to the amide N atoms. The presence of this reactive sulfide bridge appears to be essential for biological activity. The sulfur bridge in the chaetocin type is antipodal to all other types. In this type the two asymmetric centers (C-3 and C-6) have S configuration in the diketopiperazine ring, compared to R configuration occurring in the other types. These compounds show very moderate, if any, antiviral activity.

The biological properties described for these antibiotics include inhibition of various bacteria (both Gram-positive and Gram-negative), fungi, and viruses and also toxicity in animals, plants, and tissue cultures derived therefrom. Recently attention has been focused on the antiviral activities of these compounds, which are directed against RNA viruses, such as polio-, entero-, and rhinoviruses. Some compounds (chaetocins, sporidesmins) exhibit strong cytotoxic properties, and some of them possess antitumor activity also. Sporidesmins are hepatotoxic mycotoxins, causing facial eczema in sheep. Generally, these antibiotics are toxic compounds, without practical utility in medicine. Melinacidins inhibit nicotinic acid biosynthesis, and other compounds result in chromosome abnormalities.

Biosynthesis from tryptophane and alanine or valine is a possible pathway to sporidesmins, while the precursor of gliotoxin is phenylalanine rather than tyrosine. During the biosynthesis of aranotin-type compounds a novel biogenetic transformation of a benzene ring, by intervention of benzene oxide-oxepine, appears to be functioning.

The microbiological effect of these antibiotics may be a result of their ability to specifically inhibit the preformed RNA-dependent RNA polymerase induced by viruses, without inhibiting the normal cellular RNA polymerase.

Structures

41310

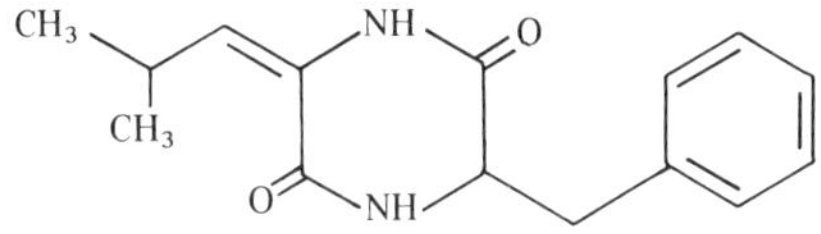

albonoursin

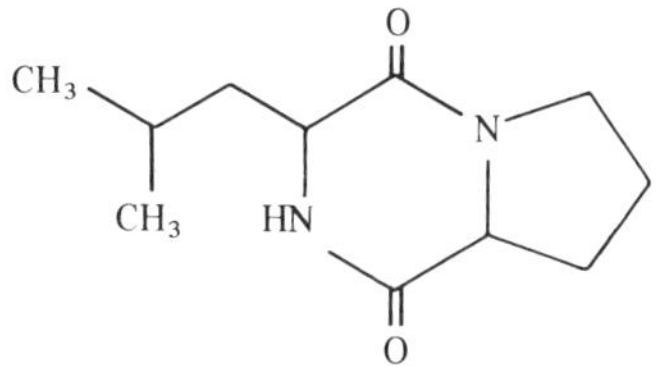

gancidin W

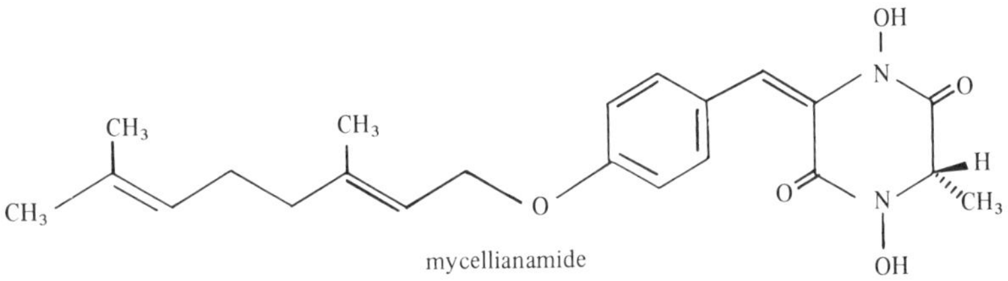

mycellianamide

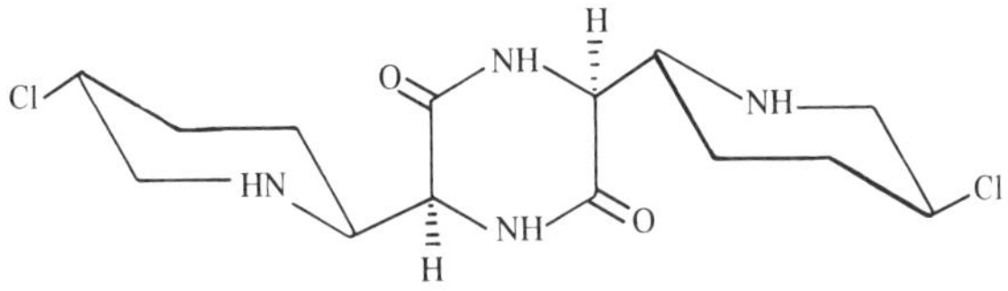

piperazinedione
(593 A)

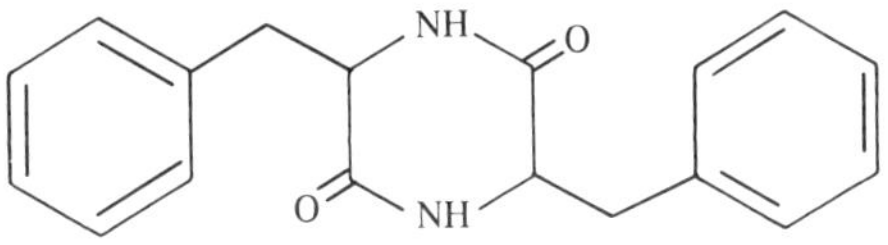

3,6-dibenzyl-2,5-dioxopiperazine

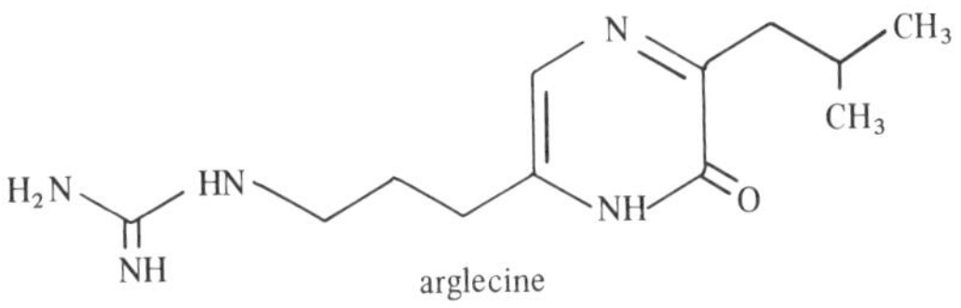

arglecine

41321

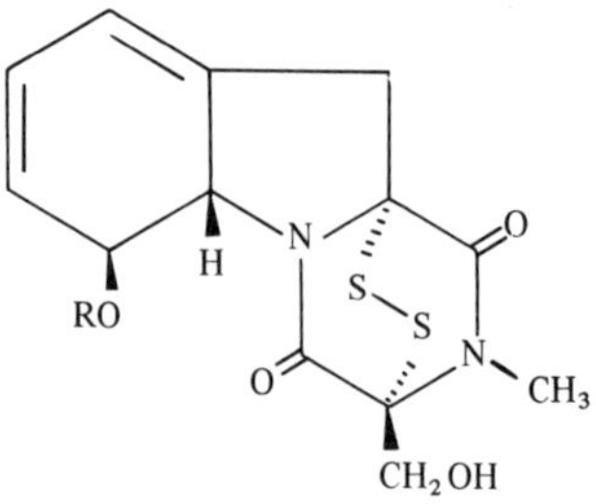

gliotoxin R = H
gliotoxin-monoacetate R = $COCH_3$

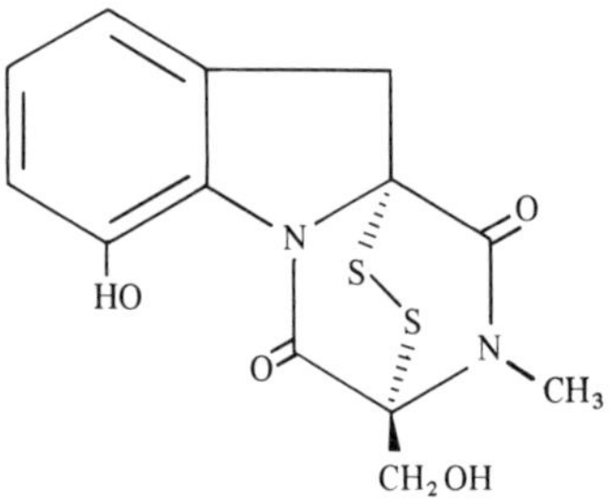

dehydrogliotoxin

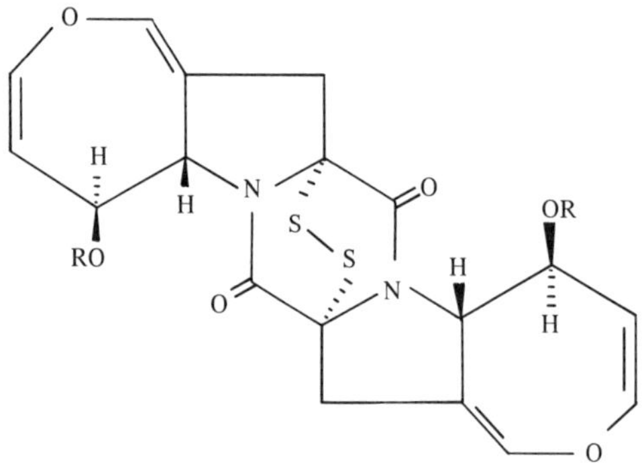

aranotin R = H
acetylaranotin (LL-S-88α) R = $COOH_3$

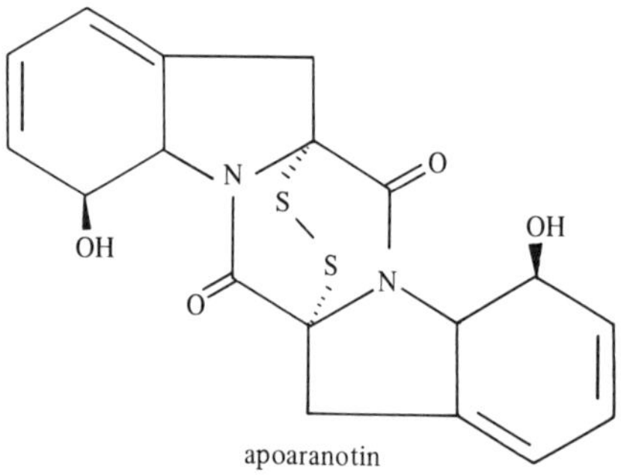

apoaranotin

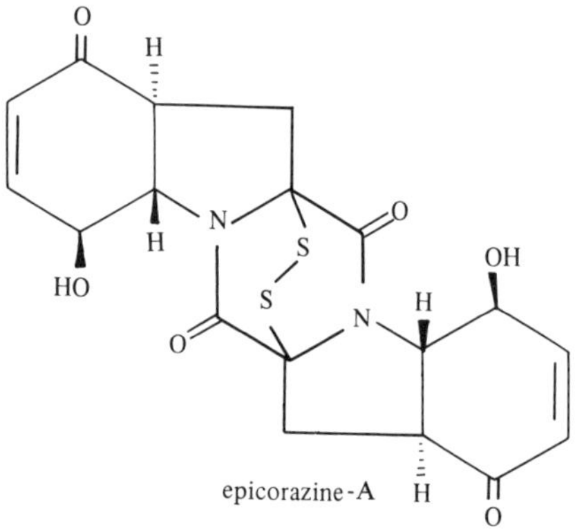

epicorazine-A

41322

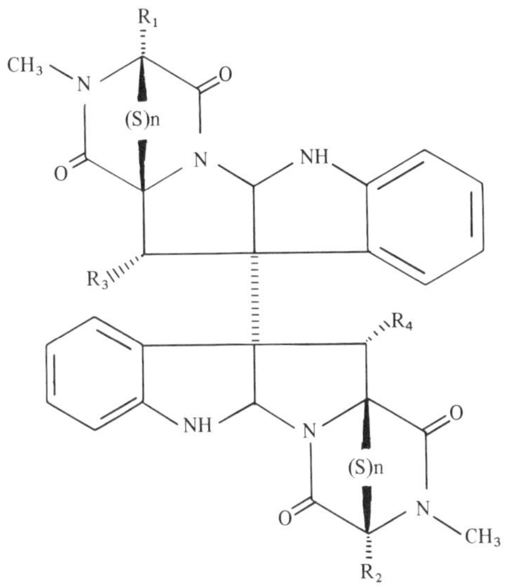

Antibiotic	**R_1**	**R_2**	**R_3**	**R_4**	n
Chaetocin	CH_2OH	CH_2OH	H	H	2
Verticillin A	CH_3	CH_3	OH	OH	2
Verticillin B	CH_3	CH_2OH	OH	OH	2
Verticillin C	CH_3	CH_2OH	OH	OH	3
Melinacidin II	CH_3	CH_2OH	OH	H	2
Melinacidin III	CH_2OH	CH_2OH	OH	H	2
Melinacidin IV (11α, 11′α-Dihydroxychaetocin)	CH_2OH	CH_2OH	OH	OH	2

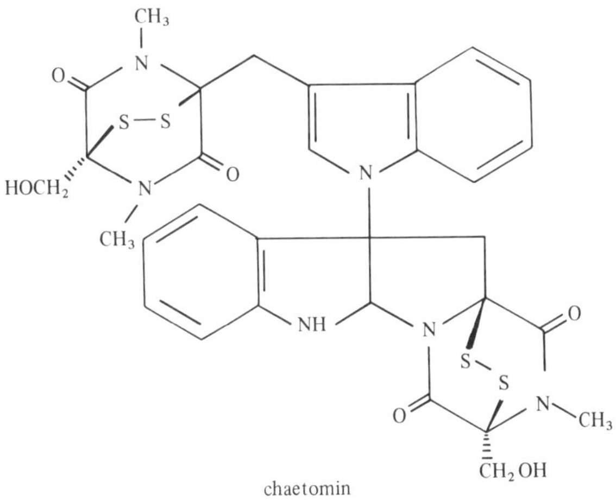

chaetomin

41323

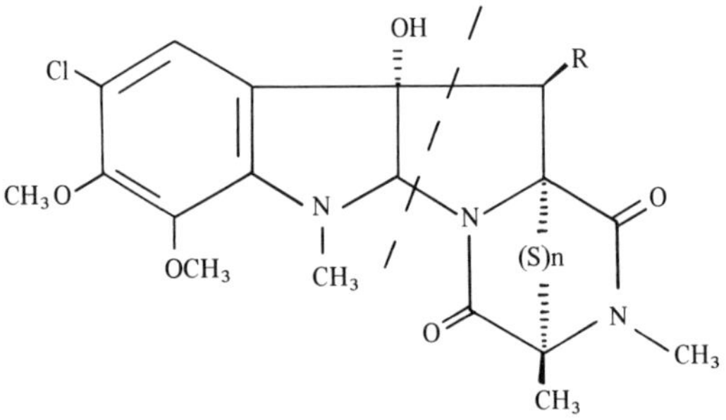

Antibiotic	R	n
Sporidesmin A	OH	2
Sporidesmin B	H	2
Sporidesmin E	OH	3
Sporidesmin G	OH	4

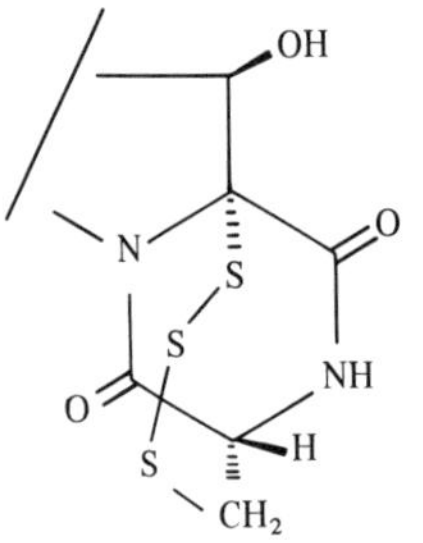

sporidesmin C

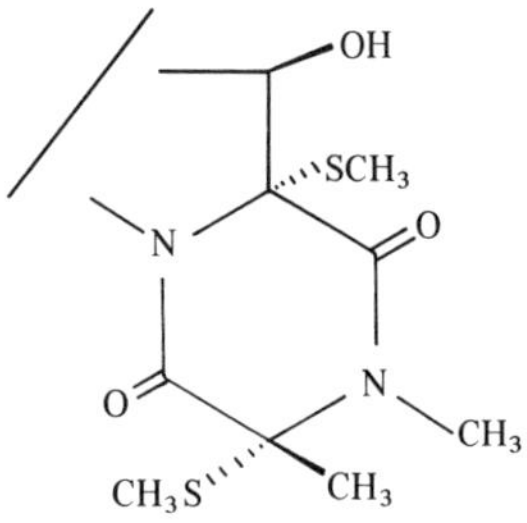

sporidesmin D

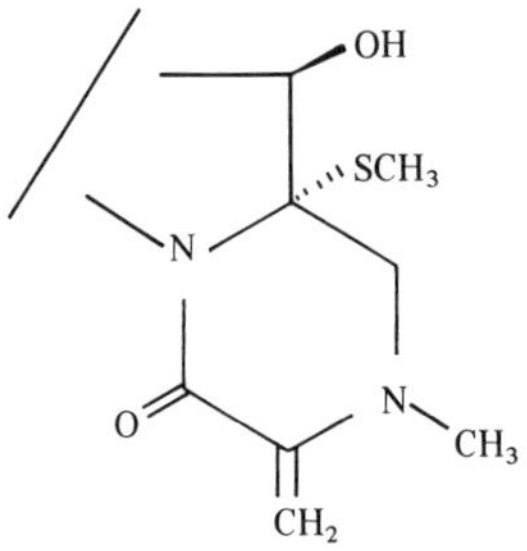

sporidesmin F

41324

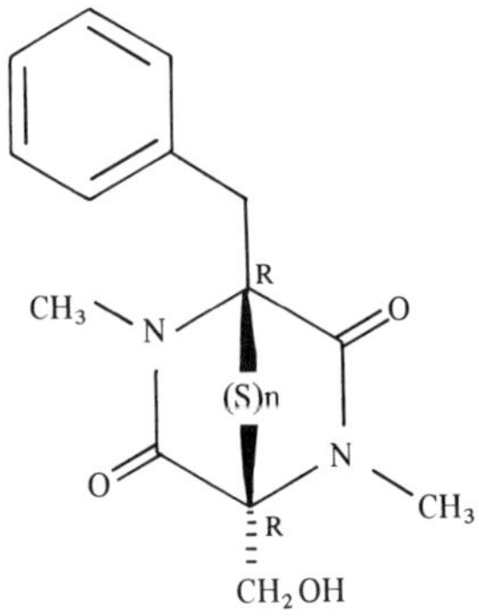

Antibiotic

Antibiotic	n
Hyalodendrin I (A-26771 A)	n = 2
Hyalodendrin II	n = 3
Hyalodendrin III (A-26771 C)	n = 4

41325

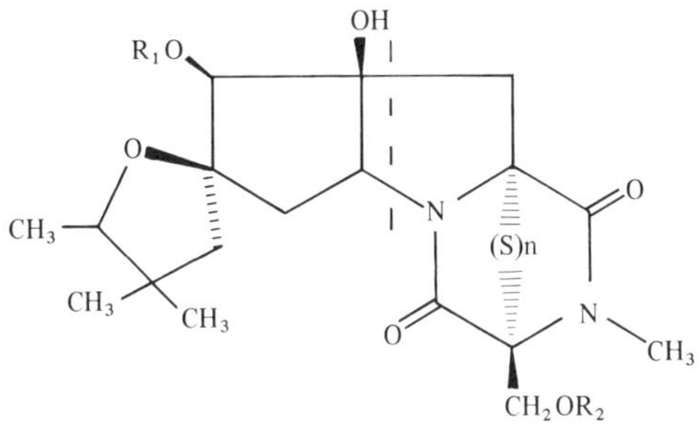

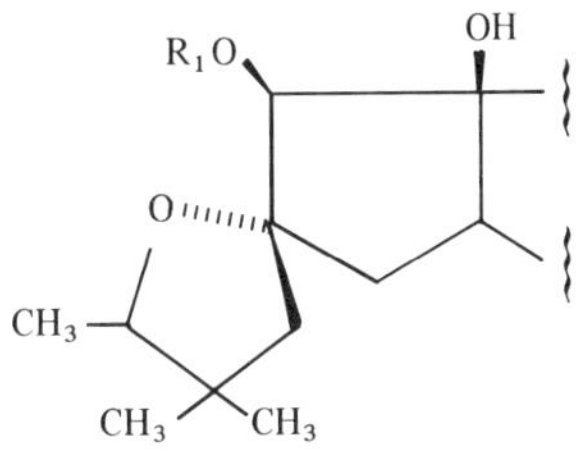

Antibiotic	R_1	R_2	n
Sirodesmin A	CH_3CO	H	2
Sirodesmin B	CH_3CO	H	4
Sirodesmin C	CH_3CO	H	3
Sirodesmin D	H	CH_3CO	4
Sirodesmin J	H	H	2

Antibiotic	R_1	R_2	n
Sirodesmin E	CH_3CO	H	4
Sirodesmin F	CH_3CO	H	3
Sirodesmin G	CH_3CO	H	2

41326

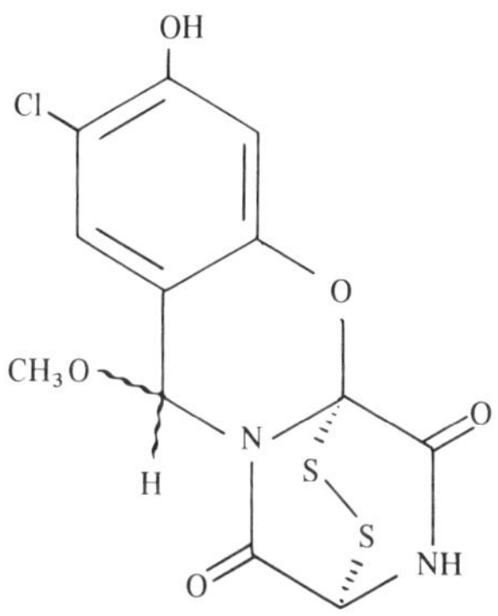

A-30641

41321-1543

NAME:	GLIOTOXIN, NSC-102866
IDENTICAL:	ASPERGILIN, 13, S-82
PO:	ASP.FUMIGATUS, ASP.CHAVALLIERI, TRICHODERMA VIRIDAE, GLIOCLADIUM FIMBRIATUM, P.TERLIKOWSKII, P.OBSCURUM, P.CINERASCENS
CT:	EPIDIKETOOLIGOTHIAPIPERAZINE, NEUTRAL, GLIOTOXIN T.
FORMULA:	C13H14N2O4S2
EA:	(N, 9) (S, 20)
MW:	347, 328
PC:	WH., CRYST.
OR:	(-290, ETOH) (-255, CHL) (-272, DIOXAN)
UV:	ETOH: (267, , 4360) (216, , 9330) (272, , 6300)
SOL-GOOD:	DIOXAN, CHL, DMFA, ACOH, ACET, ETOAC, BUOH, PYR, BENZ, ETOH, ET2O
SOL-FAIR:	MEOH
SOL-POOR:	W, HEX
STAB:	(ACID, +) (HEAT, +) (BASE, -) (LIGHT, -)
TO:	(S.AUREUS, .2) (B.SUBT., .10) (SHYG., 2) (E.COLI, 10) (K.PNEUM., 20) (C.ALB., 5) (PHYT.FUNGI, .1)
LD50:	(55|10, IP)
TV:	KB, GARDNER LY., ANTIVIRAL, COXSACKIE, LS
IS-EXT:	(ET2O, 2, FILT.)
IS-CRY:	(CRYST., ETOH)

REFERENCES:

Ann. Appl. Biol., 32, 214, 1945; 41, 280, 461, 1954; *Phytopath.*, 22, 839, 1932; 24, 1153, 1934; 31, 991, 1941; *J. Bact.*, 42, 815, 1941; 47, 391, 1944; *JACS*, 65, 2005, 1943; 66, 501, 614, 617, 619, 1944; 67, 1626, 1736, 1945; *J. Biol. Chem.*, 152, 419, 1944; *Nature*, 154, 667, 1944; 155, 637, 1945; 204, 1333, 1964; *Can. J. Micr.*, 12, 1187, 1962; 13, 1577, 1963; *TL*, 3131, 3139, 1966; *JACS*, 98, 6723, 1976; 95, 1989, 1973; 80, 1001, 1958; *Pak. J. Sci. Ind. Res.*, 18, 221, 1976; *Sci.*, 159, 431, 1968; *J. Med. Chem.*, 21, 796, 799, 1978

41321-1544

NAME: GLIOTOXIN-MONOACETATE
PO: P.TERLIKOWSKII, P.OBSCURUM
CT: EPIDIKETOOLIGOTHIAPIPERAZINE, NEUTRAL, GLIOTOXIN T.
FORMULA: C15H16N2O5S2
EA: (N, 8) (S, 18)
PC: YELLOW, CRYST.
OR: (-197, CHL)
UV: ETOH: (268, , 6300)
SOL-GOOD: MEOH, ET2O
SOL-POOR: W
TO: (S.AUREUS, 1) (B.SUBT., 3) (E.COLI, 10) (K.PNEUM., 10) (SHYG., 5) (C.ALB., 2)
LD50: (50, IP)
TV: ANTIVIRAL, COXSACKIE
IS-EXT: (BENZ, , FILT.)
IS-CRY: (CRYST., ETOH)
REFERENCES:
JACS, 75, 2110, 1953; 67, 1626, 1945

41321-1545

PO: P.OBSCURUM
CT: EPIDIKETOOLIGOTHIAPIPERAZINE, NEUTRAL, GLIOTOXIN T.
FORMULA: C14H16N2O4S2
EA: (N, 8) (S, 19)
MW: 188|6
OR: (-197, CHL)
UV: ETOH: (270, ,)
SOL-GOOD: MEOH, CHL
SOL-POOR: W, HEX
TO: (S.AUREUS, 20) (E.COLI, 100) (C.ALB., 200) (PHYT.FUNGI, 200)
LD50: (100|50, IP)
IS-EXT: (BENZ, 2, FILT.)
IS-CHR: (AL, BENZ-MEOH)
IS-CRY: (PREC., BENZ, HEX) (CRYST., BENZ-HEX)
REFERENCES:
JACS, 67, 1626, 1945

41321-1546

NAME:	GLIOTOXIN-B
PO:	P.TERLIKOWSKII
CT:	EPIDIKETOOLIGOTHIAPIPERAZINE, NEUTRAL, GLIOTOXIN T.
PC:	WH., CRYST.
OR:	(-171, CHL)
STAB:	(BASE, -)
TO:	(B.SUBT., .8)

REFERENCES:

Can. J. Micr., 12, 1187, 1966; 13, 1451, 1577, 1967

41321-1547

NAME:	DEHYDROGLIOTOXIN
PO:	P.TERLIKOWSKII
CT:	EPIDIKETOOLIGOTHIAPIPERAZINE, NEUTRAL, GLIOTOXIN T., ACIDIC
FORMULA:	C13H12N2O4S2
EA:	(N, 9) (S, 20)
PC:	YELLOW, CRYST.
OR:	(-382, CHL)
UV:	ETOH: (215, , 21900) (272, , 5370) (300, , 4680)
SOL-GOOD:	MEOH, ET2O
SOL-POOR:	W
TO:	(B.SUBT., 2.5) (S.AUREUS,) (E.COLI,)
TV:	ANTITUMOR, ANTIVIRAL

REFERENCES:

JCSC, 1799, 1966; *Diss. Abst.*, 25, 6955, 1965; *JACS*, 95, 6492, 1973; *JCS*, 4315, 1964

41321-1548

PO:	ASP.CHAVALLIERI
CT:	EPIDIKETOOLIGOTHIAPIPERAZINE, NEUTRAL, GLIOTOXIN T.
TO:	(B.SUBT.,) (E.COLI,)
IS-EXT:	(ET2O, , WB.)

REFERENCES:

Curr. Sci., 38, 518, 1969

41321-1549

NAME: VIROCYTIN, 13
PO: ASP.FUMIGATUS
CT: EPIDIKETOOLIGOTHIAPIPERAZINE, NEUTRAL, GLIOTOXIN T.
FORMULA: C13H14N2O4S2
EA: (N, 9) (S, 20)
MW: 300
PC: WH., YELLOW, CRYST.
OR: (-285, ETOH)
UV: ETOH: (245, , 3270) (270, , 4430)
SOL-GOOD: MEOH, CHL
SOL-POOR: W
TO: (S.AUREUS, .6) (FUNGI,)
LD50: (7, IP)
TV: EHRLICH, S-37, S-45, ANTITUMOR, ANTIVIRAL
IS-EXT: (ETOAC, , FILT.)
IS-CRY: (CRYST., MEOH)
REFERENCES:
Antib., 316, 1968; 522, 525, 1969

41321-1550

NAME: ARANOTIN, A-21101-III, ARIOTIN
PO: ARACHNIOTUS AUREUS
CT: EPIDIKETOOLIGOTHIAPIPERAZINE, NEUTRAL, GLIOTOXIN T.
FORMULA: C20H18N2O6S2
EA: (N, 6) (S, 14)
MW: 462, 446
PC: WH., YELLOW, CRYST.
UV: ETOH: (295, , 2380)
SOL-GOOD: ETOAC, CHL
SOL-POOR: W, HEX
LD50: (35, IP)
TV: POLIO, MEASLES, COXSACKIE
IS-EXT: (ETOAC, , WB.)
IS-CHR: (SILG, TOL-ETOAC)
REFERENCES:
JACS, 90, 2980, 6518, 6529, 1968; *AAC 1968*, 213; *TL*, 4467, 1968; *BBRC*, 33, 219, 1968; *CC*, 359, 1969; *J. Med. Chem.*, 17, 827, 1974; USP 3907988

41321-1551

NAME: LL-S-88-A"
IDENTICAL: ACETYL-ARANOTIN
PO: ASP.TERREUS
CT: EPIDIKETOOLIGOTHIAPIPERAZINE, NEUTRAL, GLIOTOXIN T.
FORMULA: C22H20N208S2
EA: (N, 5) (S, 12)
MW: 504
PC: YELLOW, CRYST.
OR: (-579.7, CHL)
UV: MEOH: (200, ,) (225, , 10200) (270, , 1800)
SOL-GOOD: MEOH, ET20
SOL-POOR: W, HEX
STAB: (ACID, +)
TO: (S.AUREUS, 100) (MYCOB.SP., 2.5) (C.ALB., 10)
LD50: (40, IP)
TV: COXSACKIE, POLIO
IS-FIL: ORIG.
IS-EXT: (CHL, , FILT.)
IS-CHR: (SILG, CHL)
IS-CRY: (CRYST., ETOH)
REFERENCES:

JACS, 90, 2980, 6518, 6529, 1968; *AAC 1968*, 213; *TL*, 4467, 1968; *BBRC*, 33, 219, 1968; *CC*, 359, 1969; *J. Med. Chem.*, 17, 827, 1974; USP 3907988

41321-1552

NAME: APOARANOTIN, A-21101-IV
PO: ARACHNIOTUS AUREUS
CT: EPIDIKETOOLIGOTHIAPIPERAZINE, NEUTRAL, GLIOTOXIN T.
FORMULA: C20H18N206S2
EA: (N, 6) (S, 14)
MW: 446
PC: WH., CRYST.
OR: (-492, CHL)
UV: ETOH: (265, , 3880)
SOL-GOOD: MEOH, ET20
SOL-POOR: W, HEX
LD50: (60, IP)
TV: COXSACKIE, POLIO
IS-CHR: (SILG, TOL-ETOAC)
REFERENCES:

JACS, 90, 2980, 6518, 6529, 1968; *AAC 1968*, 213; *TL*, 4467, 1968; *BBRC*, 33, 219, 1968; *CC*, 359, 1969; *J. Med. Chem.*, 17, 827, 1974; USP 3907988

41321-1553

NAME:	ACETYLARANOTIN, A-21101-II
IDENTICAL:	LL-S-88-A"
PO:	ARACHNIOTUS AUREUS
CT:	EPIDIKETOOLIGOTHIAPIPERAZINE, NEUTRAL, GLIOTOXIN T.
FORMULA:	C22H20N2O8S2
EA:	(N, 5) (S, 12)
MW:	504
PC:	YELLOW, CRYST.
OR:	(-549.7, CHL)
UV:	ETOH: (200, ,) (222, , 10200) (270, , 1800)
SOL-GOOD:	MEOH, ET2O
SOL-POOR:	W, HEX
TV:	COXSACKIE, POLIO

REFERENCES:
JACS, 90, 2980, 6518, 6529, 1968; *AAC 1968*, 213; *TL*, 4467, 1968; *BBRC*, 33, 219, 1968; *CC*, 359, 1969; *J. Med. Chem.*, 17, 827, 1974; USP 3907988

41321-5295

NAME:	EPICORAZINE-A
PO:	EPICOCCUM NIGRUM
CT:	EPIDIKETOOLIGOTHIAPIPERAZINE, GLIOTOXIN T.
FORMULA:	C18H16N2O6S2
MW:	420
PC:	WH., CRYST.
OR:	(-293, CHL)
SOL-GOOD:	MEOH, CHL
SOL-POOR:	W
TO:	ANTIBACTERIAL
TV:	ANTIVIRAL
IS-EXT:	(CHL, , FILT.)

REFERENCES:
TL, 3943, 1976; *Acta Cryst. Sect. B*, 33, 1474, 1977

41322-1554

NAME:	CHAETOCIN
PO:	CHAETOMIUM MINUTUM
CT:	EPIDIKETOOLIGOTHIAPIPERAZINE, NEUTRAL, CHAETOCIN T.
FORMULA:	C30H28N6O6S4
EA:	(N, 12) (S, 18)
MW:	696, 645
EW:	727
PC:	WH., YELLOW, CRYST.
OR:	(+379, PYR) (+789, DMSO)
UV:	DMSO: (306, , 6040)
SOL-GOOD:	PYR, ETOAC, DMSO, MEOH
SOL-POOR:	W
TO:	(S.AUREUS, .001) (S.LUTEA, 31.6) (SHYG., 50) (E.COLI, 50) (P.VULG., 50)
LD50:	(1.7, IP) (1200, PEROS)
TV:	P-815
IS-EXT:	(ETOAC, , WB.)
IS-CRY:	(CRYST., PYR-MEOH-ET2O)

REFERENCES:

Helv., 53, 1061, 1970

41322-1555

NAME:	11.11-DIHYDROXYCHAETOCIN
IDENTICAL:	MELINACIDIN-IV
PO:	VERTICILLIUM TERERUM
CT:	EPIDIKETOOLIGOTHIAPIPERAZINE, NEUTRAL, CHAETOCIN T.
FORMULA:	C30H28N6O8S4
EA:	(N, 11) (S, 18)
MW:	839, 728
PC:	YELLOW, CRYST.
OR:	(+758, DMSO) (+730, PYR)
UV:	DMSO: (308, , 5750)
SOL-GOOD:	PYR, DMSO, ETOAC, MEOH
SOL-POOR:	W
TO:	(S.AUREUS, .1) (B.SUBT., 1)
LD50:	(4, IP)
TV:	P-815
IS-EXT:	(CH2CL2, , FILT.) (MEOH, , MIC.)

REFERENCES:

Helv., 55, 2182, 1972; *JA*, 30, 468, 1977

41322-1556

NAME:	VERTICILLIN-A
PO:	VERTICILLIUM SP.
CT:	EPIDIKETOOLIGOTHIAPIPERAZINE, NEUTRAL, CHAETOCIN T.
FORMULA:	C30H28N6O6S4.CHCL3
EA:	(N, 12) (S, 18)
MW:	674
PC:	YELLOW, CRYST.
OR:	(+727, DIOXAN) (+703, DMSO)
UV:	DIOXAN: (306, , 6300)
SOL-GOOD:	MEOH, CHL, PYR, DIOXAN
SOL-POOR:	W, HEX
TO:	(B.SUBT., 2) (S.AUREUS, 2) (MYCOB.SP., 1)
LD50:	(7.6, IP)
TV:	HELA, EHRLICH, ANTIVIRAL
IS-EXT:	(ACET, , MIC.)
IS-CRY:	(CRYST., PYR-ACET)

REFERENCES:

JA, 23, 420, 1970; *JCS Perkin I*, 1819, 1973; *CC*, 44, 1971; JP 74/18232

41322-1557

NAME:	VERTICILLIN-B, 11-HYDROXYVERTICILLIN-A
PO:	VERTICILLIUM SP.
CT:	EPIDIKETOOLIGOTHIAPIPERAZINE, NEUTRAL, CHAETOCIN T.
FORMULA:	C30H28N6O7S4.CHCL3
EA:	(N, 11) (S, 17)
MW:	690
PC:	YELLOW, CRYST.
OR:	(+704, DIOXAN)
UV:	DIOXAN: (306, , 5600)
SOL-GOOD:	MEOH, CHL, PYR, DIOXAN
SOL-POOR:	W, HEX, ET2O
TO:	(G.POS.,) (MYCOB.SP.,)
TV:	HELA
IS-CHR:	(SILG, CHL-MEOH)

REFERENCES:

JA, 23, 420, 1970; *JCS Perkin I*, 1819, 1973; *CC*, 44, 1971; JP 74/18232

41322-1558

NAME:	VERTICILLIN-C
PO:	VERTICILLIUM SP.
CT:	EPIDIKETOOLIGOTHIAPIPERAZINE, NEUTRAL, CHAETOCIN T.
FORMULA:	C30H28N6O7S6
EA:	(N, 11) (S, 21)
MW:	754
PC:	YELLOW, POW.
OR:	(+765, DIOXAN)
UV:	DIOXAN: (303, , 5500)
SOL-GOOD:	MEOH, CHL
SOL-POOR:	W
TO:	(G.POS.,)
TV:	HELA

REFERENCES:

JA, 23, 420, 1970; *JCS Perkin I*, 1819, 1973; *CC*, 44, 1971; JP 74/18232

41322-1559

NAME:	MELINACIDIN, U-26362
PO:	ACROSTALAGMUS CINNABARINUS
CT:	EPIDIKETOOLIGOTHIAPIPERAZINE, NEUTRAL, CHAETOCIN T.
FORMULA:	C16H17N3O4S2
EA:	(N, 10) (S, 18)
MW:	1290, 1380
PC:	WH., CRYST.
OR:	(+736, CHL)
UV:	ETOH: (300, 79,)
SOL-GOOD:	CHL, DMFA, DMSO
SOL-FAIR:	MEOH, ETOH, ACET
SOL-POOR:	W, HEX
TO:	(S.AUREUS, 1.5) (B.SUBT., .5) (P.VULG., 25) (SHYG., 25)
LD50:	TOXIC
TV:	KB, ANTIVIRAL, HERPES
IS-EXT:	(CH2CL2, 7, FILT.+NACL)
IS-CHR:	(FLORISIL, ACET-HEX)
IS-CRY:	(PREC., CH2CL2, HEX) (CRYST., ETOH-W)

REFERENCES:

J. Bact., 96, 1285, 1968; *JA*, 24, 383, 1971; 25, 171, 1972; DT 1804519; USP 3857936

41322-1560

NAME: MELINACIDIN-II
PO: ACROSTALAGMUS CINNABARINUS
CT: EPIDIKETOOLIGOTHIAPIPERAZINE, NEUTRAL, CHAETOCIN T.
FORMULA: C30H28N606S4
EA: (N, 11) (S, 17)
MW: 855
PC: WH., CRYST.
OR: (+726, CHL)
UV: MEOH: (300, 73,)
SOL-GOOD: CHL, DMFA, DMSO
SOL-FAIR: MEOH, ETOH, ACET
SOL-POOR: W, HEX
TO: (S.AUREUS, 1) (B.SUBT., 1) (P.VULG., 10) (SHYG., 50)
TV: L-1210
IS-CHR: (SILG, TOL-ETOAC)
IS-CRY: (CRYST., ETOH)
REFERENCES:
JA, 30, 468, 1977; USP 3857936; BP 1229297

41322-1561

NAME: MELINACIDIN-III
PO: ACROSTALAGMUS CINNABARINUS
CT: DIKETODITHIOPIPERAZINE, NEUTRAL, CHAETOCIN T.
FORMULA: C30H28N607S4
EA: (N, 11) (S, 17)
MW: 820
PC: WH., CRYST.
OR: (+776, CHL)
UV: MEOH: (300, 75,)
SOL-GOOD: CHL, DMFA, DMSO
SOL-FAIR: MEOH, ETOH, ACET
SOL-POOR: W, HEX
TO: (S.AUREUS, .1) (B.SUBT.,) (P.VULG., 10) (E.COLI, 50) (K.PNEUM., 50) (SHYG., 50)
TV: L-1210
REFERENCES:
JA, 30, 468, 1977; USP 3857936; BP 1229297

41322-1562

NAME: MELINACIDIN-IV
IDENTICAL: 11.11-DIHYDROXYCHAETOCIN
PO: ACROSTALAGMUS CINNABARINUS
CT: EPIDIKETOOLIGOTHIAPIPERAZINE, NEUTRAL, CHAETOCIN T.
FORMULA: C30H28N608S4
EA: (N, 11) (S, 17)
MW: 1200
PC: WH., CRYST.
OR: (+718, CHL)
UV: MEOH: (301, 60,)
TO: (S.AUREUS, .1) (B.SUBT.,) (P.VULG., 50) (SHYG., 50) (E.COLI, 100) (K.PNEUM., 100)
TV: L-1210
REFERENCES:

JA, 30, 468, 1977; USP 3857936; BP 1229297

41322-1563

NAME: CHAETOMIN
PO: CHAETOMIUM COCHLIODES, CHAETOMIUM GLOBOSUM, CHAETOMIUM UMBONATUM
CT: EPIDIKETOOLIGOTHIAPIPERAZINE, NEUTRAL, CHAETOCIN T.
FORMULA: C31H30N606S4
EA: (N, 11) (S, 17)
MW: 546, 710
PC: WH., POW.
OR: (+360, CHL)
UV: ETOH: (276, 170,) (284, 185,) (293, 172,)
UV: MEOH: (275, , 9100) (284, , 9000) (295, , 8250)
SOL-GOOD: ACET, ETOAC, CHL, BENZ, DIOXAN, PYR
SOL-FAIR: MEOH, ETOH, ET2O
SOL-POOR: W, HEX
QUAL: (BIURET, -)
STAB: (HEAT, +) (ACID, +) (BASE, -)
TO: (S.AUREUS, .002) (B.SUBT., .08) (S.LUTEA, .01) (E.COLI, 10) (FUNGI, .3)
LD50: (75, PEROS-RATS)
TV: HELA, COXSACKIE
IS-EXT: (ACET, , MIC.) (ETOAC, , W)
IS-CHR: (AL, BENZ)
REFERENCES:

J. Bact., 48, 527, 531, 1944; *Mycol.*, 35, 47, 1943; *Arch. Bioch.*, 21, 125, 1949; *Proc. Soc. Exp. B.M.*, 57, 244, 1945; *Nature*, 172, 39, 1953; *Can. J. Micr.*, 18, 1129, 1972; 13, 1577, 1967; *JCSC*, 472, 1972; *JACS*, 98, 6741, 1976

41323-1564

NAME: SPORIDESMIN-A, SPORIDESMIN
PO: PITHOMYCES CHARTARUM
CT: EPIDIKETOOLIGOTHIAPIPERAZINE, NEUTRAL, SPORIDESMIN T.
FORMULA: C18H20N3O6S2CL
EA: (N, 9) (S, 14) (CL, 8)
MW: 615
PC: WH., CRYST.
OR: (-45, MEOH) (+15, CHL)
UV: ET2O: (218.5, 700,) (252.5, 220,) (305, 40,)
UV: ETOH: (218, , 39820) (254, , 13200) (302, , 2820)
SOL-GOOD: MEOH, ET2O, BASE
SOL-POOR: W, HEX
TO: (B.SUBT., 80) (E.COLI, 5)
LD50: (1, IV)
TV: HELA, EHRLICH
IS-EXT: (MEOH, , WB.)
IS-CRY: (CRYST., MEOH-W)
REFERENCES:

Chem. & Ind., 1546, 1959; *JCS*, 26, 1964; *JACS*, 95, 6493, 1973; 85, 1520, 1963; *Aust. J. Chem.*, 19, 1059, 1966; *Can. J. Micr.*, 12, 1287, 1966; 13, 1451, 1517; 1967; *TL*, 3131, 1966

41323-1565

NAME: SPORIDESMIN-B
PO: PITHOMYCES CHARTARUM
CT: EPIDIKETOOLIGOTHIAPIPERAZINE, NEUTRAL, SPORIDESMIN T.
FORMULA: C18H20N3O5S2CL
EA: (N, 9) (S, 14) (CL, 8)
MW: 380
PC: WH., CRYST.
OR: (-27, MEOH) (+12, CHL)
UV: ETOH: (218, , 31620) (256, , 12000) (307, , 2570)
SOL-GOOD: MEOH, CHL
SOL-FAIR: ET2O, HEX, BENZ
SOL-POOR: W
TO: (B.SUBT., 400)
LD50: TOXIC
TV: HELA, EARLE, EHRLICH
REFERENCES:

Chem. & Ind., 42, 1963; *TL*, 2087, 1964; *J. New Zealand Inst. Chem.*, 25, 207, 1961; *JCS*, 3172, 1963

41323-1566

NAME:	SPORIDESMIN-C
PO:	PITHOMYCES CHARTARUM
CT:	EPIDIKETOOLIGOTHIAPIPERAZINE, NEUTRAL, SPORIDESMIN T.
FORMULA:	C17H17N3O6S3CL
EA:	(N, 8) (S, 16) (CL, 7)
PC:	WH., CRYST.
TO:	(B.SUBT., 400)
LD50:	TOXIC
TV:	HELA

REFERENCES:

Aust. J. Chem., 19, 1059, 1966; *JCSC*, 1803, 1966

41323-1567

NAME:	SPORIDESMIN-D
PO:	PITHOMYCES CHARTARUM
CT:	EPIDIKETOOLIGOTHIAPIPERAZINE, NEUTRAL, SPORIDESMIN T.
FORMULA:	C20H26N3O6S2CL
EA:	(N, 8) (S, 13) (CL, 7)
MW:	503
PC:	WH., CRYST.
OR:	(+58, CHL)
UV:	ETOH: (216, , 28200) (252, , 10000) (300, , 1900)
SOL-GOOD:	MEOH, CHL
SOL-FAIR:	ET2O
SOL-POOR:	W, HEX
TO:	(B.SUBT., 1000)
IS-CHR:	(SILG, BENZ-ET2O-ACOH)
IS-CRY:	(CRYST., ET2O)

REFERENCES:

CC, 1032, 1967; *JCSC*, 1564, 1969

41323-1568

NAME: SPORIDESMIN-E
PO: PITHOMYCES CHARTARUM
CT: EPIDIKETOOLIGOTHIAPIPERAZINE, NEUTRAL, SPORIDESMIN T.
FORMULA: C19H20N3O6S3CL
EA: (N, 7) (S, 17) (CL, 7)
PC: WH., CRYST.
OR: (-132, CHL)
UV: ETOH: (217, , 33100) (252, , 16600) (295, , 3160)
TO: (B.SUBT., 10)
TV: KB, HELA, EHRLICH
IS-CHR: (SILG, PENTANE-BUOH)
IS-CRY: (CRYST., ETOH)
REFERENCES:
CC, 1571, 1968; *JCSC*, 1665, 1969

41323-1569

NAME: SPORIDESMIN-F
PO: PITHOMYCES CHARTARUM
CT: EPIDIKETOOLIGOTHIAPIPERAZINE, NEUTRAL, SPORIDESMIN T.
FORMULA: C19H21N3O6SCL
EA: (N, 9) (S, 7) (CL, 8)
MW: 457
PC: WH., POW.
UV: ETOH: (216, , 28840) (250, , 13800) (298, , 2000)
REFERENCES:
JCSC, 1564, 1969; *CC*, 1571, 1968

41323-1570

NAME:	<u>SPORIDESMIN-G</u>
PO:	PITHOMYCES CHARTARUM
CT:	EPIDIKETOOLIGOTHIAPIPERAZINE, NEUTRAL, SPORIDESMIN T.
FORMULA:	C18H20N3O6S4CL
EA:	(N, 7) (S, 21) (CL, 7)
MW:	623
PC:	WH., CRYST.
OR:	(-217, CHL)
UV:	ETOH: (216, , 44700) (250, , 11500) (298, , 2950)
TV:	HELA
IS-CHR:	(SILG, HEX)

REFERENCES:

JCSC, 470, 1972

41323-6495

NAME:	<u>SPORIDESMIN-H</u>
PO:	PITHOMYCES CHARTARUM
CT:	EPIDIKETO OLIGOTHIAPIPERAZINE, SPORIDESMIN T.
FORMULA:	C18H20N3O4S2CL
EA:	(N, 9) (CL, 8) (S, 14)
MW:	459
PC:	WH., CRYST.
OR:	(+43, CHL)
TV:	HELA
IS-CHR:	(SILG, BENZ-ETOAC)

REFERENCES:

JCS Perkin I, 1476, 1978

41324-1571

NAME: HYALODENDRIN
PO: HYALODENDRON SP., TORULA SP.
CT: EPIDIKETOOLIGOTHIAPIPERAZINE, NEUTRAL, HYALODENDRIN T.
FORMULA: C14H16N2O3S2
EA: (N, 8) (S, 19)
MW: 324
PC: WH., CRYST.
OR: (+26, CHL)
UV: ETOH: (200, ,) (260, , 1000)
SOL-GOOD: MEOH, ET2O
SOL-POOR: W
QUAL: (EHRL., +) (NINH., +)
TO: (C.ALB., 6.2) (FUNGI, .7) (B.SUBT.,) (K.PNEUM., 50) (P.VULG., 50)
LD50: (75, IP)
IS-EXT: (CHL, , FILT.)
IS-CHR: (SILG, BENZ-CHL)
IS-CRY: (CRYST., ET2O)
REFERENCES:
JA, 26, 532, 1973; *Can. J. Micr.*, 20, 759, 1974; *Exp.*, 30, 719, 1974; *JCS Perkin I*, 2600, 1973; *Diss. Abst.*, 35, 4837, 1975; USP 3715352; *CA*, 79, 73866

41324-1572

NAME: HYALODENDRIN-II
PO: HYALODENDRON SP.
CT: EPIDIKETOOLIGOTHIAPIPERAZINE, NEUTRAL, HYALODENDRIN T.
FORMULA: C14H16N2O3S3
EA: (N, 6) (S, 26)
MW: 356
PC: YELLOW, OIL
TO: (C.ALB., 12.5) (FUNGI, 3.1)
LD50: (32|8, IP)
IS-EXT: (MEOH-W, , MIC.) (ETOAC, , W)
IS-CHR: (SILG, TOL-ETOAC)
IS-CRY: (DRY, TOL-ETOAC)
REFERENCES:
JA, 26, 532, 1973; *Can. J. Micr.*, 20, 759, 1974; *Exp.*, 30, 719, 1974; *JCS Perkin I*, 2600, 1973; *Diss. Abst.*, 35, 4837, 1975; USP 3715352; *CA*, 79, 73866

41324-1573

NAME: A-26771-A
PO: P.TUBERATUM
CT: EPIDIKETOOLIGOTHIAPIPERAZINE, NEUTRAL, HYALODENDRIN T.
FORMULA: C14H16N2O3S2
EA: (N, 8) (S, 19)
MW: 324
PC: YELLOW, WH., CRYST.
OR: (-88, MEOH) (-85, CHL)
UV: ETOH: (200, ,)
SOL-GOOD: MEOH, CHL
SOL-POOR: W
TO: (S.AUREUS, 8) (S.LUTEA, .5) (B.SUBT., .5) (E.COLI, 32) (K.PNEUM., 16) (P.VULG., .25) (PS.AER., .25) (SHYG., 8) (S.CEREV., .1) (C.ALB., .5)
TV: POLIO, COXSACKIE
IS-EXT: (ETOAC, , FILT.)
IS-CHR: (SILG, ETOAC-MEOH)
IS-CRY: (CRYST., ACET-ET2O-HEX)
REFERENCES:
JA, 27, 57, 1974; USP 3883561, 3932219, 3954972

41324-1574

NAME: A-26771-C
PO: P.TUBERATUM
CT: EPIDIKETOOLIGOTHIAPIPERAZINE, NEUTRAL, HYALODENDRIN T.
FORMULA: C14H16N2O3S4
EA: (N, 7) (S, 33)
MW: 388
PC: YELLOW, CRYST.
OR: (-187, CHL)
UV: ETOH: (275, , 10000)
SOL-GOOD: MEOH, CHL
SOL-POOR: W, HEX
TO: (S.AUREUS, 8) (S.LUTEA, 2) (B.SUBT., 8) (E.COLI, 64) (K.PNEUM., 32) (P.VULG., .2) (PS.AER., .2) (SHYG., .5) (S.CEREV., 8) (C.ALB., 30)
TV: POLIO, COXSACKIE
IS-CHR: (SILG, ETOAC-HEX)
IS-CRY: (CRYST., ACET-ET2O-HEX)
REFERENCES:
JA, 27, 57, 1974; USP 3883561, 3932219, 3954972

41324-5679

NAME: HYALODENDRIN-III, 3-BENZYL-6-HYDROXYMETHYL-1.4-DIMETHYL-3.6-EPITETRATHIOPIPERAZINE-2.6-DIONE
PO: HYALODENDRON SP.
CT: EPIDIKETOOLIGOTHIAPIPERAZINE, HYALODENDRIN T.
FORMULA: C14H16N2O3S4
EA: (N, 7) (S, 33)
PC: WH., CRYST.
TO: (S.AUREUS,) (B.SUBT.,) (C.ALB.,)
IS-CHR: (SILG, BENZ-CHL)
REFERENCES:

Can. J. Chem., 53, 295, 1975

41325-1575

NAME:	SIRODESMIN-A
PO:	SIRODESMIUM DIVERSUM
CT:	EPIDIKETOOLIGOTHIAPIPERAZINE, NEUTRAL, SIRODESMIN T.
FORMULA:	C20H26N2O8S2
EA:	(N, 6) (S, 13)
MW:	486
PC:	WH., POW., YELLOW
SOL-GOOD:	MEOH, ET2O
SOL-POOR:	W, HEX
TV:	RHINO, COXSACKIE
IS-EXT:	(CHL, , FILT.) (TOL, 6.5, FILT.)
IS-CHR:	(SILG, ETOAC-TOL) (SILG, ET2O-ETOAC)
IS-CRY:	(PREC., ET2O, HEX)

REFERENCES:

JCS Perkin I, 180, 1977; DT 2346389; BP 1387504

41325-1576

NAME:	SIRODESMIN-B
PO:	SIRODESMIUM DIVERSUM
CT:	EPIDIKETOOLIGOTHIAPIPERAZINE, NEUTRAL, SIRODESMIN T.
FORMULA:	C20H26N2O8S4
EA:	(N, 5) (S, 23)
MW:	540
PC:	WH., POW., YELLOW
SOL-GOOD:	MEOH, ET2O
SOL-POOR:	W, HEX
TV:	COXSACKIE, RHINO
IS-EXT:	(CHL, , FILT.)
IS-CHR:	(SILG, ETOAC-TOL)
IS-CRY:	(PREC., ET2O, HEX)

REFERENCES:

JCS Perkin I, 180, 1977; DT 2346389; BP 1387504

41325-1577

NAME: SIRODESMIN-G
PO: SIRODESMIUM DIVERSUM
CT: EPIDIKETOOLIGOTHIAPIPERAZINE, NEUTRAL, SIRODESMIN T.
FORMULA: C20H26N2O8S2
EA: (N, 6) (S, 13)
MW: 486
PC: WH., POW., YELLOW
SOL-GOOD: MEOH, ET2O
SOL-POOR: W, HEX
TV: COXSACKIE, RHINO
IS-EXT: (CHL, , FILT.)
IS-CHR: (SILG, ETOAC-TOL)
IS-CRY: (PREC., ET2O, HEX)
REFERENCES:
JCS Perkin I, 180, 1977; DT 2346389; BP 1387504

41325-1578

NAME: SIRODESMIN-J
PO: SIRODESMIUM DIVERSUM
CT: EPIDIKETOOLIGOTHIAPIPERAZINE, NEUTRAL, SIRODESMIN T.
FORMULA: C18H22N2O7S2
EA: (N, 5) (S, 12)
MW: 486
PC: WH., POW., YELLOW
SOL-GOOD: MEOH, ET2O
SOL-POOR: W, HEX
TV: COXSACKIE, RHINO
IS-EXT: (CHL, , FILT.)
IS-CHR: (SILG, ETOAC-TOL)
IS-CRY: (PREC., ET2O, HEX)
REFERENCES:
JCS Perkin I, 180, 1977; DT 2346389; BP 1387504

41325-1579

NAME:	SIRODESMIN-C, SIRODESMIN-F
PO:	SIRODESMIUM DIVERSUM
CT:	EPIDIKETOOLIGOTHIAPIPERAZINE, NEUTRAL, SIRODESMIN T.
FORMULA:	C20H26N2O8S3
EA:	(N, 6) (S, 18)
MW:	518
PC:	WH., POW., YELLOW
SOL-POOR:	HEX
TV:	COXSACKIE, RHINO
IS-EXT:	(CHL, , FILT.)
IS-CHR:	(SILG, ETOAC-TOL)
IS-CRY:	(PREC., ET2O, HEX)

REFERENCES:

JCS Perkin I, 180, 1977; DT 2346389; BP 1387504

41325-1580

NAME:	SIRODESMIN-D, SIRODESMIN-F
PO:	SIRODESMIUM DIVERSUM
CT:	EPIDIKETOOLIGOTHIAPIPERAZINE, NEUTRAL, SIRODESMIN T.
FORMULA:	C20H26N2O8S4
EA:	(N,) (S,)
PC:	WH., POW., YELLOW
SOL-POOR:	HEX
TV:	COXSACKIE, RHINO
IS-EXT:	(CHL, , FILT.)
IS-CHR:	(SILG, ETOAC-TOL)
IS-CRY:	(PREC., ET2O, HEX)

REFERENCES:

JCS Perkin I, 180, 1977; DT 2346389; BP 1387504

41326-1581

NAME:	<u>ORYZACHLORIN</u>
PO:	ASP.ORYZAE
CT:	EPIDIKETOOLIGOTHIAPIPERAZINE
FORMULA:	C26H31N2O8S2CL
EA:	(N, 5) (S, 11) (CL, 7)
MW:	362
PC:	YELLOW, POW.
UV:	MEOH: (298, 117,)
SOL-GOOD:	MEOH, CHL
SOL-FAIR:	BENZ
SOL-POOR:	HEX
STAB:	(HEAT, +) (LIGHT, +)
TO:	(C.ALB., .3) (B.SP., 100)
TV:	EHRLICH, ANTITUMOR, NDV
IS-EXT:	(ACET, , MIC.)
IS-CHR:	(SILG, BENZ-MEOH)
IS-CRY:	(DRY,)

REFERENCES:

JA, 22, 322, 1969; JP 72/35

41326-4785

NAME:	<u>A-30641</u>
PO:	ASP.TAMARII
CT:	EPIDIKETOOLIGOTHIAPIPERAZINE
FORMULA:	C12H9N2O5S2CL
EA:	(N, 8) (S, 18) (CL, 10)
MW:	360
PC:	WH., POW.
OR:	(+73, MEOH)
UV:	ETOH: (208, , 36800) (300, , 6300)
UV:	ETOH-NAOH: (314, , 8100)
SOL-GOOD:	CHL, MEOH, ET2O
SOL-POOR:	HEX, W
TO:	(S.AUREUS, .78) (C.ALB., 1.50)
LD50:	(106, IP)
IS-FIL:	3
IS-EXT:	(MEOH, 3, MIC.) (CHL, 3, FILT.)
IS-ION:	(XAD-2, MEOH)
IS-CHR:	(SILG, BENZ-ETOAC)
IS-CRY:	(PREC., CHL, HEX)

REFERENCES:

JA, 29, 394, 1976; USP 3991052, 4001086 *Abst. AAC*, 15, 429, 1975

41326-5678

NAME:	TRICHORIN-A
PO:	TRICHODERMA SP.
CT:	DIKETODITHIOPIPERAZINE
FORMULA:	C20H20N2O8S2
EA:	(N, 6) (S, 13)
MW:	480
PC:	WH., CRYST.
OR:	(-190, DIOXAN)
UV:	ETOH: (205, , 38000) (240, , 11000) (280, , 3100)
TO:	(G.NEG., 50)
IS-EXT:	(ACET-ETOAC, , MTC.)
IS-CHR:	(SILG, BENZ)
IS-CRY:	(CRYST., AC-HEX)

REFERENCES:

JA, 30, 429, 1977

4133
Aspergillic Acid Type

These antibiotics may belong to the group of microbial pyrazines. They have cyclic hydroxamic acid structures existing in a tautomeric mixture of the α-pyrazinones (pyrazine hydroxamic acids) (I) and the corresponding 2-hydroxypyrazole-1-oxides (II).

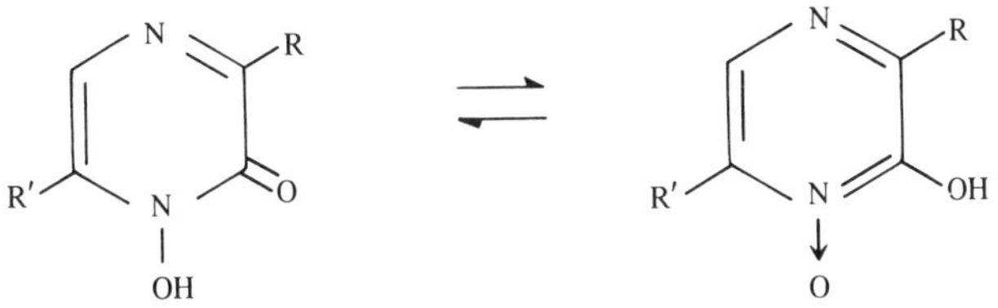

3R,6R′-1-hydroxy-2(1H)pyrazinone hydroxamic acid (I) hydroxamic acid form

3R,6R′-2-hydroxypyrazine-1-oxide (II) N-oxide form

Each compound differs only in the alkyl substituents present on the C-6 position. The C-3 substituent in all known antibiotics is isobutyl group (isoleucine).

These antibiotics show characteristic UV absorption maxima at 235 to 238 and 325 to 330 nm. According to the hydroxamic acid structure they give a deep red color with ferric chloride. They are active against Gram-positive and Gram-negative bacteria. All of these compounds are produced by *Aspergillus* species.

These compounds are considered to be condensation products of two amino acids (e.g., leucine, isoleucine, or valine) without the intermediate formation of 2,5-diketopiperazines. Aspergillic acid was among the first antibiotics isolated from a filtrate of fungal cultures (1940), but because of its toxicity it never found medical use.

Structures

41330

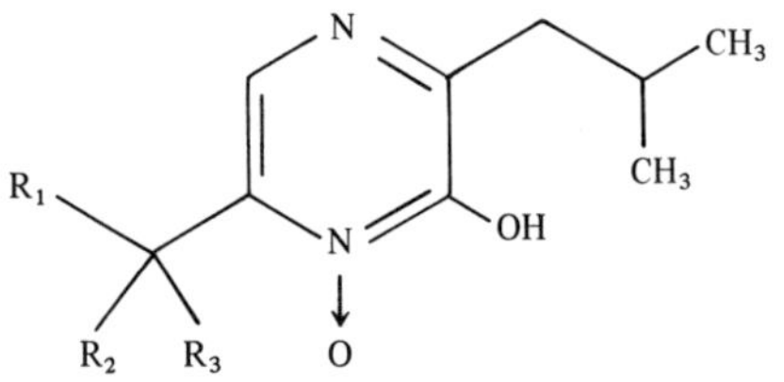

Antibiotic	R_1	R_2	R_3
Aspergillic acid	C_2H_5	CH_3	H
Hydroxyaspergillic acid	C_2H_5	CH_3	OH
Neoaspergillic acid	$CH(CH_3)_2$	H	H
Neohydroxyaspergillic acid	$CH(CH_3)_2$	H	OH
Muta-aspergillic acid	CH_3	CH_3	OH

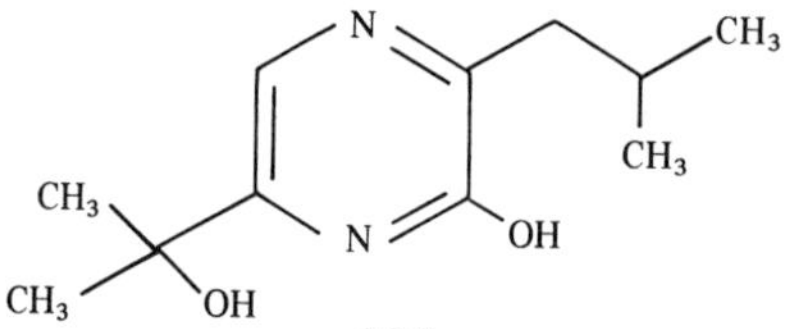

AO-3

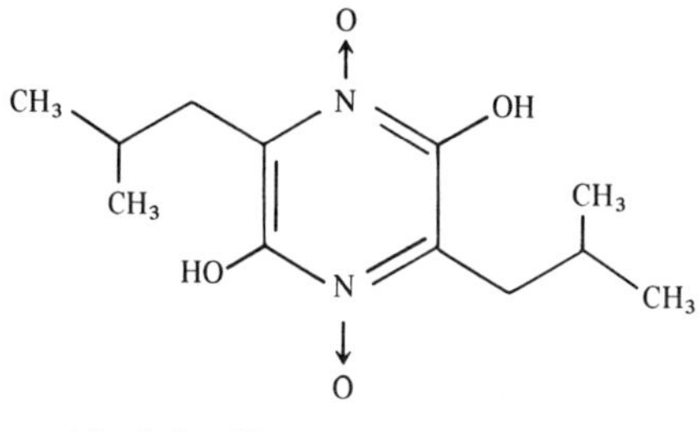

pulcherrimic acid
pulcherrimin is a Fe^{+++} salt of pulcherrimic acid

41330-1582

NAME:	ASPERGILLIC ACID
IDENTICAL:	GRANEGILLIN
PO:	ASP.FLAVUS, ASP.SOJAE
CT:	ASPERGILLIC ACID T., ACIDIC
FORMULA:	C12H20N2O2
EA:	(N, 13)
MW:	224, 220
EW:	223
PC:	YELLOW, CRYST.
OR:	(+13.3, ETOH) (+18.5, MEOH)
UV:	7.5: (235, , 15900) (332, , 10400)
UV:	ETOH: (238, , 10900) (326, , 8900)
UV:	HCL: (242, , 7300) (350|2, , 9700)
SOL-GOOD:	MEOH, ET2O, BASE
SOL-FAIR:	W
SOL-POOR:	HEX
QUAL:	(FECL3, +) (DNPH, +) (NINH., -) (BIURET, -) (FEHL., -)
STAB:	(ACID, +) (BASE, +) (HEAT, +)
TO:	(S.AUREUS, 10) (K.PNEUM., 8) (E.COLI, 30)
LD50:	(150, IP) (250, PEROS)
IS-FIL:	2
IS-ABS:	(CARBON, ET2O)
IS-CRY:	(CRYST., MEOH)

REFERENCES:

Sci., 92, 127, 1940; *Nature*, 148, 470, 1941; 162, 779, 1947; *Proc. Soc. Exp. B.M.*, 51, 273, 1942; *J. Bact.*, 45, 433, 1943; 46, 109, 1943; 52, 614, 1946; 54, 375, 543, 1947; *J. Biol. Chem.*, 152, 419, 1944; 155, 359, 1944; 171, 321, 341, 1947; *JCS Suppl.*, 126, 131, 1969; *JCS*, 2679, 1951; 4870, 1952; *Bull. Ch. Soc. Jap.*, 39, 632, 1966; *JOC*, 31, 4143, 1966; *Can. J. Bioch.*, 48, 1165, 1970; 50, 543, 1972; 51, 1311, 1973; *Cancer Res.*, 13, 684, 1953; USP 2500921

41330-1583

NAME:	HYDROXYASPERGILLIC ACID
PO:	ASP.FLAVUS, ASP.ORYZAE, ASP.SOJAE
CT:	ASPERGILLIC ACID T., ACIDIC
FORMULA:	C12H20N2O3
EA:	(N, 12)
MW:	276
EW:	240
PC:	YELLOW, CRYST.
OR:	(+36, ETOH)
UV:	ETOH: (235, , 8250) (328, , 8800)
UV:	H3PO4: (245, 440,) (363, 310,)
UV:	MEOH: (232, , 7500) (330, , 7900)
SOL-GOOD:	MEOH, BENZ, BASE
SOL-FAIR:	ET2O
SOL-POOR:	W, HEX
QUAL:	(FECL3, +) (NINH., +) (FEHL., -) (PAULY, -)
TO:	(S.AUREUS, 100) (E.COLI, 250) (K.PNEUM., 150) (MYCOB.TUB., 8)
LD50:	(101, IV) (95|5, IP)
IS-FIL:	2.5
IS-EXT:	(ET2O, 2.5, W)
IS-ABS:	(CARBON, ACET-W)
IS-CRY:	(CRYST., ETOH-W)

REFERENCES:

J. Biol. Chem., 232, 785, 1962; 237, 1977, 1963; *Bull. Agr. Chem. Soc. Jap.*, 23, 418, 1959; *JACS*, 72, 4362, 1950; *JOC*, 21, 1077, 1956

41330-1584

NAME:	NEOASPERGILLIC ACID
PO:	ASP.SCLEROTIUM, ASP.FLAVUS, ASP.OCHRACEUS
CT:	ASPERGILLIC ACID T., ACIDIC
FORMULA:	C12H20N2O2
EA:	(N, 13)
MW:	229
PC:	WH., CRYST.
OR:	(0,)
UV:	ETOH: (236, , 9150) (328, , 10500)
SOL-GOOD:	MEOH, ET2O, BASE
SOL-POOR:	W, HEX
QUAL:	(FECL3, +)
TO:	(S.AUREUS, 10) (E.COLI, 5) (B.SUBT., 10) (C.ALB., 10)
IS-EXT:	(CHL, 3, FILT.) (NA2CO3, , CHL) (CHL, 3, NA2CO3)
IS-CRY:	(CRYST., MEOH-W)

REFERENCES:

Chem. Ph. Bull., 16, 1160, 1968; *JCS*, 1507, 1964; *Can. J. Micr.*, 10, 90, 1964; *J. Biol. Chem.*, 240, 1692, 1965; *JOC*, 31, 4143, 1966; *Chem. Ph. Bull.*, 26, 1320, 1978

41330-1585

NAME: MUTAASPERGILLIC ACID
PO: ASP.ORYZAE
CT: ASPERGILLIC ACID T., ACIDIC
FORMULA: C11H18N2O3
EA: (N, 12)
MW: 246
EW: 230
PC: YELLOW, CRYST.
OR: (0, MEOH)
UV: ETOH: (233, , 6100) (334, , 7200)
UV: MEOH: (232, , 12500) (332, , 7300)
UV: W: (242, , 5100) (335, , 8600)
SOL-GOOD: MEOH, BENZ
SOL-FAIR: ET2O
SOL-POOR: W, HEX
QUAL: (FECL3, +) (NINH., +) (FEHL., -)
TO: (LACTOBACILLUS SP., 5)
LD50: (100, IV)
IS-EXT: (ET2O, 3.5, FILT.)
IS-CRY: (CRYST., ETOH-W)
REFERENCES:
Bull. Agr. Chem. Soc. Jap., 25, 74, 1968; 24, 629, 1967; *TL*, 845, 1967; *CA*, 55, 2800, 2793

41330-1586

NAME: NEOHYDROXYASPERGILLIC ACID
PO: ASP.SCLEROTIUM, ASP.FLAVUS
CT: ASPERGILLIC ACID T., ACIDIC
FORMULA: C12H20N2O3
EA: (N, 12)
MW: 253
PC: YELLOW, WH., CRYST.
OR: (-58, ETOH)
UV: ETOH: (236, , 6450) (328, , 8350)
UV: HCL: (246, , 8000) (360, , 7550)
SOL-GOOD: MEOH, ET2O, BASE
SOL-POOR: W, HEX
QUAL: (FECL3, +)
TO: (S.AUREUS, 250) (B.SUBT., 125) (E.COLI, 125) (K.PNEUM., 125) (PHYT.FUNGI, 3)
IS-FIL: ORIG.
IS-EXT: (CHL, 3, FILT.) (NH4OH, , CHL)
IS-CRY: (PREC., W, PH3)
REFERENCES:
ABB, 74, 150, 1958; *J. Biol. Chem.*, 240, 1692, 1965; *JCS*, 1507, 1964; *Ant. & Chem.*, 4, 380, 1954

41330-1587

NAME: AO-3
PO: ASP.OCHRACEUS
CT: ASPERGILLIC ACID T., ACIDIC
FORMULA: C12H20N2O2
EA: (N, 13)
MW: 224
UV: ETOH: (230, , 5016) (326.5, , 5530)
SOL-GOOD: MEOH, CHL
SOL-POOR: W, HEX
IS-EXT: (ETOAC, , MIC.)
IS-CHR: (SILG, CHL)
REFERENCES:
Chem. Ph. Bull., 20, 2274, 1972

41330-1588

NAME: PULCHERRIMINIC ACID
PO: CANDIDA PULCHERRIMA
CT: ASPERGILLIC ACID T., ACIDIC
FORMULA: C12H20N2O4
PC: YELLOW, POW.
UV: NAOH: (243, ,) (282, ,) (410, ,)
SOL-POOR: W
QUAL: (FECL3, +)
TO: (B.CEREUS,)
REFERENCES:
Can. J. Chem., 41, 165, 1963; *Chem. Ph. Bull.*, 12, 125, 1964; *J. Bact.*, 71, 290, 1956; 111, 86, 1972; *JCS*, 4133, 1956

41330-1589

NAME: PULCHERRIMIN, PULCHERRIMINIC ACID-FE-SALT
PO: B.SUBTILIS, B.CEREUS
CT: ASPERGILLIC ACID T., ACIDIC
FORMULA: C36H60N6O12FE
EA: (N, 9) (FE, 12)
PC: RED, POW.
UV: (398, ,) (495, ,)
TO: (MYCOB.SP.,) (FUSARIUM SP.,) (P.SP.,)
REFERENCES:
Can. J. Chem., 41, 165, 1963; *JCS*, 4133, 1956; *Proc. Nat. Acad. Sci.*, 39, 583, 1953

42
HOMOPEPTIDE ANTIBIOTICS

421
Oligopeptides

Introduction

This group includes antibiotics containing two to four amino acids or amino acid like compounds. Included are the aminopyrrollecarboxylic acid containing netropsin-distamycin-type antibiotics (4211) (pyrrole-amidino group), the simple linear oligopeptide antibiotics (4212), and the group of some complicated cyclic oligopeptide-like antibiotics (4213).

These antibiotics, except several linear oligopeptides, are obtained from *Streptomyces* species. They are mainly antimetabolites of natural amino acids. Distamycin has a limited application in antiviral therapy, and negamycin and bicyclomycin are on clinical trials.

4211
Pyrrole-Amidino Antibiotics

This group of antibiotic compounds consists of about 20 *Streptomyces* metabolites. The common feature of this type is the presence of a 2-aminoethylamidine fragment **(1)** linked by a peptide bond to a chromophore system **(2)** or other five-membered ring constituent. The chromophore part of these antibiotics consists of one to three molecules of 4-amino-1-methyl-pyrrole-2-carboxylic acid units linked by peptide bonds, bearing on the N-terminus various substituents such as formyl, guanidinoacetyl **(3)**, or 2-carboxy-5-imino-pyrrolidinyl **(4)** residues.

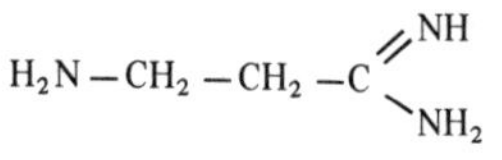

(1)

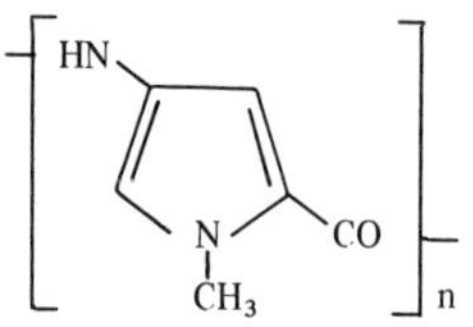

(2)

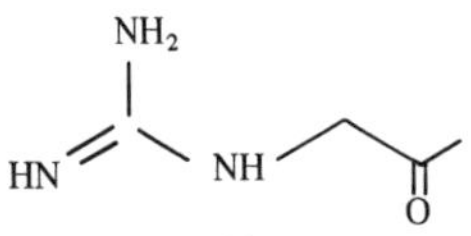

(3)

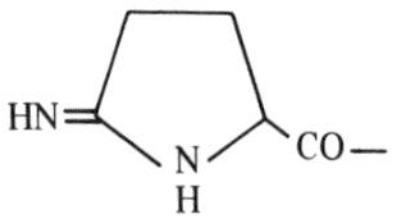

(4)

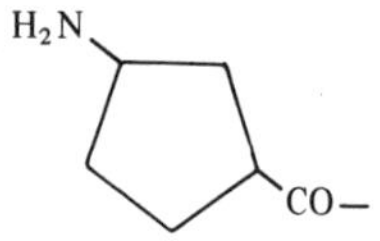

(5)

These antibiotics are subdivided into three subtypes according to their physical and the above-mentioned chemical properties. The compounds in the netropsin subtype (42111) contain two or three amino-pyrrolecarboxylic acid units, while the kikumycin type (42113) of compounds contain only a single heterocyclic unit, whereas the noformicin (42112) subtype does not contain this element. In this subtype **(4)** or 3-amino-cyclopentane-carboxaminyl **(5)** residue are only attached to the 2-amino-ethylamidine fragment, forming chromophore-free compounds.

Antibiotics in this type all are strong basic substances with good or moderate solubility in water and methanol, but they are insoluble in other organic solvents. They, except the noformicin subtype, have strongly characteristic UV absorption spectra with two maxima at 235 to 238 and 295 to 300 nm (netropsin type) as well as at 238 to 240 and 322 to 325 nm (kikumycin type), exhibiting bactochromic shift in basic solution to 305, and 365 to 370 nm, respectively.

They show a wide range of antimicrobial spectra and possess activity against Gram-positive, Gram-negative, and mycobacteria, as well as fungi, yeasts, and protozoa. Some of them exhibit anthelminthic and antitumor activity. Netropsin has larvicide and molluscocide properties.

The most characteristic microbiological property of these compounds is their antiviral activity against various DNA viruses (vaccinia-, herpes-, influenza, and adenoviruses). Distamycin A, the most studied member, inhibits phage T_2 multiplication and the transfer of drug resistance factor in *E. coli,* and induces enzyme synthesis (e.g., β-galactosidase) in this bacteria. In vivo antiviral activity studies show the clinical usefulness of distamycin A for the topical treatment of ocular and cutaneous viral infections sustained by herpes simplex, herpes zooster, vaccinia, and chicken pox viruses.

The mechanism of action of these compounds is not well known. Their activity may be a result of the interaction with the membrane. Distamycin A does not affect transcription and translation of viral DNA.

Structures

42111

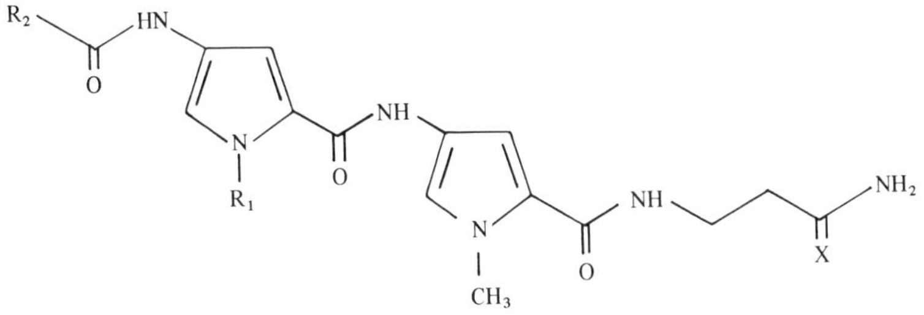

Antibiotic	X	R_1	R_2
Netropsin	=NH	CH_3	$-CH_2-NH-C(=NH)-NH_2$
Congocidin	=O	CH_3	$-CH_2-NH-C(=NH)-NH_2$
Distamycin	=NH	CH_3	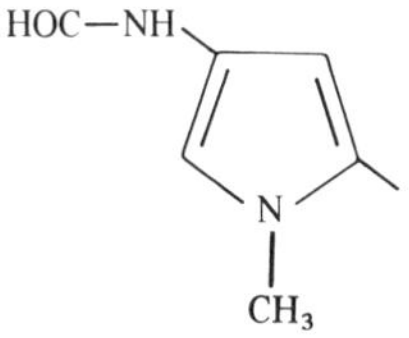
Anthelvencin	=NH	H	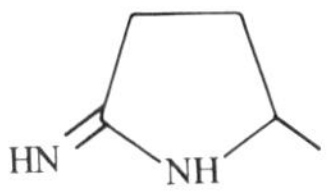

42112

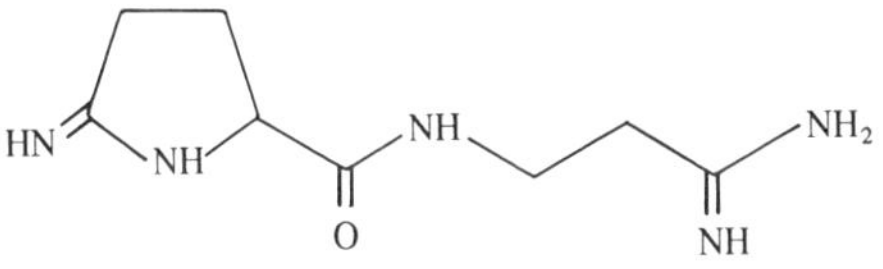

noformicin

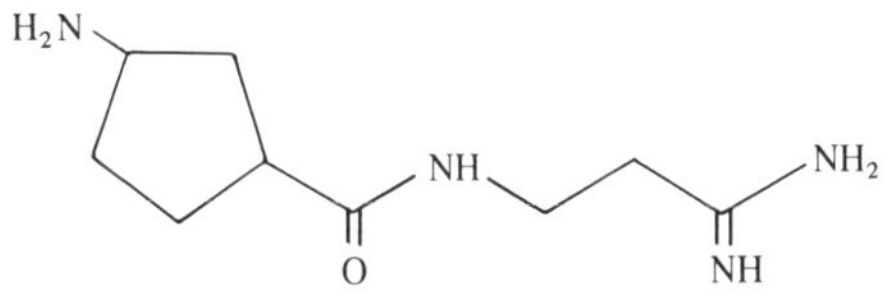

myxoviromycin (amidinomycin)

42113

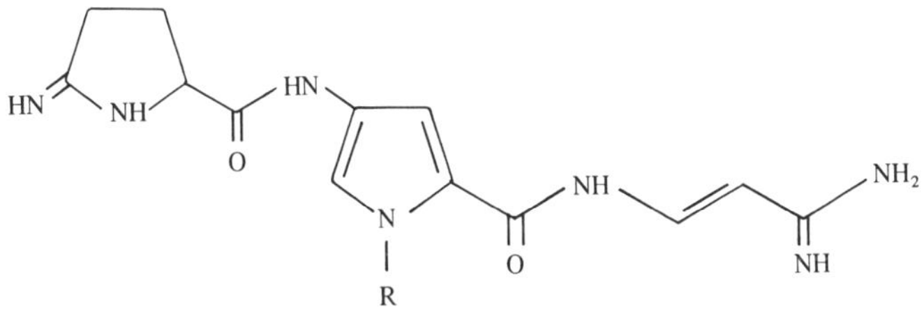

kikumycin A R = H; kikumycin B R = CH_3

42111-1590

NAME:	NETROPSIN, F-6
IDENTICAL:	SINANOMYCIN, IA-887, T-1384, 2814-A, K-117, 12782, CH-777-A
PO:	S.NETROPSIS, S.RETICULI, S.CHROMOGENES, S.SP.
CT:	OLIGOPEPTIDE, NETROPSIN T., BASIC
FORMULA:	C18H26N10O3
EA:	(N, 29)
MW:	360, 430
PC:	WH., CRYST.
OR:	(0, W)
UV:	HCL: (234, 420,) (295, 440,)
UV:	NAOH: (303.5, 520,)
UV:	W: (236, 429,) (296, 436,)
SOL-GOOD:	MEOH, ETOH
SOL-FAIR:	W, BUOH
SOL-POOR:	ACET, HEX
QUAL:	(SAKA., +) (EHRL., +) (NINH., -) (FECL3, -) (DNPH, -) (BIURET, -) (FEHL., -)
STAB:	(ACID, +) (HEAT, +) (BASE, -)
TO:	(B.SUBT., 3) (S.AUREUS, 3) (E.COLI, 5) (SHYG., 10) (K.PNEUM., 5) (P.VULG., 40) (MYCOB.SP., 5) (C.ALB., 50) (S.CEREV., 100)
LD50:	(17, IV) (70, SC)
TV:	ANTIVIRAL, ANTIPHAGE
IS-FIL:	2
IS-ION:	(IRC-50-NA, HCL)
IS-CRY:	(CRYST., W)
UTILITY:	VETERINARY DRUG

REFERENCES:

JACS, 73, 341, 1951; 78, 2157, 1956; 79, 66, 1265, 1957; *Chem. & Ind.*, 365, 1957; *Proc. Soc. Exp. B.M.*, 83, 1, 1953; *JA*, 8, 19, 1955; 9, 102, 1956; 17, 220, 1964; *Naturwiss.*, 46, 87, 1959; *J. Trop. Med. Hyg.*, 2, 1045, 1959; *Ant. An.*, 1045, 1957—58; *Cancer Res.*, 3, (Suppl.), 18, 1957; USP 2586762

42111-1591

NAME:	<u>CONGOCIDIN</u>
PO:	S.AMBOFACIENS
CT:	OLIGOPEPTIDE, NETROPSIN T., BASIC
FORMULA:	C18H26N9O4
EA:	(N, 26)
MW:	432
PC:	WH., CRYST.
OR:	(0, W)
UV:	13: (305, ,)
UV:	NAOH: (305, ,)
UV:	W: (235, , 23440) (296, , 24550)
SOL-GOOD:	MEOH, ETOH, W
SOL-FAIR:	BUOH
SOL-POOR:	ACET, HEX
QUAL:	(SAKA., +) (EHRL., +) (FECL3, -) (DNPH, -)
TO:	(G.POS., 5) (G.NEG., 10)
LD50:	(75, IV) (200, SC) (5000, PEROS)

REFERENCES:

CR Soc. Biol., 234, 1498, 1954; 243, 961, 1956; *CR Soc. Biol.*, 257, 1115, 1960; *Bull. Soc. Chim. Fr.*, 4348, 1967; *AAC*, 1, 483, 1972

42111-1592

NAME:	<u>VIOLACETIN</u>
PO:	S.PURPEOCHROMOGENES
CT:	OLIGOPEPTIDE, NETROPSIN T., BASIC
FORMULA:	C18H28N10O16.2HCL
EA:	(C, 38) (H, 7) (N, 25)
PC:	WH., YELLOW, CRYST.
OR:	(+4.32, MEOH)
UV:	MEOH: (293, ,)
UV:	W: (235, 498,) (296, 518,)
SOL-GOOD:	W, MEOH, ETOH
SOL-FAIR:	BUOH
SOL-POOR:	ACET, HEX
QUAL:	(NINH., +) (PAULY, +) (SAKA., -) (FEHL., -) (FECL3, -)
STAB:	(ACID, +) (HEAT, +) (BASE, -)
TO:	(S.AUREUS, .5) (B.SUBT., .3) (E.COLI, 1) (K.PNEUM., 5) (P.VULG., 20) (C.ALB., 25)
LD50:	(37, IV) (45, IP) (75, SC) (375, PEROS)
TV:	ANTIVIRAL
IS-FIL:	2
IS-ION:	(IRC-50, HCL)
IS-ABS:	(DIATOM., ACET-HCL)
IS-CHR:	(AL, ETOH-MEOH)

REFERENCES:

JA, 8, 33, 1955; 9, 226, 1956; *Jap. J. Ant.*, 8, 118, 1955; 9, 238, 1956; *Fukui Kenkyu Ho*, 7, 123, 1954; 8, 99, 1955; *CA*, 53, 18169

42111-1593

NAME: EM-98
PO: S.VENEZUELAE
CT: OLIGOPEPTIDE, NETROPSIN T., BASIC
FORMULA: C18H30N9O5
EA: (N, 28)
MW: 452
EW: 449
PC: WH., CRYST.
UV: MEOH: (240, 375,) (300, 390,)
SOL-GOOD: MEOH, W
SOL-POOR: ACET, HEX
QUAL: (NINH., -) (SAKA., -) (FECL3, -)
TO: (S.AUREUS, 75) (E.COLI, 100) (PS.AER., 100)
LD50: (300, IP)
IS-EXT: (MEOH, , MIC.) (BUOH, 9.1, FILT.)
IS-CHR: (DEAE-CEL, MEOH) (SILG, MEOH)
IS-CRY: (PREC., BUOH, ACET) (CRYST., MEOH-ACET)
REFERENCES:
DT 2316893; USP 3853992

42111-1594

NAME: 583
PO: S.ORIENTALIS
CT: OLIGOPEPTIDE, NETROPSIN T., BASIC
FORMULA: C19H27N9O8
EA: (N, 26)
MW: 430
PC: WH., POW.
OR: (+8.4, W)
UV: MEOH: (235, 335,) (298, 350,)
UV: NAOH: (304, 345,)
SOL-GOOD: MEOH, W
SOL-FAIR: ETOH, BUOH
SOL-POOR: ACET, HEX
QUAL: (SAKA., +) (EHRL., +) (NINH., -) (BIURET, -) (FEHL., -)
STAB: (HEAT, +) (BASE, -) (ACID, +)
TO: (S.AUREUS, 1.56) (S.LUTEA, .39) (B.SUBT., 3.12) (SHYG., .78) (E.COLI, 6) (P.VULG., 25) (C.ALB., 50)
LD50: (42, IV) (144, SC)
IS-FIL: 2
IS-ION: (IRC-50-NA, H2SO4)
IS-ABS: (CARBON, MEOH-W)
IS-CHR: (AL, MEOH-W)
IS-CRY: (PREC., W, MEOH+H2SO4)
REFERENCES:
JP 70/17596

42111-1595

NAME:	ANTHELVENCIN-A
PO:	S.VENEZUELAE
CT:	OLIGOPEPTIDE, NETROPSIN T., BASIC
FORMULA:	C19H28N9O3
EA:	(N, 30)
PC:	WH., POW.
OR:	(+9.7, W)
UV:	W: (235, 437,) (300, 451,)
SOL-GOOD:	MEOH, ACID
SOL-FAIR:	W
SOL-POOR:	ACET, HEX
QUAL:	(EHRL., +) (SAKA., -) (NINH., -) (FECL3, -)
TO:	(S.AUREUS, 25) (B.SUBT., 6) (S.LUTEA, 1.56) (E.COLI, 12) (P.VULG., 12) (K.PNEUM., 25) (C.ALB., 50) (S.CEREV., 3.13)
LD50:	(177, IP)
TV:	ANTIVIRAL
IS-FIL:	3.5
IS-EXT:	(BUOH, 8.5, W)
IS-ION:	(IRC-50-H, ACET-HCL)

REFERENCES:

AAC 1965, 789; USP 3467750; *CA*, 65, 6261

42111-1596

NAME:	ANTHELVENCIN-B
PO:	S.VENEZUELAE
CT:	OLIGOPEPTIDE, NETROPSIN T., BASIC
FORMULA:	C19H27N9O3
EA:	(N, 28)
PC:	WH., POW.
UV:	W: (235, ,) (300, ,)
SOL-GOOD:	W, MEOH
SOL-FAIR:	BUOH
SOL-POOR:	ACET, HEX
TO:	(S.AUREUS, 25) (B.SUBT., 12) (S.LUTEA, 1.5) (S.CEREV., 6) (C.ALB., 100) (E.COLI, 12) (P.VULG., 25) (K.PNEUM., 250)
TV:	ANTIVIRAL

REFERENCES:

AAC 1965, 789; USP 3467750; *CA*, 65, 6261

42111-1597

NAME:	12782
PO:	ACT.NETROPSIS, S.NETROPSIS
CT:	OLIGOPEPTIDE, NETROPSIN T., BASIC
PC:	WH., POW.
UV:	W: (235, 279,) (295, 787,)
SOL-GOOD:	MEOH, W
SOL-POOR:	ACET, HEX
STAB:	(ACID, +) (HEAT, +)
TO:	(B.SUBT., 6.5) (S.AUREUS, 5) (S.LUTEA, 1.4) (E.COLI, 1.4) (P.VULG., 12) (K.PNEUM., 25) (PS.AER., 100) (C.ALB., 500)
LD50:	(168, SC)

REFERENCES:

Antib., 234, 1966

42111-1598

NAME:	DISTAMYCIN-A, DISTAMYCIN
TRADE NAMES:	STALLIMYCIN
PO:	S.DISTALLICUS
CT:	OLIGOPEPTIDE, NETROPSIN T., BASIC
FORMULA:	C22H27N9O4
EA:	(N, 25)
MW:	481
PC:	YELLOW, WH., CRYST.
OR:	(0, W)
UV:	ETOH: (237, , 30000) (303, , 37000)
UV:	HCL: (235, 470,) (302, 565,)
UV:	W: (236.5, 591,) (305, 723,)
SOL-GOOD:	W, MEOH
SOL-POOR:	BUOH, HEX
QUAL:	(EHRL., +) (SAKA., -) (NINH., -) (FECL3, -)
TO:	(S.AUREUS, 50) (E.COLI, 100) (PS.AER., 100) (MYCOB.TUB., 5) (FUNGI, 10)
LD50:	(75, IV) (500, IP)
TV:	ANTIVIRAL, POLIO, EHRLICH, S-180, WALKER-256, INFL, NDV, TMV, ANTIPHAGE
IS-EXT:	(MEOH, , MIC.)
IS-CHR:	(AL, ETOH)
IS-CRY:	(CRYST., BUOH)
UTILITY:	ANTIVIRAL DRUG

REFERENCES:

Nature, 203, 1064; 1964; *Canc. Chemoth. Rep.*, 18, 15, 1962; *Chemother.*, 9, 65, 80, 144, 1965; *Gazz.*, 97, 1097, 1110, 1967; *Giorn. Micr.*, 11, 87, 1963; *Giorn. Hal. Chemother.*, 6—9, 271, 1962; *AAC 1965*, 593, 599; *J. Gen. Micr.*, 43, 369, 1966

AAC, 1, 483, 1972; *FEBS Lett.*, 19, 154, 327, 1972; 21, 154, 1972; USP 3190801

42111-1599

NAME:	<u>S-685</u>
PO:	S.SP.
CT:	OLIGOPEPTIDE, NETROPSIN T., BASIC
FORMULA:	C10H13N5O4
EA:	(N, 22)
MW:	285
PC:	WH., POW.
OR:	(-37, W)
UV:	HCL: (232, 510,) (295, 560,)
UV:	MEOH: (290, ,)
UV:	NAOH: (239, ,) (305, ,)
SOL-GOOD:	W
SOL-POOR:	BUOH, HEX
QUAL:	(NINH., -) (DNPH, -) (SAKA., -) (PAULY, -) (EHRL., -)
STAB:	(HEAT, +) (BASE, +)
TO:	(XANTHOMONAS ORYZAE, 1)
TV:	ANTIVIRAL
IS-ION:	(DX-50-H, NH4OH)
IS-ABS:	(CARBON, ACET-HCL)
IS-CHR:	(SEPHADEX G-25, W)
IS-CRY:	(DRY,)

REFERENCES:

JP 70/5435; *CA*, 73, 2657

42112-1600

NAME:	NOFORMICIN, MK-61
PO:	NOC.FORMICA
CT:	OLIGOPEPTIDE, NOFORMICIN T., BASIC
FORMULA:	C8H15N5O.2HCL
EA:	(N, 30)
EW:	268
PC:	WH., CRYST.
OR:	(+.7, W) (-16, MEOH) (+8.8, MEOH)
UV:	W: (200, ,)
SOL-GOOD:	MEOH, W
SOL-POOR:	ACET, HEX
QUAL:	(FEHL., -) (FECL3, -)
STAB:	(ACID, +) (BASE, -)
TO:	(CORYNEBACT.SP.,) (K.PNEUM.,)
LD50:	(5, IV) (10, SC)
TV:	INFL, NDV, ANTIVIRAL, POLIO
IS-ABS:	(CARBON, MEOH-HCL)
IS-CRY:	(CRYST., MEOH)

REFERENCES:

Ant. An., 609, 615, 1953—54; 1045, 1957—58; *J. Med. Chem.*, 16, 857, 1973; *An. Phytop. Soc. Jap.*, 21, 1, 1956; *Phytopath.*, 44, 328, 1954; 45, 281, 1955

42112-1601

NAME:	MYXOVIROMYCIN, M-141
IDENTICAL:	AMIDINOMYCIN
PO:	S.SP., S.KASUGAENSIS, S.FLAVOCHROMOGENES
CT:	OLIGOPEPTIDE, NOFORMICIN T., BASIC
FORMULA:	C9H18N4O.H2SO4
EA:	(N, 27)
MW:	198
EW:	200
PC:	WH., CRYST.
OR:	(-3.9, W)
UV:	HCL: (205, 225,)
UV:	NAOH: (219, 79,)
UV:	W: (212, 59,)
SOL-GOOD:	W, MEOH, ETOH
SOL-POOR:	BUOH, HEX
QUAL:	(NINH., +) (BIURET, +) (SAKA., -) (FEHL., -) (FECL3, -)
STAB:	(ACID, +) (BASE, -)
TO:	(B.SUBT., 5) (S.LUTEA, 5) (S.AUREUS, 100)
LD50:	(18, IV) (200, IP)
TV:	ANTIVIRAL
IS-FIL:	ORIG.
IS-ION:	(IRC-50-NA, HCL)
IS-CHR:	(AL, ACET-MEOH)
IS-CRY:	(DRY,)

REFERENCES:

JA, 13, 362, 1960; 14, 103, 163, 165, 251, 1961; *Jap. J. Micr.*, 1, 85, 90, 1957; 2, 54, 63, 117, 1958; *An. Rep. Shionogi*, 7, 715, 1957; *Tohoku J. Exp. Med.*, 70, 95, 102, 1967; *Chem. Ph. Bull.*, 9, 641, 1961; 16, 232, 1968; JP 61/4598; *CA*, 52, 13859, 20389; 55, 25157

42113-1602

NAME:	KIKUMYCIN-A, R-719
PO:	S.PHAEOCHROMOGENES
CT:	OLIGOPEPTIDE, KIKUMYCIN T., BASIC
FORMULA:	C13H17N7O2
EA:	(N, 18)
MW:	303
PC:	WH., CRYST.
OR:	(+13.3, HCL)
UV:	HCL: (235, 310,) (323, 647,)
UV:	NAOH: (356, 805,)
UV:	W: (235, 360,) (323, 720,)
SOL-GOOD:	ACID, BASE
SOL-FAIR:	W, MEOH, DMFA, MEOH
SOL-POOR:	BUOH, HEX
QUAL:	(EHRL., +) (NINH., -) (BIURET, -) (SAKA., -) (FEHL., -)
STAB:	(ACID, +) (HEAT, +) (BASE, -)
TO:	(B.SUBT., 6) (S.AUREUS, 12) (S.LUTEA, 3) (E.COLI, 6) (SHYG., 12) (PS.AER., 25) (P.VULG., 12)
LD50:	(150, IP)
TV:	ANTIVIRAL, HELA
IS-FIL:	2
IS-ION:	(IRC-50-H, ACET-HCL)

REFERENCES:

JA, 18, 243, 1965; *TL*, 1873, 1972; *Org. Mass. Spectrom.*, 9, 635, 1974; JP 67/3077; *CA*, 66, 114593

42113-1603

NAME:	KIKUMYCIN-B
PO:	S.PHAEOCHROMOGENES
CT:	OLIGOPEPTIDE, KIKUMYCIN T., BASIC
FORMULA:	C14H19N7O2
EA:	(N, 27)
MW:	440
PC:	WH., YELLOW, CRYST.
OR:	(+20, W) (+14, HCL)
UV:	HCL: (242, , 10500) (320, , 19500)
UV:	NAOH: (357, 560,)
UV:	W: (239, 430,) (328, 790,)
SOL-GOOD:	W
SOL-FAIR:	MEOH
SOL-POOR:	BUOH, HEX
QUAL:	(EHRL., +) (FEHL., -) (BIURET, -) (SAKA., -) (NINH., -)
STAB:	(ACID, +) (BASE, -) (HEAT, +)
TO:	(B.SUBT., 3) (S.AUREUS, 25) (E.COLI, 6) (PS.AER., 100) (P.VULG., 12.5) (K.PNEUM., 100)
LD50:	(200, IP)
TV:	ANTIVIRAL, HELA
IS-FIL:	2
IS-ION:	(IRC-50-NA, ACET-HCL)

REFERENCES:

JA, 18, 243, 1965; *TL*, 1873, 1972; *Org. Mass. Spectrom.*, 9, 635, 1974; JP 67/3077; *CA*, 66, 114593

42113-1604

NAME:	A-4993-A
PO:	S.KENTUCKENSIS
CT:	OLIGOPEPTIDE, KIKUMYCIN T., BASIC
FORMULA:	C28H44N12O8
EA:	(N, 26)
EW:	623
PC:	WH., CRYST.
UV:	HCL: (240, ,) (325, ,)
UV:	NAOH: (233, ,) (367, ,)
UV:	W: (232, 250,) (324, 342,)
SOL-GOOD:	W
SOL-POOR:	BUOH, HEX
TO:	(S.AUREUS, 100) (B.SUBT., 25) (E.COLI, 50) (P.VULG., 25) (SHYG., 12) (PHYT.BACT., 12) (C.ALB., 100) (PHYT.FUNGI, 6)
IS-FIL:	4.5
IS-ION:	(IRC-50, H2SO4)
IS-CHR:	(SEPHADEX G-25, W) (CEL, PROH-PYR-ACOH-W)

REFERENCES:

USP 3629405

42113-1605

NAME: A-4993-B
PO: S.KENTUCKENSIS
CT: OLIGOPEPTIDE, KIKUMYCIN T., BASIC
EA: (C, 42) (H, 7) (N, 28)
PC: WH., CRYST.
UV: HCL: (232, ,) (326, ,)
UV: NAOH: (366, ,)
UV: W: (233, 332,) (321, 480,)
SOL-GOOD: W
SOL-POOR: BUOH, HEX
TO: (S.AUREUS, 100) (B.SUBT., 25) (P.VULG., 25) (E.COLI, 50) (PHYT.BACT., 12) (PHYT.FUNGI, 6) (C.ALB., 50)
REFERENCES:
USP 3629405

42113-1606

NAME: AZOMULTIN
PO: S.NOBORITOENSIS
CT: OLIGOPEPTIDE, KIKUMYCIN T., BASIC
FORMULA: C13H22N6O4.H2SO4
EA: (N, 26)
MW: 440
PC: YELLOW, WH., POW.
OR: (+12.5, W)
UV: W: (240, 360,) (325, 620,)
SOL-GOOD: W, MEOH, ETOH
SOL-POOR: BUOH, HEX
QUAL: (SAKA., +) (NINH., -) (FEHL., -) (FECL3, -)
TO: (B.SUBT., 20) (S.AUREUS, 20) (E.COLI, 20) (K.PNEUM., 100) (SHYG., 50) (C.ALB., 200)
LD50: (50, IV)
IS-FIL: 2
IS-ION: (IRC-50-NA, HCL)
IS-CHR: (AL,) (CARBON,)
IS-CRY: (PREC., MEOH, ETOAC)
REFERENCES:
JP 70/6073; *CA*, 73, 2667

42113-3895

NAME: LL-BL-869-B"
PO: S.SP.
CT: OLIGOPEPTIDE, KIKUMYCIN T., BASIC
EA: (N, 21)
PC: YELLOW, WH., POW.
OR: (+,)
UV: MEOH: (236, ,) (322, ,)
SOL-GOOD: W, MEOH
SOL-POOR: ETOAC, HEX
TO: (S.AUREUS, 2) (E.COLI, 5) (SHYG., 20) (PS.AER., 50)
REFERENCES:
USP 3856939

42113-5681

NAME: LIA-0832-D
PO: ACT.CHROMOGENES-GRAECUS, S.CHROMOGENES-GRAECUS
CT: NETROPSIN T., OLIGOPEPTIDE, BASIC
EA: (N,)
PC: WH.
UV: MEOH: (235, ,) (323, ,)
UV: MEOH-HCL: (234, ,) (325, ,)
UV: MEOH-NAOH: (241, ,) (266, ,)
TO: (G.POS.,) (G.NEG.,)
IS-EXT: (MEOH, , MIC.)
REFERENCES:
Antib., 832, 1977

42110-1607

NAME:	GRISEOCOCCIN
PO:	S.GRISEUS
CT:	OLIGOPEPTIDE, BASIC, NETROPSIN L.
PC:	YELLOW, CRYST.
UV:	MEOH: (239, 172,) (291, 162,)
SOL-GOOD:	ACET, CHL, BENZ, THF
SOL-FAIR:	MEOH, ETOH
SOL-POOR:	W, HEX
STAB:	(ACID, -)
TO:	(S.AUREUS, .78) (S.LUTEA, 1) (B.SUBT., 1)
IS-EXT:	(BUOH, 8, FILT.)
IS-CRY:	(CRYST., BENZ-W) (PREC., BUOH, HEX)

REFERENCES:

JA, 15, 141, 1962

42110-1608

NAME:	GRISEOCOCCIN-D
PO:	S.GRISEUS
CT:	OLIGOPEPTIDE, BASIC, NETROPSIN L.
FORMULA:	C21H36N4O12
EA:	(N, 11)
MW:	532
PC:	YELLOW, CRYST.
OR:	(+227, ACET)
UV:	MEOH: (243, 213,) (290, 218,)
SOL-GOOD:	ACET, THF, CHL, DMFA, BENZ
SOL-FAIR:	MEOH, ETOH
SOL-POOR:	W, HEX
QUAL:	(FECL3, +) (NINH., -) (BIURET, -) (SAKA., -)
TO:	(S.AUREUS, 50) (S.LUTEA, 50) (B.SUBT., 50)

REFERENCES:

JA, 15, 141, 1962

4212
Linear Oligopeptide Antibiotics

These oligopeptide compounds cover about 30 antibiotics (mainly antimetabolites) built up from two, three, or four specific or common amino acids or sometimes other simple amino acid-like constituents.

These specific, unusual amino acids and amino acid-like constituents, obtained by acidic or basic hydrolysis, are the following:

(1) Phosphinothricine (L-2-amino-4-methylphosphinobutyric acid, or MPGA)
(2) D-2-Amino-5-phosphono-3-*cis*-pentenoic acid
(3) L-Methionine-sulfoximine
(4) Homoserine
(5) 2,3-Epoxy-4-oxo-hexahydro-L-phenylalanine (anticapsin)
(6) 2-Amino-4(cyclohexa-2,5-dienylaminyl)-butyric acid
(7) (2S,3R)-2-Hydroxy-3-amino-4-phenylbutyric acid
(8) δ-Hydroxy-β-lysine [(3R,5R)-3,6-diamino-5-hydroxyhexanoic acid]
(9) L-β-Lysine [(2S)-diaminohexanoic acid)]
(10) L-2,3-Diaminopropionic acid
(11) Feldamycic acid
(12) 1-Methylhydrazino acetic acid
(13) L-Prolinol
(14) D-(+)-Pentylsuccinic acid (1,3-dicarboxyheptan)

Some other specific amino acid fragments, which were never obtained by degradation, are as follows:

(15) 1(S)-Hydroxy-2(S)-aminocyclobutane-1-acetic acid
(16) 3-[(S)-Chloro-3(S)-hydroxy-2-oxo-3-azetidinylmethyl]-(S)-alanine
(17) Aminomalonyl-tetramic acid fragment of malonomycin

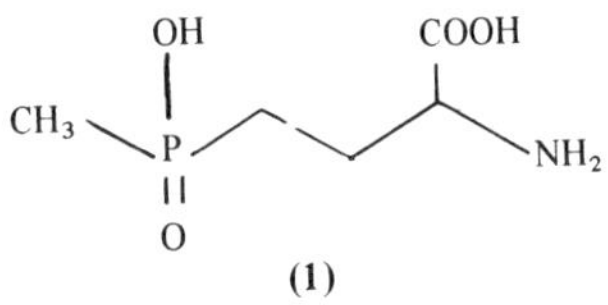

(1)

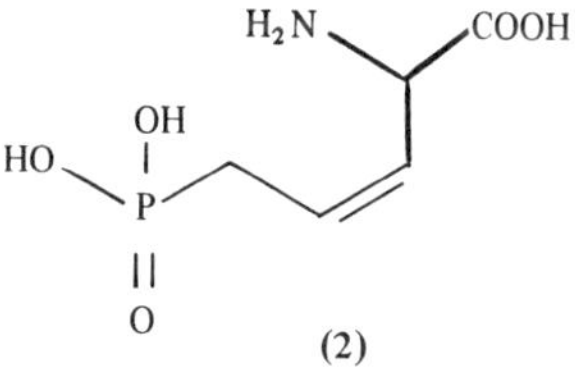

(2)

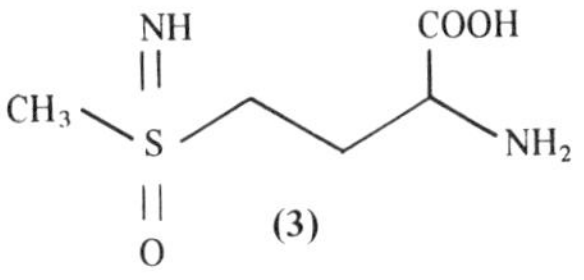

(3)

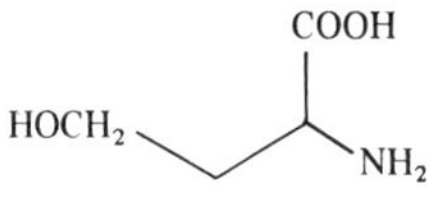

(4)

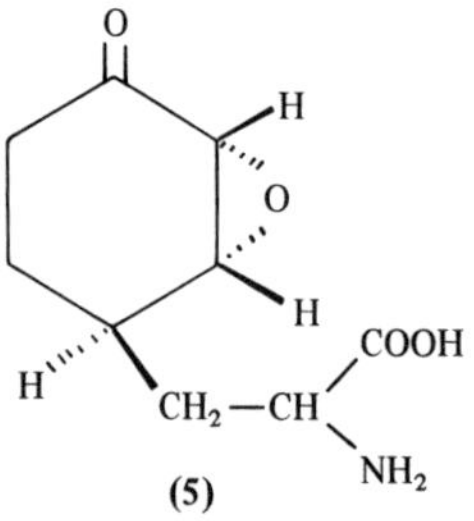

(5)

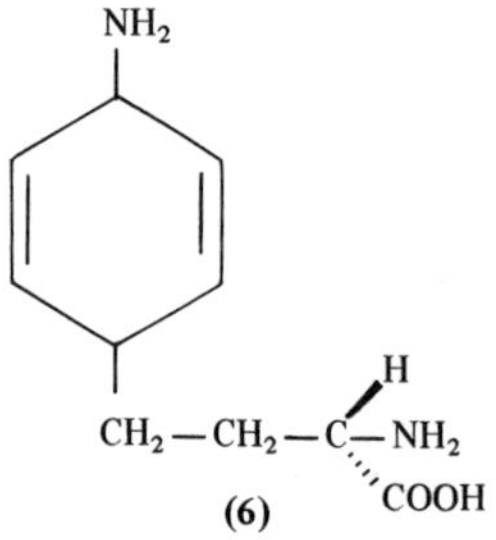

(6)

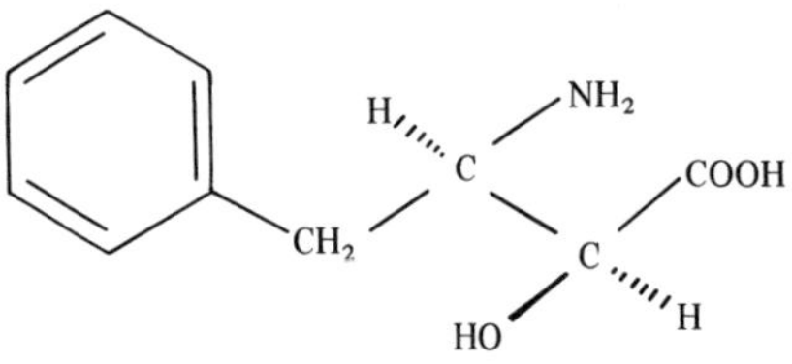

(7)

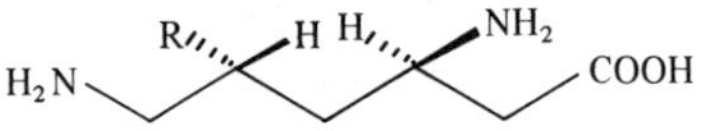

(8) R = OH
(9) R = H

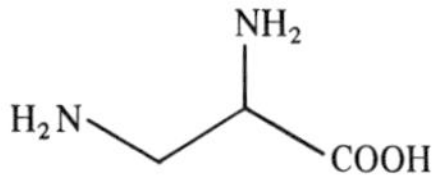

(10)

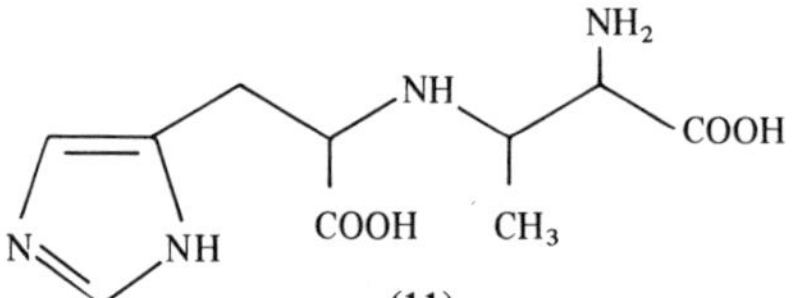

(11)

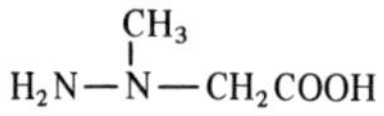

(12)

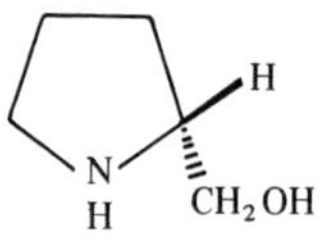

(13)

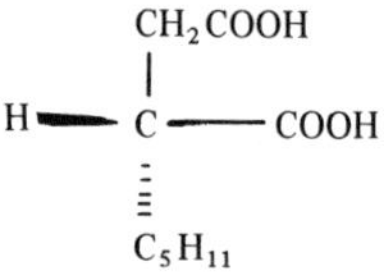

(14)

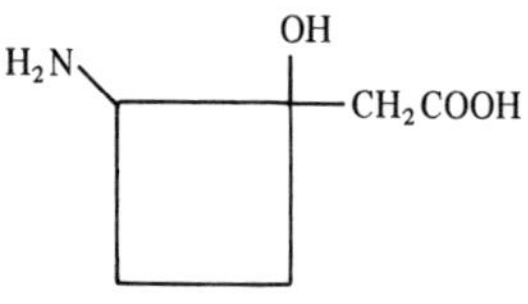

(15)

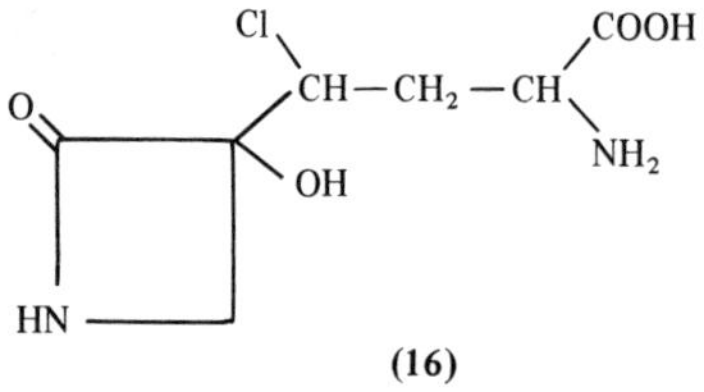

(16)

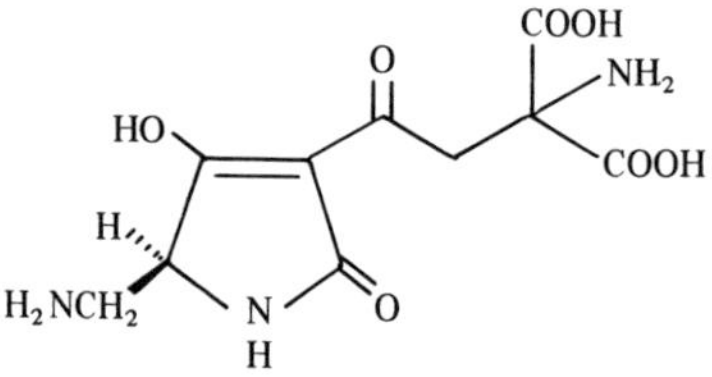

(17)

The origin (actinomycetes, fungi, or bacteria) and biological activities (antibacterial, antifungal, antimetabolite, etc.) are variable in this heterogeneous group of compounds.

The isolation of phosphino (phosphono) oligopeptide antimetabolite antibiotics from streptomycetes has special interest. These compounds contain a biologically active phosphor-containing unique amino acid (**1**, **2**, or **3**) and usually two common amino acids (ala) providing only transport properties of the active fragment.

Negamycin is potentially a clinically useful antibiotic active against multiple drug-resistant Gram-negative bacteria, including *Pseudomonas* species carrying R factor. This dipeptide-type basic compound is a specific inhibitor of protein synthesis inhibiting the termination step and causing misreading of the genetic code. The mechanism of action of negamycin is similar to that of aminoglycosides, but their binding locus on the ribosome is not identical. The three-dimensional structure of active negamycin reveals it to be related to aminoglycosides.

The aminopeptidase inhibitor bestatin might be used in cancer therapy because it increases the effectiveness of some anticancer agents owing to its immunosuppressive effect.

Structures

42120

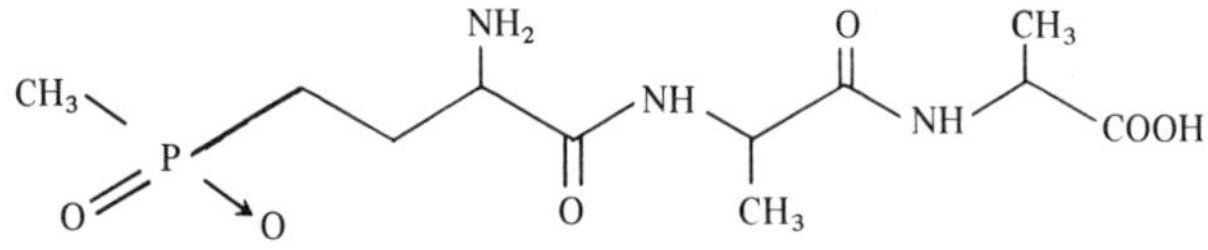

phosphotrycinyl-alanyl-alanine (SF-1293)

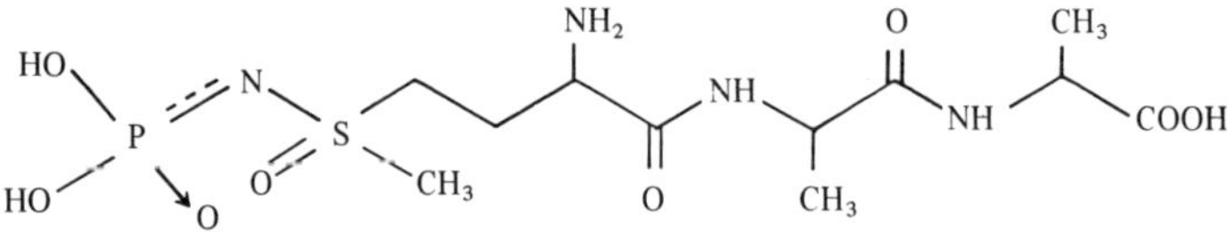

L-N^5-phosphono-methionine-S-sulfoxyminyl-alanyl-alanine

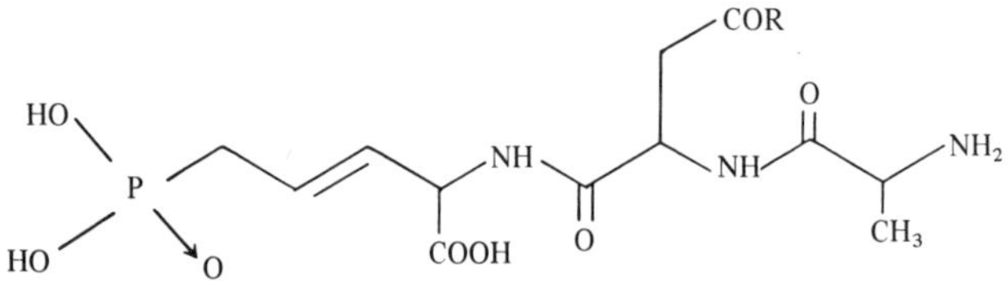

plumbemycin A R = OH; plumbemycin B R = NH_2

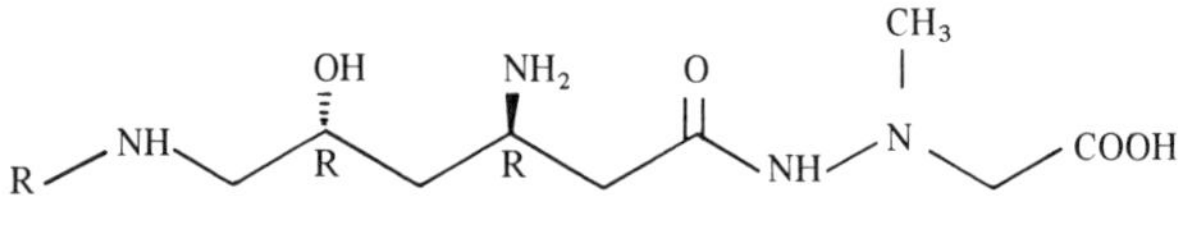

negamycin R = H

leucylnegamycin R = $CO-\overset{S}{C}H(NH_2)-CH_2-CH(CH_3)_2$

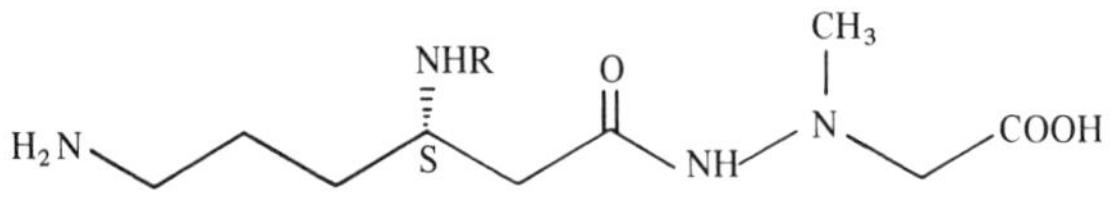

3-*epi*-deoxynegamycin R = H

leucyl-3-*epi*-deoxynegamycin R = $CO-\overset{S}{C}H(NH_2)-CH_2-CH(CH_3)_2$

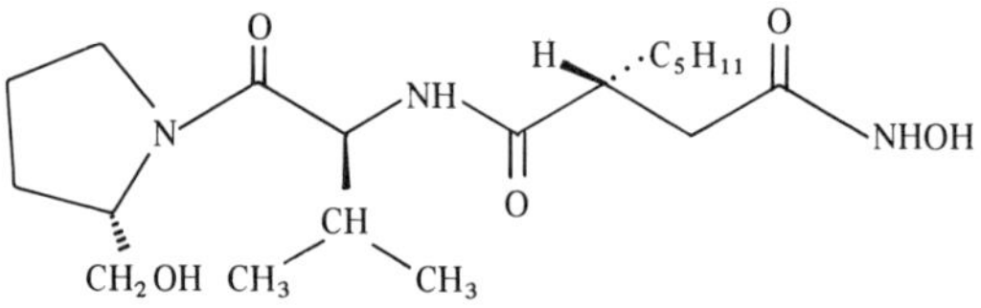

actinonin

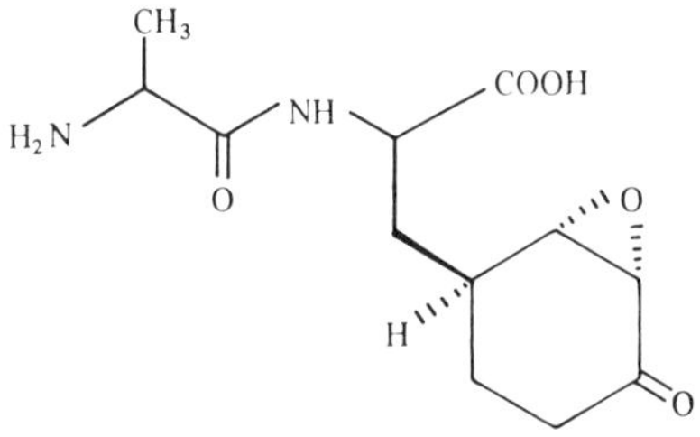

tetain (bacilysin, bacillin)

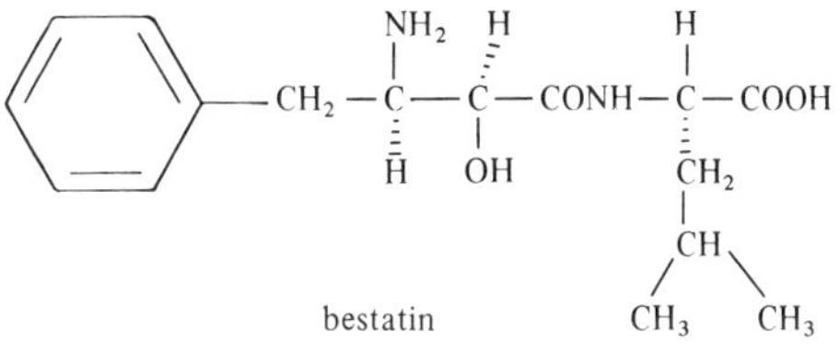

bestatin

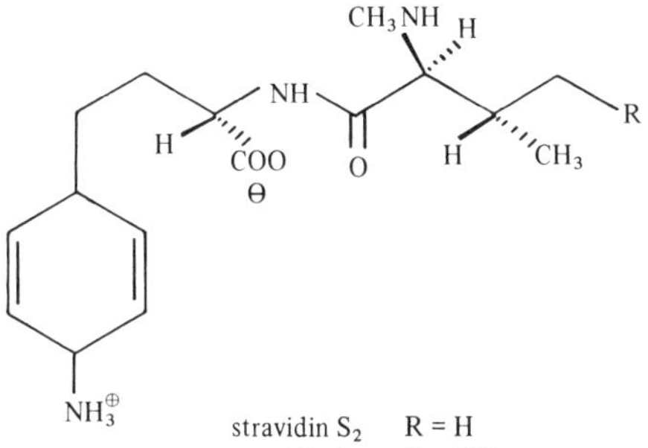

stravidin S_2 $R = H$
stravidin S_3 $R = CH_3$

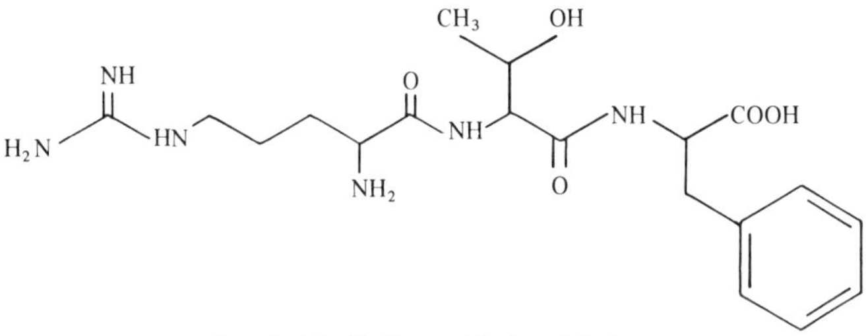

L-arginyl-D-*allo*-threonyl-L-phenylalanine

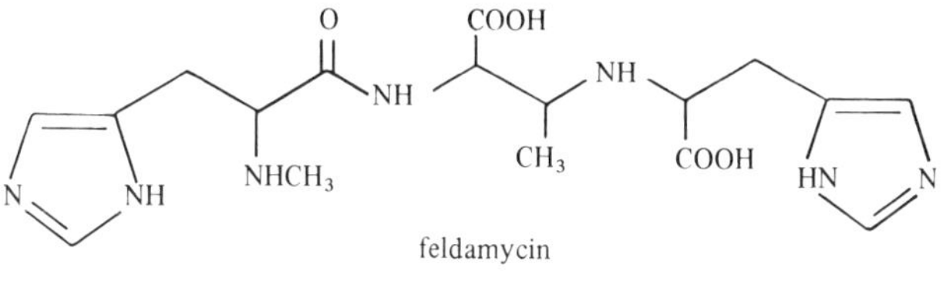

feldamycin

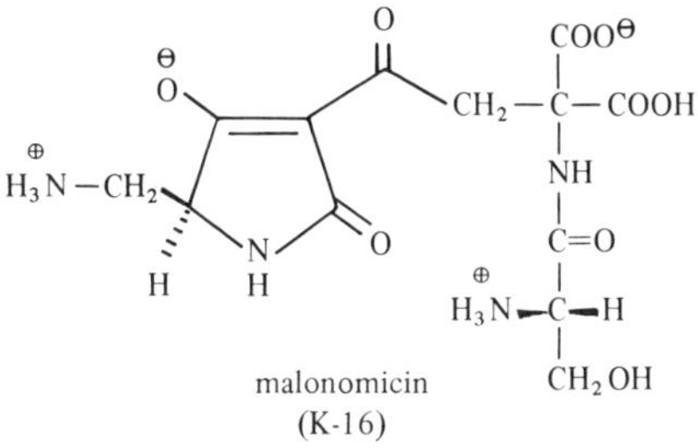

malonomicin
(K-16)

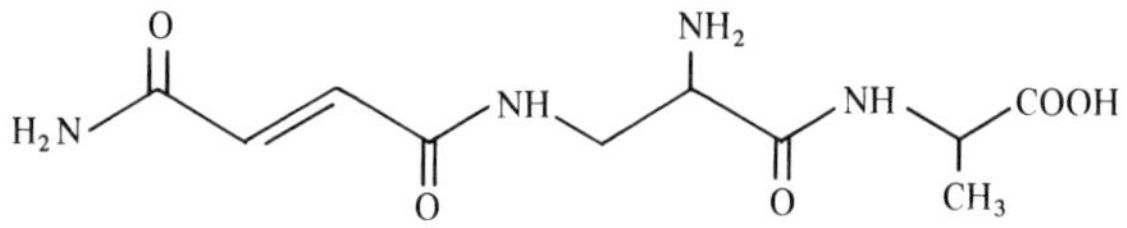

A-19009

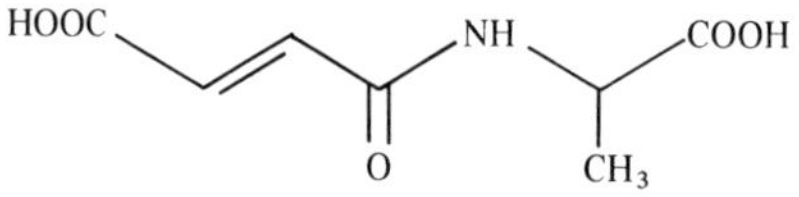

fumarylalanine

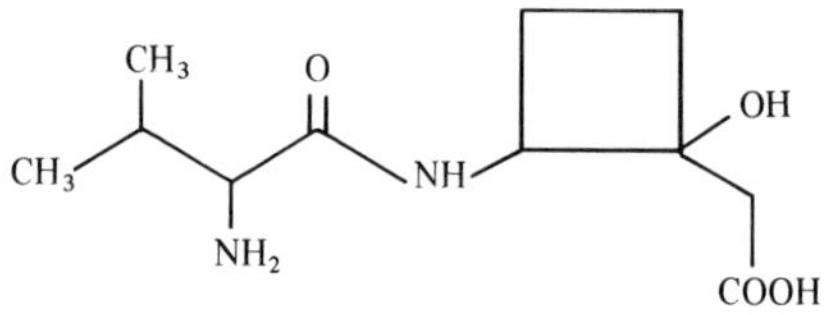

1-(S)-hydroxy-2-(S,S)-valylamido-cyclobutane-1-acetic acid

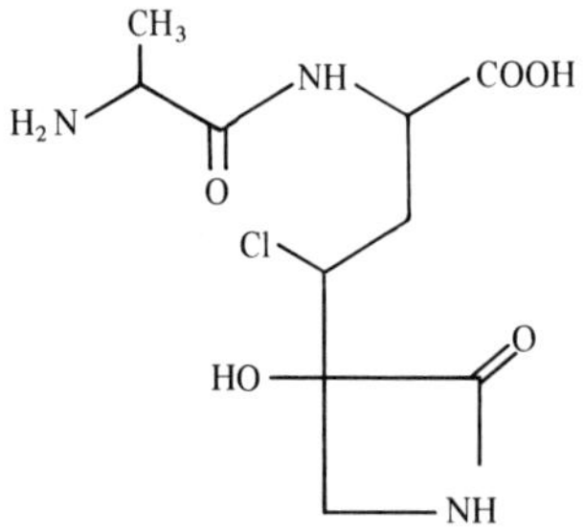

(S)-alanyl-3 [α-(S)-chloro-3-(S)-hydroxy-2-oxo-3-azetidinylmethyl] -(S)-alanine

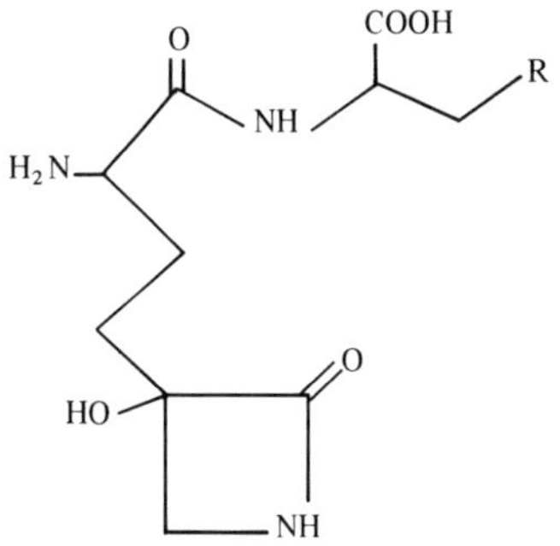

Tabtoxin R = H, CH_3

	42120-1482
NAME:	1-S-HYDROXY-2.5.5-VALYLAMIDO-CYCLOBUTANE-1-ACETIC ACID, X-1092
PO:	S.SP.
CT:	OLIGOPEPTIDE, AMPHOTER
FORMULA:	C11H20N2O4
EA:	(N, 12)
MW:	244
PC:	WH., CRYST.
OR:	(+8.4, W) (-31.2, HCL)
UV:	W: (200, ,)
SOL-GOOD:	W
SOL-POOR:	BUOH, HEX
QUAL:	(NINH., +)
TO:	(B.SUBT.,)
IS-ION:	(DX-50-H, PYR-W) (AG-50-NA, PH4.2 PUFF)
IS-CRY:	(CRYST., ETOH-W)

REFERENCES:

JA, 27, 754, 1974; USP 3939139

42120-1609

NAME:	NEGAMYCIN
PO:	S.PURPEOFUSCUS, S.SP.
CT:	BASIC, OLIGOPEPTIDE
FORMULA:	C9H20N4O4
EA:	(N, 21)
MW:	248
EW:	287
PC:	WH., POW.
OR:	(+2.5, W)
UV:	W: (200, ,)
SOL-GOOD:	W
SOL-POOR:	MEOH, HEX
QUAL:	(NINH., +) (SAKA., -)
STAB:	(ACID, +) (BASE, +)
TO:	(S.AUREUS, 1.5) (S.LUTEA, 1.5) (B.SUBT., 12) (E.COLI, 1.5) (SHYG., 3) (P.VULG., 6) (PS.AER., 6) (K.PNEUM., 3)
LD50:	(500, IV)
IS-FIL:	3
IS-ION:	(IRC-50-NH4, NH4OH) (DX-1, HCL)
IS-CHR:	(CG-50-NH4, NH4OH)
IS-CRY:	(LIOF.,)
UTILITY:	ON CLINICAL TRIAL

REFERENCES:

JA, 23, 170, 1970; 25, 685, 1972; 29, 937, 1976; *JACS*, 93, 6305, 1971; 94, 4353, 1972; *BBA*, 374, 82, 1974; Belg. P 750096; DT 2022311; USP 3743580

42120-1610

NAME:	LEUCYLNEGAMYCIN
PO:	S.PURPEOFUSCUS, S.SP.
CT:	BASIC, AMPHOTER, OLIGOPEPTIDE
FORMULA:	C15H31N5O5
EA:	(N, 19)
MW:	361
PC:	WH., POW.
OR:	(+4.8, W)
UV:	W: (200, ,)
SOL-GOOD:	W
SOL-POOR:	MEOH, HEX
QUAL:	(NINH., +)
TO:	(S.AUREUS, 25) (S.LUTEA, 100) (E.COLI, 6) (SHYG., 1.56) (K.PNEUM., 25) (P.VULG., 1.56) (PS.AER., 50)
LD50:	(500, IV)
IS-FIL:	3
IS-ION:	(IRC-50-NH4, NH4OH)
IS-CHR:	(CG-50-NH4, NH4OH)
IS-CRY:	(LIOF.,)

REFERENCES:

JA, 24, 732, 1971

42120-1611

NAME:	ACTINONIN
PO:	S.FELIS, S.ROSEOPALLIDUS
CT:	ACIDIC, OLIGOPEPTIDE
FORMULA:	C19H35N3O5
EA:	(N, 11)
MW:	385
PC:	WH., CRYST.
OR:	(-65, W) (-53.9, ETOH)
UV:	W: (200, ,)
SOL-GOOD:	W, MEOH, ETOH, BUOH, PYR, ETOAC
SOL-POOR:	CHL, HEX
QUAL:	(BIURET, +) (NINH., +)
TO:	(S.AUREUS, 20) (B.SUBT., 20) (SHYG., 20) (K.PNEUM., 20)
LD50:	NONTOXIC
TV:	ANTIPHAGE
IS-FIL:	ORIG.
IS-EXT:	(BUOH, 7, FILT.)
IS-CRY:	(CRYST., ETOH-ET2O)

REFERENCES:

Nature, 195, 701, 1962; *CC*, 420, 421, 1974; *JCS Perkin I*, 819, 1975; USP 3240787

42120-1612

NAME:	MALONOMYCIN, K-16
PO:	S.RIMOSUS-PAROMOMYCETICUS
CT:	AMPHOTER, ACIDIC, OLIGOPEPTIDE
FORMULA:	C14H18N4O10
EA:	(N, 14)
MW:	402
PC:	WH., CRYST.
OR:	(-68.8, W) (-64, PH7 PUFF)
UV:	HCL: (274, , 6700)
UV:	W: (242, 290,) (278, 313,)
SOL-GOOD:	ACID, BASE
SOL-FAIR:	W, DMSO, DMFA, THF, PYR, DIOXAN
SOL-POOR:	MEOH, HEX
QUAL:	(NINH., +) (FECL3, +)
STAB:	(BASE, +) (HEAT, -)
TO:	(TRYPANOSOMA SP.,)
LD50:	(1000, IP)
IS-FIL:	2
IS-CRY:	(PREC., NH4-VERSENATE, FILT.)

REFERENCES:

Tetr., 34, 223, 1978; *TL*, 3103, 3107, 1972; Holl. P 67/1356; *CA*, 70, 27642; BP 1178783

42120-1613

NAME:	STRAVIDIN-S2, MSD-235-S2
PO:	S.AVIDINII, S.LAVENDULAE, S.SP.
CT:	AMPHOTER, OLIGOPEPTIDE
FORMULA:	C16H27N3O3
EA:	(N, 13)
MW:	309
PC:	WH., POW.
UV:	W: (200, ,)
SOL-GOOD:	W, MEOH
SOL-POOR:	ACET, HEX
QUAL:	(NINH., +) (BIURET, +)
STAB:	(BASE, +)
TO:	(E.COLI, 25)
LD50:	NONTOXIC

REFERENCES:

AAC 1963, 20, 28, 33; *CC*, 101, 1969; DT 1232315; BP 1077999

42120-1614

NAME: STRAVIDIN-S3, MSD-235-S3
PO: S.AVIDINII, S.LAVENDULAE, S.SP.
CT: AMPHOTER, OLIGOPEPTIDE
FORMULA: C17H29N3O3
EA: (N, 13)
MW: 323, 327, 322
EW: 373
PC: WH., CRYST.
OR: (+9.5, HCL)
UV: MEOH: (200, ,)
SOL-GOOD: W, MEOH, ETOH, BUOH
SOL-POOR: ACET, HEX
QUAL: (NINH., +) (BIURET, -)
STAB: (BASE, +)
TO: (E.COLI, 10) (SHYG.,)
LD50: (1000, IP)
IS-FIL: 4
IS-EXT: (BUOH, 8.5, FILT.)
IS-ION: (DX-50-H, NH4OH)
IS-CRY: (LIOF.,)
REFERENCES:
AAC 1963, 20, 28, 33; *CC*, 101, 1969; DT 1232315; BP 1077999

42120-1615

NAME: A-19009, FUMARYLCARBOXAMIDO-L-2.3-DIAMINOPROIONYL-L-ALANINE
PO: S.COLLINUS
CT: AMPHOTER, BASIC, OLIGOPEPTIDE
FORMULA: C10H16N4O5
EA: (N, 20)
MW: 294
PC: WH., CRYST.
OR: (+107, W)
UV: MEOH: (213, , 16300) (241, , 6462)
SOL-GOOD: W
SOL-FAIR: MEOH
SOL-POOR: BUOH, HEX
TO: (SALMONELLA GALLINARUM, 8) (FUNGI, 25)
LD50: (600, IP)
IS-FIL: 4
IS-ABS: (CARBON, ACET-W)
IS-CHR: (AL, W)
IS-CRY: (CRYST., MEOH-W)
REFERENCES:
JA, 25, 137, 1972; USP 3832287

42120-1617

NAME:	TETAINE
IDENTICAL:	BACILLIN, BACILYSIN, KM-208
PO:	B.PUMILUS
CT:	AMPHOTER, OLIGOPEPTIDE
FORMULA:	C12H18N2O5
EA:	(N, 10)
MW:	270
PC:	WH., POW., HYGROSCOPIC
SOL-GOOD:	W, MEOH, ETOH, PHENOL, ACOH
SOL-POOR:	BUOH, HEX
QUAL:	(NINH., +)
STAB:	(ACID, +) (HEAT, +)
TO:	(SHYG.,) (P.VULG.,) (K.PNEUM.,) (S.AUREUS,)
LD50:	(500, IV)
IS-FIL:	9
IS-ABS:	(CARBON, BUOH)
IS-CHR:	(AL, W)
IS-CRY:	(LIOF.,)

REFERENCES:

Acta Polon. Pharm., 2, 85, 1955; *Med. Dosw.*, 7, 155, 1955; *Acta Biochem. Pol.*, 4, 231, 241, 1957; *Acta Micr. Pol.*, 12, 131, 1957; *Roznickzky Chem.*, 39, 405, 1965; *JA*, 26, 184, 1973; 28, 77, 1975; *CA*, 47, 7954, 48, 11000; 49, 16061, 1088; 51, 3092; 52, 660; 53, 3092

42120-1618

NAME:	BACILYSIN
IDENTICAL:	TETAINE, BACILLIN
PO:	B.SUBTILIS
CT:	OLIGOPEPTIDE
FORMULA:	C12H18N2O5
EA:	(N, 11)
MW:	270
EW:	280
PC:	WH., POW.
OR:	(+103, W)
UV:	W: (200, ,)
SOL-GOOD:	W, MEOH, ETOH, PHENOL, ACOH
SOL-FAIR:	ETOH
SOL-POOR:	BUOH, HEX
QUAL:	(NINH., +) (PAULY, +)
STAB:	(ACID, +) (HEAT, +) (BASE, -)
TO:	(S.AUREUS,)
LD50:	(450, IV)
IS-FIL:	3
IS-ION:	(ZEOCARB-225-H, PYR-W)
IS-ABS:	(CARBON, ETOH-W)
IS-CHR:	(AL, ETOH-W)
IS-CRY:	(LIOF.,)

REFERENCES:

Brit. J. Exp. Path., 30, 306, 1949; *Bioch. J.*, 97, 573, 579, 1965; 118, 557, 563; 1970; *JA*, 28, 77, 1975; *J. Gen. Micr.*, 94, 34, 46, 1976

42120-1621

NAME:	L-ARGINYL-D-ALLOTHREONYL-L-PHENYLALANINE
PO:	KERATINOPHYTON TERREUM, TRICHOPHYTON INDICUM
CT:	BASIC, AMPHOTER, OLIGOPEPTIDE
FORMULA:	C19H30N6O5
EA:	(N, 20)
MW:	682
PC:	WH., POW.
OR:	(+17.6, W)
UV:	W: (251.2, ,) (258, ,) (264, ,)
SOL-GOOD:	W
SOL-POOR:	BUOH, HEX
QUAL:	(NINH., +)
TO:	(PAECYLOMYCES VARIOTI,) (FUNGI,)
IS-FIL:	7
IS-ION:	(DX-50, W-PH9.8)
IS-CHR:	(BIOGEL P-2, W)
IS-CRY:	(LIOF.,)

REFERENCES:

Ber., 106, 816, 1973

42120-1622

NAME:	FUMARYL-ALANINE
PO:	P.RESTICULOSUM, ASP.INDICUS
CT:	ACIDIC, OLIGOPEPTIDE
FORMULA:	C7H9NO5
EA:	(N, 8)
MW:	187
PC:	WH., CRYST.
OR:	(-10.2, ETOH)
UV:	MEOH: (200, ,) (244, ,)
SOL-GOOD:	MEOH, ETOAC, BASE
SOL-POOR:	HEX
TO:	(S.AUREUS,)
IS-EXT:	(ETOAC, , FILT.)
IS-CRY:	(CRYST., ACOH)

REFERENCES:

Bioch. J., 36, 829, 1942; *Aust. J. Chem.*, 21, 2775, 1968

42120-1623

NAME:	PHOSPHOTHRYCINYL-ALANYL-ALANINE
IDENTICAL:	SF-1293
PO:	S.VIRIDOCHROMOGENES
CT:	AMPHOTER, OLIGOPEPTIDE
FORMULA:	C11H22N3O6P
EA:	(N, 13) (P, 9)
MW:	323
PC:	WH., POW.
UV:	W: (200, ,)
SOL-GOOD:	W
SOL-FAIR:	MEOH
SOL-POOR:	BUOH, HEX
QUAL:	(NINH., +)
TO:	(B.SUBT., .01) (E.COLI, .01) (PS.AER., .1) (PHYT.FUNGI, .1)
IS-ION:	(DX-1-AC, ACOH)
IS-CHR:	(BIOGEL P-2, W)
IS-CRY:	(LIOF.,)

REFERENCES:

Helv., 55, 224, 1972; Holl. P 72/10308; *Pharm.*, 30, 815, 1975

42120-1624

NAME: SF-1293
IDENTICAL: PHOSPHOTHRYCINYL-ALANYL-ALANINE
PO: S.HYGROSCOPICUS
CT: AMPHOTER, OLIGOPEPTIDE
FORMULA: C11H22N3O6
EA: (N, 12) (P, 9)
MW: 320
EW: 355
PC: WH., POW.
OR: (-34, W)
UV: W: (200, ,)
SOL-GOOD: W, MEOH
SOL-POOR: ETOH, HEX
QUAL: (NINH., +) (BIURET, +) (FECL3, -) (FEHL., -)
STAB: (ACID, +) (BASE, +) (HEAT, +)
TO: (FUNGI, 3.1) (PHYT.FUNGI, .09)
LD50: (500, PEROS) (80, IV)
IS-ION: (DX-50-H, NH4OH)
IS-CHR: (SEPHADEX G-10, W)
IS-CRY: (LIOF.,)
REFERENCES:
Sci. Rep. Meiji, 13, 34, 42, 49, 54, 1973; BP 1356723; JP 73/85538, 75/13322, 13592; DT 2236599; *CA*, 80, 60035; 81, 37788, 37806, 89705

42120-1625

NAME: L-N5-PHOSPHONO-METHIONINE-S-SULPHOXYMINYL-ALANYL-ALANINE
PO: S.SP.
CT: AMPHOTER, OLIGOPEPTIDE
FORMULA: C11H23N4O8SP
EA: (N, 14) (S, 8) (P, 7)
PC: WH., POW.
UV: W: (200, ,)
SOL-GOOD: W
SOL-POOR: BUOH, HEX
QUAL: (NINH., +)
TO: (B.SUBT.,) (E.COLI,) (SERRATIA MARCESCENS,)
IS-ION: (DX-50-H, PYR-W) (AG-50-H, HCL)
IS-CHR: (CARBON, W-HCL)
IS-CRY: (PREC., W, MEOH)
REFERENCES:
JA, 26, 261, 1973

42120-1631

NAME: MORIMYCIN
PO: S.DIASTATOCHROMOGENES-LUTEUS
CT: OLIGOPEPTIDE, NEUTRAL
FORMULA: C8H12N2O7
EA: (N, 15)
MW: 184
PC: WH., CRYST.
OR: (0,)
UV: MEOH: (259, 700,)
UV: W: (255, 630,)
SOL-GOOD: MEOH, W, ACET
SOL-POOR: CHL, BENZ, ET2O, HEX
QUAL: (PAULY, +) (FEHL., +) (NINH., -) (FECL3, -) (EHRL., -)
TO: (B.SUBT., 1000) (S.AUREUS, 1000) (E.COLI, 100) (PHYT.BACT., 20)
LD50: (150, IV) (200, PEROS)
IS-ABS: (CARBON, ACET-W)
IS-CHR: (CARBON, MEOH-ET2O)
IS-CRY: (CRYST., ET2O)
REFERENCES:
JP 70/955

42120-2109

NAME: BACILLIN
IDENTICAL: TETAINE, BACILYSIN, KM-208
PO: B.SUBTILIS
CT: NEUTRAL, OLIGOPEPTIDE
FORMULA: C12H18N2O5
EA: (N, 11)
SOL-GOOD: MEOH, ETOH
SOL-FAIR: BUOH
SOL-POOR: ACET, HEX
QUAL: (DNPH, +)
STAB: (ACID, +) (HEAT, +)
TO: (E.COLI,) (S.AUREUS,)
LD50: (1000, IP)
IS-ABS: (CARBON, ETOH)
REFERENCES:
J. Bact., 84, 1148, 1962; *Dev. Ind. Micr.*, 5, 237, 1963; *J. Bact.*, 51, 371, 1946; 54, 793, 1947; *JA*, 28, 77, 1975

42120-3896

NAME: S-ALANYL-3-A"-S-CHLORO-3-S-HYDROXY-2-OXO-3-AZETIDINYLMETHYL-S-ALANINE, X-372-A
CT: OLIGOPEPTIDE, AMPHOTER
FORMULA: C10H16N3O5CL
EA: (N, 14) (CL, 12)
PC: WH., CRYST.
UV: W: (200, ,)
SOL-GOOD: W
SOL-POOR: ACET, HEX
QUAL: (NINH., +)
TO: (S.AUREUS, 5) (B.SUBT., 50) (E.COLI, 5) (K.PNEUM., 5) (S.LUTEA, 10) (S.AUREUS, 100)
IS-ION: (DX-50-H, PYR-W)
IS-CHR: (AG-50-NA, PH3.55 PUFF) (CEL, BUOH-ACOH-W)
IS-CRY: (LIOF.,)
REFERENCES:

JA, 28, 1, 1975; USP 3901880, 3956067

42120-3897

NAME: TABTOXIN, WILDFIRE TOXIN
PO: PS.TABACI, PS.SP.
CT: OLIGOPEPTIDE, AMPHOTER
FORMULA: C11H19N3O6
EA: (N, 14)
PC: WH., POW.
UV: W: (200, ,)
SOL-GOOD: W
QUAL: (NINH., +)
TO: (CHLORELLA VULGARIS,)
LD50: TOXIC
IS-FIL: 2.5
IS-ION: (AG-50, PYR-W)
REFERENCES:

Nature, 219, 379, 1968; 229, 174, 1971; *BBA*, 26, 107, 1972; *JA*, 28, 1, 1975; *Wisconsin Agric. Exp. Sta. Res. Bull.*, 62, 1—34

42120-4940

NAME:	E-64
PO:	ASP.JAPONICUS
CT:	OLIGOPEPTIDE
FORMULA:	C15H27N5O5
EA:	(N, 8)
MW:	357
OR:	(+24.4, HCL)
UV:	MEOH: (200, ,)
SOL-GOOD:	MEOH-W, ACOH, PYR, DMSO
SOL-FAIR:	ETOH
SOL-POOR:	ACET, HEX.

REFERENCES:

Agr. Biol. Ch., 42, 523, 529, 1978

42120-5112

NAME:	FICELLOMYCIN, U-47929
PO:	S.FICELLUS
CT:	BASIC, OLIGOPEPTIDE
FORMULA:	C13H32N4O5
EA:	(N, 25)
MW:	312
EW:	290|2
PC:	WH., CRYST.
OR:	(+39, W)
UV:	W: (200, ,)
SOL-GOOD:	W, MEOH, ETOH
SOL-POOR:	ACET, HEX
QUAL:	(NINH., +)
STAB:	(ACID, -) (BASE, +)
TO:	(S.AUREUS, 62) (S.LUTEA,) (PENICILLIUM OXALICUM,)
LD50:	(800, IV) (800, IP)
IS-ION:	(XAD-4, MEOH-W)
IS-ABS:	(FLORISIL, ACET-W)
IS-CHR:	(DX-1-OH, W)
IS-CRY:	(LIOF.,)

REFERENCES:

JA, 29, 1001, 1976; *Biochem.*, 16, 3406, 1977; USP 3993748

42120-5188

NAME:	BSA
PO:	B.SUBTILIS
CT:	OLIGOPEPTIDE
EA:	(C, 51) (H, 7) (N, 9)
MW:	1100|400
PC:	WH., POW.
OR:	(+57.5, W)
UV:	W: (200, ,)
SOL-GOOD:	W
SOL-POOR:	BUOH, HEX
TO:	(S.AUREUS, 125) (E.COLI, 500) (C.ALB., 1) (S.CEREV., 2)
LD50:	(3000, IV) (5000, IP)
IS-ABS:	(CARBON,)
IS-CHR:	(CM-SEPHADEX D-25,)

REFERENCES:

JP 75/132188, 76/11198; *CA*, 84, 162881

42120-5249

NAME:	FELDAMYCIN, U-48266
PO:	S.FICELLUS
CT:	OLIGOPEPTIDE, AMPHOTER, BASIC
FORMULA:	C17H25N7O5
EA:	(N, 24)
MW:	407
EW:	210, 241
PC:	WH., POW.
OR:	(-6.6, W)
UV:	MEOH: (200, ,)
UV:	W: (259, ,) (265, ,)
SOL-GOOD:	W, MEOH, ETOH
SOL-POOR:	ACET, HEX
QUAL:	(NINH., +)
STAB:	(BASE, +)
TO:	(S.LUTEA, .01) (B.SUBT., .1) (S.AUREUS,) (E.COLI, 1) (SHYG., 1) (P.VULG., 1) (K.PNEUM., .05)
TV:	L-1210
IS-ION:	(XAD-4, W) (IRC-50-H, NH4OH)
IS-ABS:	(FLORISIL, ACET-W)
IS-CHR:	(SILG, ETOH-W)
IS-CRY:	(DRY, ETOH-W)

REFERENCES:

JA, 29, 1001, 1117, 1976; *Biochem.*, 16, 3406, 1977; USP 3965515; *CA*, 85, 141320

42120-5298

NAME:	<u>122110</u>
CT:	OLIGOPEPTIDE
EA:	(N,)
SOL-GOOD:	W
TO:	(G.POS.,) (G.NEG.,) (S.CEREV.,)
TV:	CYTOTOXIC

REFERENCES:

Pers. Comm. (D. Perlman)

42120-5417

NAME:	<u>102804</u>
PO:	B.CEREUS
CT:	BASIC, OLIGOPEPTIDE
FORMULA:	C12H16N2O5
EA:	(N, 10)
MW:	268
PC:	WH., CRYST.
OR:	(+16, W)
UV:	MEOH: (280, 40,)
SOL-GOOD:	W, MEOH
SOL-POOR:	ACET, HEX
QUAL:	(NINH., +)
TO:	(S.AUREUS, .4) (E.COLI, 3.2) (C.ALB., 1000) (B.SUBT., 25)
IS-FIL:	3
IS-ION:	(IR-120-H, PYR)
IS-CHR:	(DX-50X4-H, PH3.5 PUFF)
IS-CRY:	(LIOF.,) (CRYST., ACET-W)

REFERENCES:

JA, 30, 283, 1977

42120-5420

NAME: PLUMBEMYCIN-A
PO: S.PLUMBEUS
CT: OLIGOPEPTIDE, AMPHOTER
FORMULA: C12H20N3O9P
EA: (N, 10) (P, 8)
EW: 400|20
PC: WH., POW.
OR: (-10.93, W) (+4.65, HCL)
UV: (200, ,)
SOL-GOOD: W
SOL-FAIR: MEOH
SOL-POOR: ACET, HEX
QUAL: (NINH., +)
TO: (B.SUBT., 100) (E.COLI, 10)
LD50: (750|250, IV)
IS-FIL: 2
IS-ION: (DX-50X4-H, W)
IS-ABS: (CARBON, MEOH-W)
IS-CHR: (DX-50X2-H, HCL)
REFERENCES:
Agr. Biol. Ch., 40, 1905, 1976; 41, 573, 1977

42120-5421

NAME: PLUMBEMYCIN-B, N-1409
PO: S.PLUMBEUS
CT: OLIGOPEPTIDE, AMPHOTER
FORMULA: C12H21N4O8P
EA: (N, 13) (P, 8)
EW: 405
PC: WH., CRYST.
OR: (-6.57, W) (+3.66, HCL)
UV: HCL: (202.5, ,)
UV: NAOH: (214.5, ,)
UV: W: (203, ,)
SOL-GOOD: W
SOL-FAIR: MEOH
SOL-POOR: ACET, HEX
QUAL: (NINH., +)
TO: (B.SUBT., 100) (E.COLI, 10)
LD50: (750|250, IV)
IS-FIL: 2
IS-ION: (DX-50X4-H, W)
IS-ABS: (CARBON, MEOH-W)
IS-CHR: (DX-50X2-H, HCL) (DX-1X4-OH, W)
IS-CRY: (CRYST., ETOH-W)
REFERENCES:
Agr. Biol. Ch., 40, 1905, 1976; 41, 161, 573, 1977

42120-5984

NAME: 3-EPIDEOXYNEGAMYCIN
PO: S.GOSHIKIENSIS
CT: OLIGOPEPTIDE, AMPHOTER
FORMULA: C9H20N4O3
EA: (N, 23)
MW: 232
PC: WH., POW.
OR: (+5, W)
UV: W: (200, ,)
SOL-GOOD: W
SOL-POOR: ACET, HEX
TO: (S.AUREUS, 6.25) (B.SUBT., 25) (S.LUTEA, 100) (E.COLI, 50) (P.VULG., 12.5) (PS.AER., 100)
LD50: (600|200, IV)
IS-FIL: 8
IS-ION: (IRC-50-NH4, NH4OH)
IS-CHR: (CG-50-NH4, NH4OH) (SILG, MEOH-CHL-NH4OH)
IS-CRY: (LIOF.,)
REFERENCES:
JA, 30, 1137, 1977

42120-5985

NAME: LEUCYL-3-EPIDEOXYNEGAMYCIN
PO: S.GOSHIKIENSIS
CT: OLIGOPEPTIDE, AMPHOTER
FORMULA: C15H31N5O4
EA: (N, 20)
MW: 345
PC: WH., POW.
OR: (-4, W)
UV: W: (200, ,)
SOL-GOOD: W
SOL-POOR: ACET, HEX
TO: (P.VULG., 25)
LD50: NONTOXIC
IS-FIL: 8
IS-ION: (IRC-50-NH4, NH4OH)
IS-CHR: (CG-50-NH4, W)
REFERENCES:
JA, 30, 1137, 1977

42120-5989

NAME:	BESTATIN
PO:	S.OLIVORETICULI
CT:	OLIGOPEPTIDE, AMPHOTER
FORMULA:	C16H24N2O4
EA:	(N, 9)
MW:	308
EW:	310
PC:	WH., CRYST.
OR:	(-15.5, HCL)
UV:	MEOH: (248, , 104) (253, , 130) (258.5, , 172) (264.5, , 132)
SOL-GOOD:	MEOH, DMSO, ACOH
SOL-FAIR:	W
SOL-POOR:	ETOAC, CHL, BENZ, HEX
QUAL:	(NINH., +) (EHRL., -) (SAKA., -)
LD50:	(500|200, IP)
TV:	ANTITUMOR, GARDNER, CA
IS-EXT:	(BUOH, 2, W)
IS-ION:	(XAD-4, MEOH-W)
IS-CHR:	(DX-50X8, PUFF) (SILG, BUOH-BUOAC-ACOH-W)
IS-CRY:	(DRY,)
UTILITY:	ON CLINICAL TRIAL

REFERENCES:

JA, 28, 857, 1975; 29, 100, 102, 600, 1976; *J. Med. Chem.*, 20, 510, 1977; DT 2628354; JP 77/116435; *CA*, 88, 61132

4213
Cyclic Oligopeptide-Like Antibiotics

This group contains only a few antibiotics with rather unique structures. The antibacterials bicyclomycin and cairomycin have bridged diketopiperazine-type structures, while ikaraguamycin, which is an antiprotozoal antibiotic, is an acyltetramic acid derivative.

The less toxic bicyclomycin is active in vivo against many Gram-negative bacteria and does not show cross resistance to the other known antibacterial drugs. Its in vitro activity, however, surprisingly is very poor. Initial clinical trials are encouraging. This compound represents a highly functionalized derivative of cyclo-leu-ileu. Bicyclomycin affects the biosynthesis of lipoproteins existing in the membrane of Gram-negative bacteria.

The special structure of ikarugamycin is constructed from two hexa-acetate units and L-ornithine forming the *trans*-anti-*cis*-decahydro-*as*-indacene skeleton.

All of these compounds are *Streptomyces* metabolites.

Structures

42130

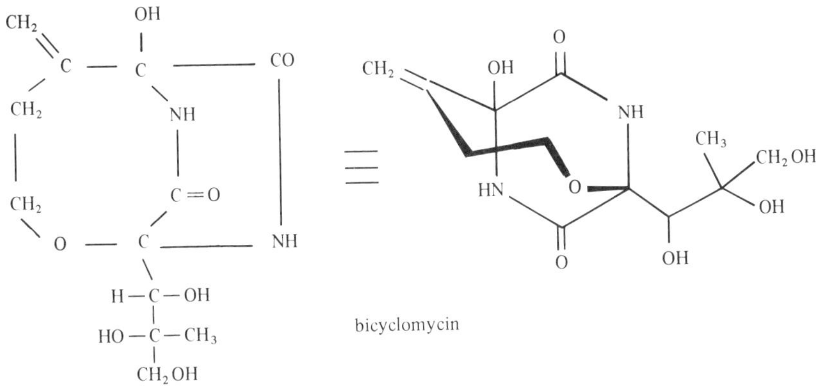

bicyclomycin

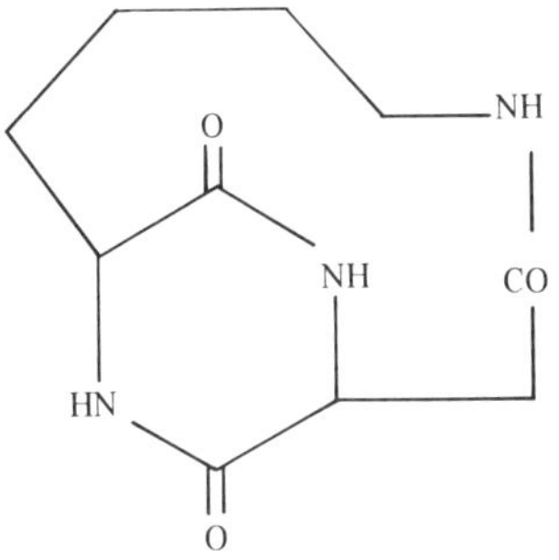

cairomycin B

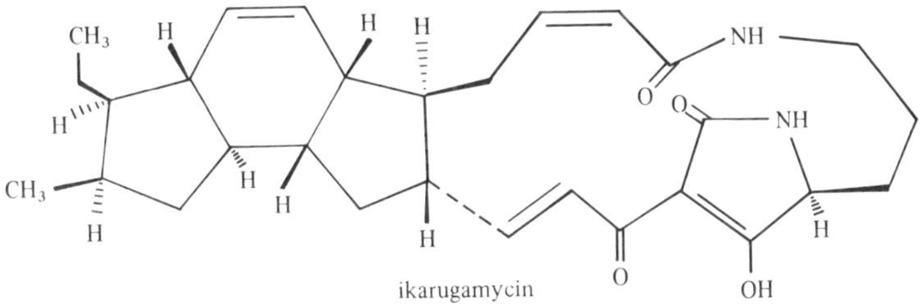

ikarugamycin

42130-1626

NAME: IKARUGAMYCIN
PO: S.PHAEOCHROMOGENES
CT: CYCLIC OLIGOPEPTIDE L., ACIDIC
FORMULA: C29H38N2O4
EA: (N, 6)
MW: 478
PC: WH., CRYST.
OR: (+390, DMFA)
UV: MEOH: (227, , 20700) (327, , 17300)
UV: MEOH-HCL: (220, , 28700) (325, , 20000)
UV: MEOH-NAOH: (243, , 21400) (321, , 13300)
SOL-GOOD: DMFA, DMSO, THF
SOL-FAIR: MEOH, CHL
SOL-POOR: W, ET2O, HEX
QUAL: (FECL3, +) (NINH., -) (EHRL., -)
STAB: (ACID, -) (BASE, +)
TO: (S.AUREUS, 6) (B.SUBT., 6) (S.LUTEA, 50)
(PS.AER., 100) (TRICHOMONAS SP., .1)
LD50: (6, IP)
IS-EXT: (CHL-MEOH, , MIC.)
IS-ABS: (CARBON, MEOH-CHL)
IS-CRY: (PREC., THF, W-HCL) (CRYST., CHL-MEOH)
REFERENCES:

JA, 25, 271, 1972; *TL*, 1181, 1185, 2557, 1972; *Bull. Ch. Soc. Jap.*, 50, 1813, 1977; JP 71/88833

42130-1627

NAME:	BICYCLOMYCIN, WS-4545
IDENTICAL:	AIZUMYCIN, 5879
PO:	S.SAPPOROENSIS, S.IRABENSIS
CT:	CYCLIC OLIGOPEPTIDE L., DIKETOPIPERAZINE DERIV., BASIC
FORMULA:	C12H18N2O7
EA:	(N, 9)
MW:	302
PC:	WH., CRYST.
OR:	(+63.5, MEOH)
UV:	MEOH: (200, ,)
SOL-GOOD:	W, MEOH, ETOH, PYR
SOL-FAIR:	ACET, ETOAC
SOL-POOR:	CHL, HEX
QUAL:	(FEHL., +) (FECL3, +) (EHRL., -) (NINH., -)
STAB:	(ACID, +) (BASE, -)
TO:	(E.COLI, 25) (SHYG., 18) (K.PNEUM., 25) (S.LUTEA, 250)
LD50:	(3000, IV) (5000, IP)
IS-FIL:	7
IS-ABS:	(CARBON, ACET-W)
IS-CHR:	(CEL, BUOH-W) (SILG, CHL-MEOH)
IS-CRY:	(CRYST., ACET)
UTILITY:	ON CLINICAL TRIAL, FEED ADDITIVE

REFERENCES:

JA, 25, 569, 576, 582, 1972; 27, 976, 1974; 29, 155, 1976; *Bull. Ch. Soc. Jap.*, 47, 18, 1974; *JA*, 29, 155, 1976; USP 3784447; DT 2150593, 2501958; JP 77/108093, 108092

42130-1628

NAME: AIZUMYCIN
IDENTICAL: BICYCLOMYCIN, 5879
PO: S.AIZUENSIS
CT: CYCLIC OLIGOPEPTIDE L., DIKETOPIPERAZINE DERIV., BASIC
FORMULA: C12H18N2O7
EA: (N, 9)
MW: 302
PC: WH., CRYST.
OR: (+82.6, W)
UV: MEOH: (200, ,)
SOL-GOOD: W, MEOH
SOL-FAIR: ETOH
SOL-POOR: BUOH, HEX
QUAL: (FEHL., +)
TO: (S.AUREUS, 500) (S.LUTEA, 62) (K.PNEUM., 15) (SHYG., 15) (E.COLI, 31)
LD50: (2000, IV)
IS-FIL: 2
IS-ION: (IRC-50-H, HCL)
IS-CHR: (CEL, BUOH) (SILG, BUOH-MEOH)
IS-CRY: (CRYST., MEOH-ACET)
REFERENCES:
JA, 25, 610, 1972; 26, 479, 1973; Holl. P 73/10943

42130-5422

NAME: CAIROMYCIN-B
PO: S.SP.
CT: CYCLIC OLIGOPEPTIDE L., DIKETOPIPERAZINE DERIV., NEUTRAL
FORMULA: C10H15N3O3
EA: (N, 19)
MW: 226
PC: WH.
UV: (228, ,) (290, ,)
SOL-GOOD: CHL, ETOAC, ACET
SOL-POOR: W, HEX
QUAL: (FEHL., -) (BIURET, -) (SAKA., -) (NINH., -) (FECL3, -)
TO: (S.AUREUS, .78) (B.SUBT., .78) (S.LUTEA, .78) (E.COLI, 100) (K.PNEUM., 100) (PS.AER., 50) (C.ALB., 50)
IS-EXT: (ETOAC-CHL, 7, FILT.)
IS-CHR: (CEL, CHL-HEX)
IS-CRY: (PREC., CHL, HEX)
REFERENCES:
AAC, 11, 373, 1977

422
Linear Homopeptides

Introduction

In this group some linear polypeptide-type compounds are included in which the peptide chain is built up only by peptide linkages. The N and/or C terminal in these peptides is generally terminated by simple molecules, other than amino acids, such as amines or fatty acids.

The bacterial metabolites gramicidins (4221), edeins (4222), and cerexins (4226); the fungal peptaibophol antibiotics (4225); several minute types of streptomycetal antibiotics [cinnamycins (4223) and stenothricins (4224)] are also included in this group.

The uncommon amino acids and the other terminating constituents are summarized in the following table:

Uncommon amino acids	Other constituents
Gramicidin Type	
Only common (L and D) amino acids occur	N terminal: formyl group C terminal: ethanolamine
Edein Type	
Isoserine **(1)** β-Isotyrosine **(2)** β-Phenyl-β-alanine **(3)** 2,3-Diaminopropionic acid **(4)** 2,6-Diamino-7-hydroxyazelaic acid **(5)**	C terminal: spermidine **(6)**, N-guanyl-spermidine **(7)**
Cinnamycin-Duramycin	
Meso-lanthionine **(8)** Cystationine **(9)**	No other constituent was identified
Stenothricin	
L-2,3-Diaminopropionic acid **(4)** Cysteinic acid **(10)** cys (O_3H)	N terminal: β-keto fatty acids **(11)**, C_{14} to C_{17} *normal* acids
Peptaibophol Type	
α-Amino-isobutyric acid or 2-methylalanine **(12)** aib L-Isovaline **(13)** L-iva	N terminal: acetyl C terminal: phenylalaninol **(14)**L- phol
Cerexin Type	
L-*threo*-γ-Hydroxylysine **(15)** D-*allo*-Threonine D-*allo*- Isoleucine	N terminal: β-hydroxy fatty acids, C_{11} to C_{12} *normal, iso,* and *anteiso* acids

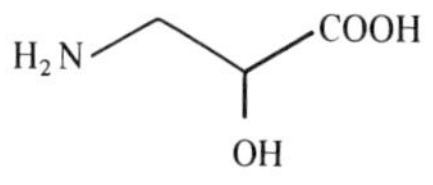

(1)

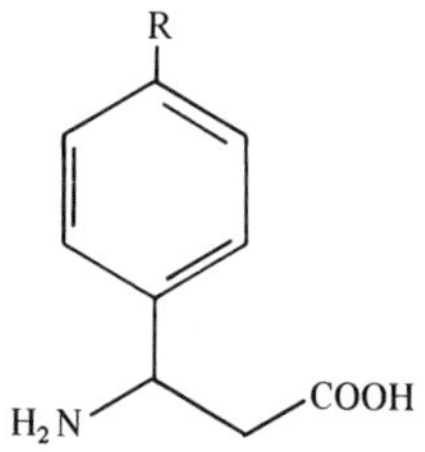

(2) R = OH
(3) R = H

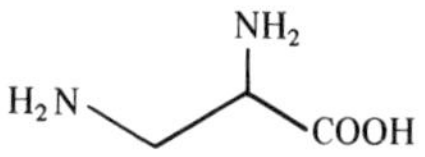

(4)

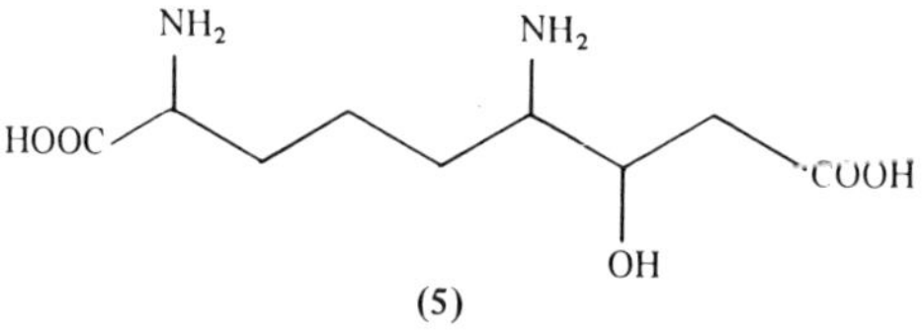

(5)

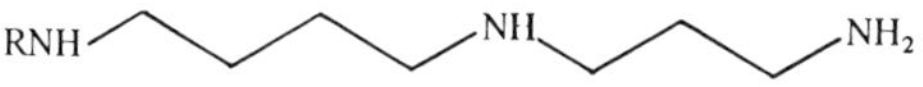

(6) R = H; (7) R = $-C(=NH)-NH_2$

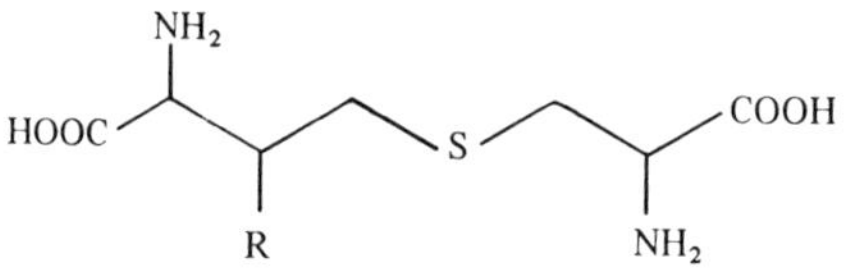

(8) R = CH_3; (9) R = H

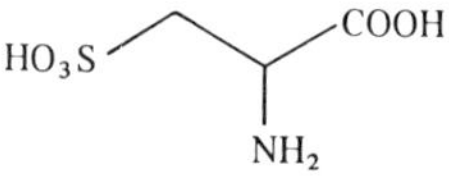

(10)

$$CH_3-(CH_2)_n-\underset{\underset{O}{\|}}{C}-CH_2-COOH$$

(11) n = 10–13

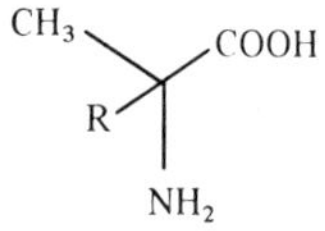

(12) R = CH_3
(13) R = C_2H_5

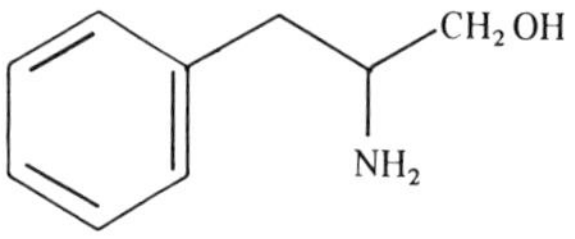

(14)

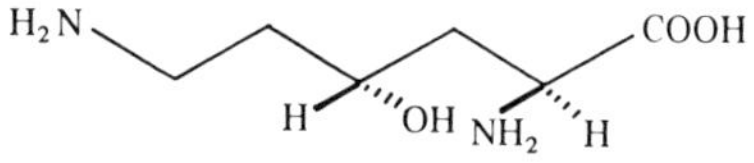

(15)

4221
Gramicidin Type

Gramicidin, a component of tyrothricin, discovered by Dubois in 1939, is one of the earlier known antibiotic. The components of the gramicidin complex (which consists of a mixture of valyl- and isoleucyl-gramicidins A, B, and C) are linear N-formylated pentadecapeptide ethanolamides.

These neutral lipophylic peptides differ from each other in the nature of the first (valine or isoleucine) and the eleventh aromatic amino acids (tryptophane, phenylalanine, or tyrosine) in the chain. The configuration of amino acids is alternating (L, D, L, D...) along the chain.

Gramicidins display strong bacteriostatic action against Gram-positive bacteria, but apart from limited topical use, they find no therapeutic application because of their marked parenteral toxicity. Gramicidins cause hemolysis of red blood cells. The gramicidin peptide has an α-helical configuration. It has the capacity to selectively transport different cations across the lipid bilayers of various organism by formation of transmembrane channels.

Structure

42210

HC = O
|
X → gly → L-ala → D-leu → L-ala → D-val → L-val → D-val → L-try →

→ D-leu → Y → D-leu → L-try → D-leu → L-try → $NH-CH_2-CH_2-OH$

Antibiotic	X	Y
Valine-gramacidin A	L-val	L -try
Isoleucine-gramicidin A	L-ileu	L-try
Valine-gramicidin B	L-val	L-phe
Isoleucine-gramicidin B	L-ileu	L-phe
Valine-gramicidin C	L-val	L-tyr
Isoleucine-gramicidin C	L-ileu	L-tyr

42210-1632

NAME:	GRAMICIDIN-A, VALYL-GRAMICIDIN-A
CT:	PEPTIDE, GRAMICIDIN T., NEUTRAL
FORMULA:	C148H210N30026
EA:	(N, 15)
MW:	3800, 3100
EW:	3011|25
PC:	WH., CRYST.
OR:	(+3, ETOH) (+5.1, DMFA)
UV:	ETOH: (272, ,) (280, ,) (292, ,)
UV:	MEOH: (271, ,) (281.5, ,) (290.5, ,)
SOL-GOOD:	MEOH, CHL, DIOXAN, ACOH, PYR, DMFA
SOL-POOR:	BENZ, HEX, TOL, W
QUAL:	(BIURET, +) (EHRL., +) (PAULY, +)
STAB:	(HEAT, +)
TO:	(S.AUREUS, 5) (S.LUTEA, 3) (B.SUBT., 10)
LD50:	(5, IV) (60, IP) (1000, PEROS)
IS-EXT:	(ET20-ACET, , TYROTHRICIN)
IS-CRY:	(CRYST., DIOXAN-ACET)
UTILITY:	ANTIBACTERIAL DRUG

REFERENCES:

Nature, 195, 1067, 1962; *J. Exp. Med.,* 73, 629, 1941; *JACS,* 85, 3397, 1862, 1963; 87, 2011, 2020, 2027, 1965; *J. Biol. Chem.,* 132, 791, 1940; 141, 155, 197, 1944; 172, 839, 1948; *Bioch. J.,* 39, 351, 355, 1944; 50, 109, 1951; *Biochem.,* 2, 1138, 1963; 4, 2491, 2495, 1965; 13, 5249, 1974; 11, 477, 487, 1972; *Ant. & Chem.,* 5, 561, 1955; *Tetr.,* 19, 1661, 1966; 21, 138, 1968; *J. Chrom.,* 92, 147, 1974; *Proc. Nat. Acad. Sci.,* 68, 672, 1971; *Ind. J. Bioch. Biophys.,* 9, 21, 225, 1972; USP 2453534, 2438209

42210-1633

NAME: <u>GRAMICIDIN-B</u>, VALYL-GRAMICIDIN-B
PO: B.BREVIS
CT: PEPTIDE, GRAMICIDIN T., NEUTRAL
EA: (C, 63) (H, 8) (N, 15)
MW: 3000|100
PC: WH., CRYST.
OR: (+6, DMFA)
UV: ETOH: (280, ,) (292, ,)
SOL-GOOD: MEOH, CHL, DMFA
SOL-POOR: BENZ, HEX, W
QUAL: (BIURET, +)
TO: (S.AUREUS, 5) (B.SUBT., 20)
REFERENCES:

Nature, 195, 1067, 1962; *J. Exp. Med.,* 73, 629, 1941; *JACS,* 85, 3397, 1862, 1963; 87, 2011, 2020, 2027, 1965; *J. Biol. Chem.,* 132, 791, 1940; 141, 155, 197, 1944; 172, 839, 1948; *Bioch. J.,* 39, 351, 355, 1944; 50, 109, 1951; *Biochem.,* 2, 1138, 1963; 4, 2491, 2495, 1965; 13, 5249, 1974; 11, 477, 487, 1972; *Ant. & Chem.,* 5, 561, 1955; *Tetr.,* 19, 1661, 1966; 21, 138, 1968; *J. Chrom.,* 92, 147, 1974; *Proc. Nat. Acad. Sci.,* 68, 672, 1971; *Ind. J. Bioch. Biophys.,* 9, 21, 225, 1972; USP 2453534, 2438209

42210-1634

NAME: <u>GRAMICIDIN-C</u>, VALYL-GRAMICIDIN-C
PO: B.BREVIS
CT: PEPTIDE, GRAMICIDIN T., NEUTRAL
EA: (C, 62) (H, 8) (N, 15)
MW: 3000|100
PC: WH., CRYST.
OR: (+11.4, DMFA)
UV: ETOH: (280, ,) (290, ,)
SOL-GOOD: MEOH, CHL
SOL-POOR: W, BENZ, HEX
QUAL: (BIURET, +)
TO: (S.AUREUS, 1) (B.SUBT., 10)
REFERENCES:

Nature, 195, 1067, 1962; *J. Exp. Med.,* 73, 629, 1941; *JACS,* 85, 3397, 1862, 1963; 87, 2011, 2020, 2027, 1965; *J. Biol. Chem.,* 132, 791, 1940; 141, 155, 197, 1944; 172, 839, 1948; *Bioch. J.,* 39, 351, 355, 1944; 50, 109, 1951; *Biochem.,* 2, 1138, 1963; 4, 2491, 2495, 1965; 13, 5249, 1974; 11, 477, 487, 1972; *Ant. & Chem.,* 5, 561, 1955; *Tetr.,* 19, 1661, 1966; 21, 138, 1968; *J. Chrom.,* 92, 147, 1974; *Proc. Nat. Acad. Sci.,* 68, 672, 1971; *Ind. J. Bioch. Biophys.,* 9, 21, 225, 1972; USP 2453534, 2438209

42210-1635

NAME: GRAMICIDIN-D
PO: B.BREVIS
CT: PEPTIDE, GRAMICIDIN T., NEUTRAL
MW: 1900|100
TO: (S.AUREUS, .15)
REFERENCES:
Biochem., 4, 2495, 1965

42210-1636

NAME: GRAMICIDIN LIKE SUBST.
PO: B.BREVIS
CT: PEPTIDE, GRAMICIDIN T., NEUTRAL
EA: (N, 15)
MW: 2500
PC: WH., POW.
UV: MEOH: (270, ,) (281.5, ,) (290, ,)
SOL-GOOD: MEOH, BUOH, ACET
SOL-POOR: ET2O, W, HEX
QUAL: (BIURET, +)
TO: (G.POS.,)
REFERENCES:
CA, 55, 1804

42210-1637

NAME: COLISAN, RB-103
PO: B.SP.
CT: BASIC, PEPTIDE, GRAMICIDIN T., NEUTRAL
EA: (N, 15)
EW: 1500
PC: WH., POW.
OR: (-8.2, W)
UV: W: (274, ,)
SOL-GOOD: MEOH, ETOH, CHL, ACOH, DMFA, ACID
SOL-POOR: W, BASE, HEX
QUAL: (NINH., +) (BIURET, +)
STAB: (ACID, +)
TO: (G.POS.,) (PARAMECIUM CANDIDATUM,)
LD50: (7.8, IP)
IS-EXT: (ACID, 2, MIC.)
REFERENCES:
Brit. J. Pharm., 15, 313, 1960; *Nature*, 158, 26, 1946; *Biotech. Bioeng.*, 10, 424, 1968

42210-1638

NAME: ESEIN
PO: B.BREVIS
CT: PEPTIDE, GRAMICIDIN T., NEUTRAL
PC: WH., POW.
SOL-GOOD: MEOH
TO: (B.SUBT.,) (S.LUTEA,)
IS-EXT: (MEOH, , MIC.)
IS-CRY: (PREC., MEOH, BENZ)
REFERENCES:

Dokl., 204, 405, 1972; *CA*, 69, 142; 77, 44577, 59979; *Antib.*, 583, 1971; *Vestn. Moskow. Univ.*, 23, 42, 1968

4222
Edein Type

Edein type of antibiotics are rare examples of peptides, containing mostly unusual amino acids in their molecules. They bear little structural resemblance to other naturally occurring peptides. These strongly basic antibiotics show broad antimicrobial spectra. They interfere with protein biosynthesis in a rather interesting way, namely by inhibiting DNA synthesis in very low concentration with the inhibition of bacterial DNA polymerase, without the direct effect on protein and RNA synthesis. Edein does not react covalently with DNA.

Structures

42220

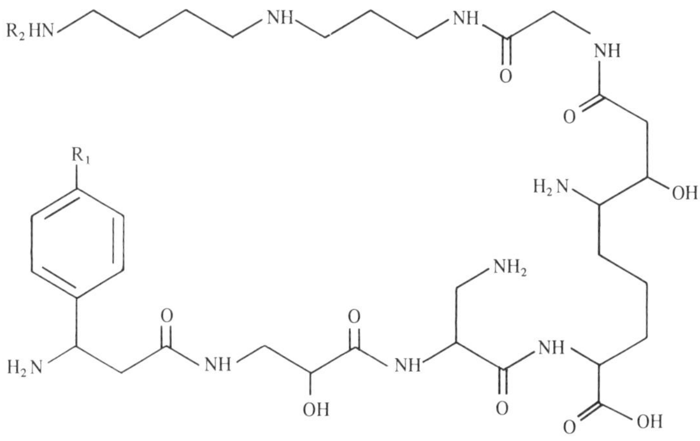

Antibiotic	**R_1**	**R_2**
Edein A	OH	H
Edein B	OH	$-C(=NH)-NH_2$
Edein D	H	H
Edein F	H	$-C(=NH)-NH_2$

42240

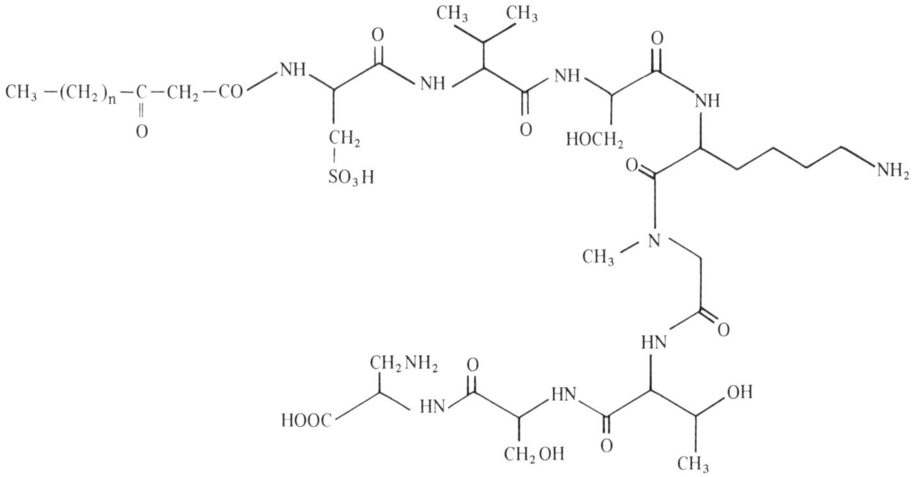

β-ketoacyl — D-cys(O_3H) — L-val — D-ser — L-lys — sar — *a*thr — L-ser — L-Dap-OH

stenothricin (n=10–13)

42220-1639

NAME:	EDEIN-A1
PO:	B.BREVIS
CT:	PEPTIDE, BASIC, AMPHOTER, EDEIN T.
FORMULA:	C30H57N10O10
EA:	(N, 18)
MW:	1600, 753
EW:	860
PC:	WH., POW.
UV:	HCL: (270, ,)
UV:	NAOH: (240, ,) (290, ,)
UV:	W: (270, ,)
SOL-GOOD:	W
SOL-FAIR:	MEOH
SOL-POOR:	BUOH, HEX
QUAL:	(BIURET, +) (NINH., +) (SAKA., +) (PAULY, +) (FEHL., -)
TO:	(E.COLI,) (P.VULG.,) (PS.AER.,) (SHYG.,) (S.AUREUS,) (B.SUBT.,) (S.LUTEA,)
TV:	ANTITUMOR
IS-EXT:	(PHENOL, 7.5, WB.)
IS-ION:	(IRC-50,)
IS-ABS:	(CARBON,)
IS-CHR:	(CM-CEL, NACL) (SILG, I.PROH-MEOH-W)
IS-CRY:	(DRY,)

REFERENCES:

Bull. Inst. Marine Med. (Gdansk), 10, 151, 1959; *Acta Micr. Pol.,* 15, 223, 235, 1966; 16, 159, 1967; *Chemother.,* 12, 12, 1967; *Biochem.,* 5, 2153, 1966; 7, 4147, 4153, 1968; 9, 1224, 1970; *BBA,* 130, 560, 1966; 131, 206, 1966; *An. N.Y. Acad. Sci.,* 171, 1002, 1970; *CA,* 54, 2495, 3862

42220-1640

NAME: EDEIN-B1, GUANYL-EDEIN-A1
PO: B.BREVIS
CT: PEPTIDE, BASIC, AMPHOTER, EDEIN T.
FORMULA: C34H60N12O10
EA: (N, 20)
MW: 800, 796
PC: WH., POW.
UV: HCL: (270, ,)
UV: NAOH: (240, ,) (290, ,)
UV: W: (270, ,)
SOL-GOOD: W
SOL-POOR: BUOH, HEX
QUAL: (NINH., +) (PAULY, +) (SAKA., +)
TO: (S.LUTEA,) (E.COLI,)
IS-ION: (DX-50-H, NH4OH)
IS-CHR: (SEPHADEX G-25, W)
IS-CRY: (DRY,)
REFERENCES:
Bull. Inst. Marine Med. (Gdansk), 10, 151, 1959; *Acta Micr. Pol.*, 15, 223, 235, 1966; 16, 159, 1967; *Chemother.*, 12, 12, 1967; *Biochem.*, 5, 2153, 1966; 7, 4147, 4153, 1968; 9, 1224, 1970; *BBA*, 130, 560, 1966; 131, 206, 1966; *An. N.Y. Acad. Sci.*, 171, 1002, 1970; *CA*, 54, 7495, 3862

42220-1641

NAME: EDEIN-D
PO: B.BREVIS
CT: PEPTIDE, BASIC, AMPHOTER, EDEIN T.
FORMULA: C33H57N10O9
EA: (N, 18)
PC: WH., POW.
SOL-GOOD: W, MEOH
SOL-POOR: BUOH, HEX
QUAL: (NINH., +) (BIURET, +) (SAKA., -) (PAULY, -)
TO: (G.POS.,) (G.NEG.,)
IS-CHR: (SILG, I.PROH-NH4OH-W) (CEL,)
REFERENCES:
Exp., 28, 1423, 1972

42220-6122

NAME:	EDEIN-F
CT:	BASIC, PEPTIDE, EDEIN T.
FORMULA:	C31H59N12O9
EA:	(N, 15)
PC:	WH., POW.
TO:	(G.POS.,)

REFERENCES:

Proc. IUPAC, 1, 210, 1978; *Biochem.*, 9, 1224, 1970

42230-1642

NAME:	CINNAMYCIN, NSC-71936
PO:	S.CINNAMONEUS
CT:	PEPTIDE, AMPHOTER
EA:	(C,) (H,) (N, 15) (S, 4)
PC:	WH., POW.
OR:	(-,)
UV:	W: (200, ,) (255|5, ,)
SOL-GOOD:	W, BUOH-W, ACOH
SOL-FAIR:	MEOH
SOL-POOR:	BUOH, HEX
QUAL:	(BIURET, +) (SAKA., +) (NINH., -) (FEHL., -) (FECL3, -)
STAB:	(ACID, +) (BASE, +) (HEAT, +)
TO:	(B.SUBT., 2) (MYCOB.SP., 1) (E.COLI, 50) (P.VULG., 100)
LD50:	(7.5|2.5, IV) (10|2, IP) (400, SC)
IS-FIL:	ORIG.
IS-ION:	(IRC-50-H, HCL)
IS-CHR:	(AL, MEOH-W)
IS-CRY:	(DRY,)

REFERENCES:

Ant. & Chem., 2, 591, 1952; 4, 1135, 1242, 1954; *Appl. Micr.*, 6, 52, 1958; *Bot. Rev.*, 19, 229, 1953

42230-1643

NAME:	DURAMYCIN, F-17-B, NSC-71935
PO:	S.CINNAMONEUS-AZACOLUTA
CT:	PEPTIDE, AMPHOTER
EA:	(C, 51) (H, 6) (N, 17) (S, 3)
PC:	WH., POW.
OR:	(-6.4, W)
UV:	(200, ,)
SOL-GOOD:	W, MEOH, ETOH, BUOH
SOL-POOR:	ETOAC, HEX
QUAL:	(BIURET, +) (FECL3, -) (PAULY, -) (SAKA., -)
STAB:	(ACID, +) (HEAT, +)
TO:	(B.SUBT., .2) (C.ALB., 50) (PHYT.BACT., 30)
IS-EXT:	(BUOH, , FILT.)
IS-CHR:	(AL, MEOH-W)
IS-CRY:	(DRY,)

REFERENCES:

Ant. An., 241, 1957—58; *JACS*, 80, 3912, 1958; *Phytopath.*, 46, 568, 575, 1956

42240-2101

NAME:	STENOTHRICIN, STENOTHRICIN COMPLEX
PO:	S.SP.
CT:	PEPTIDE, BASIC, AMPHOTER
FORMULA:	C43H82N10017S
EA:	(N, 12) (S, 2)
PC:	WH., POW.
SOL-GOOD:	W, BUOH
SOL-POOR:	CCL4, HEX
TO:	(S.LUTEA,) (STREPTOMYRES VIRIDOCHROMOGENES, .005) (ARTHROBACTER SP., .01)
IS-FIL:	ORIG.
IS-EXT:	(BUOH, 7, FILT.)
IS-CHR:	(AVICEL, PROH-W) (DEAE-SEPHADEX A-25, ACOH-W)
IS-CRY:	(LIOF.,)

REFERENCES:

Arch. Mikr., 99, 307, 1974; *Z. Naturforsch. Ser. B*, 29, 679, 1974; *Liebigs Ann.*, 2011, 1976; *CA*, 82, 58096

4225
Peptaibophol (Alamethicin) Type

The recently expanding group of peptaibophol antibiotics is defined as a class of linear *peptides* containing several molecules of α-aminoisobutyric acid (*aib*) and one molecule of phenylalaninol (*phol*) in their molecules. They have an acetylated aib or phe N-terminal and phenylalaninol C-terminal fragments and contain altogether 16 to 24 amino acids.

These compounds have aroused considerable interest in molecular biology for their ability to alter ionic conductance or permeability across membranes. These lipophylic peptides exhibit right-handed α-helical configuration and they cause hemolysis of human erythrocytes. In very low levels they induce a voltage-dependent ionic conductance in bilayer lipid membranes of various cells, and they can serve as a new pore-forming model system for molecular biological studies.

Structures

42250

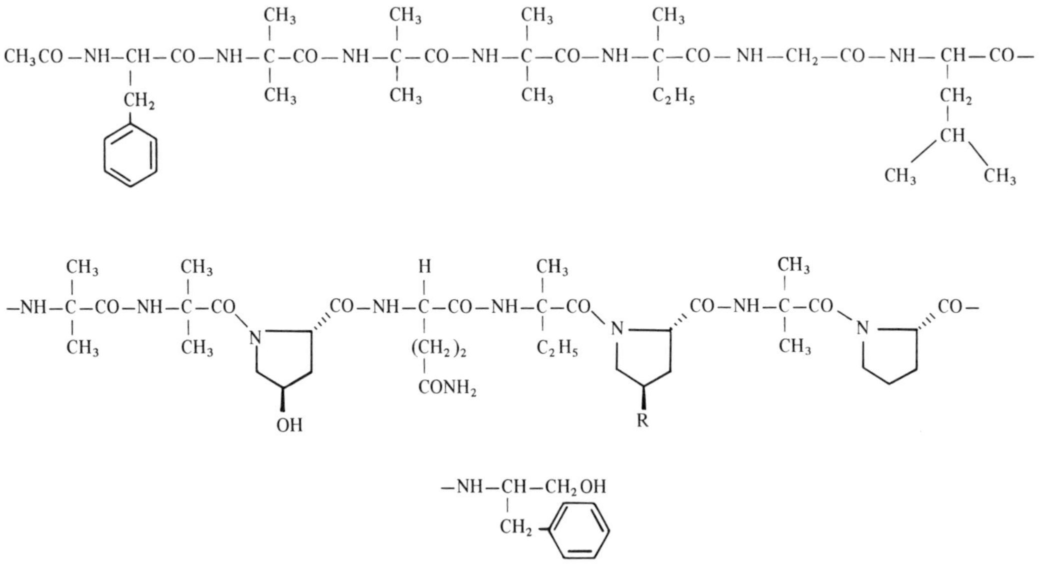

Ac → L-phe → aib → aib → aib → L-iva → gly → L-leu— → aib → aib → L-hyp → L-gln → L-iva → X → aib → L-pro → L-phol

antiamoebin I R = OH; X = L-hyp

antiamoebin II R = H; X = L-pro

Ac → aib → L-pro → aib → L-ala → aib → X → L-gln → aib → L-val → aib →

→ gly → L-leu → aib → L-pro → L-val → aib → aib → L-glu $\xrightarrow{\alpha}$ L-gln → L-phol
γ↓
OH

alamethicin I X = L-ala; alamethicin II X = aib

Ac → aib → L-pro → L-val → aib → L-val → L-ala → aib → L-ala → aib →

→ aib → L-gln → aib → L-leu → aib → gly → L-leu → aib → L pro → L-val →

→ aib → aib → L-glu $\xrightarrow{\alpha}$ L-gln → L-phol
γ↓
OH

suzukacillin A

Ac → L-phe → aib → aib → aib → L-val → gly → L-leu → aib → aib → L-hyp →

→ L-gln → L-iva → L-hyp → X → L-phol

emerimycin III X = L-ala; emerimycin IV X = aib

42260

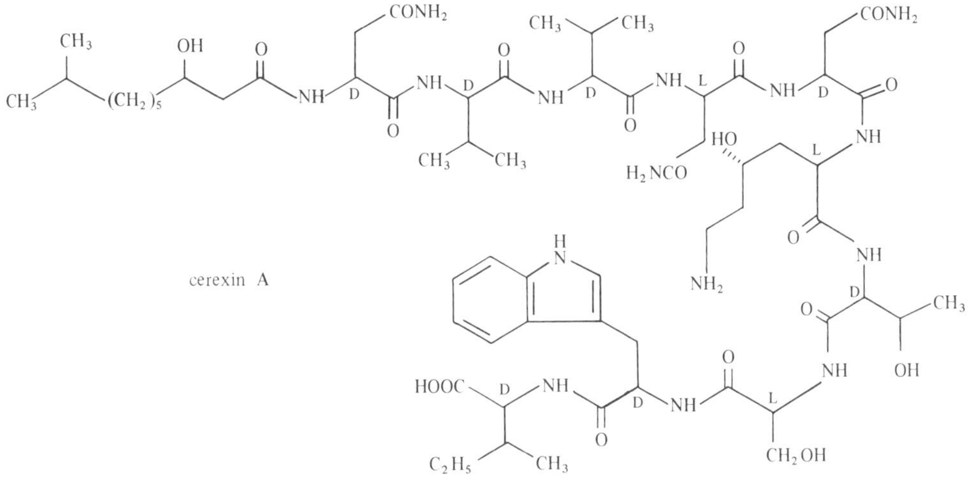

FA → D-asn → D-val → D-val → L-asn → D-asn → L-γ-hyl → D-*α*thr → L-ser → D-try → D-*α*ile

FA: *β*-hydroxy-isoundecanoyl **(Q)**
γ-hyl: L-*threo*-γ-hydroxylysine **(15)**

FA → D-asn → D-val → D-X → L-asn → D-asn → L-Y → D-*α*thr → Z → D-try → D-*α*ile-OH

Antibiotic	FA	X	Y	Z
Cerexin A	$COCH_2CH(OH)(CH_2)_5CH(CH_3)_2$ = **Q**	val	γ-hyl	ser (L)
Cerexin B	$COCH_2CH(OH)(CH_2)_4CH(CH_3)_2$, or $COCH_2CH(OH)(CH_2)_6CH_3$, or **Q**, or $COCH_2CH(OH)(CH_2)_4CH(CH_3)(C_2H_5)$	phe	γ-hyl	gly
Cerexin C	Q	val	lys	ser (L)
Cerexin D	$COCH_2CH(OH)(CH_2)_4CH(CH_3)_2$,or $COCH_2CH(OH)(CH_2)_6CH_3$, or Q, or $COCH_2CH(OH)(CH_2)_4CH(CH_3)(C_2H_5)$	phe	lys	gly

42250-1697

NAME: ALAMETHICIN-I, ALAMETHICIN, U-22324, F-30, F-50
PO: TRICHODERMA VIRIDAE
CT: ACIDIC, AMPHOTER, PEPTAIBOPHOL, PEPTIDE
FORMULA: C92H150N22025
EA: (N, 16)
MW: 1962
EW: 1960
PC: WH., CRYST.
OR: (-5.0, ETOH)
UV: (200, ,)
UV: MEOH: (258, , 296) (264, , 226) (268, , 184)
SOL-GOOD: MEOH, ETOH, ACET, BUOH, CHL
SOL-FAIR: ETOAC
SOL-POOR: ET20, W
QUAL: (NINH., -)
TO: (S.LUTEA, 62) (S.AUREUS, 62) (B.SUBT., 100)
LD50: (40, SC) (80, PEROS)
TV: KB
IS-FIL: 3
IS-EXT: (CHL, 3, FILT.)
IS-CHR: (SEPHADEX LH-20, MEOH)
IS-CRY: (CRYST., ETOH-ET20)
REFERENCES:

Exp., 23, 85, 1967; *Bioch. J.*, 117, 757, 1970; 153, 181, 1976; 119, 10P, 11P; *BBA*, 433, 164, 1976; *Eur. J. Bioch.*, 54, 395, 1975; *Bioch. Soc. Trans.*, 3, 166, 1975; *Chem. Ztg.*, 101, 196, 1977; *JACS*, 99, 8469, 1977; *Nature*, 224, 5219, 1969; USP 3833723; BP 1152659

42250-1701

NAME: TRICHOTOXIN-A, TRICHOTOXIN-A-40
PO: TRICHODERMA VIRIDAE
CT: AMPHOTER, PEPTAIBOPHOL
FORMULA: C58H95N15017
EA: (N, 16)
PC: WH., CRYST.
UV: (215, ,)
SOL-GOOD: MEOH
SOL-FAIR: CHL
SOL-POOR: HEX
QUAL: (NINH., -)
TO: (S.AUREUS, 1000) (PHYT.FUNGI, 100)
LD50: (4.36, IP)
TV: ANTITUMOR
IS-EXT: (CHL-MEOH, , MIC.)
IS-CHR: (FLORISIL, CHL-MEOH) (SEPHADEX LH-20, MEOH)
REFERENCES:

Appl. Micr., 23, 183, 1972; *Chem. Ztg.* 101, 196, 1977; *Eur. J. Bioch.*, 54, 166, 1975; *BBA*, 507, 470, 485, 1978

42250-1747

NAME: STILBELLIN
IDENTICAL: ANTIAMOEBIN
PO: STILBELLA SP.
CT: PEPTAIBOPHOL, NEUTRAL, PEPTIDE
EA: (C, 57) (H, 7) (N, 15)
MW: 1470, 1500
PC: WH., CRYST.
OR: (+15.9, MEOH)
UV: (200, ,)
SOL-GOOD: MEOH, ETOH, BUOH, PYR, DMFA
SOL-POOR: W, ACET, HEX
QUAL: (NINH., -) (FECL3, -)
TO: (B.SUBT., 21) (S.AUREUS, 20) (PROTOZOA, 1)
LD50: (47.5, IP)
IS-EXT: (MEOH, , MIC.)
IS-CRY: (CRYST., MEOH)
REFERENCES:

JA, 24, 67, 1971

42250-1748

NAME: ANTIAMOEBIN-I, ANTIAMOEBIN
IDENTICAL: STILBELLIN
PO: EMERICELLOPSIS SALMOSYNNEMATA, EMERICELLOPSIS POONENSIS, CEP.PIMPRINAE
CT: PEPTAIBOPHOL, NEUTRAL, PEPTIDE
FORMULA: C82H127N17O20
EA: (C, 56) (H, 8) (N, 14)
MW: 1669
PC: WH., CRYST.
OR: (+10, MEOH) (+17.8, MEOH)
UV: (200, ,)
SOL-GOOD: MEOH, ETOH, BUOH, PYR, DMFA
SOL-POOR: W, ACET, HEX
QUAL: (FEHL., -) (FECL3, -) (NINH., -) (BIURET, -) (SAKA., -)
TO: (PROTOZOA, .1) (S.AUREUS, 62) (B.SUBT., 31) (S.LUTEA, 31) (E.COLI, 500)
IS-FIL: 5
IS-EXT: (BUOH, 5, FILT.)
IS-CRY: (CRYST., MEOH)
REFERENCES:

Nature, 217, 849, 1968; *Curr. Sci.*, 36, 347, 1967; *HAB*, 10, 287, 299, 1967; 11, 81, 1968; *JA*, 27, 274, 1974; *JACS*, 99, 5203, 1977; DT 1467945; USP 3657419

42250-1869

NAME:	EMERIMICIN-II, EM-2, U-40588
PO:	EMERICELLOPSIS MICROSPORA
CT:	PEPTIDE, PEPTAIBOPHOL, NEUTRAL
FORMULA:	C91H146N18O26
EA:	(N, 13)
MW:	1929
PC:	WH., CRYST.
OR:	(+5, MEOH)
UV:	MEOH: (273, 28,) (281, 30,) (289, 26,)
SOL-GOOD:	MEOH, BUOH, DMFA, DMSO
SOL-FAIR:	ETOAC, CHL
SOL-POOR:	ACET, ET2O, BENZ, HEX
TO:	(S.AUREUS, 4) (B.SUBT., 8) (S.LUTEA, 5) (SHYG., 500) (PS.AER., 500)
IS-EXT:	(MEOH, , MIC.) (BUOH, , FILT.)
IS-CHR:	(SILG, CHL-MEOH)
IS-CRY:	(PREC., MEOH, ACET) (CRYST., MEOH-ACET)

REFERENCES:

JA, 27, 274, 1974; *JACS*, 99, 5205, 1977; DT 2352693; USP 3821367

42250-1870

NAME:	EMERIMICIN-III, EM-3, U-40589
PO:	EMERICELLOPSIS MICROSPORA
CT:	PEPTIDE, PEPTAIBOPHOL, NEUTRAL
FORMULA:	C76H118N16O19
EA:	(N, 13)
MW:	1558
PC:	WH., CRYST.
OR:	(+12, MEOH)
UV:	MEOH: (253, 4.3,) (257, 4.6,) (264, 4.4,) (267, 4.1,)
SOL-GOOD:	MEOH, BUOH, DMFA, DMSO
SOL-FAIR:	CHL, ETOAC
SOL-POOR:	ACET, ET2O, BENZ, HEX
TO:	(S.AUREUS, 31) (B.SUBT., 31) (S.LUTEA, 8)

REFERENCES:

JA, 72, 274, 1974; *JACS*, 99, 5205, 1977; DT 2352693; USP 3821367

42250-1871

NAME:	EMERIMICIN-IV, EM-4, U-40590
PO:	EMERICELLOPSIS MICROSPORA
CT:	PEPTIDE, PEPTAIBOPHOL
FORMULA:	C77H120N16019
EA:	(N, 14)
MW:	1572
PC:	WH., CRYST.
OR:	(+13.5, MEOH)
UV:	MEOH: (252, 2.4,) (257, 2.6,) (264, 2.6,) (267, 2.5,)
SOL-GOOD:	MEOH, BUOH, DMFA, DMSO, CHL
SOL-FAIR:	ETOAC, BENZ
SOL-POOR:	ACET, ET20, HEX
TO:	(S.AUREUS, 31) (B.SUBT., 31) (S.LUTEA, 16) (E.COLI, 500)

REFERENCES:

JA, 72, 274, 1974; *JACS*, 99, 5205, 1977; DT 2352693; USP 3821367

42250-1872

NAME:	ZERVAMICIN-I, ZERVACIN-1
PO:	EMERICELLOPSIS SALMOSYNNEMATA
CT:	PEPTIDE, PEPTAIBOPHOL, ACIDIC, AMPHOTER
FORMULA:	C70H114N14021
EA:	(N, 13)
EW:	1513
PC:	WH., CRYST.
OR:	(+16, MEOH)
UV:	MEOH: (273, 28,) (282, 30,) (289, 27,) (315, 4,)
SOL-GOOD:	MEOH, BUOH, DMFA, DMSO
SOL-FAIR:	CHL, ETOAC
SOL-POOR:	ACET, ET20, HEX
TO:	(S.AUREUS, 500) (S.LUTEA, 250) (B.SUBT., 500) (E.COLI, 500) (P.VULG., 500)
IS-EXT:	(BUOH, , FILT.)
IS-CHR:	(SILG, CHL-MEOH)
IS-CRY:	(CRYST., CHL-ACET)

REFERENCES:

JA, 27, 321, 1974; USP 3907990

42250-1873

NAME:	ZERVAMICIN-II, ZERVACIN-2
PO:	EMERICELLOPSIS SALMOSYNNEMATA
CT:	PEPTIDE, PEPTAIBOPHOL, NEUTRAL
FORMULA:	C93H152N19029
EW:	1998
PC:	WH., CRYST.
OR:	(+4.5, MEOH)
UV:	MEOH: (274, 26,) (281, 29,) (289, 26,)
SOL-GOOD:	MEOH, ETOH, BUOH, DMFA, DMSO
SOL-FAIR:	CHL, ETOAC
SOL-POOR:	ACET, ET2O, HEX
TO:	(S.LUTEA, 4) (S.AUREUS, 8) (B.SUBT., 8) (E.COLI, 250) (K.PNEUM., 250) (PS.AER., 125)
IS-CRY:	(CRYST., MEOH-W)

REFERENCES:

JA, 27, 321, 1974; USP 3907990

42250-2081

NAME:	SUZUKACILLIN-A
PO:	TRICHODERMA VIRIDAE
CT:	ACIDIC, AMPHOTER, PEPTAIBOPHOL, PEPTIDE
FORMULA:	C109H184N26029
EA:	(N, 17)
MW:	2500|100
PC:	WH., CRYST.
OR:	(-85.7,) (-8.5, MEOH)
UV:	ETOH: (258, ,) (265, ,) (271, ,)
UV:	MEOH: (258, , 312) (264, , 245) (268, , 204)
SOL-GOOD:	MEOH, ETOH, BUOH, CHL
SOL-POOR:	W, ACET, HEX, ETOAC, DIOXAN, CCL4, ET2O, BENZ, ETOAC
QUAL:	(BIURET, +) (FECL3, -) (SAKA., -) (EHRL., -)
TO:	(B.SUBT., 10) (S.AUREUS, 20) (S.LUTEA, 20) (S.CEREV., 100) (PHYT.BACT., 20)
IS-EXT:	(BUOH, , FILT.) (MEOH, , MIC.)
IS-CHR:	(AL, MEOH)
IS-CRY:	(PREC., MEOH, W) (CRYST., CHL)

REFERENCES:

Agr. Biol. Ch., 30, 700, 1966; 36, 112, 1972; 38, 19, 1974; *Trans. Brit. Mycol. Soc.*, 57, 25, 1974; *Eur. J. Bioch.*, 54, 166, 1975; *BBA*, 433, 164, 1976; *JACS*, 99, 8469, 1977; JP 65/13795

42250-2082
NAME: SUZUKACILLIN-B
PO: TRICHODERMA VIRIDAE
CT: PEPTAIBOPHOL, PEPTIDE, ACIDIC
TO: (S.LUTEA,)
REFERENCES:
Agr. Biol. Ch., 36, 112, 1972

42250-5193
NAME: SAMAROSPORIN
PO: SAMAROSPORA SP.
CT: PEPTAIBOPHOL, PEPTIDE, NEUTRAL
FORMULA: C72H111N15O19
EA: (N, 14)
MW: 1480|20
PC: WH., CRYST.
OR: (+16.5, MEOH)
UV: MEOH: (200, ,)
SOL-GOOD: MEOH, ETOH, PYR, DMSO, ACOH, ACET-W
SOL-POOR: , ACET, HEX, W
QUAL: (BIURET, -) (FECL3, -) (DNPH, -)
TO: (S.AUREUS, 15.6) (S.LUTEA, 15.6) (B.SUBT., 31.2) (SHYG., 31.2) (E.COLI, 62) (C.ALB., 62) (S.CEREV., 31.2)
LD50: (27, IP) (750, PEROS)
IS-EXT: (MEOH, , MIC.)
IS-CRY: (PREC., MEOH, ACET) (CRYST., MEOH)
REFERENCES:
JA, 29, 618, 1976

42250-5878
NAME: 1037
PO: TRICHODERMA VIRIDAE
CT: PEPTIDE, PEPTAIBOPHOL
FORMULA: C105H217N23O53
EA: (N, 12)
MW: 2618
PC: WH., CRYST.
OR: (-8, MEOH)
SOL-GOOD: MEOH, ETOH, BUOH, T.BUOH
SOL-FAIR: PYR
SOL-POOR: ACET, HEX, DIOXAN
QUAL: (NINH., -) (EHRL., -) (SAKA., -)
TO: (G.POS.,) (PROTOZOA,)
IS-EXT: (BUOH, , FILT.) (MEOH, , MIC.)
IS-CHR: (XAD-2, MEOH-W)
IS-CRY: (CRYST., ACET)
REFERENCES:
JP 77/72891; *CA*, 87, 166000

42250-5986

NAME: ALAMETHICIN-II
PO: TRICHODERMA VIRIDAE
CT: PEPTIDE, PEPTAIBOPHOL, ACIDIC, AMPHOTER
FORMULA: C93H152N22025
EA: (N, 15)
EW: 1976
PC: WH., POW.
OR: (-30.6, MEOH)
UV: ETOH: (241.5, 3.8,) (248, 4,) (253, 5,) (258, 6,) (264.5, 4.6,) (268, 2.7,)
UV: W: (252, , 299) (257, , 279) (263, , 199) (267, , 149)
SOL-FAIR: BUOH
REFERENCES:
JACS, 99, 8469, 1977

42250-6071

NAME: ANTIAMOEBIN-II
PO: EMERICELLOPSIS POONENSIS, EMERICELLOPSIS SYNNEMINTICOLA, CEPH.PIMPRINA
CT: PEPTIDE, PEPTAIBOPHOL T.
FORMULA: C82H127N17019
EA: (N, 14)
MW: 1653
PC: WH., CRYST.
OR: (+16.1, MEOH)
TO: (S.AUREUS, 100)
REFERENCES:
JA, 31, 241, 1978

42250-6612

PO: TRICHODERMA SP.
CT: PEPTIDE, PEPTAIBOPHOL
EA: (N,)
MW: 4051
PC: WH., CRYST.
TO: (S.LUTEA,)
IS-EXT: (MEOH+CHL, 7, WB.)
IS-CHR: (HYFLO, CHL-MEOH-W)
REFERENCES:
Exp., 35, 294, 1979

42260-3905

NAME: CEREXIN-A, 60-6
PO: B.CEREUS
CT: PEPTIDE, AMPHOTER, ACIDIC, CEREXIN T.
FORMULA: C63H103N15O19
EA: (N, 15)
MW: 1600
EW: 1517
PC: WH., POW.
OR: (+19.5, DMFA)
UV: MEOH: (275, 36,) (282, 38,) (290, 33,)
SOL-GOOD: DMFA, DMSO, BASE
SOL-FAIR: MEOH-W, BUOH-W
SOL-POOR: ETOH, HEX, W
QUAL: (NINH., +) (EHRL., +)
TO: (B.SUBT., 6.25) (S.AUREUS, 50)
LD50: (75|25, IV) (150|50, IP) (1000|500, SC)
IS-EXT: (ACET-W, , MIC.) (BUOH, 7, FILT.)
IS-CRY: (PREC., CHL-MEOH-W, ETOH)
REFERENCES:
JA, 28, 48, 56, 60, 764; 1975; 29, 1268, 1275, 1281, 1976; DT 2420103

42260-3906

NAME: CEREXIN-B, GP-3
PO: B.CEREUS
CT: PEPTIDE, AMPHOTER, ACIDIC, CEREXIN T.
FORMULA: C65H90N15O18
EA: (N, 15)
MW: 1416
PC: WH., POW.
OR: (+19.8, DMFA)
UV: MEOH: (275, 36,) (282, 38,) (290, 34,)
SOL-GOOD: DMFA, DMSO, BASE
SOL-FAIR: MEOH-W, ACET-W
SOL-POOR: ETOH, HEX, W
QUAL: (EHRL., +) (NINH., +)
TO: (B.SUBT., 6.25) (S.AUREUS, 50)
LD50: (100, IP)
IS-EXT: (ACET-W, , WB.) (BUOH, , W)
IS-CRY: (PREC., BUOH, ETOH)
REFERENCES:
JA, 28, 56, 60, 764, 1975; 29, 1275, 1976; DT 2420104; USP 3590436

42260-5424

NAME: CEREXIN-C
PO: B.CEREUS
CT: PEPTIDE, AMPHOTER, CEREXIN T.
FORMULA: C63H103N15O18
EA: (N, 14)
PC: WH., POW.
OR: (+16.4, DMFA)
UV: MEOH: (276, 35,) (283, 38,) (290.5, 33,)
SOL-GOOD: DMFA, DMSO
SOL-FAIR: MEOH-W, ACET-W
SOL-POOR: BASE, ETOH, HEX
QUAL: (NINH., +) (EHRL., +)
TO: (B.SUBT., 6.25) (S.AUREUS, 6.25)
IS-FIL: 3
IS-EXT: (ACET-W, , MIC.) (CHL-MEOH, , MIC.) (BUOH, , W)
IS-CHR: (SILG, CHL-ETOH-NH4OH)
IS-CRY: (DRY, BUOH)
REFERENCES:

JA, 29, 1281, 1976

42260-5425

NAME: CEREXIN-D
PO: B.CEREUS
CT: PEPTIDE, AMPHOTER, CEREXIN T.
FORMULA: C65H99N15O17
EA: (N, 14)
PC: WH., POW.
OR: (+11.7, DMFA)
UV: MEOH: (275, 33,) (283, 36,) (290.5, 31,)
SOL-GOOD: DMFA, DMSO
SOL-FAIR: ETOH-W, ACET-W
SOL-POOR: BUOH, HEX, BASE
QUAL: (NINH., +) (EHRL., +)
TO: (B.SUBT., 6.25) (S.AUREUS, 12.5)
REFERENCES:

JA, 29, 1281, 1976

423
Cyclic Homopeptides

Introduction

Various cyclopeptides, including other types such as heteromeric peptides and peptolide-type compounds also, are well known for their biological importance not only as antibiotics but as toxins, hormones, and ion transport regulators. Macrocyclic structure (they are at least cyclic tetrapeptides) without other nonamino acid-type constituents is the characteristic fragment of the cyclic homopeptide antibiotics.

Their biological activity very strongly depends on the spatial arrangement of the whole molecules. PMR, X-ray, ORD, and CD studies have shown that a common conformational feature of most cyclopeptide antibiotics, including the cyclopeptide lactones and depsipeptides (441 to 445), is the β-turn (or loop) frequently associated with antiparallel pleated sheet structures (gramicidin S, viomycin, ilamycin), due to the intramolecular hydrogen bonds. D-Amino acids (I) or glycine and dehydro amino acids (II) are energetically favored to form the corner of these β-turns. In this respect the D and dehydro amino acids occupy exchangeable positions in all of the peptide antibiotics.

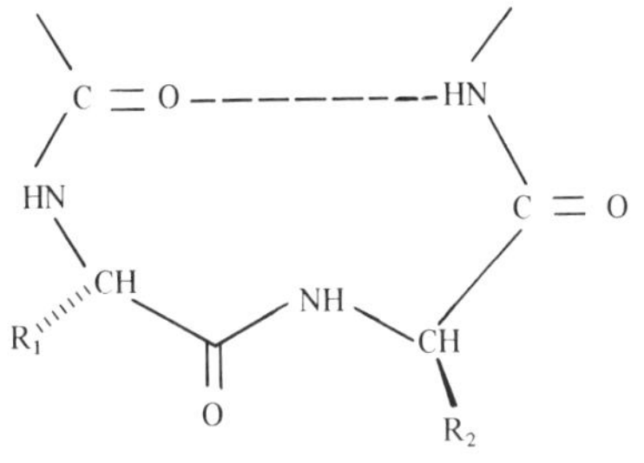

I

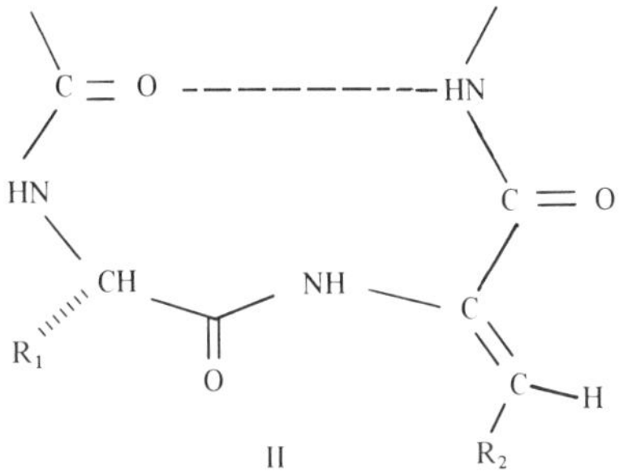

II

This group of antibiotics covers the *Bacillus*-produced tyrocidine (4231) and bacitracin (4232) type peptides, the viomycin(4233) and ilamycin (4234) type antibiotics which are *Streptomyces* metabolites, the fungal cyclosporin antibiotics (4235), and several less characterized cyclopeptides with various origins (423) such as malformins or mycobacillin. The cyclic lipopeptides (polymyxins, bacillomycins, etc.) and the cyclic peptolides and depsipeptides (431 and 44) are listed under heteromeric peptides and peptolides, respectively.

In the bacterial cyclopeptides (tyrocidines, bacitracins) only D amino acids occur as unusual constituents (D-phe, D-tyr, D-glu, D-asp, D-orn), but the other types are a unique collection of uncommon amino acids. The amino acids in the *Streptomyces* peptides all have L configuration, while in the bacterial peptides the abundance of D acids is very high. Apart from the N-methyl amino acids (N-methylvaline, N-methylleucine, N-methylalanine, sarcosine) the following unique amino acids occur in these antibiotics:

Viomycin type

(1) L-β-Lysine
(2) L-*erythro*-γ-Hydroxy-β-lysine

(3) L-N-β-Methyl-β-arginine
(4) L-α,β-Diaminopropionic acid (derived also from **(5)** during the acidic hydrolysis)
(5) β-Ureido-dehydroalanine
(6) Tuberactidin [α-(6-hydroxy-2-iminohexahydro-4-pyrimidinyl)-glicine]
(7) Capreomycidin [α-(2-iminohexahydro-4-pyrimidinyl)-glicine]
(8) Viomycidin — it is an artefact, obtained by rearrangement of **(6)**

Ilamycin type

(9) L-3-Nitrotyrosine (L-3-nitro-4-hydroxyphenylalanine)
(10) L-γ-Formyl-N-methylnorvaline (N,4-dimethylglutamic-γ-semialdehyde)
(11) Dehydronorleucine (2-amino-*trans*-4-hexenoic acid)
(12) L-1(2-methyl-3-buten-2-yl) tryptophane
(13) L-1(1,1-Dimethylpropyl) tryptophane
(14) L-1(1,1-Dimethyl-2,3-epoxypropyl) tryptophane

Cyclosporin and other types

(15) 2S-Methylamino-3R-hydroxy-4R-methyloct-6-*trans*-en-1-oic acid
(16) L-2-Amino-9,10-epoxy-8-oxo-decanoic acid
α-aminobutyric acid, γ-aminobutyric acid, α-aminoisobutyric acid

In this group there are some antibiotics with practical importance. Bacitracin is useful in human therapy and in animal feeding; viomycin, cpareomycin, and tuberactinomycin N (enviomycin) are antitubercular drugs, while gramicidin S and tyrocidines have empirical importance in molecular biology.

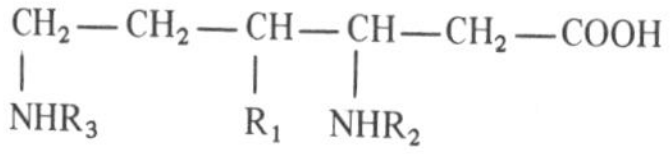

	R₁	**R₂**	**R₃**
(1)	H	H	H
(2)	OH	H	H
(3)	H	CH_3	$-C(=NH)-NH_2$

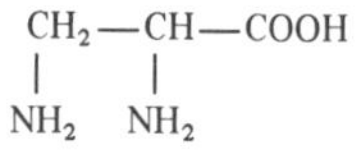

(4)

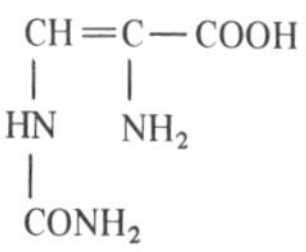

(5)

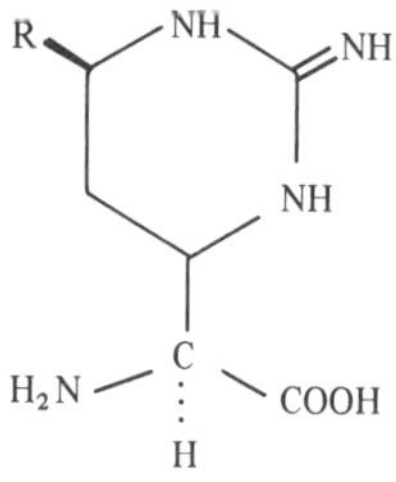

(6) R = OH
(7) R = H

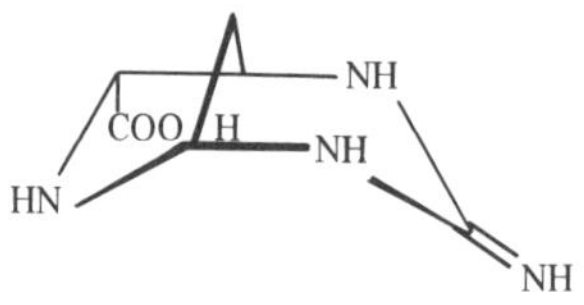

(8)

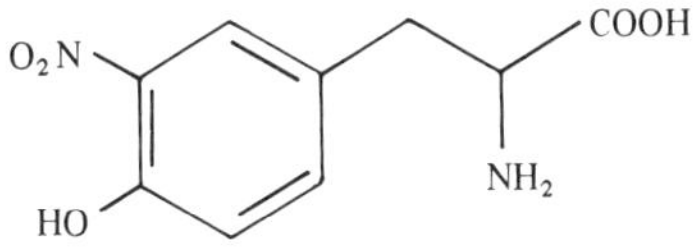

(9)

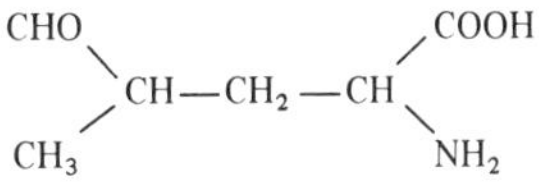

(10)

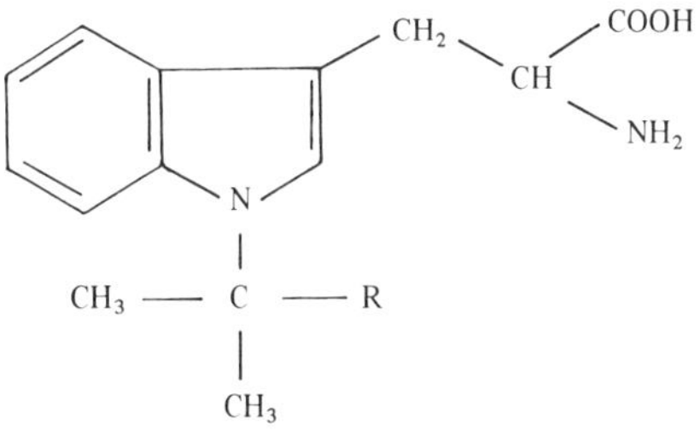

(12) R = $-CH{=}CH_2$
(13) R = $-CH_2-CH_2OH$
(14) R = 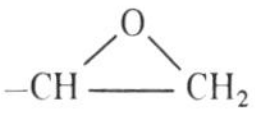

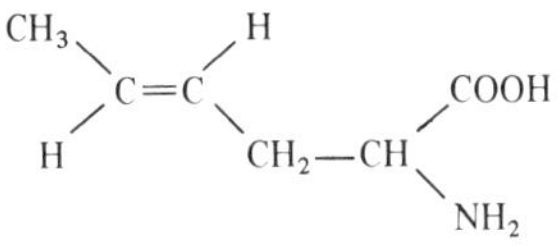

(11)

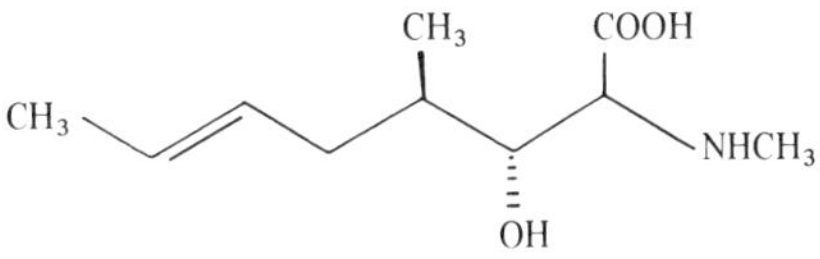

(15)

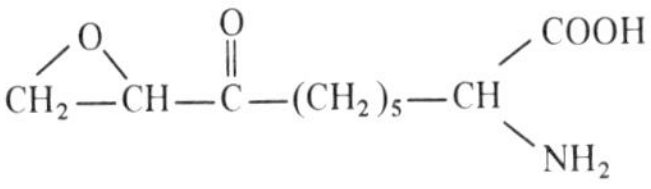

(16)

4231
Tyrocidine Type

All compounds in this type are cyclic decapeptides differing by one or two amino acid constituents. Gramicidin S, which should have a more adequate name — tyrocidine S, is also a cyclic decapeptide in which the same pentapeptide sequence occurs twice. In all tyrocidines this sequence is also present. Gramicidin S is one of the most popular subjects in the conformation study of cyclopeptides. The most probable "pleated sheet" structure is shown in the following figure:

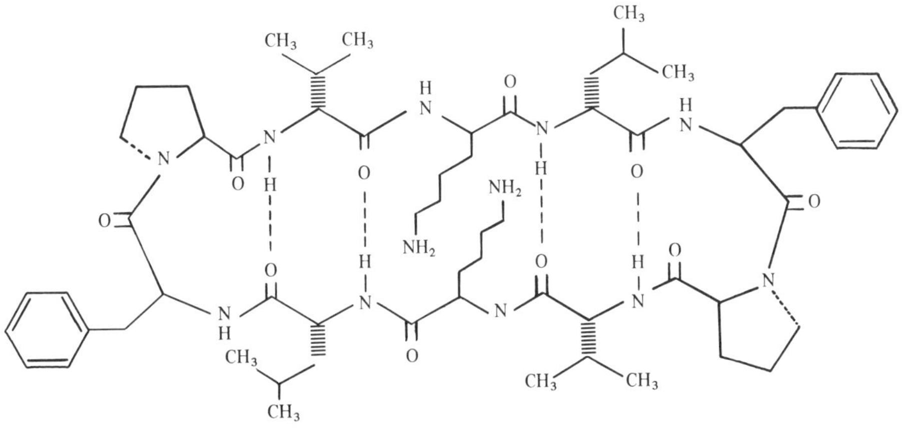

Gramicidin S

These compounds are one of the longest known antibiotics. Gramicidin S was the first naturally occurring cyclic peptide to be synthesized (in 1957). Tyrocidines are produced together with the linear gramicidins by a *Bacillus brevis* strain. This complex, tyrothricine, has limited local use in human therapy. These cyclic peptides cause hemolysis of erythrocytes, making them unsuitable for treatment of systemic infections. They are active against Gram-positive bacteria.

The whole character — stereostructure and functional groups — of the molecule is responsible for their biological activity. The cyclic decapeptide structure is one of the essential factors for bioactivity. The presence of free ornithine amino groups and their spatial proximity are both important factors in the antimicrobial activity of gramicidin S. The interaction of the protonated amino groups and the lipoprotein-phospholipid complex of bacterial membranes is the primary site of action of these compounds. The presence of several basic groups and a number of apolar side chains appears to give these compounds properties of cationic detergents; consequently they have surfactant activity.

The biosynthesis of these cyclic peptides is a typical, and exhaustively studied example of peptide biosynthesis which occurs without RNA template, but by stepwise enzymatic addition of the amino acids. This biosynthetic process features the involvement of thiol groups of synthetizing enzyme in activating the (constituent) amino acids and participation of 4′-phosphopanthotheine in the transfer of peptides to make head-to-tail condensation to the next amino acid residue.

Structures

42310

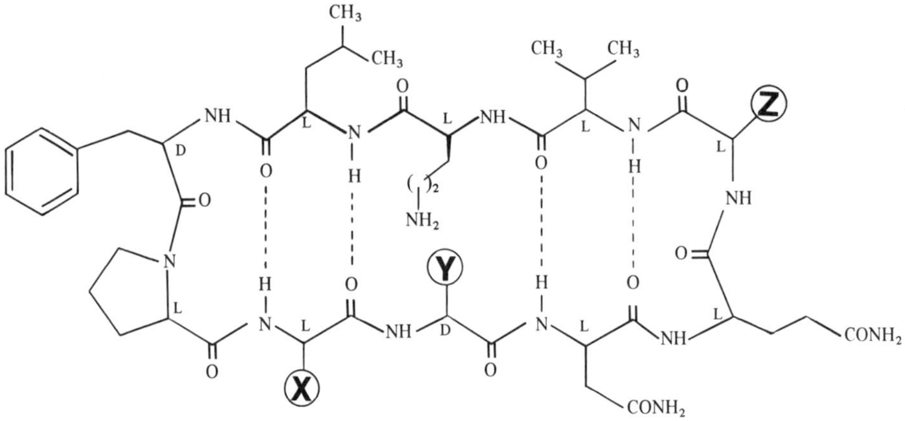

Antibiotic	X	Y	Z
Tyrocidine A	$CH_2-C_6H_5$	$CH_2-C_6H_5$	
Tyrocidine B	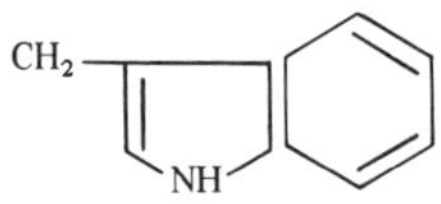		
Tyrocidine C		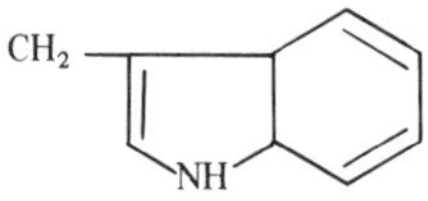	
Tyrocidine D			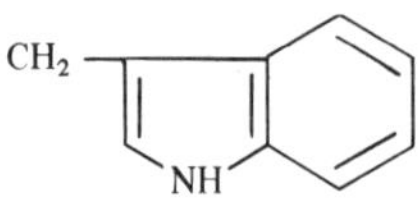
Tyrocidine E	$CH_2-C_6H_5$	$CH_2-C_6H_5$	$CH_2C_6H_5$

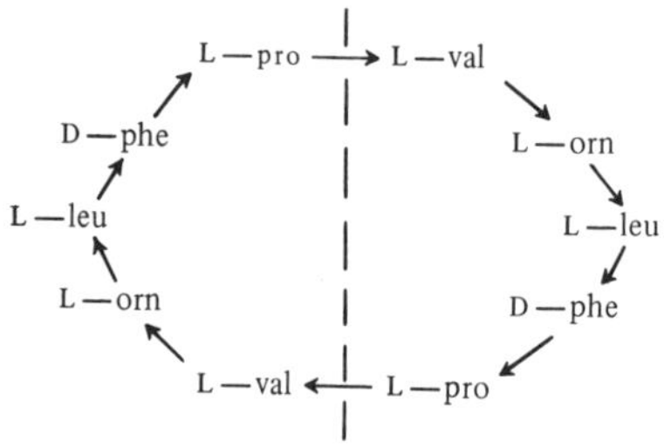

gramicidin S

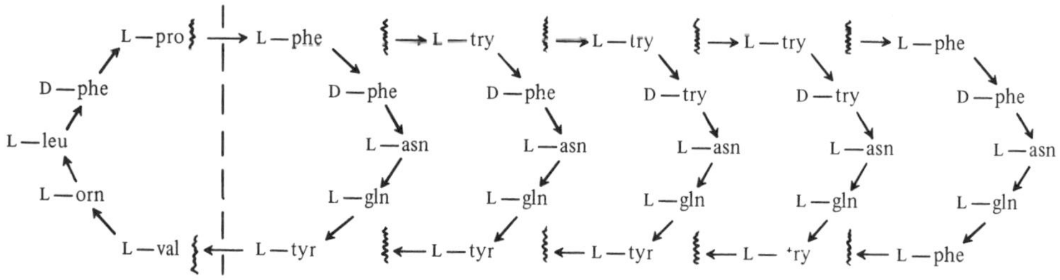

tyrocidine A B C D E

42310-1664

NAME: TYROCIDINE-A, GRAMINIC ACID
PO: B.BREVIS, B.SP.
CT: BASIC, AMPHOTER, CYCLOPEPTIDE, TYROCYDINE T.
FORMULA: C66H86N13O13.HCL
EA: (N, 14)
MW: 1300|20, 1268
PC: WH., CRYST.
OR: (-112, ETOH) (-10, ETOH-W)
UV: NAOH: (291, ,)
UV: W: (280, ,) (292, ,)
SOL-GOOD: MEOH, ETOH, ACOH, PYR
SOL-FAIR: W, ACET, DIOXAN
SOL-POOR: ETOAC, HEX
QUAL: (NINH., +) (EHRL., +) (BIURET, +)
STAB: (HEAT, +)
TO: (B.SUBT., 1) (S.AUREUS, 10) (S.LUTEA, 3)
LD50: (15, IV) (40, IP) (1000, PEROS)
REFERENCES:

JACS, 74, 4019, 4023, 1952; 76, 688, 1954; *Biochem.,* 4, 11, 1965; 5, 2857; 2864, 1966; 9, 4839, 1970; *Bull. Ch. Soc. Jap.,* 39, 1738, 1966; *Exp.,* 26, 476, 587, 1970; *TL,* 1471, 1970, *BBA,* 169, 520, 1968; *Adv. Enzymol.,* 4, 153, 1944; *Proc.Nat. Acad. Sci.,* 50, 175, 1963

42310-1665

NAME: TYROCIDINE-B
PO: B.BREVIS, B.SP.
CT: BASIC, AMPHOTER, CYCLOPEPTIDE, TYROCYDINE T.
FORMULA: C68H88N14O13.HCL
EA: (N, 14)
MW: 1660
PC: WH., CRYST.
OR: (-106, MEOH)
UV: NAOH: (291, ,)
UV: W: (280, ,) (292, ,)
SOL-GOOD: MEOH, ETOH, ACOH, PYR
SOL-FAIR: W, ACET, DIOXAN
SOL-POOR: ETOAC, HEX
QUAL: (NINH., +) (EHRL., +) (BIURET, +)
STAB: (HEAT, +)
TO: (B.SUBT., 5) (S.AUREUS, 20) (S.LUTEA, 10)
LD50: (15, IV) (40, IP) (1000, PEROS)
REFERENCES:

JACS, 77, 6624, 6627, 1955; *AAC 1968,* 87

42310-1666

NAME: TYROCIDINE-C
PO: B.BREVIS, B.SP.
CT: AMPHOTER, BASIC, CYCLOPEPTIDE, TYROCYDINE T.
FORMULA: C70H89N15O13.HCL
EA: (N, 15)
MW: 1500|100
PC: WH., POW.
OR: (-98, MEOH) (-84.3, ETOH-W)
UV: W: (280, ,) (292, ,)
SOL-GOOD: MEOH, PYR
SOL-POOR: W
QUAL: (NINH., +) (BIURET, +)
TO: (B.SUBT., 1) (S.AUREUS, 20)
REFERENCES:

Biochem., 4, 11, 1965; *TL*, 1471, 1970; *Exp.*, 26, 476, 587, 1970; *Biochem.*, 5, 2857, 2864, 1966; *J. Chrom.*, 92, 147, 1974

42310-1667

NAME: TYROCIDINE-D
PO: B.SP.
CT: NEUTRAL, CYCLOPEPTIDE, TYROCYDINE T.
FORMULA: C72H90N16O13
EA: (N, 15)
PC: WH., POW.
QUAL: (NINH., +) (BIURET, +)
TO: (B.SUBT.,) (S.AUREUS,)
REFERENCES:

Exp., 26, 476, 587, 1970; *Proc. Nat. Acad. Sci.*, 52, 876, 1964; *Biochem.*, 5, 2864, 1966

42310-1668

NAME: TYROCIDINE-E
PO: B.BREVIS
CT: AMPHOTER, CYCLOPEPTIDE, TYROCYDINE T.
FORMULA: C66H86N13O12
EA: (N, 15)
PC: WH., POW.
OR: (-116, MEOH)
QUAL: (NINH., +) (BIURET, +)
TO: (B.SUBT., 10) (S.AUREUS, 10)
REFERENCES:

Exp., 26, 476, 1970; *BBA*, 169, 520, 1968

42310-1669

NAME:	GRAMICIDIN-S
IDENTICAL:	GRAMICIDIN-J
PO:	B.BREVIS, B.NAGANO, B.SP.
CT:	NEUTRAL, CYCLOPEPTIDE, TYROCYDINE T.
FORMULA:	C60H92N12O10
EA:	(N, 13)
MW:	1248
PC:	WH., CRYST.
OR:	(-295, ETOH)
UV:	(200, ,)
SOL-GOOD:	MEOH-W, ACET, CHL
SOL-FAIR:	ETOH
SOL-POOR:	W, ET2O, HEX
QUAL:	(NINH., +) (BIURET, +) (PAULY, -) (SAKA., -)
STAB:	(ACID, +) (HEAT, +)
TO:	(S.AUREUS, 2) (B.SUBT., 1) (SHYG., 12) (E.COLI, 25) (P.VULG., 100)
LD50:	(17, IV-RATS)
IS-CRY:	(PREC., FILT., HCL) (CRYST., ETOH)
UTILITY:	BIOCHEMICAL REAGENT

REFERENCES:

CA, 39, 1893, 1894, 1945; *Nature*, 154, 703, 1944; 190, 120, 1961; 217, 635, 1968; *Bioch. J.*, 39, 363, 1945; 40, 261, 624, 1946; 41, 596, 1947; *Nature*, 227, 480, 1970; 174, 840, 1954; 211, 1039, 1966; *Helv.*, 40, 624, 1957; *Antib.*, 38, 1972; *TL*, 1267, 1970; *CC*, 1073, 1970; *Proc. Nat. Acad. Sci.*, 61, 374, 1968; *BBRC*, 36, 194, 1969; *Dokl.*, 74, 111, 1950; *Biokhim.*, 27, 849, 1962; *Antib.*, 6, 33, 1958

42310-1670

NAME: GRAMICIDIN-J
IDENTICAL: GRAMICIDIN-S
PO: B.BREVIS, B.NAGANO
CT: BASIC, CYCLOPEPTIDE, TYROCYDINE T.
FORMULA: C44H65N907
EA: (N, 14)
MW: 820|30
OR: (-318.8, ETOH)
UV: ETOH: (249, ,) (258, ,) (265, ,)
SOL-GOOD: ETOH, MEOH, CHL
SOL-FAIR: ACET, W
SOL-POOR: BENZ, ET20, HEX
QUAL: (BIURET, +) (NINH., +)
TO: (S.AUREUS, .8) (B.SUBT., .8) (E.COLI, 20) (P.VULG., 40) (PS.AER., 40) (SHYG., 40) (C.ALB., 8)
LD50: (20.8, IP)
IS-ABS: (DIATOM., MEOH)
IS-CRY: (CRYST., MEOH-BUOAC)
REFERENCES:

Proc. Jap. Acad., 30, 991, 1954; *Osaka Shiritsu Daigaku Zasshi*, 7, 640, 1958; *J. Bioch. (Tokyo)*, 56, 101, 103, 1964; *Med. Dosw.*, 13, 377, 1961; *J. Osaka City Med. Cent.*, 6, 89, 1957; 7, 1, 40, 1958; *CA*, 54, 17516; 55, 9519; *Bull. Ch. Soc. Jap.*, 33, 753, 1960

42310-1671

NAME: B-456
PO: B.SUBTILIS
CT: AMPHOTER, CYCLOPEPTIDE, TYROCYDINE T.
EA: (C, 58) (H, 7) (N, 11)
PC: WH., POW.
OR: (-229, MEOH)
UV: MEOH: (278, 1010,)
SOL-GOOD: MEOH, ETOH, PYR, ACID, BASE
SOL-FAIR: BUOH
SOL-POOR: W, ACET, HEX
QUAL: (NINH., +) (BIURET, +)
STAB: (HEAT, -) (BASE, -)
TO: (C.ALB., 6)
LD50: (85, IP)
IS-EXT: (MEOH, ,)
IS-CRY: (PREC., FILT., HCL)
REFERENCES:

Jap. J. Ant., 9, 1, 1956; *CA*, 53, 20250

42310-1672

NAME: <u>BRESEIN</u>
PO: B.BREVIS
CT: BASIC, CYCLOPEPTIDE, TYROCYDINE T.
EA: (N, 15)
PC: WH., POW.
QUAL: (BIURET, +)
TO: (B.SUBT.,)
IS-EXT: (MEOH, , MIC.)
IS-CRY: (DRY, ETOH)
REFERENCES:
Vestn. Moscow Univ. Biol. Fac., 23, 42, 1968; *CA*, 69, 142; *Antib.*, 583, 1971; *Dokl.*, 204, 465, 1972; *CA*, 77, 59979

42310-1706

NAME: <u>GRATIZIN</u>
PO: B.BREVIS
CT: CYCLOPEPTIDE, TYROCYDINE T.
EA: (N,)
PC: WH., CRYST.
UV: HCL: (270, ,)
SOL-GOOD: MEOH, ETOH, ACOH, ACET-W
SOL-FAIR: W
SOL-POOR: CHL, HEX
TO: (G.POS., 1)
IS-EXT: (ETOH, , MIC.)
REFERENCES:
Vestn. Moscow Univ. Biol. Fac., 27, 110, 1972; *CA*, 77, 162982

4232
Bacitracin Type

Bacitracin is a complex mixture of polypeptides in which the major peptide is bacitracin A representing a unique dodecapeptide structure. In the molecule of bacitracin A a cyclic hexapeptide ring occurs and in the peptide side chain a thiazolidine structure occurs, formed by ring closure between the amino and mercapto groups of cysteine and the carboxyl group of the terminal isoleucine. Probably no single structural formula can represent the true state of active peptide bacitracin A, since numerous tautomeric or resonating forms with various intramolecular interactions depending on the pH or solvent environment are possible.

Commercial bacitracin is a mixture of at least ten peptides. Some of them are inactive products, maybe artefacts, formed by rearrangement of the active peptides (bacitracins A, B, and C). Isolation of individual peptides presents a difficult separation problem, because bacitracin is unstable outside the pH region 4.5 to 6.5. The stability and potency of bacitracin are enhanced by Zn^{++}.

Bacitracin is bactericidal against Gram-positive bacteria. It is effective in a number of systemic and local infections when administered parenterally or intramuscularly. Presently bacitracin is used only for topical application, but it is widely used as an animal feed supplement.

Bacitracin exerts its activity through the inhibition of mucopeptide cell wall synthesis. Its bactericidal action is a result of the inhibition of the pyrophosphatase which catalyzes the cleavage of the C_{55}-isoprenylpyrophosphate to the corresponding phosphate, which is required for regeneration of the lipid carrier in peptidoglycan synthesis.

Structure

42320

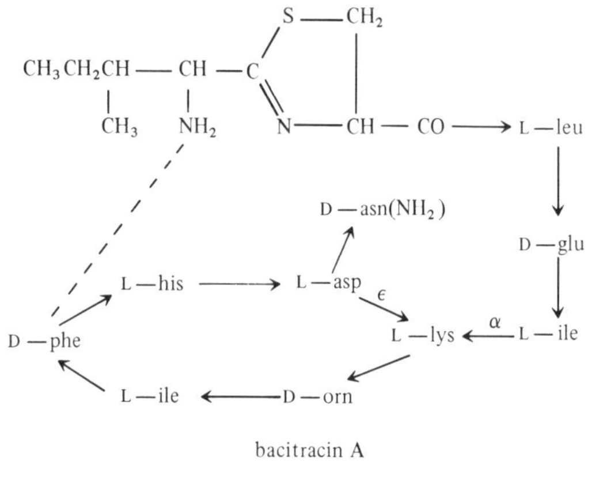

bacitracin A

42320-1673

NAME:	BACITRACIN-A
IDENTICAL:	AYFIVIN
PO:	B.SUBTILIS, B.LICHENIFORMIS
CT:	BACITRACIN T., CYCLOPEPTIDE, BASIC, AMPHOTER
FORMULA:	C66H103N17O16S
EA:	(N, 16) (S, 2)
MW:	1470
PC:	WH., POW.
OR:	(+5, HCL) (-3.6, NAOH)
UV:	W: (254, 21.4,)
SOL-GOOD:	W, MEOH, ETOH, PYR, FA, I.PROH
SOL-FAIR:	ACET, BUOH, DIOXAN
SOL-POOR:	ETOAC, HEX
QUAL:	(NINH., +) (BIURET, +)
STAB:	(HEAT, +) (BASE, -)
TO:	(S.AUREUS, .002)
LD50:	(360, IV) (420|220, IP) (1900|600, SC)
IS-EXT:	(BUOH, , FILT.)
UTILITY:	FEED ADDITIVE, ANTIBACTERIAL DRUG

REFERENCES:

Brit. J. Exp. Path., 30, 425, 427, 444, 458, 1949; *Sci.*, 102, 376, 1945; *J. Bact.*, 55, 249, 1948; 56, 507, 1948; *J. Clin. Invest.*, 28, 1019, 1949; *Bioch. J.*, 61, 534, 1955; *JACS*, 77, 731, 3123, 1955; 88, 2025, 1966; 83, 145, 1961; *Nature*, 179, 536, 1957; *Biochem.*, 8, 2348, 1969; *J. Chrom.*, 99, 597, 1974; *JOC*, 22, 1395, 1957 *Acta Chem. Scand.*, 6, 1237, 1952

42320-1674

NAME:	BACITRACIN-B
PO:	B.SUBTILIS, B.LICHENIFORMIS
CT:	BACITRACIN T., CYCLOPEPTIDE, BASIC, AMPHOTER
FORMULA:	C73H117N18O19S
EA:	(N, 16) (S, 2)
PC:	WH., POW.
OR:	(-2.8, HCL)
UV:	W: (253, ,)
SOL-GOOD:	W, MEOH
SOL-FAIR:	ACET, BUOH
SOL-POOR:	ETOAC, HEX
QUAL:	(NINH., +) (BIURET, +)
TO:	(G.POS.,)

REFERENCES:

Brit. J. Exp. Path., 30, 444, 1949; *Bioch. J.*, 47, 257, 1950; 58, 633, 1954; 53, 597, 1953; *JACS*, 76, 2839, 1954; 77, 721, 723, 3123, 1955

42320-1675

NAME: BACITRACIN-C
PO: B.LICHENIFORMIS
CT: BACITRACIN T., CYCLOPEPTIDE
EA: (N,) (S,)
PC: WH.
UV: W: (258, ,)
SOL-GOOD: W, MEOH
QUAL: (BIURET, +)
TO: (G.POS.,)
REFERENCES:

Brit. J. Exp. Path., 30, 444, 1949; *Bioch. J.*, 47, 257, 1950; 58, 633, 1954; 53, 597, 1953; *JACS*, 76, 2839, 1954; 77, 721, 723, 3123, 1955

42320-1676

NAME: BACITRACIN-G, BACITRACIN-X, BACITRACIN-F
CT: BACITRACIN T., CYCLOPEPTIDE, AMPHOTER
TO: (G.POS.,)
IS-CHR: (CEL,)
REFERENCES:

BBRC, 40, 530, 1970; *JOC*, 27, 934, 1962; *Ant. An.*, 1118, 1954-55; *CA*, 62, 2213; *J. Agr. Chem. Soc. Jap.*, 33, 325, 329, 936, 1959; 36, 793, 797, 1962

4233
Viomycin Type

The antibiotics in the viomycin type are hexapeptides consisting of a peptide ring and a basic amino acid side chain. The 16-membered macro ring contains β-ureido-dehydroalanine chromophore, α,β-diaminopropionic acid units in the branching position, and a novel guanidine carbinol system.

The structure of these antibiotics has been the subject of considerable controversy. The determination of the structure of the chromophore and the guanidine-containing fragments has proved to be a difficult task. Their structures were revised several times and it is interesting that according to very recent results capreomycins have a different amino acid sequence compared to other congeners of this type.

All amino acids occurring in these antibiotics have L configuration. A significant feature of these compounds is the presence of the hydrogen-bound 10-membered ring (β-turn) structure due to the presence of dehydroamino acid. These antibiotics are water-soluble basic substances, effective against mycobacteria and several Gram-positive and Gram-negative bacteria. The in vitro potency of these antibiotics is low. They show a strong and characteristic UV absorption maximum at 266 to 268 nm, with a batochromic shift to 285 to 290 nm in alcalic solution.

Some of these antibiotics, namely viomycin, capreomycin, and tuberactinomycin N (enviomycin), gained limited clinical application in the chemotherapy of tuberculosis, mainly in combination with other antitubercular drugs. They are the prototypes of the minor antituberculotic drugs. These antibiotics have relatively low acute toxicity, but long-term treatment produced rather serious side effects. Chronic toxicity is primarily associated with damage to the eighth cranial nerve and to the kidney. The nephrotoxic effects are manifested by albuminuria, cylindurine, etc. Partial loss of hearing and allergenic reactions have also been observed. The ototoxicity of tuberactinomycin N seems to be less pronounced compared to other members.

Their mode of action apparently is inhibition of protein synthesis at the stage of amino acid transfer from the tRNA-ribosome complex.

4234, 4235, and 423
Other Cyclic Homopeptides

Ilamycins (4234) are homodetic cycloheptapeptides built up solely from L-amino acids, among which some have unique chemical structures **(9 to 14)**. In ilamycin A the aldehyde group is in hemiacetal (cyclol) structure, as shown in the following figure:

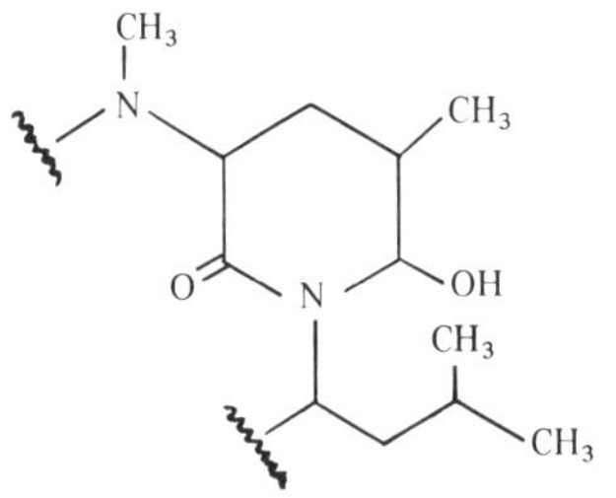

Due to the 3-nitrotyrosine fragment these yellow-colored compounds show UV absorption at 278 to 280 and 355 to 360 nm. These antibiotics exhibit antimycobacterial activity.

Cyclosporin antibiotics (4235), produced by fungi, are neutral undecapeptides whose structures are rich in hydrophobic amino acids, including an unusual new nine carbon containing-acid **(15)**. They exhibit weak antifungal, immunosuppressive, and antiphlogistic activities. Cyclosporin, rather than being cytostatic or lympholytic, affects an early stage of mitogenic triggering of the immunocompetent lymphoid cells.

Malformins are cyclic pentapeptides with an intramolecular -S-S- bridge. These plant growth regulators induce malformation of bean plants and exhibit antimicrobial and cytostatic properties. Mycobacillin, the cyclic tridecapeptide from *B. subtilis,* is similar to bacillomycins (4314) in its amino acid composition and biological activity. The 43-membered ring of mycobacillin contains two γ-glutamyl linkages.

Structures

42330

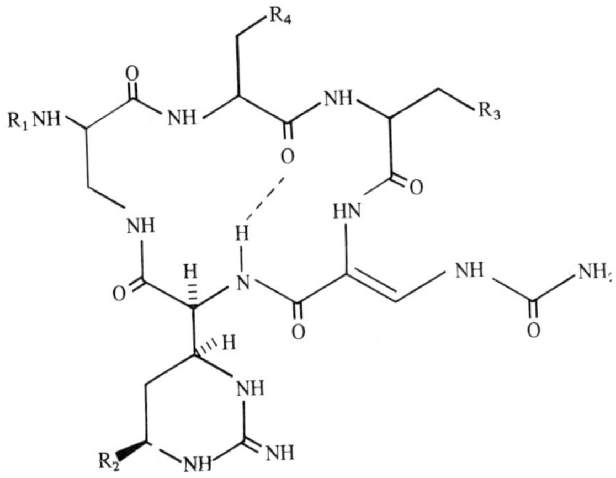

Antibiotic	R_1	R_2	R_3	R_4
Viomycin (tuberactinomycin B)	X	OH	OH	OH
Tuberactinomycin A	Y	OH	OH	OH
Tuberactinomycin N	Y	H	OH	OH
Tuberactinomycin O	X	H	OH	OH
Deslysil-viomycin (LL-BM-547α)	H	OH	OH	OH
LL-BM-547β	Z	OH	OH	OH
Capreomycin IA	H	H	NH-X	OH
Capreomycin IB	H	H	NH-X	H
Capreomycin IIA	H	H	NH_2	OH?
Capreomycin IIB	H	H	NH_2	H?

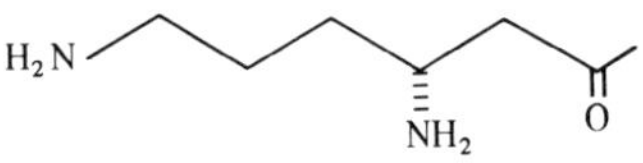

X

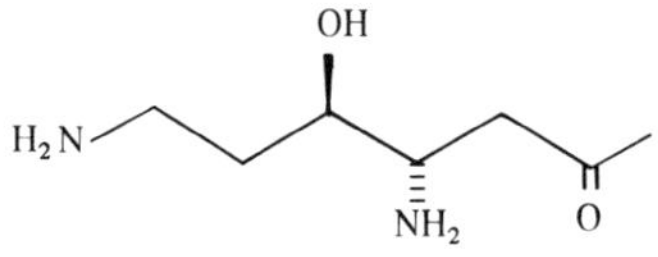

Y

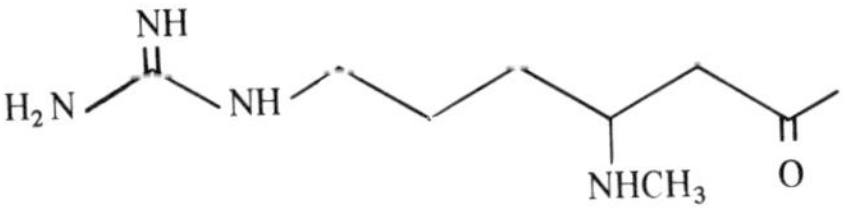

Z

42340

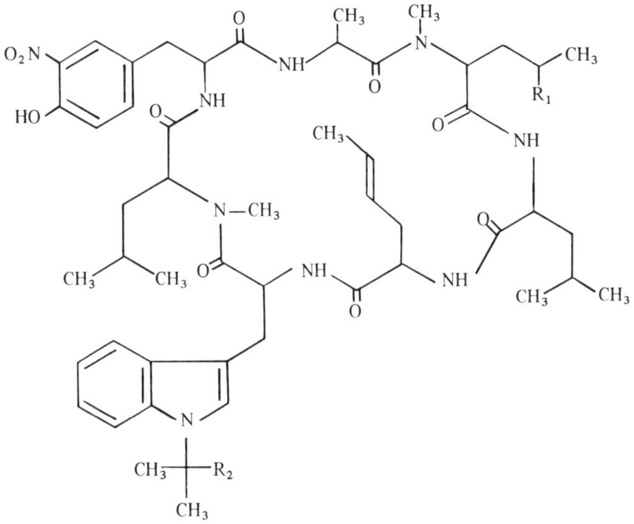

Antibiotic	R_1	R_2
Ilamycin A (rufomycin III)	CHO	$-CH(O)CH_2$ (epoxide)
Ilamycin B_1 (rufomycin I)	CH_3	$-CH{=}CH_2$
Ilamycin B_2	CH_3	$-CH(O)CH_2$ (epoxide)
Ilamycin C_1	CHO	$-CH_2CH_2OH$

42350

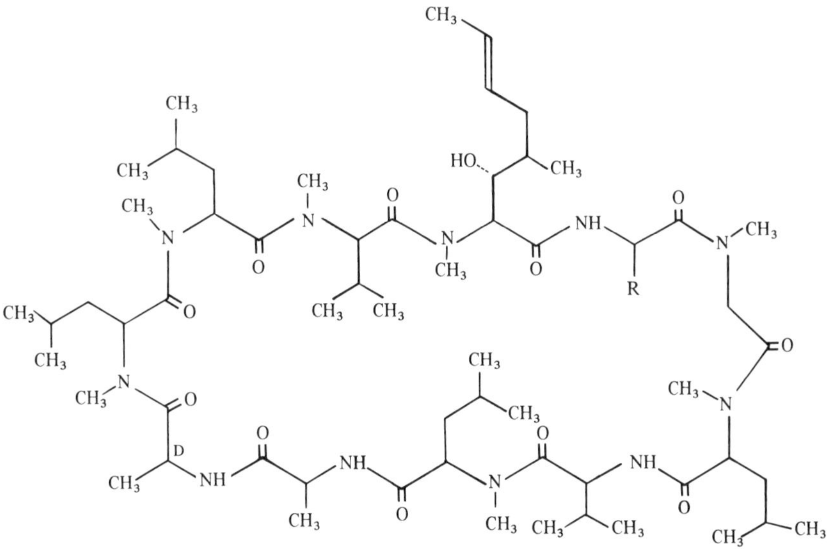

cyclosporin A $R = C_2H_5$
cyclosporin B $R = CH_3$
cyclosporin C $R = CH(OH)CH_3$
cyclosporin D $R = CH(CH_3)_2$

42300

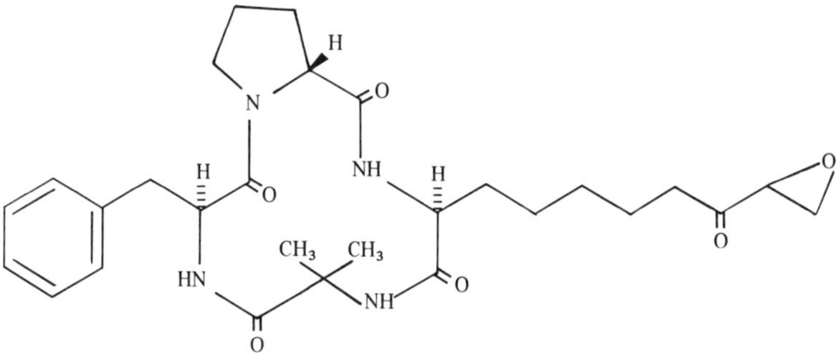

chlamydocin (SL-3440)

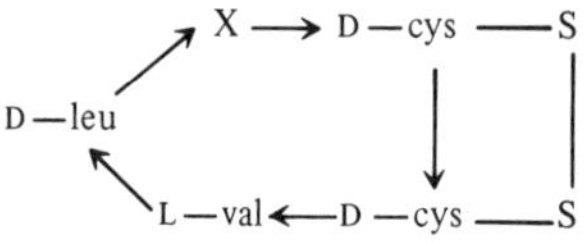

malformin A_1	X = L-ile
malformin B_1	X = L-*a*ile
malformin B_2	X = L-val

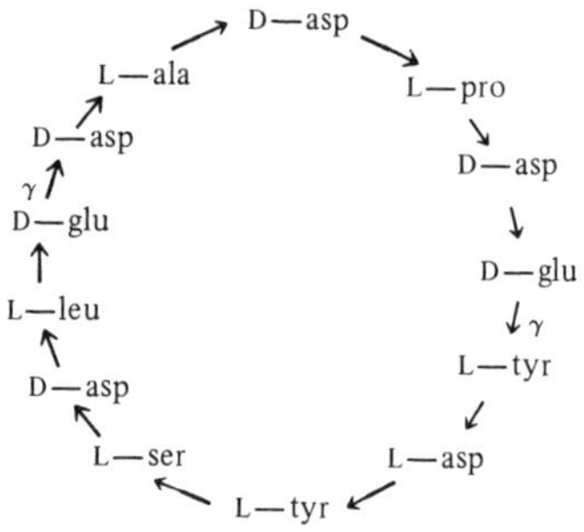

mycobacillin

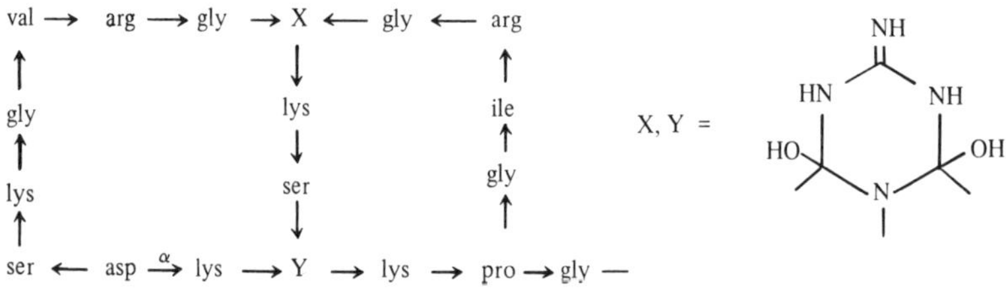

triculamin (partial structure)

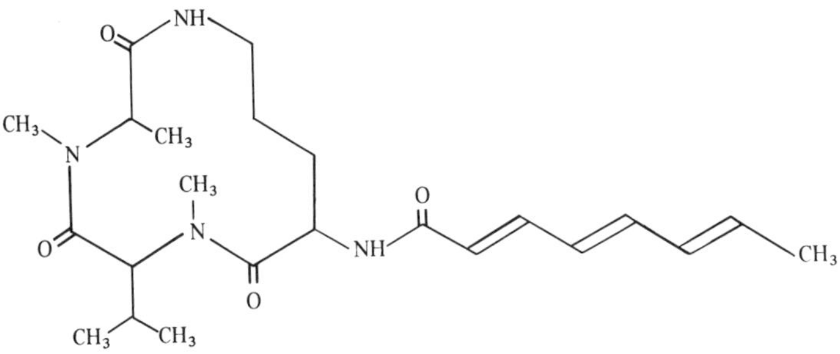

aspochracin

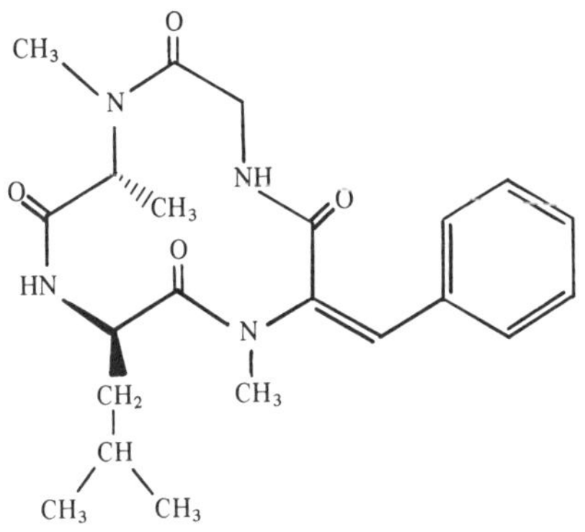

isotentoxin

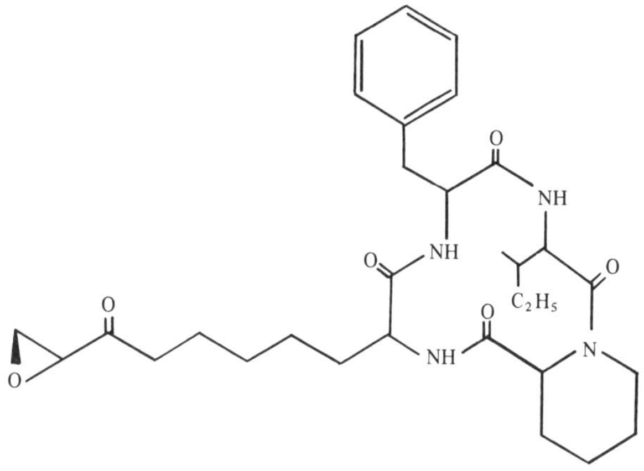

CYL-2

42330-1677

NAME:	VIOMYCIN, VINACTIN
TRADE NAMES:	VINACTANE, VIOCIN
IDENTICAL:	FLORIMYCIN, TUBERACTINOMYCIN-B, KOLUOPTHISIN, S-300, PHTIOMYCIN
PO:	S.VINACEUS, S.PUNICEUS, S.FLORIDAE, S.ABIKOENSIS, S.OLIVORETICULI, S.CALIFORNICUS, S.GRISEUS-PURPUREUS
CT:	CYCLOPEPTIDE, VIOMYCIN T., BASIC
FORMULA:	C25H43N13O10
EA:	(N, 26)
MW:	686
PC:	WH., CRYST.
OR:	(-39.8, W)
UV:	HCL: (268, 339, 20000)
UV:	NAOH: (285, , 15000)
UV:	W: (268, 328, 24000)
SOL-GOOD:	W
SOL-FAIR:	MEOH
SOL-POOR:	BUOH, HEX
QUAL:	(SAKA., +) (BIURET, +) (NINH., +) (FEHL., +)
STAB:	(ACID, +) (BASE, -) (HEAT, +)
TO:	(B.SUBT., 3.2) (S.AUREUS, 25) (S.LUTEA, 100) (K.PNEUM., 10) (E.COLI, 1) (SHYG., 2.5) (P.VULG., 6.3) (PS.AER., 6.3) (MYCOB.TUB., .7)
LD50:	(200|40, IV) (400, IV) (1381, SC)
IS-FIL:	2
IS-ION:	(IRC-50-NA, HCL)
IS-CRY:	(PREC., MEOH, BUOH) (CRYST., MEOH-W)
UTILITY:	ANTIBACTERIAL DRUG

REFERENCES:

JACS, 74, 599, 1952; 86, 5363, 1967; *Am. Rev. Tub.*, 63, 1, 4, 7, 17, 44, 1951; *Ant. & Chem.*, 1, 203, 1951; 4, 1210, 1954; 7, 435, 1957; *Chem. Ph. Bull.*, 20, 2176, 1972; 22, 1527, 1974; 23, 2113, 1975; 24, 1324, 1976; 25, 280, 1977; *Exp.*, 27, 801, 1971; *TL*, 2043, 1971; 3305, 1964; 585, 1965; 5901, 1968; *CC*, 660, 1972; *JCS Perkin I*, 820, 827, 1972; *JA*, 21, 512, 1968; 22, 39, 1969; 25, 427, 1972; 26, 528, 1973; *Antib.*, 872, 997, 1965; *Exp.*, 27, 501, 1971; Hung. P 153683; *CA*, 67, 62992; USP 2828245, 2633445; BP 651269

42330-1678

NAME: PHTIOMYCIN
IDENTICAL: VIOMYCIN
PO: S.SP.
CT: CYCLOPEPTIDE, VIOMYCIN T., BASIC
EA: (C,) (H,) (N,)
PC: WH., POW.
OR: (-11, W-HCL)
UV: HCL: (268, 171,)
UV: NAOH: (282, 157,)
UV: W: (268, 171,)
SOL-GOOD: W
SOL-POOR: BUOH, HEX
QUAL: (SAKA., +) (NINH., +) (BIURET, +) (FECL3, -)
STAB: (ACID, +)
TO: (B.SUBT., 25) (MYCOB.SP., 10)
LD50: (600, IV)
IS-ION: (IRC-50, HCL)
IS-CRY: (PREC., W, MEOH)
REFERENCES:
JA, 6, 183, 1953; 7, 17, 1954; JP 55/3096; *CA*, 51, 13323

42330-1679

NAME: DESLYSIL-VIOMYCIN
IDENTICAL: LL-BM-547A"
PO: S.SP., NOC.SP.
CT: CYCLOPEPTIDE, VIOMYCIN T., BASIC
FORMULA: C19H31N11O9
EA: (N, 25)
PC: WH., POW.
UV: (256, ,)
UV: NAOH: (281, ,)
UV: W: (268, ,)
SOL-GOOD: W
SOL-POOR: BUOH, HEX
QUAL: (NINH., +) (FEHL., +) (SAKA., +)
TO: (B.SUBT.,) (MYCOB.TUB.,) (MYCOB.SP., 25)
(K.PNEUM., 100)
IS-ION: (IRC-50, H2SO4)
IS-CHR: (CEL, PROH-PYR-ACOH-W)
IS-CRY: (PREC., W, MEOH)
REFERENCES:
Acta Polon. Pharm., 30, 431, 1973; *Med. Dosw.*, 22, 95; *JOC*, 42, 1282, 1977; *CA*, 73, 33864; 83, 41522; Pol. P, 71192

42330-1680

NAME:	CAPREOMYCIN-I-A, CAPROMYCIN, A-250-II, 29275
TRADE NAMES:	CAPSTAT
PO:	S.CAPREOLUS, DACTYLOSPORANGIUM VARIESPORUM
CT:	CYCLOPEPTIDE, VIOMYCIN T., BASIC
FORMULA:	C25H44N14O8
EA:	(N, 28)
MW:	750, 1115
EW:	740
PC:	WH., POW.
OR:	(-29.7, W) (-21.9, W)
UV:	HCL: (268, 269,) (269, , 24000)
UV:	NAOH: (283, 175,) (289, , 15900)
UV:	W: (267, 280, 26050) (268, , 23000)
SOL-GOOD:	W
SOL-POOR:	MEOH, HEX
QUAL:	(BIURET, +) (NINH., +) (EHRL., -)
STAB:	(HEAT, +)
TO:	(B.SUBT., 6) (S.AUREUS, 100) (K.PNEUM., 62) (E.COLI, 100) (P.VULG., 100) (SHYG., 100) (MYCOB.TUB., 3) (FUNGI, 25)
LD50:	(250, IV) (514, SC) (10000, PEROS)
TV:	ANTITUMOR
IS-FIL:	3
IS-ION:	(IRC-50-NH4, HCL)
IS-ABS:	(CARBON, HCL) (CARBON, BUOH-W-HCL) (CARBON, BUOH-HCL)
IS-CHR:	(DX-50-H, ET3N) (SILG, ACET-NH4OAC-NH4OH) (IRC-50, NH4OAC)
IS-CRY:	(PREC., W, MEOH)
UTILITY:	ANTIBACTERIAL DRUG

REFERENCES:

Nature, 231, 301, 1971; *AAC 1962*, 201, 596; *Sci.*, 146, 403, 1964; *CC*, 1301, 1968; *JCSC*, 3040, 1971; *An. N.Y. Acad. Sci.*, 135, 940—1200, 1966; *TL*, 2925, 1968; 3907, 1976; *Exp.*, 32, 1109, 1976; *JA*, 30, 955, 1971; *Tetr.*, 34, 921, 1978; *Butler Univ. Botan. Stud.*, 14, 1, 1964; *Praxis Pneumol.*, 18, 798, 1964; *Tox. Appl. Pharm.*, 12, 350, 1968; USP 3143468, 4026766; BP 920563

42330-1681

NAME:	CAPREOMYCIN-II-A
PO:	S.CAPREOLUS, DACTYLOSPORANGIUM VARIESPORUM
CT:	CYCLOPEPTIDE, VIOMYCIN T., BASIC
FORMULA:	C19H32N12O7
EA:	(N, 28)
MW:	770
EW:	740
PC:	WH., POW.
OR:	(+2.5, W)
UV:	HCL: (267, 300,)
UV:	NAOH: (272, 183,)
UV:	W: (266, , 26400)
SOL-GOOD:	W
SOL-POOR:	MEOH, HEX
QUAL:	(NINH., +) (BIURET, +) (EHRL., -)
TO:	(S.AUREUS, 100) (B.SUBT., 12.5) (K.PNEUM., 100) (E.COLI, 100) (P.VULG., 100) (SHYG., 100)
LD50:	(750, IV)

REFERENCES:

Nature, 231, 301, 1971; *JCS,* 3040, 1971; *JA,* 30, 955, 1977; *Tetr.,* 34, 921, 1978

42330-1682

NAME:	CAPREOMYCIN-I-B
PO:	S.CAPREOLUS, DACTYLOSPORANGIUM VARIESPORUM
CT:	CYCLOPEPTIDE, VIOMYCIN T., BASIC
FORMULA:	C25H44N14O7
EA:	(N, 28)
MW:	1050
PC:	WH., POW.
OR:	(-27.6, W) (-44.6, W)
UV:	HCL: (268, , 22700)
UV:	NAOH: (283, ,) (290, , 14400)
UV:	W: (266, , 24050) (268, , 22300)
SOL-GOOD:	W
SOL-POOR:	MEOH, HEX
QUAL:	(NINH., +) (BIURET, +)
TO:	(S.AUREUS, 100) (B.SUBT., 20) (K.PNEUM., 62) (MYCOB.SP., 3)
LD50:	(250, IV)
IS-ABS:	(CARBON, BUOH-HCL)
IS-CHR:	(CG-50-NH4, PH9 PUFF) (IRC-50, NH4OAC)

REFERENCES:

JA, 30, 955, 1977; *Tetr.,* 34, 921, 1978

42330-1683

NAME:	CAPREOMYCIN-II-B
PO:	S.CAPREOLUS, DACTYLOSPORANGIUM VARIESPORUM
CT:	CYCLOPEPTIDE, VIOMYCIN T., BASIC
FORMULA:	C19H32N12O6
EA:	(N, 28)
MW:	790
EW:	740
PC:	WH., POW.
OR:	(+2.5, W)
UV:	HCL: (267, 300,)
UV:	NAOH: (272, 183,)
UV:	W: (266, , 26950)
SOL-GOOD:	W
SOL-POOR:	MEOH, HEX
QUAL:	(BIURET, +) (NINH., +) (EHRL., -)
TO:	(S.AUREUS, 100) (B.SUBT., 12.5) (E.COLI, 100) (P.VULG., 100) (K.PNEUM., 50) (SHYG., 100)
LD50:	(750, IV)

REFERENCES:

JA, 30, 955, 1977; *Tetr.*, 34, 921, 1978

42330-1684

NAME:	TUBERACTINOMYCIN-A, TUBERACTIN, HYDROXYVIOMYCIN
PO:	S.GRISEOVERTICILLATUS-TUBERACTICUS, STV.SP., STV.SP.
CT:	CYCLOPEPTIDE, VIOMYCIN T., BASIC
FORMULA:	C25H43N13O11
MW:	701
EW:	484|2
PC:	WH., CRYST.
OR:	(-31.5, W)
UV:	HCL: (268.5, 313,)
UV:	NAOH: (285.5, 206.5,)
UV:	W: (268, 330,)
SOL-GOOD:	W, DMFA
SOL-FAIR:	MEOH
SOL-POOR:	BUOH, HEX
QUAL:	(NINH., +) (SAKA., +) (BIURET, +) (PAULY, -) (EHRL., -)
STAB:	(ACID, +)
TO:	(S.AUREUS, 30) (B.SUBT., 12.5) (S.LUTEA, 100) (PS.AER., 12.5) (E.COLI, 25) (SHYG., 50) (MYCOB.TUB., 4) (C.ALB., 200)
LD50:	(200, IV) (507, IV)
IS-FIL:	2
IS-ION:	(IRC-50-NA, HCL)
IS-CHR:	(SEPHADEX G-25, W)
IS-CRY:	(CRYST., MEOH-W)

REFERENCES:

JA, 21, 681, 1968; 24, 680, 1971; 25, 201, 1972; 27, 900, 1976; 28, 292, 1975; 30, 1008, 1977; *TL*, 3497, 1970; 2043, 1971; *Bull. Ch. Soc. Jap.*, 45, 3668, 1972; 46, 949, 1973; *Bull. Ch. Soc. Jap.*, 47, 2292, 1974; *JOC*, 42, 1282, 1977; *Tuberculosis*, 43, 245, 249, 1969; *Am. Rev. Resp. Dis.*, 100, 228, 1969; Holl. P 71/9029

	42330-1685
NAME:	TUBERACTINOMYCIN-N
TRADE NAMES:	ENVIOMYCIN
PO:	S.GRISEOVERTICILLATUS-TUBERACTICUS
CT:	CYCLOPEPTIDE, VIOMYCIN T., BASIC
FORMULA:	C25H43N13O10
EA:	(N, 27)
EW:	778
PC:	WH., CRYST.
OR:	(-19.1, W) (-50.8, W)
UV:	HCL: (268, 342,)
UV:	NAOH: (288, 215,) (286, , 14000)
UV:	W: (268, 342,) (268, , 22000)
SOL-GOOD:	W
SOL-FAIR:	MEOH, ETOH
SOL-POOR:	BUOH, HEX
QUAL:	(NINH., +) (BIURET, +) (SAKA., -) (PAULY, -)
TO:	(B.SUBT., 12) (S.AUREUS, 100) (S.LUTEA, 100) (E.COLI, 50) (PS.AER., 100) (SHYG., 100) (MYCOB.TUB., 3)
LD50:	(385, IV)
IS-ION:	(IRC-50-NA, HCL)
UTILITY:	ANTIBACTERIAL DRUG

REFERENCES:

JA, 25, 201, 1972; 28, 292, 1975; 30, 1073, 1977; *Audiology Japan,* 15, 69, 1972; *TL,* 2043, 1971; *Chemother. (Tokyo),* 19, 289, 1971; JP 73/30396; USP 3892732

	42330-1686
NAME:	TUBERACTINOMYCIN-O
PO:	S.GRISEOVERTICILLATUS-TUBERACTICUS
CT:	CYCLOPEPTIDE, VIOMYCIN T., BASIC
FORMULA:	C25H43N13O9
EA:	(N, 28)
PC:	WH., POW.
OR:	(-19, W) (-16, W)
UV:	HCL: (268, 320,)
UV:	NAOH: (288, 170,)
UV:	W: (268, 305,)
SOL-GOOD:	W
SOL-FAIR:	MEOH, ETOH
SOL-POOR:	BUOH, HEX
QUAL:	(NINH., +) (BIURET, +) (SAKA., -) (PAULY, -)
TO:	(B.SUBT., 10) (S.AUREUS, 100) (S.LUTEA, 50) (E.COLI, 100) (SHYG., 100) (K.PNEUM., 50) (MYCOB.TUB., 5)
LD50:	(375, IV)

REFERENCES:

JA, 25, 201, 1972; 28, 292, 1975; 30, 1073, 1977; *Audiology Japan,* 15, 69, 1972; *TL,* 2043, 1971; *Chemother. (Tokyo),* 19, 289, 1971; JP 73/30396; USP 3892732

42330-1687

NAME: XK-33-F-2
PO: S.OLIVORETICULI-CELLULOPHYLUS
CT: CYCLOPEPTIDE, VIOMYCIN T., BASIC
EA: (N, 22) (C, 38) (H, 6)
PC: WH., POW.
OR: (-12.4, W)
UV: NAOH: (286, 240,)
UV: W: (268, 348,)
SOL-GOOD: W
SOL-FAIR: MEOH
SOL-POOR: BUOH, HEX
QUAL: (NINH., +) (SAKA., +) (FEHL., -)
STAB: (ACID, +) (HEAT, +) (BASE, -)
TO: (B.SUBT., 10) (S.AUREUS, 100) (E.COLI, 13) (P.VULG., 52) (SHYG.,) (K.PNEUM., 26) (PS.AER., 52)
LD50: (1000|250, IV)
REFERENCES:
Holl. P 71/18132; DT 2165644; BP 1368153; JP 73/30400

42330-5682

NAME: LL-BB-547-B"
PO: NOC.SP.
CT: VIOMYCIN T., CYCLOPEPTIDE, BASIC
FORMULA: C26H45N15O10
EA: (N, 28)
MW: 727
PC: WH., POW.
OR: (-33, W)
UV: NAOH: (281, ,)
UV: W: (268, ,)
SOL-GOOD: W
SOL-POOR: ACET, ET2O, HEX
QUAL: (NINH., +) (SAKA., -)
TO: (B.SUBT.,) (K.PNEUM., 10) (MYCOB.TUB., 2.5)
LD50: (15|5, IV)
IS-ION: (IRC-50-NA, H2SO4)
IS-ABS: (CARBON, ACET-W)
IS-CHR: (CM-SEPHADEX-NA, NH4CL) (SILG, NH4OAC-ETOH--W)
IS-CRY: (LIOF.,)
REFERENCES:
JOC, 42, 1282, 1977

42340-1688

NAME: <u>ILAMYCIN-A</u>, ILAMYCIN
IDENTICAL: RUFOMYCIN-A
PO: S.ISLANDICUS, S.INSUBTUS
CT: CYCLOPEPTIDE, ILAMYCIN T., ACIDIC
FORMULA: C54H75N9O12
EA: (N, 12)
MW: 1170
PC: YELLOW, POW.
OR: (-78, MEOH)
UV: MEOH: (223, 448,) (278, 116,) (355, 29,)
UV: MEOH-HCL: (223, 448,) (278, 117,) (355, 29,)
UV: MEOH-NAOH: (226, 446,) (284, 102,) (425, 44,)
SOL-GOOD: MEOH, BENZ
SOL-FAIR: ET2O
SOL-POOR: W, HEX
QUAL: (FECL3, -) (NINH., -) (EHRL., -)
TO: (S.LUTEA, .5) (MYCOB.SP., .1)
LD50: (400, IP)
IS-FIL: ORIG.
IS-EXT: (ETOAC, 7, FILT.)
IS-CHR: (AL, BENZ)
REFERENCES:
JA, 15, 46, 49, 1962; 16, 175, 211, 1963; 17, 90, 117, 265, 1964; 18, 135, 1965; *FEBS Lett.*, 17, 145, 1971; JP 64/1657

42340-1689

NAME: <u>ILAMYCIN-B</u>, ILAMYCIN-B1+ILAMYCIN-B2
IDENTICAL: RUFOMYCIN-B
PO: S.ISLANDICUS
CT: CYCLOPEPTIDE, ILAMYCIN T., ACIDIC
FORMULA: C60H90N10O14
EA: (N, 12)
MW: 1148
PC: YELLOW, CRYST.
OR: (-76, MEOH)
UV: MEOH: (221, 465,) (278, 118,) (355, 32,)
SOL-GOOD: MEOH, CHL
SOL-POOR: W, BENZ, HEX
QUAL: (NINH., -) (FECL3, -)
TO: (S.LUTEA, .5) (MYCOB.SP., 3)
IS-CRY: (CRYST., ETOH)
REFERENCES:
JA, 15, 46, 49, 1962; 16, 175, 211; 1963; 17, 90, 117, 265, 1964; 18, 135, 1965; *FEBS Lett.*, 17, 145, 1971; JP 64/1657

42340-1690

NAME: ILAMYCIN-C1
PO: S.INSUBTUS, S.ISLANDICUS
CT: CYCLOPEPTIDE, ILAMYCIN T., ACIDIC
FORMULA: C54H77N9O12
EA: (N, 12)
PC: YELLOW, CRYST.
OR: (-54, MEOH)
UV: MEOH: (221, ,) (278, ,) (355, ,)
SOL-GOOD: MEOH, CHL
SOL-POOR: W, HEX
TO: (MYCOB.SP.,)
REFERENCES:
JA, 18, 135, 1965

42340-1691

NAME: ILAMYCIN-C2
PO: S.INSUBTUS, S.ISLANDICUS
CT: CYCLOPEPTIDE, ILAMYCIN T., ACIDIC
FORMULA: C54H77N9O12
EA: (N, 12)
PC: YELLOW, CRYST.
OR: (+27, MEOH)
UV: MEOH: (221, ,) (278, ,) (355, ,)
SOL-GOOD: MEOH, CHL
SOL-POOR: W, HEX
TO: (MYCOB.SP.,)
REFERENCES:
JA, 18, 135, 1965

42340-1692

NAME: RUFOMYCIN-A, RUFOMYCIN-III
IDENTICAL: ILAMYCIN-A
PO: S.ATRATUS, S.SP.
CT: CYCLOPEPTIDE, ILAMYCIN T., ACIDIC
FORMULA: C54H75N9012
EA: (N, 12)
MW: 1050
PC: YELLOW, CRYST.
OR: (-58, MEOH) (-64, ETOH)
UV: ETOH: (222, 450,) (282, 100,) (355, 28,)
SOL-GOOD: MEOH, CHL
SOL-FAIR: ET2O, BENZ, HEX
SOL-POOR: W
QUAL: (PAULY, +) (NINH., -) (FEHL., -) (SAKA., -) (FECL3, -)
STAB: (ACID, -) (BASE, -) (HEAT, -)
TO: (S.LUTEA, 100) (MYCOB.SP., .1)
LD50: (400, IP)
IS-FIL: 2
IS-EXT: (ETOAC, 2, FILT.) (MEOH, , MIC.)
IS-CHR: (AL, ETOAC)
IS-CRY: (CRYST., ETOH)
REFERENCES:

Agr. Biol. Ch., 26, 228, 234, 1961; *JA*, 16, 246, 1963; *JACS*, 86, 4698, 1964; *Chem. Ph. Bull.*, 12, 1390, 1964; *Agr. Chem. Soc. Jap.*, 42, 394, 401, 1968; BP 923938; DT 1113851, 1181230

42340-1693

NAME: RUFOMYCIN-B, RUFOMYCIN-I
PO: S.ATRATUS
CT: CYCLOPEPTIDE, ILAMYCIN T., ACIDIC
FORMULA: C54H79N9013
EA: (N, 12)
PC: YELLOW, CRYST.
OR: (-73, MEOH) (-120, MEOH)
UV: ETOH: (222, 524,) (282, 113,) (355, 28,)
SOL-GOOD: MEOH, CHL, ETOAC, PYR, DIOXAN, ACOH
SOL-FAIR: ETOH, BUOH, ET2O, BENZ, HEX
SOL-POOR: W
QUAL: (NINH., -) (FEHL., -) (SAKA., -) (FECL3, -)
TO: (MYCOB.SP., .5)
LD50: (2000, IP)
IS-EXT: (ETOAC, 2, FILT.)
IS-CHR: (AL, ETOH-W)
IS-CRY: (CRYST., ETOH)
REFERENCES:

Agr. Biol. Ch., 26, 228, 234, 1961; *JA*, 16, 246, 1963; *JACS*, 86, 4698, 1964; *Chem. Ph. Bull.*, 12, 1390, 1964; *Agr. Chem. Soc. Jap.*, 42, 394, 401, 1968; BP 923938; DT 1113851, 1181230

42340-1694

NAME: ILAMYCIN-B1
IDENTICAL: RUFOMYCIN-B1
PO: S.SP.
CT: CYCLOPEPTIDE, ILAMYCIN T., ACIDIC
FORMULA: C54H77N9O10
EA: (N, 12)
EW: 1020
PC: YELLOW, CRYST.
OR: (-77, MEOH)
UV: ETOH: (282, 100,) (365, 25,)
SOL-GOOD: MEOH, CHL
SOL-POOR: W, ET2O, BENZ, HEX
QUAL: (EHRL., +)
TO: (MYCOB.SP.,)
IS-EXT: (BUOAC, , WB.)
IS-CHR: (SILG, ETOAC)
IS-CRY: (CRYST., ETOH)
REFERENCES:
JA, 17, 90, 117, 1964; *Acta Cryst.*, 30B, 2817, 1974; *FEBS Lett.*, 17, 145, 1971

42340-1695

NAME: ILAMYCIN-B2
IDENTICAL: RUFOMYCIN-B2
PO: S.ISLANDICUS, S.SP.
CT: CYCLOPEPTIDE, ILAMYCIN T., ACIDIC
FORMULA: C54H77N9O11
EA: (N, 12)
EW: 1020
PC: YELLOW, CRYST.
OR: (-77, MEOH)
UV: ETOH: (282, 110,) (362, 30,)
SOL-GOOD: MEOH, CHL
SOL-POOR: W, HEX, ET2O, BENZ
QUAL: (EHRL., -)
TO: (MYCOB.SP.,)
REFERENCES:
JA, 17, 90, 117, 1964; *Acta Cryst.*, 30B, 2817, 1974; *FEBS Lett.*, 17, 145, 1971

42350-1879

NAME:	RADICICOLIN
PO:	CYLINDROCARPON RADICICOLA
CT:	AMPHOTER, CYCLOPEPTIDE, CYCLOSPORIN T.
EA:	(C, 62) (H, 9) (N, 12)
MW:	2000
PC:	WH., POW.
OR:	(-193.5, MEOH)
SOL-GOOD:	MEOH, ET2O
SOL-POOR:	W, HEX
QUAL:	(BIURET, +) (FEHL., -)
TO:	(FUNGI, .25) (B.SUBT., 200) (E.COLI, 200)

REFERENCES:

Nature, 195, 406, 1962; *Aust. J. Chem.*, 19, 1265, 1966; *Trans. Brit. Mycol. Soc.*, 49, 563, 1966; BP 1006724

42350-4873

NAME:	CYCLOSPORIN-A, S-7481-F1
PO:	CYLINDROCARPON LUCIDUM, TRICHODERMA POLYSPORUM
CT:	CYCLOPEPTIDE, NEUTRAL, CYCLOSPORIN T.
FORMULA:	C62H111N11O12
EA:	(N, 13)
MW:	1201
PC:	WH., CRYST.
OR:	(-244, CHL) (-189, MEOH)
UV:	MEOH: (200, ,)
SOL-GOOD:	MEOH, CHL, ET2O
SOL-POOR:	W, HEX
TO:	(ASP.NIGER,) (PHYT.FUNGI,)
TV:	ANTITUMOR
IS-EXT:	(MEOH, , MIC.) (CH2CL2, , W) (BUOAC, 7, FILT.)
IS-CHR:	(SILG, CHL-MEOH) (SEPHADEX LH-20, MEOH)
IS-CRY:	(CRYST., ACET)

REFERENCES:

Helv., 59, 1075, 1480, 1976; *Agents & Action*, 6, 432, 1976; *Eur. J. Appl. Micr.*, 3, 125, 1976; Belg. P 823008; DT 2455859

42350-4874

NAME: CYCLOSPORIN-B, S-7481-F2
PO: CYLINDROCARPON LUCIDUM, TRICHODERMA POLYSPORUM
CT: CYCLOPEPTIDE, NEUTRAL, CYCLOSPORIN T.
FORMULA: C61H109N11O12
EA: (N, 15)
MW: 1189
PC: WH., CRYST.
OR: (-243, CHL) (-168, MEOH)
UV: MEOH: (200, ,)
SOL-GOOD: MEOH, CHL
SOL-POOR: W, HEX
TO: (ASP.NIGER,) (PHYT.FUNGI, 1)
TV: ANTITUMOR
REFERENCES:
Helv., 59, 1075, 1480, 1976; *Agents & Action*, 6, 432, 1976; *Eur. J. Appl. Micr.*, 3, 125, 1976; Belg. P 823008; DT 2455859

42350-5060

NAME: CYCLOSPORIN-C
PO: TRICHODERMA POLYSPORUM, CYLINDROCARPON LUCIDUM
CT: NEUTRAL, CYCLOPEPTIDE, CYCLOSPORIN T.
FORMULA: C62H111N11O13
EA: (N, 13)
MW: 1217
PC: WH., POW.
OR: (-255, CHL) (-182, MEOH)
UV: MEOH: (200, ,)
SOL-GOOD: MEOH, ET2O
SOL-POOR: W, HEX
TO: (ASP.NIGER,) (PHYT.FUNGI, 1)
IS-EXT: (BUOAC, , FILT.)
IS-CHR: (SILG, CHL-MEOH) (SEPHADEX LH-20, MEOH)
REFERENCES:
Helv., 59, 1075, 1480, 1976; *Agents & Action*, 6, 432, 1976; *Eur. J. Appl. Micr.*, 3, 125, 1976; Belg. P 823008; DT 2455859

42350-5575

NAME: CYCLOSPORIN-D
PO: TRICHODERMA POLYSPORUM, GYLINDROCARPON LUCIDUM
CT: NEUTRAL, CYCLOPEPTIDE, CYCLOSPORIN T.
FORMULA: C63H113N11O12
EA: (N, 13)
MW: 1215
PC: WH., CRYST.
OR: (-211, MEOH) (-245, CHL)
UV: (200, ,)
SOL-GOOD: MEOH, ACET, CHL, ET2O
SOL-POOR: W, BENZ, HEX
TO: (PHYT.FUNGI, 1)
IS-CHR: (SILG, ET2O-MEOH)
IS-CRY: (CRYST., ACET)
REFERENCES:

Helv., 60, 1568, 1977

42350-5576

NAME: CYCLOSPORIN-E
PO: TRICHODERMA POLYSPORUM, CYLINDROCARPON LUCIDUM
CT: NEUTRAL, CYCLOPEPTIDE, CYCLOSPORIN T.
FORMULA: C61H109N11O12
EA: (N, 13)
MW: 1187
PC: WH., CRYST.
OR: (-186, MEOH) (-179, CHL)
UV: (200, ,)
SOL-GOOD: MEOH, ACET, CHL, ET2O
SOL-POOR: W, BENZ, HEX
TO: (PHYT.FUNGI,)
IS-CRY: (CRYST., ET2O)
REFERENCES:

Helv., 60, 1568, 1977

42300-1661

NAME: B-344-A
PO: B.SUBTILIS
CT: CYCLOPEPTIDE, ACIDIC, AMPHOTER
EA: (N,)
PC: YELLOW, WH., POW.
SOL-GOOD: MEOH, ETOH, ACET, BENZ
SOL-POOR: ET2O, W
QUAL: (NINH., -)
STAB: (HEAT, -) (ACID, -)
TO: (FUNGI,) (G.POS.,) (G.NEG.,)
REFERENCES:
Ind. J. Chem., 1, 135, 1963

42300-1662

NAME: B-344-B
PO: B.SUBTILIS
CT: CYCLOPEPTIDE, ACIDIC, AMPHOTER
EA: (N,)
PC: RED, POW.
SOL-GOOD: ETOH, MEOH, ET2O
SOL-POOR: W
TO: (FUNGI, 100)
REFERENCES:
Ind. J. Chem., 1, 135, 1963

42300-1696

NAME: MYCOBACILLIN
PO: B.SUBTILIS
CT: ACIDIC, CYCLOPEPTIDE
EA: (C, 51) (H, 7) (N, 12)
MW: 1800
EW: 1775
PC: WH., CRYST.
UV: W: (277, ,)
SOL-GOOD: MEOH, ACET, BASE, PYR
SOL-POOR: W, ACET, HEX
QUAL: (BIURET, +) (NINH., -)
STAB: (ACID, +) (HEAT, +)
TO: (S.CEREV., 5) (C.ALB., 100) (PHYT.FUNGI, 1.5)
LD50: (20, SC)
IS-EXT: (BUOH, , WB.)
IS-CRY: (PREC., BUOH, ET2O)
REFERENCES:
Nature, 181, 134, 1958; 200, 471, 1963; *ABB*, 90, 154, 1960; *Bioch. J.*, 121, 839, 1971; 74, 596, 1960; *J. Gen. Appl. Micr.*, 15, 473, 1969; *JA*, 26, 257, 1973; 28, 988, 1975; 30, 987, 1977; 31, 147, 1978; *Ind. J. Bioch. Biophys.*, 13, 187, 1976; *Naturwiss.*, 47, 39, 1960; *Ind. J. Appl. Chem.*, 22, 228, 1959

42300-1698

NAME:	CHLAMYDOCIN, SL-3440
PO:	DIHETEROSPORA CHLAMYDOSPORA
CT:	NEUTRAL, CYCLOPEPTIDE
FORMULA:	C28H38N4O6
EA:	(N, 10)
MW:	526
PC:	WH., OIL
OR:	(-147.5, BENZ)
UV:	(200, ,)
SOL-GOOD:	MEOH, BENZ
SOL-POOR:	W
QUAL:	(NINH., -)
TO:	(FUNGI, 10)
TV:	WALKER-256, ANTITUMOR, P-815
IS-FIL:	ORIG.
IS-EXT:	(CH2CL2, , FILT.)
IS-CHR:	(SILG, CHL-MEOH)

REFERENCES:

Helv., 57, 533, 1974; Belg. P 747441; BP 1300137

42300-1699

NAME:	MALFORMIN-A1
PO:	ASP.NIGER, ASP.FICUM, ASP.AWAMORI
CT:	NEUTRAL, CYCLOPEPTIDE
FORMULA:	C23H39N5O5S2
EA:	(N, 13) (S, 12)
MW:	530
PC:	WH., POW.
OR:	(-39, METILCELLOSOLVE)
UV:	MEOH: (220, , 4100)
SOL-GOOD:	MEOH, BUOH
SOL-FAIR:	ACET, ETOAC
SOL-POOR:	CHL, HEX, W
QUAL:	(PAULY, +) (FECL3, -) (EHRL., -) (NINH., -)
STAB:	(ACID, +) (BASE, -)
TO:	(B.SUBT., 2.5) (S.AUREUS,) (E.COLI, 5)
LD50:	(3.1, IP)
TV:	P-815
IS-ABS:	(CARBON, MEOH)
IS-CHR:	(SILG, TOL-ETOAC-HCOOH)

REFERENCES:

BBA, 119, 614, 1966; *Proc. Nat. Acad. Sci.*, 71, 2791, 1974; *Agr. Biol. Ch.*, 39, 1325, 1975; *Ber.*, 103, 3159, 1970; *Appl. Micr.*, 28, 362, 1974; 14, 425, 1966; 15, 1519, 1967; *Phytoch.*, 4, 263, 1965; 1, 245, 1961; 8, 1397, 1969; *Proc. Nat. Acad. Sci.*, 71, 2791, 1974; *Bioorg. Chem.*, 4, 93, 1975; *Helv.*, 59, 1127, 1976; *JACS*, 97, 2857, 1975; *JA*, 29, 549, 1976

42300-1700

NAME: MALFORMIN-B1
PO: ASP.NIGER
CT: NEUTRAL, CYCLOPEPTIDE
FORMULA: C23H39N5O5S2
PC: WH., POW.
OR: (-40.3, METILCELLOSOLVE)
UV: (200, ,)
SOL-GOOD: MEOH, ETOAC
SOL-POOR: W, BENZ, HEX
TO: (B.SUBT.,) (E.COLI,)
IS-CHR: (SILG, ETOAC)
REFERENCES:
Appl. Micr., 14, 425, 1966; 15, 1519, 1967; *Phytoch.*, 6, 287, 1967

42300-1702

NAME: I-1
PO: SACCHAROMYCES CEREVISIAE
CT: ACIDIC, CYCLOPEPTIDE
EA: (N,)
PC: WH., POW.
UV: W: (255, ,)
SOL-GOOD: W
SOL-FAIR: MEOH
SOL-POOR: ET2O
QUAL: (NINH., -) (PAULY, -) (EHRL., -)
TO: (S.AUREUS,) (E.COLI,)
IS-CHR: (CEL,)
REFERENCES:
Cereal Chem., 39, 183, 1962; *Nature*, 182, 415, 1958; *CA*, 57, 7715

42300-1703

NAME: I-2
PO: SACCHAROMYCES CEREVISIAE
CT: ACIDIC, CYCLOPEPTIDE
EA: (N,)
PC: WH., POW.
UV: W: (272, ,)
SOL-GOOD: W
SOL-FAIR: MEOH
SOL-POOR: ET2O
TO: (S.AUREUS,) (E.COLI,)
REFERENCES:
Cereal Chem., 39, 183, 1962; *Nature*, 182, 415, 1958; *CA*, 57, 7715

42300-1704

NAME: EPIDERMIDINS-A1, EPIDERMIDINS-A2, EPIDERMIDINS-B1, EPIDERMIDINS-B2
PO: STAPHYLOCOCCUS EPIDERMIDIS
CT: AMPHOTER, CYCLOPEPTIDE
EA: (N, 15)
MW: 1200|200, 1200|200
PC: WH., CRYST.
SOL-GOOD: W
SOL-POOR: MEOH, HEX
QUAL: (BIURET, +) (NINH., -) (FECL3, +)
TO: (S.AUREUS, 10)
REFERENCES:

Can. J. Micr., 13, 947, 1967; 17, 1223, 1971; 18, 121, 1972

42300-1705

NAME: CEREIN-B2
PO: B.CEREUS
CT: CYCLOPEPTIDE, AMPHOTER
EA: (C, 43) (H, 0) (N, 14)
PC: WH., POW.
SOL-GOOD: W, MEOH, ACOH
SOL-POOR: ACET, HEX
QUAL: (NINH., -)
STAB: (HEAT, +) (ACID, +)
TO: (SHYG.,) (P.VULG.,) (E.COLI,)
LD50: (12.4, IV)
IS-ABS: (CARBON, I.AMOH-W)
IS-CHR: (AL,)
REFERENCES:

Acta Biochem. Polon., 2, 389, 489, 1955; *Bull. Polon. Acad. III*, 8, 285, 1955; *J. Gen. Micr.*, 16, 1, 1957; *CA*, 51, 543

42300-1707

NAME:	ALBOVERTICILLIN
PO:	S.ALBOVERTICILLATUS
CT:	BASIC, AMPHOTER, CYCLOPEPTIDE
FORMULA:	C78H174N30O33
EA:	(N, 18)
MW:	2000
PC:	WH., POW.
OR:	(-33.5, W)
UV:	HCL: (207, 159,)
UV:	NAOH: (217, 65,)
SOL-GOOD:	W, MEOH
SOL-POOR:	ACET, HEX
QUAL:	(NINH., +) (SAKA., -) (BIURET, -) (FEHL., -)
STAB:	(ACID, +) (BASE, +) (HEAT, +)
TO:	(S.LUTEA, 15) (B.SUBT., 15) (SHYG., 100) (MYCOB.SP., 2)
LD50:	(75|25, IV)
IS-FIL:	8
IS-ION:	(IRC-50-NA, HCL)
IS-CRY:	(LIOF.,)

REFERENCES:

JA, 11, 30, 1958; JP 60/10997; *CA*, 50, 9780

42300-1708

NAME:	TRICULAMIN
PO:	S.TRICULAMINICUS
CT:	AMPHOTER, BASIC, CYCLOPEPTIDE
FORMULA:	C85H154N32O27
EA:	(N, 18)
MW:	2130
PC:	WH., CRYST.
OR:	(-65.5, W)
UV:	W: (200, ,)
SOL-GOOD:	W
SOL-POOR:	MEOH, HEX
QUAL:	(NINH., +) (SAKA., +) (FEHL., -)
TO:	(B.SUBT., 12.5) (MYCOB.SP., .02) (E.COLI, 100) (S.CEREV., 100)
LD50:	(200, IV)
IS-FIL:	3
IS-ION:	(IRC-50-NA, HCL)
IS-ABS:	(CARBON, ACET-HCL)
IS-CRY:	(LIOF.,) (CRYST., ETOH-W)

REFERENCES:

JA, 20, 126, 1967; *Agr. Biol. Ch.*, 33, 1737, 1969

42300-1709

NAME:	A-287-A
PO:	ACTINOPLANES UTAHENSIS
CT:	CYCLOPEPTIDE
EA:	(C, 45) (H, 6) (N, 10) (O, 26) (ASH, 4)
MW:	1500
PC:	WH., POW.
UV:	HCL: (273, ,)
UV:	NAOH: (273, ,)
UV:	W: (273, , 2700)
SOL-GOOD:	W, MEOH, BUOH
SOL-POOR:	ACET, HEX
STAB:	(ACID, +) (HEAT, +) (BASE, +)
TO:	(S.AUREUS, 6.25) (S.LUTEA, 50) (B.SUBT., 12.1) (P.VULG., 50) (PHYT.BACT., 50) (PHYT.FUNGI, 25)
LD50:	(1370, IP)
IS-FIL:	6.5
IS-EXT:	(BUOH, , FILT.)
IS-CHR:	(SEPHADEX G-25, W)
IS-CRY:	(PREC., MEOH, ET2O)

REFERENCES:

USP 3824305; DT 2402956

42300-1710

NAME:	A-287-B
PO:	ACTINOPLANES UTAHENSIS
CT:	CYCLOPEPTIDE
EA:	(C, 50) (H, 7) (N, 10) (O, 24) (ASH, 5)
MW:	2800
PC:	WH., POW.
UV:	HCL: (273, ,)
UV:	NAOH: (273, ,)
UV:	W: (273, , 3200)
SOL-GOOD:	W, MEOH, BUOH
SOL-POOR:	ACET, HEX
STAB:	(ACID, +) (BASE, +) (HEAT, +)
TO:	(S.AUREUS, 12) (B.SUBT., 3.1) (S.LUTEA, 6.2) (P.VULG., 50) (SHYG., 25) (PHYT.BACT., 6) (PHYT.FUNGI, 12)

REFERENCES:

USP 38224305; DT 2402956

42300-1711

NAME:	300-A-B-C
PO:	S.SP.
CT:	CYCLOPEPTIDE
PC:	WH.
SOL-GOOD:	W
QUAL:	(BIURET, +)
TO:	(E.COLI, 4) (G.POS.,) (G.NEG.,) (MYCOB.SP.,)
LD50:	(50|40,)
IS-ION:	(ABC-10, H2SO4)
IS-CHR:	(AL, MEOH-W)

REFERENCES:

Acad. Sci. Sinica Conf. Antib. 1955

42300-1712

NAME: REUMYCIN
PO: ACT.SP., S.SP.
CT: CYCLOPEPTIDE
MW: 1300
OR: (-9, W)
SOL-GOOD: W
LD50: (133, IV) (120, IP)
TV: S-180, S-45, EHRLICH, CA-755, NK-LY, S-37, WALKER-256
REFERENCES:
Antib., 892, 1967; 1014, 1968

42300-1713

NAME: ASPOCHRACIN
PO: ASP.OCHRACEUS
CT: NEUTRAL, CYCLOPEPTIDE
FORMULA: C26H36N4O4
EA: (N,)
PC: YELLOW, POW.
OR: (-76, MEOH)
UV: MEOH: (297, , 29500)
SOL-GOOD: MEOH, ET2O
SOL-POOR: W
STAB: (LIGHT, -) (HEAT, -)
TO: (INSECTICID,)
IS-EXT: (ETOAC, , FILT.)
REFERENCES:
Agr. Biol. Ch., 33, 1491, 1501, 1969; *TL*, 695, 1969; JP 71/21789

42300-5058

NAME: AS-N-136
PO: S.SP.
CT: BASIC, PEPTIDE
PC: WH., YELLOW, CRYST.
TO: (G.POS.,)
REFERENCES:
Proc. Egypt. Acad. Sci., 25, 23, 1974

42300-5191

NAME: MALFORMIN-C
PO: ASP.NIGER
CT: CYCLOPEPTIDE, NEUTRAL
FORMULA: C23H39N5O5S2
EA: (N, 13) (S, 16)
MW: 529
PC: WH., POW.
OR: (-37.4, DMSO)
SOL-GOOD: MEOH, ETOAC, CH2CL2
SOL-POOR: W, ACID, BASE
TO: (B.SUBT.,) (S.AUREUS,) (S.LUTEA.,)
LD50: (.9, IP)
IS-EXT: (CH2CL2, , MIC.)
IS-CHR: (SILG, ETOAC) (AL, ETOAC-ETOH)
IS-CRY: (DRY,)
REFERENCES:
JACS, 98, 3366, 1976; *Appl. Micr.*, 33, 996, 1977

42300-5445

NAME: MALFORMIN-B2, VALINE-MALFORMIN
PO: ASP.NIGER
CT: NEUTRAL, CYCLOPEPTIDE
FORMULA: C22H37N5O5S2
EA: (N, 13) (S, 12)
MW: 515
PC: WH., POW.
OR: (-49.5, METILCELLOSOLVE)
UV: MEOH: (220, ,)
SOL-GOOD: ETOH, MEOH, ETOAC
SOL-POOR: W, HEX
TO: (B.SUBT.,) (E.COLI,)
REFERENCES:
Appl. Micr., 14, 475, 1966; 15, 1519, 1967

42300-5446

NAME: GRACEILLIN
PO: B.BREVIS
CT: CYCLOPEPTIDE
TO: (G.POS.,)
REFERENCES:
CA, 84, 119884

42300-6072

NAME:	ISOTENTOXINE
PO:	ALT.MALI
CT:	CYCLOPEPTIDE, NEUTRAL
FORMULA:	C22H31N4O4
EA:	(N, 13)
MW:	415
TO:	(PIRICULARIA ORYZAE,) (PHYT.BACT.,)

REFERENCES:

JP 77/118487; *CA*, 88, 73011

42300-6123

NAME:	CYL-2
PO:	CYLINDROCLADIUM SCOPARIUM
CT:	NEUTRAL, CYCLOPEPTIDE
FORMULA:	C32H46N4O7
EA:	(N,)
PC:	WH., CRYST.
UV:	CHL: (276, , 1790) (283, , 1530)
SOL-GOOD:	MEOH, ETOAC
SOL-POOR:	W
QUAL:	(DNPH, +)
LD50:	PHYTOTOXIC
IS-EXT:	(ETOAC, 7, FILT.)
IS-CHR:	(SILG, BENZ-ETOAC)

REFERENCES:

Agr. Biol. Ch., 37, 643, 955, 1185, 1973

43
HETEROMER PEPTIDES

Introduction

This subfamily includes mainly cyclic peptide-type compounds, derived from amino acids, modified (oxygenated or dehydrated) amino acids, heterocyclic compounds, and aliphatic constituents (fatty acids, amines) or metal cations.

The (cyclic) lipopeptide group (431) covers homodetic peptides which are all cyclic compounds (except amphomycin type) with a fatty acid or fatty-amino acid side chain. In the thiapeptide group (432) highly modified peptides, sometimes with multiple macrocyclic structures, containing several sulfur-containing heterocycles (thiazoles) are listed. The chelate-forming peptide group (433) covers the Fe^{3+}-containing sideromycins, the Cu^{++}-containing bleomycin-type glycopeptides, and several other chelate-forming (peptide-like) compounds.

The thiapeptides (except micrococcins) and the chelate-forming compounds all are actinomycetal metabolites, while the lipopeptides are mainly bacterial products. This group includes some fungal (echinocandins) and streptomycetal (amphomycins) metabolites.

Several of these antibiotics, e.g., the antibacterial polymyxins and amphomycin, are used in human therapy. Thiostrepton is a veterinary drug, while thiopeptin, siomycin, and nosiheptid are animal feed additives. This group covers about 250 microbial metabolites.

431
Lipopeptide Antibiotics

Introduction

Chemically this group is characterized by a cyclic peptide part (usually hexa-, hepta-, or octapeptide ring) and a fatty acyl peptide side chain or a long aliphatic chain of an unusual β-hydroxy-fatty amino acid, participating in the peptide portion.

These antibiotics are grouped into the acidic amphomycin (4311) and bacillomycin (4314), the basic polymyxin-octapeptin (4312), the neutral echinocandin (4313), and the amphoteric longicatenamycin (4315) types. The polymyxin and bacillomycin types are produced by *Bacillus* species, while echinocandins are fungal metabolites.

The microorganisms which produce these antibiotics in all cases yield mixtures of closely related compounds. The differences are found in the amino acid composition and/or in the lipoid portion. In one or a few positions the amino acid may be replaced with another — most frequently homolog — amino acid, e.g., valine with isoleucine or ornithine with lysine. Moreover, all of the antibiotic peptides in this group are mixtures of compounds containing the homologs or isomers of their fatty acid constituents. This fact (obtaining the mixtures of fatty acids after hydrolysis in all cases) indicates that the number of carbon atoms in the fatty acid is not genetically determined, but rather a consequence of fermentation media and conditions. The separation of this type of congener is very difficult and sometimes practically impossible. It is interesting that each species of microorganism always produces the same peptide part with different fatty acid constituents, while the other, closely related microorganism strains usually produce compounds with a different peptide portion.

The occurrence of unusual amino acids is a common feature, especially of the streptomycetal and fungal compounds, in this group. They are as follows:

Bacterial peptides (polymyxins, bacillomycins): various D amino acids (leu, phe, ser, asp, tyr, asn) and

(1) L-α,γ-Diaminobutyric acid (dab)

Amphomycin type

(2) L-β-Methylaspartic acid (measp)
(3) D-α-Pipecolic acid (pip)
(4) L-*threo*-α,β-Diaminobutyric acid (dab^t)
(5) D-*erythro*-α,β-Diaminobutyric acid (dab^e)

Echinocandin type

(6) L-4-Hydroxyproline (hypro)
(7) L-4-Methyl-3-hydroxyproline (mehypro)
(8) 3,4-Dihydroxyhomotyrosine
(9) 4,5-Dihydroxyornithine

Longicatenamycin type

(10) L-*threo*-β-Hydroxyglutamic acid
(11) D-5- Chlorotryptophane

(12)	L-2-Amino-5-methylhexanoic acid	fatty amino acids
(13)	L-2-Amino-6-methylheptanoic acid	
(14)	L-2-Amino-7-methyloctanoic acid D-val, D-ile, D-lys, D-orn	

The lipoid constituents are fatty acids (unsaturated C_{11} to C_{16} acids in the amphomycin type, branched-chain C_6 to C_{11} acids in the polymyxin series, and C_{16} to C_{18} straight-chain acids in the echinocandins) or C_{14} to C_{16} β-amino acids in the bacillomycins and C_7 to C_9 α-amino acids **(12, 13, 14)** in the longicatenamycins, respectively.

The polymyxin-type antibiotics have continuously diminishing practical importance in human therapy, but the significance of some substances (parvulin) in animal husbandry may increase in the future.

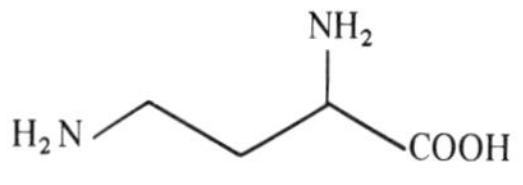

(1)

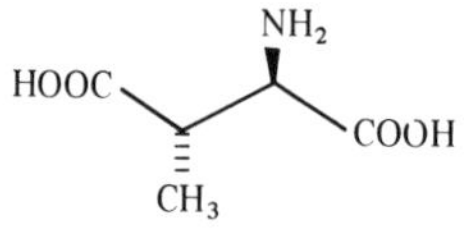

(2)

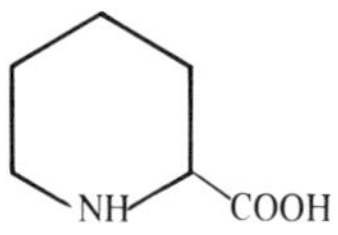

(3)

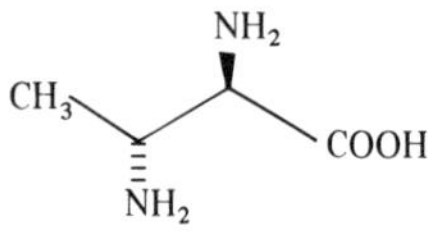

(4)

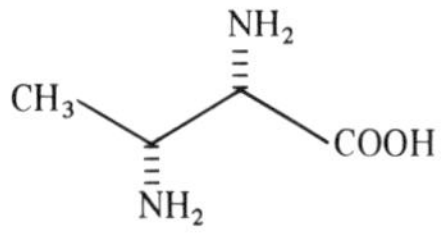

(5)

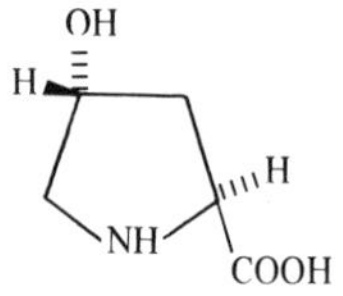

(6)

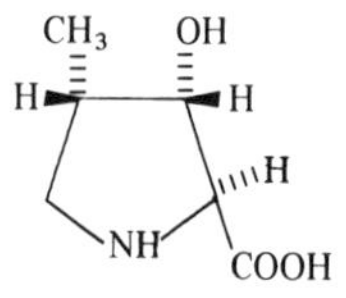

(7)

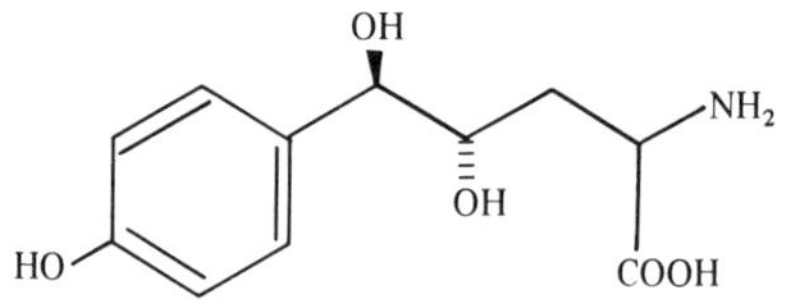

(8)

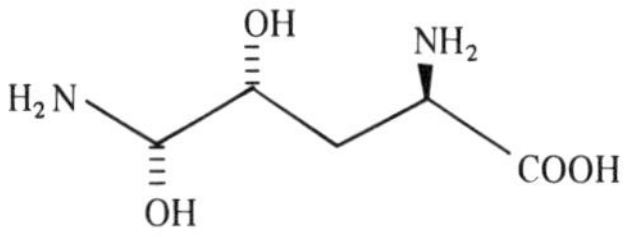

(9)

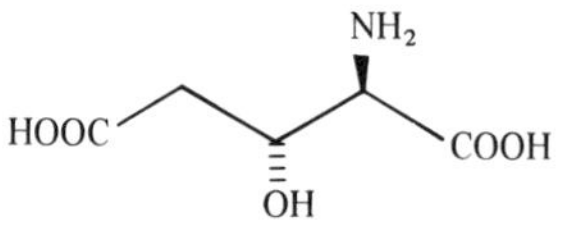

(10)

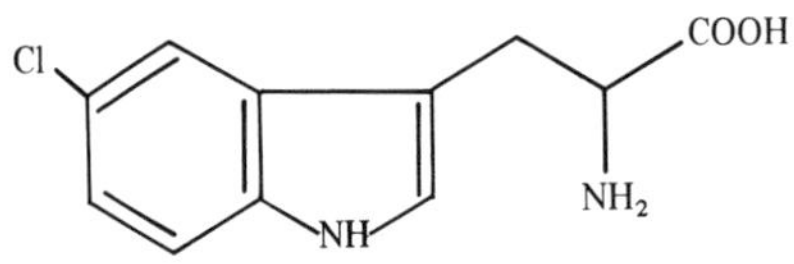

(11)

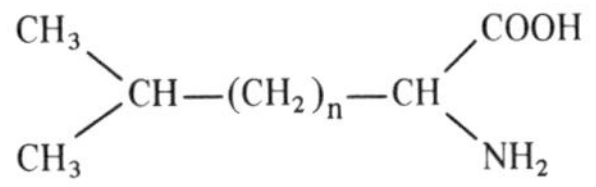

(12) n = 2
(13) n = 3
(14) n = 4

4311
Amphomycin Type

According to recent results these compounds may be linear peptides. However, for glumamycin a cyclic structure was considered — due to some biogenetic and chemical reasons.

This group is characterized as acidic undecapeptides substituted on the N terminal with various unsaturated branched-chain fatty acids. Of specific interest in the amphomycin structure is the diketopiperazine fragment formed from pipecolic acid and *threo*-α,β-diaminopropionic acid units on the C-terminus of the peptide chain.

Owing to the remarkable similarity in the amino acid composition of these antibiotics, it seems that most of the known compounds have identical (or very similar) peptide fragments acylated with different fatty acids. This situation was proved in the case of amphomycin, glumamycin, aspartocin, and tsusimycin, which differ only by their qualitative and quantitative fatty acid constitutions. The constituents of these antibiotics are summarized in the following table:

Antibiotic	Fatty acids[a]	asp	measp	pro	gly	val	pip	dab
Amphomycin	3-*anteiso*-C_{13}	3	1	1	2	1	1	2
	3-*iso*-C_{12}							
	3-*iso*-C_{13}							
Glumamycin	3-*iso*-C_{13}	3	1	1	2	1	1	2
	3-*anteiso*-C_{13}							
Aspartocin	3-*iso*-C_{15}	4[b]		1	2	1	+	+[c]
	3-*anteiso*-C_{15}							
Tsusimycin	3-*anteiso*-C_{15}	4[b]		1	2	1	+	+[c]
	3-*iso*-C_{14}, *n*-C_{14}							
	3-*iso*-C_{15}							
Zaomycin	3-*iso*-C_{11}	+		+	+	+	+	+
Parvulin	3-*iso*-C_{13}	3	1	1	2	1	1	1—2
	3-*iso*-C_{12}							
	3-*anteiso*-C_{13}							
Crystallomycin	Unidentified	8(3)		+	6(2)	3(1)	3(1)	+[c]
Laspartomycin[d]	*trans*-2-*iso*-C_{15}	4	—	1	4	—	+	1

[a] All fatty acids are *cis*-Δ^3-enoic (β, γ-unsaturated) acids, e.g., 3-*iso*-C_{13} = *cis*-Δ^3-isotridecenoic acid **(1)** 3-*anteiso*-C_{15} = *cis*-Δ^3-isopentadecenoic acid **(2)**.
[b] Including measp.
[c] Unidentified basic amino acids.
[d] Contains additional threonine and isoleucine.

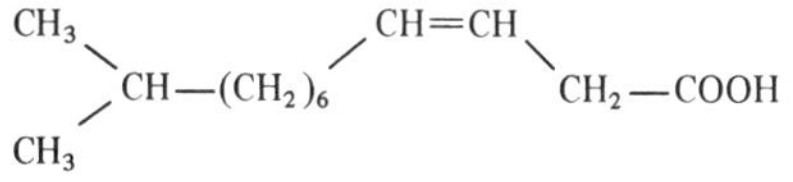

(1)

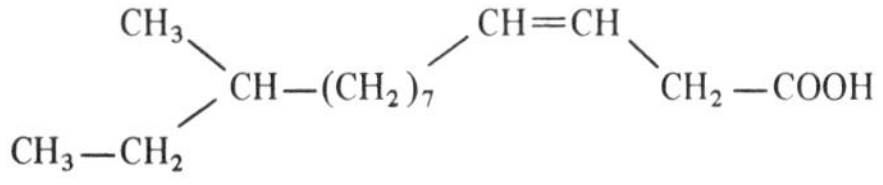

(2)

These antibiotics are acidic, surface-active substances, with isoelectric point 3,4 to 3,5, produced by *Streptomyces* species. They are active against Gram-positive bacteria and show moderate or low toxicity. Because they are poorly absorbed from the gastrointestinal tract and their potency is moderate, amphomycin has found therapeutic application as an antibacterial agent only in ointments. It is used in human and veterinary medicine for treatment of lesions infected with Gram-positive organisms. Parvulin may be used as a food additive in animal husbandry.

REFERENCES

1. *AAC 1969,* 135; *AAC 1970,* 42.
2. *JACS,* 95, 2352, 1973.

Structures

43110

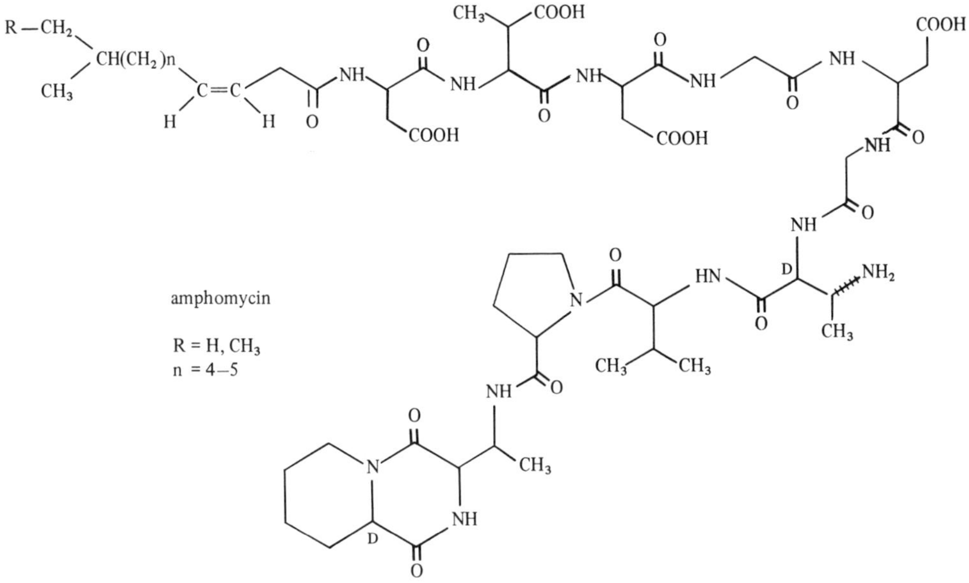

amphomycin

R = H, CH_3
n = 4–5

Fa—asp—measp—asp—gly—asp—gly—dab[e]—val—pro—dab[t]—pip

amphomycin

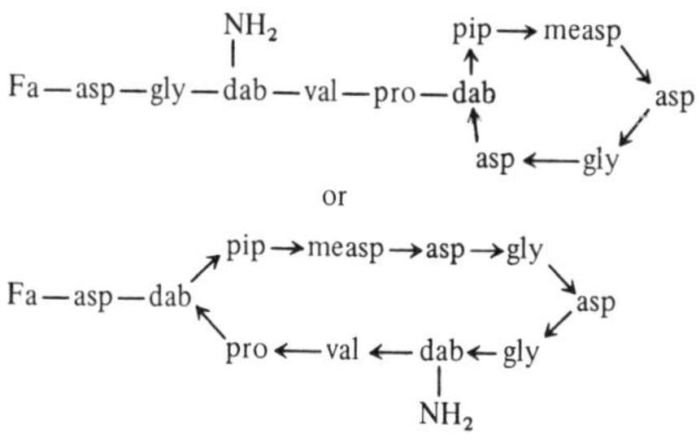

tentative structures for glumamycin

43110-1714

NAME:	AMPHOMYCIN, A-6786-52
IDENTICAL:	GLUMAMYCIN, ASPARTOCIN
PO:	S.CANUS, S.VIOLACEUS, S.SP.
CT:	LIPOPEPTIDE, AMPHOMYCIN T., ACIDIC, AMPHOTER
FORMULA:	C58H91N13O20
EA:	(N, 15)
EW:	1450|50
PC:	WH., YELLOW, POW.
OR:	(+7.5, W)
UV:	W: (200, ,)
SOL-GOOD:	W, MEOH, ETOH, PYR
SOL-FAIR:	BUOH, ETOAC
SOL-POOR:	CHL, HEX
QUAL:	(NINH., +) (BIURET, +) (FECL3, -) (SAKA., -) (EHRL., -) (PAULY, -)
STAB:	(HEAT, +) (ACID, -) (BASE, +)
TO:	(S.AUREUS, 2.5) (B.SUBT., 5)
LD50:	(120, IV) (150, IP) (500, PEROS)
IS-FIL:	8
IS-EXT:	(BUOH, 2, FILT.) (W, 6.4, BUOH)
UTILITY:	ANTIBACTERIAL DRUG

REFERENCES:

Ant. & Chem., 3, 1239, 1953; 5, 132, 1955; 6, 684, 1956; *Ant. An.*, 1011, 1954—55; *Giorn. Micr.*, 3, 70, 1951; *JA*, 22, 399, 1969; 23, 149, 238, 1970; *AAC 1969*, 135; *AAC 1970*, 42; *JACS*, 95, 2352, 1973; BP 736325; DT 1021538; Can. P 494191

43110-1715

NAME:	TSUSHIMYCIN
PO:	S.PSEUDOGRISEOLUS
CT:	LIPOPEPTIDE, AMPHOMYCIN T., ACIDIC, AMPHOTER
FORMULA:	C59H93N13O20
EA:	(N, 14)
MW:	1296, 1400
EW:	445
PC:	WH., POW.
OR:	(+11.9, MEOH) (+13.2, ETOH) (-5.6, PH6 PUFF)
UV:	MEOH: (207, ,)
SOL-GOOD:	MEOH, ETOH, BUOH
SOL-FAIR:	ACET
SOL-POOR:	CHL, HEX
QUAL:	(NINH., +) (BIURET, +)
STAB:	(BASE, +)
TO:	(B.SUBT., .5) (S.AUREUS, 1) (S.LUTEA, 1) (K.PNEUM., 1)
LD50:	(150|50, IV) (150|50, IP) (250|50, SC)
IS-FIL:	9
IS-EXT:	(BUOH, 2, FILT.) (W, 9.5, BUOH) (BUOH, 2, W)
IS-CRY:	(PREC., BUOH, ETOAC)
IS-CHR:	(SILG, ETOH-NH4OH)

REFERENCES:

JA, 21, 439, 1968; 23, 473, 1969; USP 3639582; *CA*, 71, 79719; JP 72/5717

43110-1716

NAME:	LASPARTOMYCIN
PO:	S.VIRIDOCHROMOGENES
CT:	LIPOPEPTIDE, AMPHOMYCIN T., ACIDIC, AMPHOTER
FORMULA:	C82H138N17O29
EA:	(N, 13)
MW:	1820
PC:	WH., POW.
OR:	(-17.5, MEOH)
UV:	(200, ,)
SOL-GOOD:	MEOH, BUOH
SOL-FAIR:	W
SOL-POOR:	ACET, HEX
QUAL:	(NINH., +) (BIURET, +)
STAB:	(ACID, +) (BASE, +) (HEAT, +)
TO:	(S.AUREUS, 1) (B.SUBT., 1) (C.ALB., 100) (PHYT.FUNGI, 10)

REFERENCES:

JA, 21, 55, 1968; 23, 423, 1970

43110-1717

NAME:	PARVULIN, PARVULIN-A
PO:	S.PARVULUS, S.PSEUDOGRISEOLUS
CT:	LIPOPEPTIDE, AMPHOMYCIN T., ACIDIC, AMPHOTER
FORMULA:	C57.5H90N13020
EA:	(N, 13)
MW:	1275|15
PC:	WH., POW.
OR:	(-11.54, ETOH)
UV:	MEOH: (200, ,)
SOL-GOOD:	MEOH, ETOH, BUOH
SOL-FAIR:	ETOAC, ACET
SOL-POOR:	CHL, HEX
QUAL:	(NINH., +) (BIURET, +) (FECL3, -) (FEHL., -)
STAB:	(ACID, +) (BASE, +) (HEAT, +)
TO:	(S.AUREUS, .5) (B.SUBT., .8) (S.LUTEA, .8) (E.COLI, 100)
LD50:	(300, IP)
IS-FIL:	4
IS-EXT:	(ACET, 4, MIC.) (BUOH, 3, W)
IS-CHR:	(SILG, CHL-MEOH) (SEPHADEX LH-20, MEOH)
IS-CRY:	(PREC., BUOH, ETOAC)
UTILITY:	FEED ADDITIVE

REFERENCES:

USP 3798129; Hung. P 157984; Can. P 956254; Belg. P 827051; *CA*, 82, 153748

43110-1718

NAME:	ASPARTOCIN, A-8999, T-3910
IDENTICAL:	AMPHOMYCIN, GLUMAMYCIN
PO:	S.GRISEUS-SPIRALIS, S.VIOLACEUS
CT:	LIPOPEPTIDE, AMPHOMYCIN T., ACIDIC, AMPHOTER
EA:	(C, 54) (H, 8) (N, 14)
MW:	2000
PC:	WH., POW.
OR:	(+26.4, MEOH)
UV:	(200, ,)
SOL-GOOD:	ACID, BASE, MEOH, ETOH, BUOH, ACOH
SOL-FAIR:	ACET, ETOAC
SOL-POOR:	W, CHL, HEX
QUAL:	(BIURET, +) (SAKA., -)
STAB:	(ACID, +) (BASE, +) (HEAT, +)
TO:	(B.SUBT., 4) (S.AUREUS, 15)
LD50:	NONTOXIC
IS-FIL:	3
IS-EXT:	(ACID, , MIC.) (BUOH, 3, W)
IS-CRY:	(PREC., BUOH, ACET)

REFERENCES:

Ant. An., 194-213, 1959—60; AAC 1963, 352; *JA*, 22, 207, 1969; *JACS*, 82. 2079, 1960; USP 3057779; BP 897381

43110-1719

NAME:	ZAOMYCIN
PO:	S.ZAOMYCETICUS
CT:	LIPOPEPTIDE, AMPHOMYCIN T., ACIDIC, AMPHOTER
EA:	(N, 12)
PC:	YELLOW, POW.
SOL-GOOD:	MEOH, ETOH, BUOH
SOL-FAIR:	W
SOL-POOR:	ACET, HEX
QUAL:	(NINH., +) (BIURET, +) (FECL3, +) (FEHL., -)
STAB:	(ACID, -) (HEAT, -)
TO:	(S.AUREUS, .8) (B.SUBT., .8)
LD50:	(360, IV)
IS-EXT:	(BUOH, 2, FILT.) (W, 8.5, BUOH)
IS-ABS:	(CARBON, MEOH-W-ACET)
IS-CHR:	(AL, ETOH-W)
IS-CRY:	(LIOF.,) (PREC., MEOH, ET2O)

REFERENCES:

Jap. J. Ant., 7, 83, 1954; *JA*, 7, 134, 1954; JP 55/8150

43110-1720

NAME:	CRYSTALLOMYCIN
PO:	S.VIOLACEAE-NIGER
CT:	LIPOPEPTIDE, AMPHOMYCIN T., ACIDIC, AMPHOTER
EA:	(N, 12)
MW:	1400
PC:	WH., CRYST.
UV:	MEOH: (200, ,)
SOL-GOOD:	W, MEOH, ETOH, BUOH
SOL-POOR:	ACET, HEX
QUAL:	(BIURET, +) (NINH., +)
TO:	(S.AUREUS, .39)
LD50:	(124, IV) (109, IV) (220, SC)
IS-EXT:	(BUOH, 2.5, FILT.)
IS-CRY:	(PREC., FILT., NACL-HCL)

REFERENCES:

Antib., 6, 9, 1957; 2, 45, 106, 1959; 4, 63, 1960; *Biokhim.*, 24, 399, 425, 1960; *CA*, 53, 8285, 420165

43110-1721

NAME: GLUMAMYCIN
IDENTICAL: AMPHOMYCIN, ASPARTOCIN
PO: S.ZAOMYCETICUS
CT: LIPOPEPTIDE, AMPHOMYCIN T., ACIDIC, AMPHOTER
FORMULA: C60H95N13O20
EA: (N, 14)
MW: 1800
PC: WH., CRYST.
OR: (+8, ETOH)
UV: (200, ,)
SOL-GOOD: MEOH, ACID, BASE
SOL-FAIR: ETOH, BUOH, ACET
SOL-POOR: W, CHL, HEX
QUAL: (BIURET, +) (NINH., +) (SAKA., -)
TO: (S.AUREUS, 1) (B.SUBT., .5)
LD50: (500, IP)
IS-FIL: 8
IS-EXT: (I.AMOH, 2, FILT.)
IS-CRY: (PREC., BUOH, ETOAC)
REFERENCES:
JA, 15, 1, 1962; 16, 7, 1963; *An. Rep. Takeda*, 20, 207, 1961; *Bull. Ch. Soc. Jap.*, 33, 1014, 1960; *Bull. Ch. Soc.*, 34, 740, 885, 1961: 35, 1249, 1255, 1556, 1962; 38, 515, 517, 1965; *JACS*, 95, 2352, 1973; DT 1108381; BP 923544; JP 61/8698, 67/4058

43110-5423

NAME: CP-41012, 41012
PO: ACTINOPLANES NIPPONENSIS
CT: LIPOPEPTIDE, ACIDIC, AMPHOMYCIN T.
EA: (C, 45) (H, 7) (N, 10) (O, 39)
PC: WH., POW.
OR: (-7.1, MEOH)
UV: (200, ,)
SOL-GOOD: W, MEOH, BUOH, ETOH, DMFA, DMSO
SOL-POOR: ET2O, CHL, HEX
TO: (S.AUREUS, 3.12) (B.SUBT., .78)
IS-ION: (XAD-2, MEOH)
IS-CHR: (SILG, CHL-ETOH-W)
IS-CRY: (PREC., PROH, HEX) (DRY, BUOH)
REFERENCES:
USP 4001397

4312
Polymyxin Series

The antibiotics belonging to this series are chemically, microbiologically, and biogenetically closely related cyclic lipopeptides. They are branched cycloocta, -deca, or -undecapeptides that are monoacylated in the amino acyl side chain with branched-chain fatty or β-hydroxy fatty acids. These antibiotics are characterized by a high percentage of α,γ-diaminobutyric acid (dab), the presence of several D-amino acids (leu, phe, ser), and a heptapeptide ring and by the fatty acid attachment to the N-terminal of the peptide side chain through an amide bond. The peptides are cyclized through the α-amino and carboxyl groups of a dab residue, and the side chain is attached to the γ-amino group of this residue (α-peptides)

These antibiotics are grouped into polymyxin (43121), octapeptin (43122), and polypeptin (43123) subtypes. The linear tridecaptin-type compounds (43124) are also listed here. The polymyxins contain one to three molecules of threonine and several other amino acids, besides the dab, while octapeptins contain only dab, leucine, and phenylalanine. The polymyxins are decapeptides containing C_8 or C_9 fatty acids, while octapeptins are octapeptides with C_7 to C_{11} β-hydroxy fatty acid constituents. The polypeptin subtype represents an exception, because polypeptin (the only member of this group with exactly known structure) is, in fact, a cyclononapeptolide, because the ring closure is made by ester linkage between the β-hydroxy group of the fatty acid and the C terminus.

This whole group is called polymyxin series (or polymyxin antibiotics), but the designation polymyxins is restricted to compounds belonging to the polymyxin subtype.

The amino acid sequences of these peptides are quite similar, with only a few variable positions. The individual polymyxins and octapeptins differ from each other with respect to the nature, ratio, and chirality of the constituent amino acids, as well as in the fatty acid constituents (homologs, isomers). The compounds with different amino acid composition are usually distinguished by capital letters, and those differing in the fatty acid are marked by a subscript, e.g., polymyxin A_1 and A_2 or polymyxin B_1, B_2, and B_3.

The general structural skeleton of polymyxins and octapeptins are compared in the following figure:

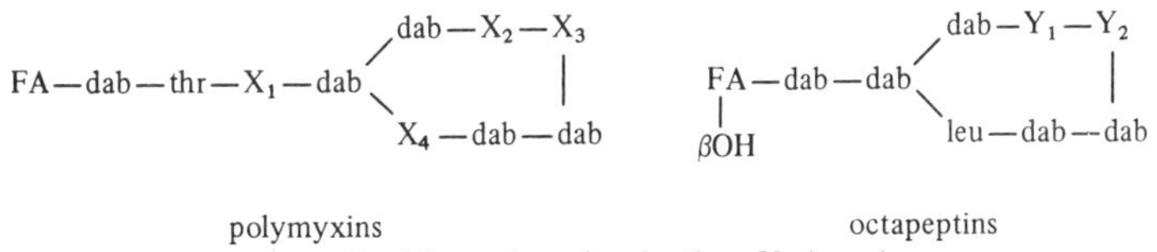

polymyxins octapeptins

X: dab, ser, leu, phe, thr, ile; Y: leu, phe

The amino acid composition of these antibiotics is summarized in the following tables.

Polymyxins	L-dab	L-thr	D-phe	D-leu	D-ser	L-ile	L-leu
A (M)	6	3		1			
B (B_1, B_2)	6	2	1	1			
C	+	+	+				
D (D_1, D_2)	5	3		1	1		
E (Colistin) (E_1, E_2)	6	2		1			1
F	5	1		1	1	1	1
K (A?)	6	3		1			
P (C?)	6	3	1				
S	5	3	1		1		
T	6	1	1	1			1
Circulin (A, B)	6	2		1		1	
Thianosin	4	2		1			

Octapeptins	D-dab	dab	L-dab	D-leu	leu	L-leu	D-phe	phe	L-phe
A (A_1, A_2, A_3)	1		4	1		2			
B	1		4	1		1			1
C (333-25)	1		4	1		1	1		
Y-8495		6			3			1	
AB-1		8			4			1	
BU-1880		5			2			1	
TM-743		5			2			1	
MX-A		4			3				

Polypeptins	dab	thr	leu	phe	ile	val	ala	ser	asp	glu	gly	try
Polypeptin	3	1	2	1	1	1						
AB-2	6		2	1	1	1		1				
B-43	3		1	1	1	2			1			
BN-7	4	1	2	1	1							
Jolipeptin	2					2	2	2		1	1	
4205 A and C	4		2	1	1	1		1				
4205 B	5		3	1	1	2		2				

In each subtype of the polymyxin series the following fatty acids occur:

Polymyxins
(1) (+)-6-Methyloctanoic acid (anteisononanoic acid) (*ai* C_9)
(2) 6-Methylheptanoic acid (isooctanoic acid, methylpellargonic acid) (*i*C_8)
(3) *n*-Octanoic acid (*n*C_8)
Octapeptins
(4) β-Hydroxy-8-methyldecanoic acid (β-OH-*ai*C_{11})
(5) β-Hydroxy-8-methylnonanoic acid (β-OH-*i*C_{10})
(6) β-Hydroxydecanoic acid (β-OH-*n*C_{10})
(7) β-Hydroxy-6-methyloctanoic acid (β-OH-*ai*C_9)
Polypeptins
(8) β-Hydroxy-4-methylhexanoic acid (β-OH-*ai*C_7)
(9) β-Hydroxy-5-methylhexanoic acid (β-OH-*i*-C_7)
(10) β-Hydroxyheptanoic acid (β-OH-*n*C_7)
(11) β-Hydroxyoctanoic acid (β-OH-*n*C_8)
(12) β-Hydroxynonanoic acid (β-OH-*n*C_9)

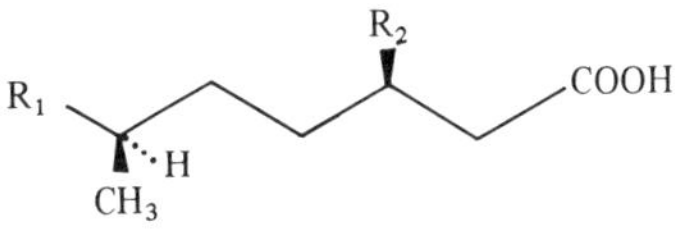

(1) $R_1=C_2H_5$; $R_2=H$ (2) $R_1=CH_3$; $R_2=H$
(7) $R_1=C_2H_5$; $R_2=OH$

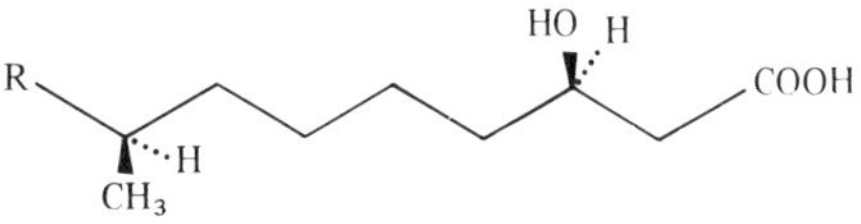

(4) $R = C_2H_5$
(5) $R = CH_3$

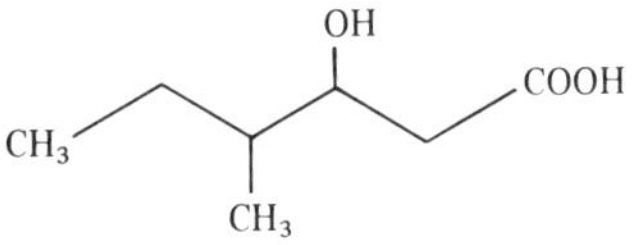

(8)

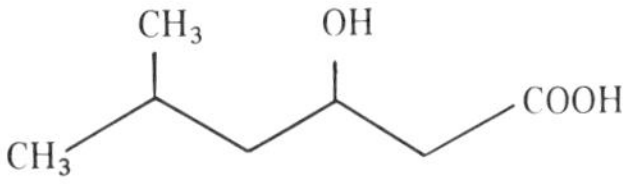

(9)

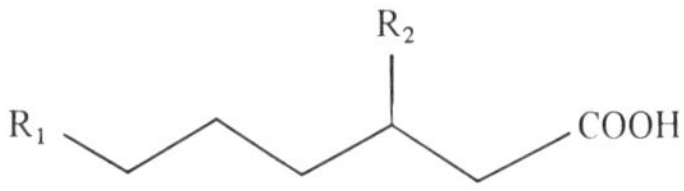

	R_1	R_2
(3)	C_2H_5	H
(6)	nC_4H_9	OH
(10)	CH_3	OH
(11)	C_2H_5	OH
(12)	nC_3H_7	OH

The carbon chains of the fatty acids of all types have the same pattern of branching. It is interesting that the β-hydroxyl group of the fatty acids in octapeptins — which contain a shorter amino-acyl side chain — occupies the same position as in the hydroxyl group of the extracyclic threonine found in all of the polymyxins.

The secondary structure of polymyxin peptides is not fully clarified yet. The common feature of the proposed conformational structures is the existence of β-loops.

These strongly basic cyclolinear peptide antibiotics are white, amorphous substances. They readily form water-soluble salts with strong mineral acids. The free bases of polymyxins B, E, and circulin are water insoluble, while polymyxins A, C, and D give water-soluble bases. All compounds show moderately negative rotation with $(\alpha)_D$ values between −40 and −80°. Only the phenylalanine-containing compounds show a few very weak UV maxima around 254 and 266 nm.

Polymyxins may be isolated from the cultural filtrates by ion-exchange processes or by precipitation methods. The separation of the bacterial mass from the culture liquid usually represents a considerable technical problem.

Compounds in the polymyxin series are produced exclusively by *Bacillus* species, mainly various *B. polymyxa* and *B. circulans* species. Each strain produces only a single polypeptide, but they are usually linked to different fatty acids.

The most important polymyxins were discovered between 1947 and 1950, but their exact chemical structures were established only after their total synthesis in 1965—66.

The structure of polypeptin (discovered in 1948) was established only in 1976. The members of the octapeptin subtype were discovered after 1973.

These antibiotics — especially polymyxins — exhibit high and specific activity against Gram-negative bacteria, including *Pseudomonas* species. Octapeptins and polypeptins are broader spectrum antibiotics exhibiting activity against Gram-positive bacteria, fungi, and protozoa, too. *Proteus* and *Neisseria* species are insensitive to polymyxins, but are sensitive against octapeptins. The antibacterial spectra of all polymyxins are almost identical. They are bacteriostatic at low and bactericidal at higher concentrations.

Development of resistance is not induced readily and there is no evidence of cross resistance with other antibiotic drugs, e.g., aminoglycosides. However, complete cross resistance exists between different polymyxins. Cross resistance between polymyxins and octapeptins was not observed, suggesting their different site of action.

The polymyxin antibiotics are slightly toxic compounds. The principal untoward effect is renal damage and some neurotoxicity. The marked nephrotoxic effects are manifested by proteinuria, cylindruria, and other renal abnormalities. Polymyxin B and E (colistin) are less damaging to the renal system than other members, and therefore they are used in human therapy. Until the development of gentamicin and carbenicillin, polymyxins were the only antibiotics available for treatment of many pseudomonal infections.

The main indication of polymyxin therapy is in the treatment of infections of the urinary tract; bacteremia, bacterial meningitis, gastroenteritis caused by Gram-negative organisms. They are frequently recommended for treatment of refractory urinary tract infections. Polymyxins are poorly absorbed from the gastrointestinal tract (except in newborn), so oral administration (polymyxin B sulfate) is useful only in the treatment of intestinal infections, such as enteritis due to *Pseudomonas* and *Shigella* species. In systemic infections they may be given intramuscularly or parenterally (colistin methanesulfonate). The methane-sulfonate sodium salt of colistin is less toxic but also less active than sulfate, and because it is highly water soluble, so it is very suitable for injection. Because of their relatively high toxicity these antibiotics are indicated only in severe infections which have proven refractory to other drugs.

The mechanism of the biosynthesis of these peptides is similar to that of gramicidin S or tyrocidines, in which aminoacyl-adenylates and aminoacyl-thioesters participate.

The antimicrobial activity of polymyxins is definitely connected with the basic amino groups (γ-amino groups of the dab). Acylation or alkylation on the amino groups leads to inactive products. The ring size (seven-membered α-ring) is also strongly connected with the activity. The synthetic cyclooctapeptide analogs (both 8α and 8β) are about ten times less active than the natural 7α peptides. The exchange of several neutral or one basic amino acids and the replacement of dab with other basic acids (lys, orn) does not have a significant influence on overall activity. The structure and the length (between C_6 and C_{11}) of the fatty acid moiety only modify the activity.

Polymyxins and octapeptins are considered as membrane-active substances. These compounds contain both hydrophobic and hydrophylic groups and carry a positive charge at neutral pH values. This amphiphatic character might suggest that their disruptive influence on membrane structure is analogous to the action of a high concentration of simple cationic detergents. Generally they are attached to the cell membranes of the sensitive organisms and disorient the protein and lipide layers; therefore, the membrane can no longer function normally as an osmotic or permeability barrier, resulting in a loss of certain cellular constituents. In this interaction both ionic (protonated amino groups) and hydrophobic (fatty acid) forces are involved.

REFERENCES

1. *Nature*,163, 611, 1949.
2. *JCS*, 4107, 1964.
3. *Bull. Inst. Chem. Res. Kyoto Univ.*, 43, 259, 1965.
4. *AAC 1966*, 651.
5. *Exp.*, 22, 345, 1966.
6. *J. Chrom.*, 52, 154, 1970.
7. *JA*, 28, 379, 1975; 29, 1241, 1976.
8. *An. Rev. Bioch.*, 46, 723, 1977.

Structures

43121

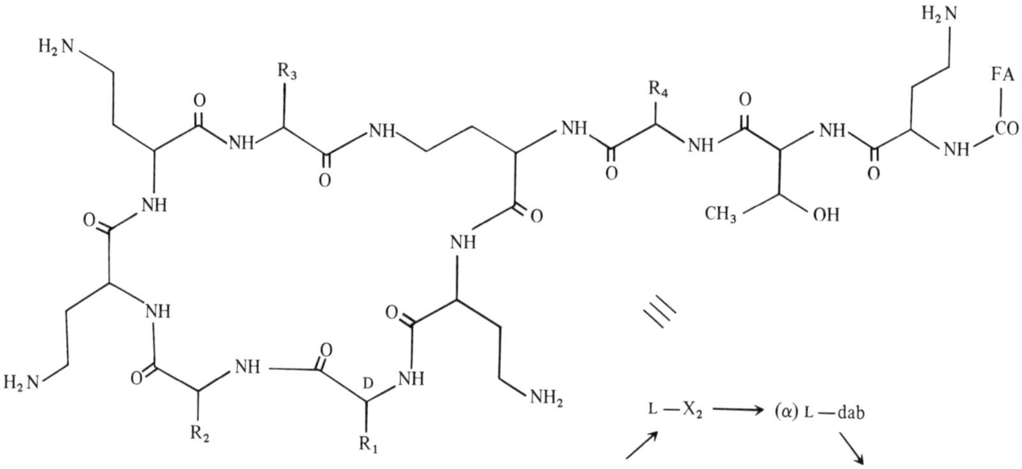

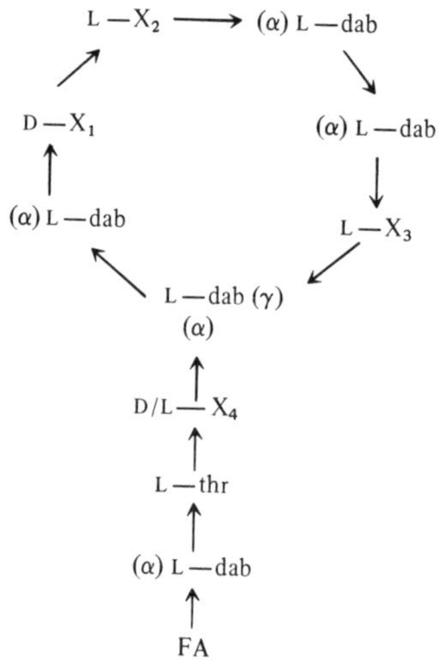

FA = fatty acid; **(1)** in N_1, **(2)** in N_2, or **(3)** in N_3 components (N = A, B, D, E, F, P, S, T)
in colistins A, B, and C, FA = **(1)**, **(2)**, and **(3)**, respectively
in circulins A and B, FA = **(1)** and **(2)**, respectively

Antibiotic	R_1 (X_1)	R_2 (X_2)	R_3 (X_3)	R_5 (X_4)
Polymyxin A	$-CH_2CH(CH_3)_2$ (leu)	$-CH(OH)CH_3$ (thr)	$-CH(OH)CH_3$ (thr)	$-(CH_2)_2NH_2$ (D — dab)
Polymyxin B	$-CH_2C_6H_5$ (phe)	$-CH_2CH(CH_3)_2$ (leu)	$-CH(OH)CH_3$ (thr)	$-(CH_2)_2NH_2$ (L — dab)

Polymyxin D

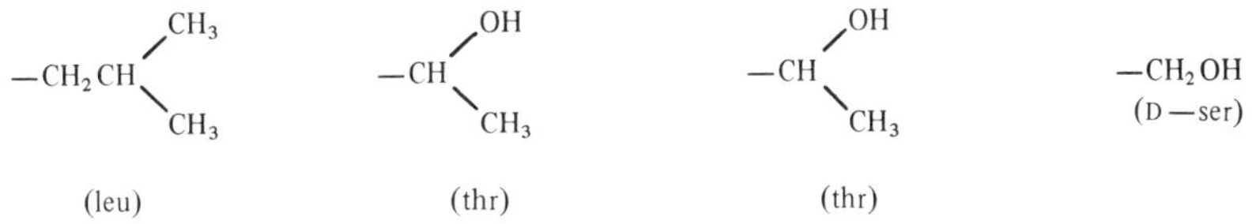

Polymyxin E

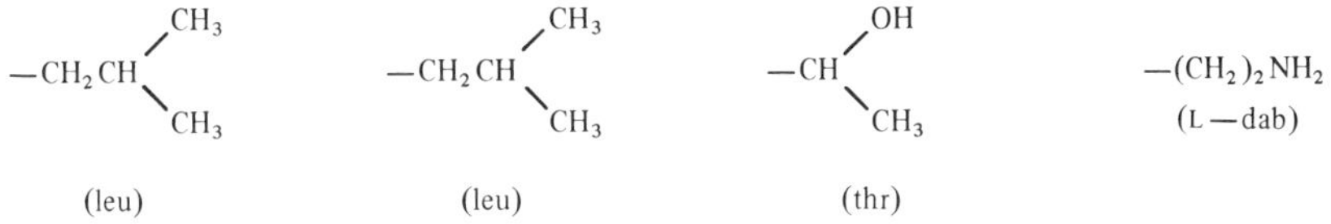

Polymyxin S

Polymyxin T

Circulin A, B

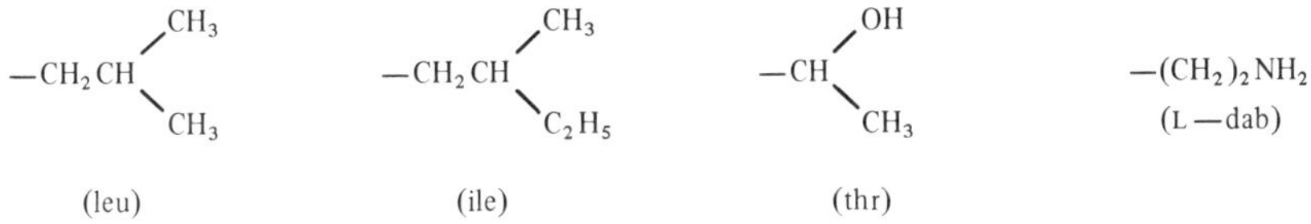

43122

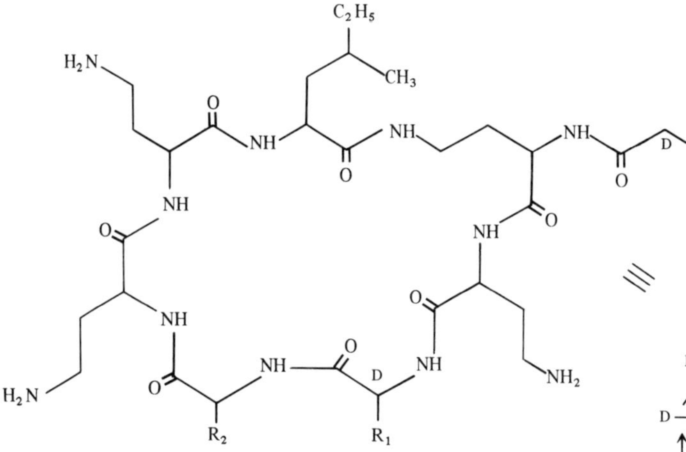

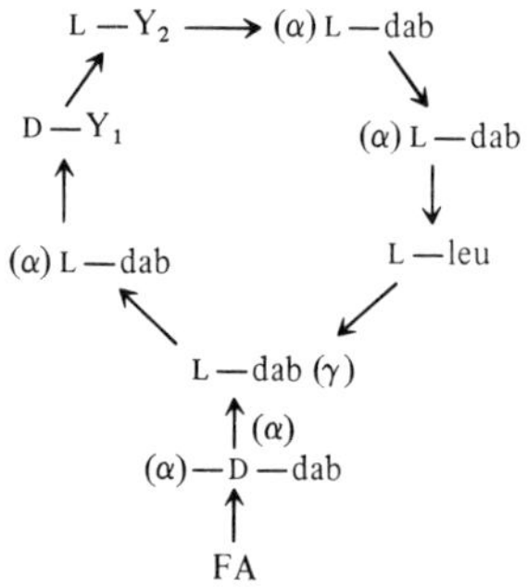

FA = β-hydroxy-fatty acid;
(4) in N_1, **(5)** in N_2, or **(6)** in N_3
(N = A, B, or C)

Antibiotic	R_1 (Y_1)	R_2 (Y_2)
Octapeptin A	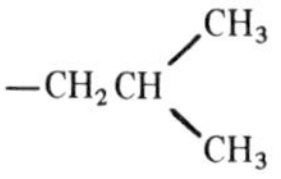 (leu)	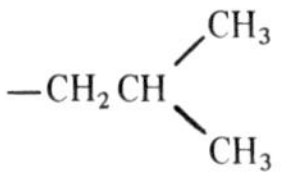 (leu)
Octapeptin B	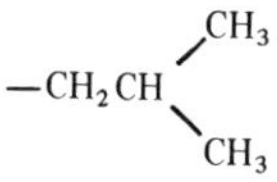 (leu)	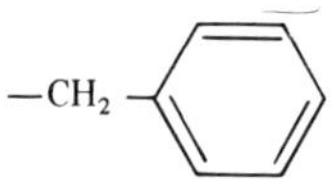 (phe)
Octapeptin C	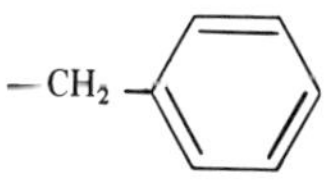 (phe)	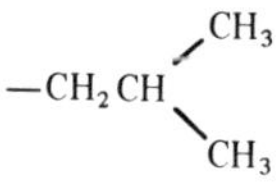 (leu)

43123

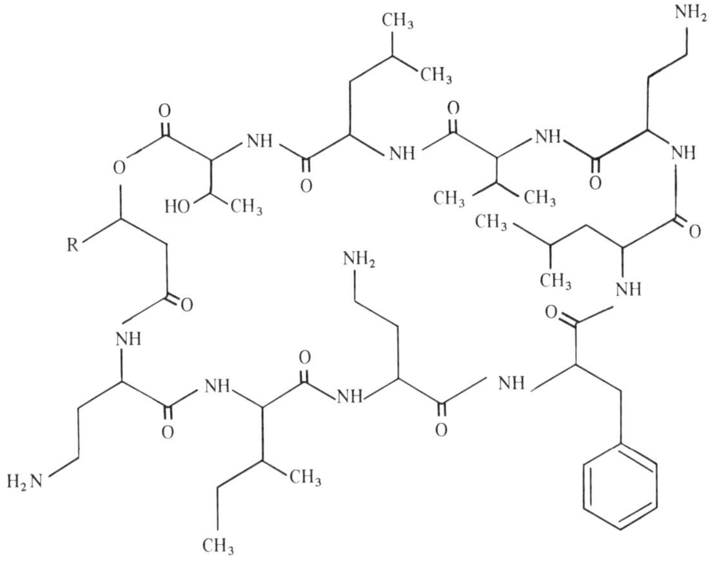

polypeptin A R = $CH(CH_3)CH_2CH_3$
polypeptin B R = $CH_2CH(CH_3)_2$

43124

FA−D-X_1−D-dab−gly−D-ser−D-try−L-ser−L-dab−D-dab−L-X_2−L-glu−L-val−D-X_3−L-X_4

		X_1	X_2	X_3	X_4	FA
Tridecaptin A	α	val	phe	aile	ala	aC_9h^3
	β	val	phe	val	ala	aC_9h^3
Tridecaptin B	α	gly	ile	aile	ser	
	β	gly	ile	val	ser	aC_9
	γ	gly	val	aile	ser	
	δ	gly	val	val	ser	
Tridecaptin C	α_1	val	phe	val	ser	$aC_{11}h^3$
	β_1	val	phe	aile	ser	$iC_{10}h^3$
	α_2	val	phe	val	ser	

Note: aC_9h^3: $-CO-CH_2CH(OH)CH_2CH_2CH(CH_3)C_2H_5$
aC_9: $-CO-(CH_2)_4CH(CH_3)C_2H_5$
$aC_{11}h^3$: $-CO-CH_2CH(OH)(CH_2)_4CH(CH_3)C_2H_5$
$iC_{10}h^3$: $-CO-CH_2CH(OH)(CH_2)_4C(CH_3)_2$

43121-1722

NAME: POLYMYXIN-A
TRADE NAMES: AEROSPORIN
IDENTICAL: POLYMYXIN-M
PO: B.POLYMYXA
CT: LIPOPEPTIDE, POLYMYXIN T., BASIC
FORMULA: C51H97N16O13.4HCL
EA: (N, 16)
MW: 1293
EW: 275
PC: WH., POW.
OR: (-42, W)
UV: W: (200, ,)
SOL-GOOD: ACID
SOL-POOR: W, MEOH, HEX
QUAL: (BIURET, +) (NINH., +) (SAKA., -) (PAULY, -)
STAB: (ACID, +) (HEAT, +) (BASE, -)
TO: (E.COLI, .2) (SHYG., 1) (K.PNEUM., .1)
(PS.AER., 1) (P.VULG., 1) (B.SUBT., 50)
LD50: (7.5|1.5, IV) (16|3, IP) (77|10, SC)
IS-FIL: 2
IS-ABS: (CARBON, MEOH-HCL)
IS-CRY: (PREC., MEOH-W, ACET)
REFERENCES:

An. N.Y. Acad. Sci., 51, 853, 1949; *Nature*, 169, 611, 1949; 160, 263, 1947; 212, 311, 1966; *AAC 1966, 651*

43121-1723

NAME:	POLYMYXIN-M
IDENTICAL:	POLYMYXIN-A
PO:	B.POLYMYXA
CT:	LIPOPEPTIDE, POLYMYXIN T., BASIC
FORMULA:	C51H96N16O14.5HCL
EA:	(N, 18)
MW:	1185
PC:	WH., POW.
OR:	(-48.1, W)
UV:	W: (200, ,)
SOL-GOOD:	ACID, MEOH
SOL-FAIR:	W
SOL-POOR:	ETOH, HEX
QUAL:	(BIURET, +) (NINH., +) (SAKA., -)
STAB:	(ACID, +) (BASE, -) (HEAT, +)
TO:	(E.COLI, .05) (SHYG., .1) (P.VULG., .05) (K.PNEUM., .02) (PS.AER., 1)
LD50:	(5.5, IV)
IS-FIL:	2.5
IS-ION:	(KB-2-NA, MEOH-HCL)
IS-CRY:	(PREC., MEOH, ACET)
UTILITY:	ANTIBACTERIAL DRUG

REFERENCES:

Antib., 250, 1971; 549, 1967; 3, 1960; 4, 6, 1958; 1, 10, 1959; *Zh. Obsch. Khim.*, 31, 297, 1961; 33, 1019, 2760, 1963; 45, 2287, 2331, 1975; *Biokhim.*, 26, 296, 1961; *Khim. Prir. Soed.*, 280, 1975; 277, 1976; *CA*, 55, 5653, 22149, 16912

43121-1724

NAME:	POLYMYXIN-B1
PO:	B.POLYMYXA
CT:	LIPOPEPTIDE, POLYMYXIN T., BASIC
FORMULA:	C56H99N16O14
EA:	(N, 18)
MW:	1220
EW:	276
PC:	WH., POW.
OR:	(-85.5, ETOH-W)
UV:	W: (252, ,) (259, ,) (264, ,)
SOL-GOOD:	ACID
SOL-FAIR:	MEOH
SOL-POOR:	W, BUOH, HEX
QUAL:	(NINH., +) (BIURET, +) (SAKA., -)
STAB:	(ACID, +) (BASE, +) (HEAT, +)
TO:	(E.COLI, .1) (SHYG., .05) (K.PNEUM., .1) (P.VULG., 2) (PS.AER., .1) (B.SUBT., 100) (C.ALB., 100)
LD50:	(7.5|1.5, IV) (19, IP) (80, SC)
IS-FIL:	2.5
IS-ION:	(IRC-50-NA, HCL)
IS-CRY:	(PREC., W, NH4OH)
UTILITY:	ANTIBACTERIAL DRUG

REFERENCES:

Lancet, 127, 1948; *Nature*, 160, 263, 1947; 164, 611, 1949; *An. N.Y. Acad. Sci.*, 51, 853, 1949; *JACS*, 76, 4892, 1954; 78, 3663, 1956; *Bull. Soc. Chim. Biol.*, 39, 795, 1957; *J. Bioch. (Tokyo)*, 54, 555, 1963; 56, 335, 1964; *Nature*, 200, 1008, 1963; 204, 185, 993, 1964; *Exp.*, 20, 365, 1964; *Helv.*, 48, 1161, 1965; *J. Chrom.*, 52, 154, 1970; *BBA*, 156, 119, 1968; *J. Inf. Dis.*, 119, 492, 504, 518, 1969; BP 646258, 645750, 658766; *JA*, 29, 774, 1976; *J. Ph. Soc.*, 53, 1536, 1969

43121-1725

NAME: POLYMYXIN-B2
PO: B.POLYMYXA
CT: LIPOPEPTIDE, POLYMYXIN T., BASIC
FORMULA: C55H97N16O14
EA: (N, 18)
PC: WH., POW.
OR: (-88, ETOH-W)
UV: W: (252, ,) (259, ,) (264, ,)
SOL-GOOD: ACID
SOL-FAIR: MEOH
SOL-POOR: W, BUOH, HEX
QUAL: (NINH., +) (BIURET, +)
STAB: (ACID, +) (BASE, +) (HEAT, +)
TO: (G.NEG., .01)
REFERENCES:

Lancet, 127, 1948 *Nature,* 160, 263, 1947; 164, 611, 1949; *An. N.Y. Acad. Sci.,* 51, 853, 1949; *JACS,* 76, 4892, 1954; 78, 3663, 1956; *Bull. Soc. Chim. Biol.,* 39, 795, 1957; *J. Bioch. (Tokyo),* 54, 555, 1963; 56, 335, 1964; *Nature,* 200, 1008, 1963; 204, 185, 993, 1964; *Exp.,* 20, 365, 1964; *Helv.,* 48, 1161, 1965; *J. Chrom.,* 52, 154, 1970; *BBA,* 156, 119, 1968; *J. Inf. Dis.,* 119, 492, 504, 518, 1969; BP 646258, 645750, 658766; *JA,* 29, 774, 1976; *J. Ph. Soc.,* 53, 1536, 1969

43121-1726

NAME: POLYMYXIN-C
PO: B.POLYMYXA
CT: LIPOPEPTIDE, POLYMYXIN T., BASIC
EA: (N, 18)
PC: WH., POW.
UV: W: (252, ,) (258, ,) (264, ,)
SOL-GOOD: ACID
SOL-POOR: W, BUOH, HEX
QUAL: (BIURET, +) (NINH., +) (SAKA., -)
STAB: (HEAT, +) (ACID, +) (BASE, -)
TO: (G.NEG., .02)
REFERENCES:

An. N.Y. Acad. Sci., 51, 853, 1949

43121-1727

NAME:	POLYMYXIN-D1
PO:	B.POLYMYXA, B.AEROSPORUS
CT:	LIPOPEPTIDE, POLYMYXIN T., BASIC
FORMULA:	C50H94N15O14
EA:	(N, 18)
MW:	1150
EW:	286
PC:	WH., POW.
OR:	(-42.1, W)
UV:	W: (200, ,)
SOL-GOOD:	ACID
SOL-FAIR:	MEOH, W
SOL-POOR:	ETOH, HEX
QUAL:	(BIURET, +) (NINH., +) (SAKA., -)
STAB:	(ACID, +) (BASE, -) (HEAT, +)
TO:	(E.COLI, .01) (SHYG., .01) (K.PNEUM., .2) (P.VULG., .5) (PS.AER., 1)
LD50:	(15|3, IV) (50|27, IP) (195|35, SC)
IS-FIL:	2.5
IS-ION:	(IRC-50,)
IS-ABS:	(CARBON, MEOH-HCL)
IS-CRY:	(PREC., MEOH, ACET)

REFERENCES:

Bull. Johns Hopkins Hosp., 81, 43, 1947; *J. Bact.*, 54, 24, 1947; JACS, 70, 3771, 1948; *An. N.Y. Acad. Sci.*, 51, 853, 1000, 1949; *J. Biol. Chem.*, 239, 502, 1964; *Exp.*, 22, 354, 1966; *Helv.*, 53, 929, 1970; *Nature*, 160, 263, 1947

43121-1728

NAME: POLYMYXIN-E
TRADE NAMES: COLIMYCIN
IDENTICAL: COLISTIN
PO: B.POLYMYXA
CT: LIPOPEPTIDE, POLYMYXIN T., BASIC
FORMULA: C53H102N16O13.5HCL
EA: (N, 16)
MW: 1250
PC: WH., POW.
UV: (200, ,)
SOL-GOOD: ACID
SOL-POOR: W, MEOH, HEX
QUAL: (NINH., +) (BIURET, +)
STAB: (ACID, +) (BASE, -) (HEAT, +)
TO: (E.COLI, .02) (SHYG., .05) (K.PNEUM., .1) (P.VULG., .1) (PS.AER., .5) (B.SUBT., 50) (C.ALB., 100)
LD50: (7.5, IV) (15, IP) (75, SC)
IS-FIL: 2
IS-ION: (IRC-50, HCL)
UTILITY: ANTIBACTERIAL DRUG
REFERENCES:
Bioch. J., 43, 26, 1948; *Lancet*, 922, 1963; *An. N.Y. Acad. Sci.*, 51, 853, 1949; *J. Bact.*, 57, 305, 1949; *Nature*, 204, 185, 993, 1964; *J. Bioch. (Tokyo)*, 57, 226, 1965; *JCS*, 4107, 1964; *Helv.*, 48, 1371, 1965; BP 742589

43121-1729

NAME: POLYMYXIN-P1
PO: B.POLYMYXA
CT: LIPOPEPTIDE, POLYMYXIN T., BASIC
FORMULA: C54H99N16O14.6HCL
EA: (N, 16)
MW: 1400
PC: WH., POW.
OR: (-37.4, W)
UV: W: (200, ,)
SOL-GOOD: W, MEOH, ETOH
SOL-POOR: BUOH, HEX
QUAL: (NINH., +) (SAKA., -) (PAULY, -) (BIURET, +)
TO: (E.COLI, .79) (K.PNEUM., .79) (SHYG., .79) (PS.AER., 3.12) (B.SUBT., 10)
IS-FIL: 2
IS-ION: (IRC-50-H, HCL)
IS-CHR: (SEPHADEX G-15, ACOH-W)
REFERENCES:
JA, 22, 449, 1969; JP 72/27038; *CA*, 77, 150576

43121-1730

NAME: POLYMYXIN-P2
PO: B.POLYMYXA
CT: LIPOPEPTIDE, POLYMYXIN T., BASIC
FORMULA: C53H97N16O14
EA: (N, 18)
MW: 1400
PC: WH., POW.
OR: (-43.3, W)
UV: W: (200, ,)
SOL-GOOD: W, MEOH, ETOH
SOL-POOR: BUOH, HEX
QUAL: (NINH., +) (SAKA., -) (PAULY, -) (BIURET, +)
TO: (G.NEG., 1) (G.POS., 20)
REFERENCES:
JA, 22, 449, 1969; JP 72/27038; *CA*, 77, 150576

43121-1731

NAME: COLISTIN-A
TRADE NAMES: COLIMYCIN, BELCOMYCIN, COLISTINAT
IDENTICAL: POLYMYXIN-E1
PO: B.COLISTINUS, B.POLYMYXA-COLISTINUS
CT: LIPOPEPTIDE, POLYMYXIN T., BASIC
FORMULA: C53H100N16O13
EA: (N, 19)
MW: 1360
PC: WH., POW.
OR: (-56.3, W)
UV: W: (200, ,)
SOL-GOOD: ACID
SOL-FAIR: MEOH
SOL-POOR: W, ETOH, HEX
QUAL: (NINH., +) (BIURET, +)
STAB: (ACID, +) (BASE, -) (HEAT, +)
TO: (E.COLI, .01) (SHYG., .05) (P.VULG., .1)
(K.PNEUM., .05) (PS.AER., 1) (B.SUBT., 50)
LD50: (23, IP)
IS-ION: (IRC-50, HCL)
IS-CHR: (XE-64-NA, HCL)
UTILITY: ANTIBACTERIAL DRUG
REFERENCES:
Jap. J. Ant., 7, 147, 1954; 12, 365, 1959; *JA*, 3, 457, 1950; 4, 7, 1951; 7, 140, 1954; *J. Ph. Soc. Jap.*, 74, 1234, 1246, 1954; 73, 414, 1953; *Ant. An.*, 41, 61, 1959—60; *J. Bioch. (Tokyo)*, 54, 25, 173, 412, 1963; 56, 182, 1965; *Nature*, 200, 1008, 1963; 204, 993, 1964; *JCS*, 4107, 1964; *Helv.*, 48, 1321, 1965; *Chem. Ph. Bull.*, 15, 1219, 1967; *Bull. Soc. Chim. Biol.*, 43, 495, 1961; *Agr. Biol. Ch.*, 30, 1112, 1967; 33, 262, 1969; 37, 2455, 1973; JP 52/1546, 56/1346, 57/4898, 6629

43121-1732

NAME: COLISTIN-B
IDENTICAL: POLYMYXIN-E2
PO: B.POLYMYXA-COLISTINUS
CT: LIPOPEPTIDE, POLYMYXIN T., BASIC
FORMULA: C52H98N16O13
EA: (N, 18)
MW: 1360
PC: WH., POW.
OR: (-57.4, W)
UV: W: (200, ,)
SOL-GOOD: W
SOL-FAIR: MEOH
SOL-POOR: ETOH, HEX
TO: (G.NEG., .01) (G.POS., 50)
REFERENCES:

Jap. J. Ant., 7, 147, 1954: 12, 365, 1959; *JA*, 3, 457, 1950; 4, 7, 1951; 7, 140, 1954; *J. Ph. Soc. Jap.*, 74, 1234, 1246, 1954; 73, 414, 1953; *Ant. An.*, 41, 61, 1959-60; *J. Bioch. (Tokyo)*, 54, 25, 173, 412, 1963; 56, 182, 1965; *Nature*, 200, 1008, 1963; 204, 993, 1964; *JCS*, 4107, 1964; *Helv.*, 48, 1321, 1965; *Chem. Ph. Bull.*, 15, 1219, 1967; *Bull. Soc. Chim. Biol.*, 43, 495, 1961; *Agr. Biol. Ch.*, 30, 1112, 1967; 33, 262, 1969; 37, 2455, 1973; JP 52/1546, 56/1346, 57/4898, 6629

43121-1733

NAME: COLISTIN-C
CT: LIPOPEPTIDE, POLYMYXIN T., BASIC
FORMULA: C51H96N16O13
PC: WH., POW.
TO: (G.NEG., 1)
REFERENCES:

J. Bioch. (Tokyo), 56, 182, 1964; *J. Ph. Soc. Jap.*, 73, 414, 1953; 74, 1243, 1246, 1954

43121-1734

NAME: CIRCULIN-A
PO: B.CIRCULANS
CT: LIPOPEPTIDE, POLYMYXIN T., BASIC
FORMULA: C53H100N16O13
EA: (N, 18)
MW: 1200
PC: WH., POW.
OR: (-61.6, W)
UV: W: (200, ,)
SOL-GOOD: W
SOL-FAIR: MEOH
SOL-POOR: BUOH, HEX
QUAL: (BIURET, +) (NINH., +) (SAKA., -)
STAB: (ACID, +) (BASE, -) (HEAT, +)
TO: (E.COLI, .4) (SHYG., .5) (K.PNEUM., .4) (PS.AER., 1) (P.VULG., 67) (B.SUBT., 100) (S.AUREUS, 100) (PHYT.BACT., .4)
LD50: (10, IV) (68, SC)
IS-FIL: ORIG.
IS-ABS: (CARBON, ACET-HCL)
IS-CHR: (SILG, BUOH-PH2 PUFF)
REFERENCES:

Proc. Soc. Am. Bact., 1, 20, 1948; *Sci.*, 116, 147, 1952; *J. Bact.*, 57, 305, 1949; 58, 115, 1949; *J. Clin. Invest.*, 28, 1032, 1053, 1949; *Exp.*, 21, 307, 1965; *J. Biol. Chem.*, 181, 95, 1949; *Fed. Proc.*, 17, 233, 1955; 19, 342, 1960; *Bact. Proc.*, 72, 1956; *Helv.*, 49, 974, 1966; USP 2779705, 2676133

43121-1735

NAME: CIRCULIN-B
PO: B.CIRCULANS
CT: LIPOPEPTIDE, POLYMYXIN T., BASIC
FORMULA: C52H98N16O13
EA: (N, 18)
PC: WH., POW.
UV: W: (200, ,)
SOL-GOOD: W
SOL-FAIR: MEOH
SOL-POOR: BUOH, HEX
TO: (G.NEG., .1)
REFERENCES:

Z. Chem., 3, 316, 1966; *Sci.*, 116, 147, 1952; *Helv.*, 49, 924, 1966; *Exp.*, 24, 656, 1968

43121-1740

NAME: THIANOSINE
PO: B.THIAMINOLYTICUS
CT: LIPOPEPTIDE, POLYMYXIN T., BASIC
EA: (C, 48) (H, 8) (N, 15)
MW: 1000|200
PC: WH., POW.
OR: (-16, MEOH)
UV: MEOH: (200, ,)
SOL-GOOD: W, MEOH
SOL-POOR: ACET, HEX
QUAL: (NINH., +) (BIURET, +)
TO: (G.NEG.,)
LD50: (68,)
IS-ION: (IRC-50-H, NH4OH)
IS-ABS: (CARBON, MEOH-HCL)
IS-CHR: (SILG, ETOAC-MEOH-ACOH-W)
IS-CRY: (DRY,)
REFERENCES:

J. Vitaminol. (Kyoto), 17, 163, 1971; JP 71/42959; *CA*, 76, 32827, 84518

43121-5683

NAME: POLYMYXIN-S1
PO: B.POLYMYXA
CT: POLYMYXIN T., LIPOPEPTIDE, BASIC
FORMULA: C53H91N15O15
EA: (N, 17)
MW: 1177
PC: WH., POW.
OR: (-54, 3, W)
UV: W: (253, 1.4,) (259, 1.5,) (264, 1.2,)
SOL-GOOD: W, MEOH
SOL-POOR: ACET-HEX
QUAL: (NINH., +)
TO: (E.COLI, .78) (K.PNEUM, .78) (PS.AER., 6.25)
LD50: (37.5|12.5, IP)
IS-FIL: 2
IS-EXT: (BUOH, 11, W)
IS-ION: (IRC-50-NA, HCL)
IS-CRY: (PREC., W, NAOH) (LIOF.,)
REFERENCES:

JA, 30, 427, 1030, 1035, 1977

43121-5684

NAME:	POLYMYXIN-T1
PO:	B.POLYMYXA
CT:	POLYMYXIN T., LIPOPEPTIDE, BASIC
FORMULA:	C58H102N16O12
EA:	(N, 18)
MW:	1214
PC:	WH., POW.
OR:	(-78, W)
UV:	W: (252, 2.3,) (258, 2.4,) (264, 2.1,)
SOL-GOOD:	W, MEOH
SOL-POOR:	ACET, HEX
QUAL:	(NINH, +)
TO:	(B.SUBT., 3.13) (S.AUREUS, 12.5) (E.COLI, 3.13) (K.PNEUM., 3.13) (PS.AER., 6.25)
LD50:	(32.4, IP)
IS-EXT:	(BUOH, 11, W)
IS-ION:	(IRC-50-NA, HCL)
IS-CRY:	(PREC., W, NAOH) (LIOF.,)

REFERENCES:

JA, 30, 427, 1030, 1042, 1977

43121-5991

NAME:	POLYMYXIN-F1
PO:	B.CIRCULANS
CT:	PEPTIDE, POLYMYXIN T., BASIC
FORMULA:	C54H101N15O13
EA:	(N, 18)
MW:	1167
PC:	WH., POW.
OR:	(-43, HCL)
UV:	W: (200, ,)
SOL-GOOD:	W
SOL-FAIR:	MEOH
SOL-POOR:	BUOH, HEX
QUAL:	(NINH., +)
TO:	(S.AUREUS, 50) (PS.AER., 1.6) (E.COLI, 2.4)
LD50:	(50, SC)
IS-FIL:	2
IS-EXT:	(BUOH, 2, FILT.)
IS-ION:	(IRC-50-NA, MEOH-HCL)
IS-CHR:	(CM-CEL, NACL)
IS-CRY:	(PREC., MEOH, ACET) (PREC., W, NAOH)

REFERENCES:

JA, 30, 767, 1977

43121-5992

NAME:	POLYMYXIN-F2
PO:	B.CIRCULANS
CT:	LIPOPEPTIDE, POLYMYXIN T., BASIC
FORMULA:	C53H99N15013
EA:	(N, 18)
PC:	WH.
UV:	W: (200, ,)
SOL-GOOD:	W
SOL-FAIR:	MEOH
SOL-POOR:	BUOH, HEX
QUAL:	(NINH., +)
TO:	(PS.AER.,) (E.COLI,)
IS-CHR:	(CM-CEL, NACL)

REFERENCES:

JA, 30, 767, 1977

43121-6073

NAME:	POLYMYXIN-K
PO:	B.SP.
CT:	BASIC, LIPOPEPTIDE, POLYMYXIN T.
EA:	(N,)
TO:	(G.NEG.,)

REFERENCES:

JP 71/16152

43121-6613

NAME:	681-17
PO:	B.BREVIS
CT:	BASIC, LIPOPEPTIDE, POLYMYXIN T.
EA:	(C, 50) (H, 8) (N, 15)
MW:	1200
PC:	WH., POW.
OR:	(-60, HCL)
UV:	W: (200, ,)
SOL-GOOD:	W, MEOH, BUOH-W
SOL-FAIR:	BUOH, W
SOL-POOR:	ACET, HEX
QUAL:	(NINH., +)
TO:	(S.AUREUS, 50) (B.SUBT., 25) (PS.AER., 6) (K.PNEUM., 6) (P.VULG., 1.5) (E.COLI, 12)
LD50:	(37.5|12.5, IV)
IS-EXT:	(BUOH, 7, W)
IS-ION:	(IRC-50-NH4, NH4OH)
IS-CHR:	(SILG, CHL-MEOH-NH4OH)
IS-CRY:	(LIOF.,)

REFERENCES:

JP 78/121703

43122-1742

NAME: OCTAPEPTIN-A2, E-49-A", OCTAPEPTIN-A3
PO: B.CIRCULANS
CT: LIPOPEPTIDE, BASIC, OCTAPEPTIN T.
FORMULA: C48H91N13O10
EA: (N, 17)
MW: 1080
EW: 255
PC: WH., POW.
OR: (-42, W)
UV: W: (200, ,)
SOL-GOOD: W, MEOH, ETOH, ACOH, DMSO
SOL-POOR: ACET, HEX
STAB: (ACID, +) (HEAT, +)
TO: (S.AUREUS, 12) (B.SUBT., .6) (E.COLI, .6) (PS.AER., .8) (K.PNEUM., .7) (P.VULG., 100) (C.ALB., 9.4) (S.CEREV., 2.4)
IS-FIL: 1
IS-EXT: (BUOH, 10, FILT.)
IS-CHR: (CM-CEL, NACL)
IS-CRY: (PREC., MEOH, ET2O)
REFERENCES:

JA, 26, 444, 449, 457, 1973; 28, 379, 1975; 30, 756, 1977; *An. N.Y. Acad. Sci.*, 235, 493, 1974; *J. Chrom.*, 97, 112, 1974; *JA*, 29, 1241, 1976; Holl. P 72/5751; DT 2219993, 2357858

43122-1743

NAME: OCTAPEPTIN-A1, E-49-B"
CT: LIPOPEPTIDE, BASIC, OCTAPEPTIN T.
FORMULA: C49H93N13O10
EA: (N, 17)
PC: WH., POW.
UV: (200, ,)
SOL-GOOD: W, MEOH
SOL-POOR: ACET, HEX
QUAL: (NINH., +) (BIURET, +)
TO: (S.AUREUS, 6.3) (E.COLI, .6) (PS.AER., .8) (C.ALB., 9.4)
IS-FIL: 2
IS-EXT: (BUOH, 10, FILT.)
REFERENCES:

JA, 26, 444, 449, 457, 1973; 28, 379, 1975; 30, 756, 1977; *An. N.Y. Acad. Sci.*, 235, 493, 1974; *J. Chrom.*, 97, 112, 1974; *JA*, 29, 1241, 1976; Holl. P 72/5751; DT 2219993, 2357858

43122-1744

NAME: OCTAPEPTIN-B2, E-49-G", OCTAPEPTIN-B3
PO: B.CIRCULANS
CT: LIPOPEPTIDE, BASIC, OCTAPEPTIN T.
FORMULA: C51H89N13O10
EA: (N, 17)
PC: WH., POW.
UV: W: (258, 4.1,) (265, 3.4,) (268, 3.2,)
SOL-GOOD: W, MEOH
SOL-POOR: ACET, HEX
QUAL: (NINH., +) (BIURET, +)
TO: (S.AUREUS, 3.1) (E.COLI, .3) (PS.AER., .4) (C.ALB., 6.3)

REFERENCES:
JA, 26, 444, 449, 457, 1973; 28, 379, 1975; 30, 756, 1977; *An. N.Y. Acad. Sci.*, 235, 493, 1974; *J. Chrom.*, 97, 112, 1974; *JA*, 29, 1241, 1976; Holl. P 72/5751; DT 2219993, 2357858

43122-1745

NAME: OCTAPEPTIN-B1, E-49-D"
CT: LIPOPEPTIDE, BASIC, OCTAPEPTIN T.
FORMULA: C52H91N13O10
EA: (N, 16)
PC: WH., POW.
UV: W: (258, ,) (265, ,) (268, ,)
SOL-GOOD: W, MEOH
SOL-POOR: ACET, HEX
QUAL: (NINH., +) (BIURET, +)
TO: (S.AUREUS, 2.4) (E.COLI, .4) (PS.AER., 1.2) (C.ALB., 4.7)

REFERENCES:
JA, 26, 444, 449, 457, 1973; 28, 379, 1975; 30, 756, 1977; *An. N.Y. Acad. Sci.*, 235, 493, 1974; *J. Chrom.*, 97, 112, 1974; *JA*, 29, 1241, 1976; Holl. P 72/5751; DT 2219993, 2357858

43122-3904

NAME:	<u>BU-1880</u>, BU-1975-B, OCTAPEPTIN
PO:	B.CIRCULANS
CT:	LIPOPEPTIDE, BASIC, OCTAPEPTIN T.
EA:	(N, 16)
PC:	WH., POW.
OR:	(-,)
UV:	W: (200, ,)
SOL-GOOD:	ACID, BASE
SOL-FAIR:	W, MEOH, BUOH
SOL-POOR:	ACET, HEX
QUAL:	(NINH., +) (EHRL., +) (SAKA., -)
TO:	(E.COLI, 3.1) (K.PNEUM., 3.1) (PS.AER., 3) (SHYG., 3.1) (P.VULG., 6) (S.AUREUS, 3) (S.LUTEA, 12) (B.SUBT., 1.6)
LD50:	(37, IV) (300, IM)
IS-EXT:	(BUOH, 9, WB.)
IS-ION:	(IRC-50-NH4, NH4OH)

REFERENCES:

JA, 27, 460, 1974; USP 3880994

43122-4786

NAME:	<u>Y-8495</u>, OCTAPEPTIN
PO:	B.BUNGOENSIS
CT:	LIPOPEPTIDE, BASIC, OCTAPEPTIN T.
EA:	(C, 45) (H, 4) (N, 16)
MW:	2000
PC:	WH., POW.
OR:	(-30, HCL)
UV:	W-HCL: (254, ,) (261, ,) (266, ,) (269, ,)
SOL-GOOD:	PYR, DMSO, ACOH, ACID
SOL-POOR:	W, MEOH, HEX
QUAL:	(NINH., +) (BIURET, +) (SAKA., -)
TO:	(S.LUTEA, 6.25) (S.AUREUS, 12) (B.SUBT., 12) (E.COLI, 1.56) (PS.AER., 3.13) (SHYG., 6.25) (K.PNEUM., 6.25) (C.ALB., 25)
LD50:	(1500|500, PEROS)
IS-EXT:	(BUOH, , FILT.)
IS-CHR:	(CM-SEPHADEX C-25-H, PYR-NH4OH-W)

REFERENCES:

JA, 29, 1241, 1976; JP 75/25795

43122-5061

NAME: TM-743
PO: B.CIRCULANS
CT: LIPOPEPTIDE, BASIC, OCTAPEPTIN T.
EA: (C, 55) (H, 9) (N, 16)
MW: 1080
PC: WH., POW.
OR: (-52, W)
UV: W: (251, 1.69,) (257, 1.85,) (263, 1.46,) (266, .94,)
SOL-GOOD: W
SOL-POOR: ACET, HEX
QUAL: (NINH., +) (BIURET, +)
TO: (S.AUREUS, 12) (B.SUBT., 12) (E.COLI, 1.6) (PS.AER., 6.25) (K.PNEUM., 6.25) (SHYG., 6.25) (C.ALB., 25)
IS-ION: (IRC-50, NH4OH)
IS-CHR: (CG-50,)
REFERENCES:
JP 76/9789; Fr. P 2277593; *CA*, 85, 31609

43122-5074

NAME: MX-A
PO: B.VITELINUS, B.CIRCULANS
CT: LIPOPEPTIDE, BASIC, OCTAPEPTIN T.
EA: (C, 53) (H, 8) (N, 16) (O, 23)
PC: WH., POW.
OR: (-59, MEOH) (-59, W)
UV: MEOH: (200, ,)
SOL-GOOD: W, MEOH, ETOH, BUOH
SOL-POOR: ACET, HEX, BENZ, ETOAC, CHL, ET2O
QUAL: (NINH., +) (BIURET, +)
TO: (PS.AER., 3.13)
LD50: (50, IV)
IS-EXT: (BUOH, 10, W)
IS-ION: (IRC-50-NH4, NH4OH)
IS-ABS: (CARBON, MEOH-HCL)
IS-CHR: (SILG, CHL-MEOH-NH4OH-W)
REFERENCES:
JP 76/15692, 29294; 77/83803; *CA*, 85, 31611

43122-5192

NAME:	<u>OCTAPEPTIN-C1</u>, 333-25
PO:	B.CIRCULANS
CT:	LIPOPEPTIDE, BASIC, OCTAPEPTIN T.
FORMULA:	C50H87N13O10
EA:	(N, 16)
MW:	1200
PC:	WH., POW.
OR:	(-65.6, HCL)
UV:	MEOH: (253, 2,) (259, 2,) (265, 2,)
SOL-GOOD:	W, MEOH, BUOH
SOL-POOR:	ETOAC, HEX
QUAL:	(NINH., +) (BIURET, +) (SAKA., -) (PAULY, -) (EHRL., -) (FECL3, -)
TO:	(B.SUBT., 6.25) (S.AUREUS, 6.25) (E.COLI, 25) (K.PNEUM., 12.5) (PS.AER., 6.25)
LD50:	(37.5|12.5, IP) (18|7, IV) (500, SC)
IS-EXT:	(MEOH-BUOH, 3, MIC.) (BUOH, 9, FILT.,) (W, 2, BUOH)
IS-CHR:	(SILG, CHL-ETOH-NH4OH)
IS-CRY:	(PREC., BUOH, ETOAC)

REFERENCES:

JA, 29, 516, 521, 1241, 1339, 1976; JP 75/160491; *CA*, 85, 3871

43122-5427

NAME:	<u>AB-1</u>
PO:	B.CIRCULANS
CT:	OCTOPEPTIN T., LIPOPEPTIDE, BASIC
EA:	(C, 53) (H, 9) (N, 15)
MW:	1250|250
PC:	WH., POW.
SOL-GOOD:	W, MEOH, ETOH, DMSO, DMFA, PYR
SOL-POOR:	ACET, HEX
QUAL:	(NINH., +) (SAKA., -)
TO:	(S.AUREUS, 7.8) (B.SUBT., 7.8) (E.COLI, 7.8) (PS.AER., 15.6) (P.VULG., 62.5) (C.ALB., 500) (PHYT.BACT., 3.9)
LD50:	(1000|500, IP)

REFERENCES:

JP 76/118828

43123-1736

NAME: 4205-A, BACTERICID-4205-A, 4204-A
PO: B.SP.
CT: LIPOPEPTIDE, BASIC, POLYPEPTIN T.
EA: (C, 50) (H, 8) (N, 14)
MW: 1160|34
PC: WH., YELLOW, POW.
OR: (-87.7, MEOH)
UV: MEOH: (252, 6.2,) (258, 6.12,) (264, 5.68,)
SOL-GOOD: W, MEOH
SOL-FAIR: BUOH
SOL-POOR: ACET, HEX
QUAL: (NINH., +) (BIURET, +)
STAB: (HEAT, +) (ACID, +) (BASE, -)
TO: (PS.AER., 20) (S.CEREV., 5) (S.AUREUS, 5) (B.SUBT., 2.5) (S.LUTEA, .7) (E.COLI, 1.6) (K.PNEUM., 1.25)
LD50: (13.5, IP)
TV: HELA, ANTIVIRAL
IS-CHR: (AL, BUOH-PROH-HCL)
REFERENCES:
An. Rep. Div. Lab. N.Y. Dept. Health, 53, 1959; 52, 1960; 112, 1966;
Appl. Micr., 14, 79, 1966; *CA,* 56, 759; 58, 14462

43123-1737

NAME: 4205-C
PO: B.SP.
CT: LIPOPEPTIDE, BASIC, POLYPEPTIN T.
EA: (C, 50) (H, 8) (N, 13)
MW: 1285|79
PC: WH., YELLOW, POW.
OR: (-89.6, MEOH)
UV: (252, ,) (258, ,) (264, ,)
SOL-GOOD: W, MEOH
SOL-FAIR: BUOH
SOL-POOR: ACET, HEX
QUAL: (NINH., +) (SAKA., -) (BIURET, +)
STAB: (ACID, +) (BASE, -) (HEAT, +)
TO: (G.NEG., 1) (G.POS., 5)
IS-EXT: (MEOH, , MIC.)
REFERENCES:
An. Rep. Div. Lab. N.Y. Dept. Health, 53, 1959; 52, 1960; 112, 1966;
Appl. Micr., 14, 79, 1966; *CA,* 56, 759; 58, 14462

43123-1738

NAME:	<u>4205-B</u>
PO:	B.SP.
CT:	LIPOPEPTIDE, BASIC, POLYPEPTIN T.
EA:	(C, 51) (H, 9) (N, 15)
MW:	1440
PC:	WH., YELLOW, POW.
OR:	(-102.3, MEOH)
UV:	MEOH: (252, 3.59,) (258, 3.89,) (264, 3.63,)
SOL-GOOD:	W, MEOH
SOL-FAIR:	BUOH
SOL-POOR:	ACET, HEX
QUAL:	(NINH., +) (BIURET, +)
STAB:	(ACID, +) (HEAT, +)
TO:	(S.AUREUS, 1) (B.SUBT., 5) (E.COLI, 1)

REFERENCES:

An. Rep. Div. Lab. N.Y. Dept. Health, 53, 1959; 52, 1960; 112, 1966; *Appl. Micr.,* 14, 79, 1966; *CA,* 56, 759; 58, 14462

43123-1739

NAME:	<u>POLYPEPTIN-A</u>
PO:	B.KRZEMIENIEWSKII, B.CIRCULANS
CT:	LIPOPEPTIDE, BASIC, POLYPEPTIN T.
FORMULA:	C55H94N12O12
EA:	(N, 14)
MW:	1150, 1050
EW:	367
PC:	WH., CRYST.
OR:	(-93.3, I.PROH-W)
UV:	ETOH-W: (252, ,) (258, ,) (264, ,)
SOL-GOOD:	MEOH, ETOH, ACID, PYR
SOL-POOR:	ACET, HEX
QUAL:	(BIURET, +) (NINH., +)
STAB:	(HEAT, +) (BASE, -)
TO:	(B.SUBT., .75) (SHYG., 1.5) (K.PNEUM., 1) (E.COLI, 1) (PS.AER., 10) (C.ALB., 1.5)
LD50:	(15, IP)
IS-FIL:	2
IS-CRY:	(CRYST., ETOH-W)

REFERENCES:

J. Bact., 56, 749, 1948; 58, 115, 1949; *Fed. Proc.,* 8, 208, 1949; *J. Biol. Chem.,* 198, 405, 1952; 186, 863, 1950; *JACS,* 76, 4892, 1954; *J. Med. Chem.,* 19, 1228, 1976

43123-1741

NAME:	BN-7
PO:	B.CIRCULANS
CT:	LIPOPEPTIDE, BASIC, POLYPEPTIN T.
EA:	(C, 53) (H, 8) (N, 14)
MW:	1230
PC:	WH., CRYST.
OR:	(-89.5, W)
UV:	W: (200, ,)
SOL-GOOD:	MEOH, W, ACOH
SOL-POOR:	ACET, HEX
QUAL:	(NINH., +) (BIURET, +) (FECL3, -)
TO:	(B.SUBT., .3) (S.AUREUS, 3.1) (S.LUTEA, .3) (E.COLI, 1.5) (PS.AER., 12.5) (P.VULG., 6.25) (FUNGI, 3)
LD50:	(10, IP)
IS-EXT:	(BUOH, 10,)
IS-ION:	(IRC-50-NA, ACET-HCL)
IS-CHR:	(SEPHADEX LH-20, MEOH)
IS-CRY:	(DRY,)

REFERENCES:

JP 73/56895; *CA*, 79, 135292

43123-1746

NAME:	JOLIPEPTIN
PO:	B.POLYMYXA-COLISTINUS, AEROBACILLUS COLISTINUS
CT:	LIPOPEPTIDE, NEUTRAL, POLYPEPTIN T.
EA:	(C, 50) (H, 7) (N, 13)
MW:	3000
PC:	WH., CRYST.
OR:	(+4, ETILENGLYCOL)
UV:	W: (200, ,)
SOL-GOOD:	MEOH, BUOH, W
SOL-POOR:	ACET, HEX
QUAL:	(NINH., +)
STAB:	(ACID, +) (BASE, +) (HEAT, +)
TO:	(S.AUREUS, .3) (B.SUBT., .6) (S.LUTEA, 2) (E.COLI, .3) (P.VULG., 10) (PS.AER., 50) (S.CEREV., 40)
LD50:	(21, IV) (62, IP)

REFERENCES:

JA, 25, 147, 304, 309, 1972; JP 72/43291; BP 1346973; USP 38833649

43123-5280

NAME:	B-43
PO:	B.CIRCULANS
CT:	LIPOPEPTIDE, BASIC, POLYPEPTIN T.
EA:	(C, 53) (H, 8) (N, 15)
PC:	WH., POW.
OR:	(-54.5, W)
UV:	MEOH: (253, 2,) (258.5, 2,) (264, 2,)
SOL-GOOD:	MEOH, BUOH-W, BASE
SOL-FAIR:	W
SOL-POOR:	ACET, HEX
QUAL:	(NINH., +) (FECL3, -) (SAKA., -)
TO:	(B.SUBT., 6.25) (S.AUREUS, 25) (E.COLI, 25) (K.PNEUM., 12.5)
LD50:	(100|50, IP)
IS-FIL:	2
IS-EXT:	(BUOH-MEOH, 2, WB) (BUOH, 8, FILT.) (W, 2, BUOH+ETOAC)
IS-CHR:	(SILG, CHL-ETOH-NH4OH) (SEPHADEX LH-20, MEOH-W)
IS-CRY:	(PREC., BUOH, ETOAC)

REFERENCES:

JA, 29, 814, 1976

43123-5428

NAME:	AB-2
PO:	B.CIRCULANS
CT:	BASIC, LIPOPEPTIDE, POLYPEPTIN T.
EA:	(C, 55) (H, 9) (N, 14)
MW:	1500
PC:	WH., POW.
OR:	(-49.8, W)
UV:	W: (252, ,) (257.5, ,) (263, 5, ,) (267, ,)
SOL-GOOD:	W, MEOH, ETOH
SOL-POOR:	ACET, BENZ, ET2O, CHL, ETOAC
QUAL:	(NINH., +) (BIURET, +) (SAKA., -)
STAB:	(ACID, +) (BASE, +)
TO:	(B.SUBT., 6.25) (S.LUTEA, 3.9) (E.COLI, 7.8) (PS.AER., 25) (P.VULG., 125) (S.AUREUS, 7.8) (PHYT.BACT., 1.25) (S.CEREV., 100) (C.ALB., 200)
IS-EXT:	(BUOH, , EVAP.FILT.)
IS-CHR:	(SEPHADEX G-25,)

REFERENCES:

JP 76/144795; *CA*, 86, 169330

43124-3903

NAME: BN-109
PO: B.POLYMYXA
CT: LIPOPEPTIDE, BASIC, TRIDECAPTIN T.
EA: (C, 53) (H, 7) (N, 13)
MW: 2050|150
PC: WH., CRYST.
OR: (-4, MEOH-ACOH)
UV: HCL: (279, 23,)
UV: NAOH: (279, 34,)
SOL-GOOD: ACID, BASE, ACOH, DMFA, DMSO
SOL-FAIR: MEOH-HCL
SOL-POOR: ETOH, HEX
TO: (E.COLI, .3) (K.PNEUM., .78) (P.VULG., 6.25) (PS.AER., 100) (B.SUBT., 6.25) (S.AUREUS, 25) (S.LUTEA, 25)
LD50: (25, IP) (1000, PEROS)
IS-EXT: (BUOH, , W+NACL)
IS-ION: (IRC-50-H, NH4OH)
IS-CHR: (CM-SEPHADEX C-25-H, NACL)
IS-CRY: (CRYST., BUOH)
REFERENCES:
DT 2433932; USP 3940479; *Sci. Rep. Meiji,* 17, 1, 1978

43124-5426

NAME: TRIDECAPTIN-A, AR-110
PO: B.POLYMYXA
CT: AMPHOTER, LIPOPEPTIDE, TRIDECAPTIN T., BASIC
FORMULA: C73H115N17O20
EA: (C, 50) (H, 7) (N, 14)
MW: 1800|100
EW: 533, 912
PC: WH., POW.
OR: (-18.2, W) (-3.5, MEOH-ACOH)
UV: W: (274, 32,) (281.5, 34,) (289, 30,)
SOL-GOOD: W, ACID, BASE, MEOH-W
SOL-FAIR: MEOH, BUOH
SOL-POOR: ACET, HEX
QUAL: (NINH., +) (EHRL., +) (SAKA., -) (PAULY, -)
TO: (B.SUBT., 12.5) (S.AUREUS, 50) (E.COLI, 3.13) (K.PNEUM., 6.25) (PS.AER., 50) (P.VULG., 50)
LD50: (18|7, IP)
IS-FIL: 2.5, 70-C
IS-EXT: (BUOH, 7, FILT.)
IS-CHR: (SEPHADEX LH-20, MEOH-W)
IS-CRY: (PREC., W, ACET)
REFERENCES:
JP 76/144796; *CA,* 86, 169331

43124-6229

NAME:	TRIDECAPTIN-B
PO:	B.POLYMYXA
CT:	LIPOPEPTIDE, TRIDECAPTIN T., BASIC, AMPHOTER
FORMULA:	C67H111N17O20
EA:	(N, 15)
PC:	WH., POW.
OR:	(-7.7, MEOH-ACOH)
UV:	W: (274, 26,) (282, 26,) (289, 19,)
SOL-GOOD:	ACID, BASE
SOL-FAIR:	MEOH-W, BUOH-W
SOL-POOR:	W, ACET, ET2O
QUAL:	(NINH., +) (EHRL., +) (SAKA., -) (PAULY, -)
TO:	(B.SUBT., 12.5) (S.AUREUS, 25) (E.COLI, 6.25) (K.PNEUM., 12.5) (PS.AER., 50)
LD50:	(75|25, IP)
IS-EXT:	(BUOH, 2, FILT.) (W, 13, BUOH) (BUOH, 8, W)
IS-CRY:	(PREC., MEOH-HCL, ACET)

REFERENCES:

JA, 31, 646, 1978

43124-6230

NAME:	TRIDECAPTIN-C
PO:	B.POLYMYXA
CT:	LIPOPEPTIDE, TRIDECAPTIN T., BASIC, AMPHOTER
FORMULA:	C74H117N17O21
EA:	(N, 14)
PC:	WH., POW.
OR:	(-3, MEOH-ACOH)
UV:	W: (274, 25,) (282, 27,) (289, 23,)
SOL-GOOD:	ACID, BASE
SOL-FAIR:	MEOH-W, BUOH-W
SOL-POOR:	W, ACET, ET2O
QUAL:	(NINH., +) (EHRL., +) (SAKA., -) (PAULY, -)
TO:	(B.SUBT., 6.25) (S.AUREUS, 12.5) (E.COLI, 3.13) (K.PNEUM., 6.25) (PS.AER., 25)
LD50:	(75|25, IP)
IS-FIL:	2
IS-EXT:	(BUOH-MEOH, 2, WB) (BUOH, 2, W)
IS-CHR:	(SEPHADEX LH-20, MEOH-W-NACL)
IS-CRY:	(LIOF.,)

REFERENCES:

JA, 31, 646, 1978

4313
Echinocandin Type

These neutral peptides are members of a recently discovered group of fungal metabolites, produced by various *Aspergillus* species. They are presumably cyclohexapeptides with a long fatty acid side chain, consisting of threonine, hydroxyproline, and several unusual amino acids (see the introduction to lipopeptide antibiotics). The fatty acid constituents may be linolenic, myristic, or palmitic acids.

These antibiotics have characteristic UV absorption at 225 to 226 and 276 to 278 nm and exhibit high antiyeast and antifungal activity and possess low toxicity.

Structure

43130

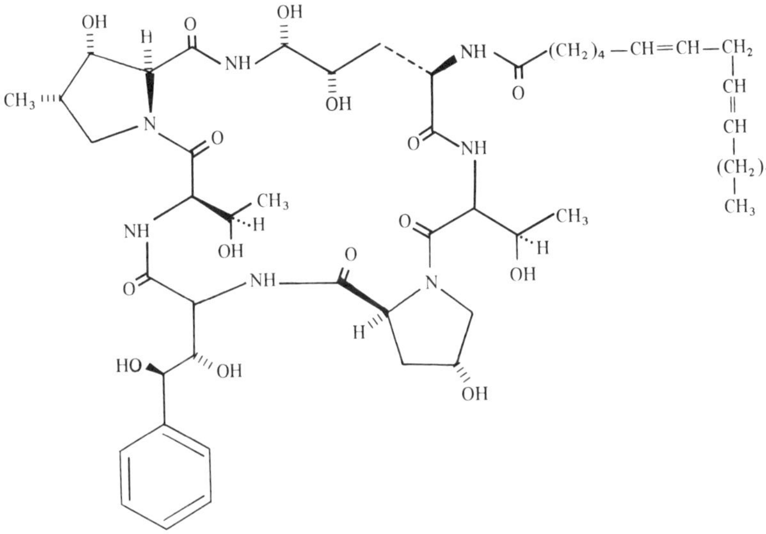

echinocandin B (SL-7810, A-32204)

43130-1749

NAME:	ECHINOCANDIN-B, A-32204-B
IDENTICAL:	SF-7810-F
PO:	ASP.NIDULANS
CT:	ENCHINOCANDIN T., NEUTRAL, PEPTIDE
FORMULA:	C52H81N7O16
EA:	(N, 9)
MW:	1100
PC:	WH., POW.
UV:	ETOH: (225, 152,) (277, 30,)
UV:	ETOH-NAOH: (225, 195,) (248, 158,) (301, 41,)
SOL-GOOD:	MEOH, ETOH, PROH, DMSO, DMFA
SOL-FAIR:	ETOAC, ACET, CHL, ET2O
SOL-POOR:	W, ACET, HEX
QUAL:	(PAULY, +)
STAB:	(BASE, -)
TO:	(C.ALB., .2)
IS-FIL:	7.7
IS-EXT:	(MEOH, , MIC.) (ETOAC, , W)
IS-CHR:	(SEPHADEX LH-20, MEOH)

REFERENCES:

Helv., 57, 2459, 1974; *TL*, 41, 47, 1976; Swiss P 568386

43130-2083

NAME:	X-73
PO:	ASP.RUGULOSUS
CT:	PEPTIDE, ACIDIC, ENCHINOCANDIN T.
EA:	(C, 54) (H, 7) (N, 9)
PC:	WH., POW.
UV:	MEOH: (271|3, 18,)
SOL-GOOD:	MEOH, ETOH, ETOAC, CHL, BENZ
SOL-POOR:	W, HEX, ET2O
TO:	(C.ALB., .00035) (S.CEREV., 6.25)
LD50:	(300, IP)
IS-EXT:	(ETOH, , MIC.)
IS-CHR:	(AL, CHL-MEOH)
IS-CRY:	(PREC., MEOH, ET2O)

REFERENCES:

Ind. J. Biochem., 7, 81, 1970

43130-3902

NAME:	ACULEACIN COMPLEX, M-4214
PO:	ASP.ACULEATUS
CT:	ENCHINOCANDIN T., PEPTIDE
EA:	(N,)
PC:	WH., POW.
OR:	(-53, MEOH)
SOL-GOOD:	MEOH, ETOH
SOL-FAIR:	W
SOL-POOR:	ACET, HEX
QUAL:	(PAULY, +) (NINH., -) (SAKA., -) (EHRL., -) (FECL3, -)
STAB:	(BASE, -) (ACID, +)
TO:	(C.ALB., 1.1) (S.CEREV., .1) (PHYT.FUNGI, .01)
LD50:	(350, IV) (600, IP)
IS-EXT:	(MEOH, , MIC.)
IS-CHR:	(AL,)

REFERENCES:

Abst. AAC, 14, 203, 1974; *JA,* 30, 297, 303, 308, 1977; USP 3978210

43130-5017

NAME:	ATHLESTAIN
PO:	ASP.NIGER
CT:	PEPTIDE, NEUTRAL, ENCHINOCANDIN T.
FORMULA:	C32H53N5O12
EA:	(N, 10)
PC:	WH., YELLOW, POW.
OR:	(-64, MEOH)
UV:	MEOH: (225, 130,) (278, 21,)
SOL-GOOD:	MEOH, ACET
SOL-FAIR:	ETOAC, CHL
SOL-POOR:	ET2O, HEX, W
QUAL:	(EHRL., -) (NINH., -) (BIURET, -) (PAULY, -) (FECL3, -)
STAB:	(ACID, +) (HEAT, +) (BASE, -)
TO:	(TRICHOPHYTON SP., 1) (C.ALB.,)
LD50:	(400|100, IP)
IS-EXT:	(ACET, , MIC.)
IS-CHR:	(SILG, ETOAC) (AL, ETOH)
IS-CRY:	(PREC., ETOH, ET2O)

REFERENCES:

Jap. J. Ant., 17, 268, 1964; *Yakugaku Kenkyu,* 39, 165, 1968; JP 66/12688; *CA,* 65, 19274; 70, 27607

43130-5063

NAME:	<u>SL-7810-F</u>
IDENTICAL:	ECHINOCANDIN-B
PO:	ASP.RUGULOSUS
CT:	ENCHINOCANDIN T., PEPTIDE, NEUTRAL
FORMULA:	C52H81N7016
EA:	(C, 57) (H, 8) (N, 9) (O, 25)
MW:	1190
PC:	WH., POW.
OR:	(-48.3, MEOH)
UV:	MEOH: (276, , 200) (194, , 100000) (276, , 20400)
SOL-GOOD:	MEOH, ETOH
SOL-FAIR:	CHL, ET2O, HEX
SOL-POOR:	W
QUAL:	(NINH., -)
STAB:	(BASE, -) (ACID, +)
TO:	(C.ALB., .3) (S.CEREV., 10)
IS-EXT:	(ETOAC, 7, FILT.)
IS-CHR:	(SILG, CHL-MEOH)

REFERENCES:

TL, 414, 1976; DT 2549127; Belg. P 834289

43130-5064

NAME:	<u>SL-7810-FII</u>
IDENTICAL:	ECHINOCANDIN-C
PO:	ASP.RUGULOSUS
CT:	ENCHINOCANDIN T., PEPTIDE, NEUTRAL
EA:	(C, 58) (H, 8) (N, 9) (O, 24)
MW:	1018
PC:	WH., POW.
OR:	(-47.9, MEOH)
UV:	MEOH: (278, , 250)
SOL-GOOD:	MEOH, ETOH
SOL-FAIR:	CHL, ET2O, HEX
SOL-POOR:	W
QUAL:	(NINH., -)
STAB:	(BASE, -)
TO:	(C.ALB., .03) (S.CEREV., 10)

REFERENCES:

TL, 4142, 1976; DT 2549127; Belg. P 834289

43130-5065

NAME:	<u>SL-7810-FIII</u>
IDENTICAL:	ECHINOCANDIN-D
PO:	ASP.RUGULOSUS
CT:	ENCHINOCANDIN T., PEPTIDE, NEUTRAL
EA:	(C, 61) (H, 8) (N, 9) (O, 22)
MW:	1000|200
PC:	WH., POW.
OR:	(-53, MEOH)
UV:	MEOH: (278, , 350)
SOL-GOOD:	MEOH, ETOH
SOL-FAIR:	CHL, ET2O, HEX
SOL-POOR:	W
QUAL:	(NINH., -)
STAB:	(BASE, -)
TO:	(C.ALB., .3) (S.CEREV., 10)

REFERENCES:

TL, 4142, 1976; DT 2549127; Belg. P 834289

43130-5066

NAME:	<u>ACULEACIN-A</u>
PO:	ASP.ACULEATUS
CT:	ENCHINOCANDIN T., PEPTIDE
FORMULA:	C57H94N8O20, C60H102N8O21
EA:	(C, 56) (H, 8) (N, 9)
MW:	1021
EW:	1200|50
PC:	WH., CRYST.
OR:	(-53, MEOH)
UV:	ETOH: (278, 15.8,)
UV:	MEOH: (277, 15.6,)
UV:	MEOH-NAOH: (247, 148,) (295.5, 22,)
SOL-GOOD:	MEOH, ETOH
SOL-FAIR:	ETOAC, W
SOL-POOR:	ACET, CHL, HEX
QUAL:	(FECL3, -) (PAULY, +) (NINH., -) (SAKA., -) (EHRL., -)
STAB:	(BASE, -) (ACID, +)
TO:	(C.ALB., .1) (S.CEREV., 1.6) (TRICHOPHYTON SP., .004)
LD50:	(350, IV) (600, IP)
IS-EXT:	(MEOH, , MIC.) (BUOH, 7, W)
IS-CHR:	(AL, ETOAC) (SILG, ETOAC-MEOH)
IS-CRY:	(PREC., MEOH, ETOAC-HEX)

REFERENCES:

JA, 30, 297, 303, 308, 1977; DT 2509820; Belg. P 826393; USP 3978210

43130-5067

NAME: ACULEACIN-B
PO: ASP.ACULEATUS
CT: ENCHINOCANDIN T., PEPTIDE, NEUTRAL
FORMULA: C58H96N8015, C61H104N8016
EA: (N, 9)
MW: 1200|50
EW: 540
PC: WH., CRYST.
OR: (-45, MEOH)
UV: MEOH: (279, 18.5,)
UV: MEOH-NAOH: (247, 104,) (297, 21.6,)
SOL-GOOD: MEOH, ETOH
SOL-FAIR: ETOAC, W
SOL-POOR: ACET, CHL, HEX
QUAL: (FECL3, -) (PAULY, +) (NINH., -) (SAKA., -) (EHRL., -)
STAB: (BASE, -) (ACID, +)
TO: (C.ALB., .4) (S.CEREV., 3.2) (TRICHOPHYTON SP., .04)
LD50: (600|300, IP)
REFERENCES:

JA, 30, 297, 303, 308, 1977; DT 2509820; Belg. P 826393; USP 3978210

43130-5068

NAME: ACULEACIN-C
PO: ASP.ACULEATUS
CT: ENCHINOCANDIN T., PEPTIDE, NEUTRAL
FORMULA: C56H92N8016, C59H100N8017
EA: (N, 10)
MW: 1166|33
EW: 540
PC: WH., CRYST.
OR: (-47.5, MEOH)
UV: MEOH: (277, 18.3,)
UV: MEOH-NAOH: (247, 100,) (295.5, 20,)
SOL-GOOD: MEOH, ETOH
SOL-FAIR: ETOAC, W
SOL-POOR: ACET, CHL, HEX
QUAL: (FECL3, -) (PAULY, +) (NINH., -) (SAKA., -) (EHRL., -)
STAB: (BASE, -) (ACID, +)
TO: (C.ALB., .1) (S.CEREV., 1.6) (TRICHOPHYTON SP., .01)
LD50: (600|300, IP)
REFERENCES:

JA, 30, 297, 303, 308, 1977; DT 2509820; Belg. P 826393; USP 3978210

43130-5069

NAME:	ACULEACIN-D
PO:	ASP.ACULEATUS
CT:	ENCHINOCANDIN T., PEPTIDE, NEUTRAL
FORMULA:	C58H96N8O19, C62H106N8O20
EA:	(N, 9)
MW:	1246|37
EW:	555
PC:	WH., CRYST.
OR:	(-46, MEOH)
UV:	MEOH: (278, 17.2,)
UV:	MEOH-NAOH: (247, 100,) (295.5, 19.5,)
SOL-GOOD:	MEOH, ETOH
SOL-FAIR:	ETOAC, W
SOL-POOR:	ACET, CHL, HEX
QUAL:	(FECL3, -) (PAULY, +) (NINH., -) (SAKA., -) (EHRL., -)
STAB:	(BASE, -) (ACID, +)
TO:	(C.ALB., .025) (S.CEREV., .2) (TRICHOPHYTON SP., .005)
LD50:	(600|300, IP)

REFERENCES:

JA, 30, 297, 303, 308, 1977; DT 2509820; Belg. P 826393; USP 3978210

43130-5070

NAME:	ACULEACIN-E
PO:	ASP.ACULEATUS
CT:	ENCHINOCANDIN T., PEPTIDE, NEUTRAL
FORMULA:	C57H94N8O19, C61H104N8O20
EA:	(N, 9)
MW:	1232|37
EW:	650
PC:	WH., CRYST.
OR:	(-66, MEOH)
UV:	MEOH: (277, 16,)
UV:	MEOH-NAOH: (247, 120,) (295, 21.2,)
SOL-GOOD:	MEOH, ETOH
SOL-FAIR:	ETOAC, W
SOL-POOR:	ACET, CHL, HEX
QUAL:	(FECL3, -) (PAULY, +) (NINH., -) (SAKA., -) (EHRL., -)
STAB:	(BASE, -) (ACID, +)
TO:	(C.ALB., 3.2) (S.CEREV., 25) (TRICHOPHYTON SP., .003)
LD50:	(1000|600, IP)

REFERENCES:

JA, 30, 297, 303, 308, 1977; DT 2509820; Belg. P 826393; USP 3978210

43130-5071

NAME:	ACULEACIN-F
PO:	ASP.ACULEATUS
CT:	ENCHINOCANDIN T., PEPTIDE, NEUTRAL
FORMULA:	C56H90N8022, C59H98N8023
EA:	(N, 9)
MW:	1257|30
EW:	565
PC:	WH., CRYST.
OR:	(-55, MEOH)
UV:	MEOH: (277, 14.5,)
UV:	MEOH-NAOH: (247, 125,) (295, 19.6,)
SOL-GOOD:	MEOH, ETOH
SOL-FAIR:	ETOAC, W
SOL-POOR:	ACET, CHL, HEX
QUAL:	(FECL3, -) (PAULY, +) (NINH., -) (SAKA., -) (EHRL., -)
STAB:	(BASE, -) (ACID, +)
TO:	(C.ALB., .2) (S.CEREV., 3.3) (TRICHOPHYTON SP., .003)

REFERENCES:

JA, 30, 297, 303, 308, 1977; DT 2509820; Belg. P 826393; USP 3978210

43130-5072

NAME:	ACULEACIN-G
PO:	ASP.ACULEATUS
CT:	ENCHINOCANDIN T., PEPTIDE, NEUTRAL
FORMULA:	C58H94N8022, C62H106N8023
EA:	(N, 9)
MW:	1292|37
EW:	710
PC:	WH., CRYST.
OR:	(-52, MEOH)
UV:	MEOH: (277, 17.4,)
UV:	MEOH-NAOH: (247, 115,) (295.5, 23,)
SOL-GOOD:	MEOH, ETOH
SOL-FAIR:	ETOAC, W
SOL-POOR:	ACET, CHL, HEX
QUAL:	(FECL3, -) (PAULY, +) (NINH., -) (SAKA., -) (EHRL., -)
STAB:	(BASE, -) (ACID, +)
TO:	(C.ALB., .2) (S.CEREV., 3.2) (TRICHOPHYTON SP., .005)

REFERENCES:

JA, 30, 297, 303, 308, 1977; DT 2509820; Belg. P 826393; USP 3978210

43130-5075

NAME: ECHINOCANDIN-A, A-32204-A
PO: ASP.NIDULANS-ECHINULATUS
CT: ENCHINOCANDIN T., PEPTIDE, NEUTRAL
EA: (N, 9)
PC: WH., POW.
SOL-GOOD: MEOH, PROH, DMSO
SOL-FAIR: ETOAC, ACET, ET2O, CHL
SOL-POOR: W
STAB: (ACID, +) (BASE, -)
TO: (C.ALB., .02)
IS-CHR: (SILG, CCL4-MEOH)
REFERENCES:
Swiss P 568386

43130-5429

NAME: S-31794-F-1
PO: ACROPHIALOPHORA LIMONISPORA
CT: ENCHINOCANDIN T., PEPTIDE, NEUTRAL
EA: (C, 56) (H, 8) (N, 11) (O, 26)
PC: WH., CRYST.
OR: (-24, MEOH) (+37, PYR)
UV: ETOH: (225, 132,) (276, 13,)
UV: MEOH: (194, 807,) (276, 13,)
SOL-GOOD: MEOH, ETOH, PYR, DMSO
SOL-POOR: W, CHL, ETOAC, ET2O, BENZ, HEX
QUAL: (NINH., -)
STAB: (BASE, -) (ACID, +)
TO: (C.ALB., .3)
IS-EXT: (ETOAC-I.PROH, , WB.)
IS-CHR: (SILG, CHL-MEOH) (SEPHADEX LH-20, MEOH)
IS-CRY: (PREC., MEOH, ET2O) (CRYST., ETOAC-MEOH-W)
REFERENCES:
DT 2628965

43130-5685

NAME:	A-30912-A
IDENTICAL:	A-22082
PO:	ASP.NIDULANS, ASP.RUGULOSUS
CT:	ECHINOCANDIN T., PEPTIDE
FORMULA:	C52H81N7O18
EA:	(N, 9)
MW:	1100
EW:	1100
PC:	WH., POW.
OR:	(-44, MEOH)
UV:	MEOH: (225, , 18000) (284, , 2500)
UV:	MEOH-HCL: (225, , 18000) (284, , 2500)
UV:	MEOH-NAOH: (245, , 16000) (290, , 3000)
SOL-GOOD:	MEOH, ETOAC, DMFA, DMSO, BASE
SOL-POOR:	ET2O, HEX
TO:	(C.ALB., .62) (FUNGI, .0098)
LD50:	(1000|400, IP)
IS-EXT:	(MEOH, , MIC.) (CHL, 3.5, W)
IS-CHR:	(SILG, ACCN-W)
IS-CRY:	(PREC., MEOH, ET2O)

REFERENCES:

USP 4074246, 4074245; DT 2643485; *CA*, 87, 20612

43130-5686

NAME:	A-30912-B
PO:	ASP.RUGULOSUS
CT:	ECHINOCANDIN T., PEPTIDE
EA:	(C, 57) (H, 6) (N, 9) (O, 26)
PC:	WH., POW.
OR:	(-47, MEOH)
UV:	MEOH: (278, , 2400)
UV:	MEOH-HCL: (278, , 2400)
UV:	MEOH-NAOH: (242, , 13900) (292, , 2800)
SOL-GOOD:	MEOH, ETOAC, DMFA, DMSO, BASE
SOL-POOR:	ET2O, HEX
TO:	(C.ALB., .5) (FUNGI, .07)
IS-FIL:	4
IS-EXT:	(CHL, 4, FILT.)
IS-CHR:	(SILG, ACCN-W) (AL, ACCN-W)
IS-CRY:	(PREC., CHL, ET2O) (PREC., MEOH, ET2O)

REFERENCES:

USP 4074245

43130-5687

NAME: A-30912-C
PO: ASP.RUGULOSUS
CT: ECHINOCANDIN T., PEPTIDE
EA: (C, 57) (H, 8) (N, 11)
PC: WH., POW.
OR: (-33, MEOH)
UV: MEOH: (275, , 1350)
UV: MEOH-HCL: (275, , 1350)
UV: MEOH-NAOH: (240, , 12400) (290, , 5200)
SOL-GOOD: MEOH, ETOAC, DMFA, DMSO, BASE, CHL
SOL-POOR: ET2O, HEX
TO: (C.ALB., .5) (FUNGI, .07)
REFERENCES:
USP 4074245

43130-5688

NAME: A-30912-D
PO: ASP.RUGULOSUS
CT: ECHINOCANDIN T., PEPTIDE
EA: (C, 56) (H, 8) (N, 9) (O, 27)
MW: 1100
PC: WH., POW.
OR: (-50, MEOH)
UV: MEOH: (225, , 18000) (275, , 2500)
UV: MEOH-HCL: (225, , 18000) (275, , 2500)
UV: MEOH-NAOH: (240, , 11000) (290, , 3000)
SOL-GOOD: MEOH, ETOAC, DMFA, DMSO, BASE
SOL-POOR: ET2O, HEX
TO: (C.ALB., .5) (FUNGI, .07)
REFERENCES:
USP 4074245

43130-6231

NAME:	ACULEACIN-A A"
PO:	ASP.ACULEATUS
CT:	NEUTRAL, PEPTIDE, ECHINOANDIN T.
EA:	(C, 56) (H, 9) (N, 10)
MW:	1015
EW:	860
PC:	WH., CRYST.
OR:	(-46.8, MEOH)
UV:	MEOH: (277, 16,) (226, 146,)
SOL-GOOD:	MEOH, BUOH
SOL-FAIR:	ETOAC
SOL-POOR:	ACET, CHL, HEX, W
QUAL:	(PAULY, +) (BIURET, +) (NINH., -) (SAKA., -) (EHRL., -) (FECL3, -) (DNPH, -)
STAB:	(ACID, +) (HEAT, +) (BASE, -)
TO:	(FUNGI, .004)
LD50:	(350, IV) (600, IP)
IS-EXT:	(MEOH, , MIC.) (BUOH, , W)
IS-CHR:	(SILG, ETOAC-I.PROH-W)
IS-CRY:	(PREC., BUOH, HEX-ETOAC)

REFERENCES:

Belg. P 866095

43130-6232

NAME:	ACULEACIN-D A"
PO:	ASP.ACULEATUS
CT:	NEUTRAL, PEPTIDE, ECHINOCANDIN T.
EA:	(C, 56) (H, 8) (N, 10)
MW:	1242
EW:	555
PC:	WH., CRYST.
OR:	(-45.7, MEOH)
UV:	MEOH: (278, 17.5,) (226, 138,)
SOL-GOOD:	MEOH, BUOH
SOL-FAIR:	ETOAC
SOL-POOR:	ACET, CHL, HEX, W
QUAL:	(PAULY, +) (BIURET, +) (NINH., -) (SAKA., -) (EHRL., -) (FECL3, -) (DNPH, -)
STAB:	(ACID, +) (HEAT, +) (BASE, -)
TO:	(FUNGI, .001)
LD50:	(400|200, IM)

REFERENCES:

Belg. P 866095

43130-6233

NAME:	ACULEACIN-A G"
PO:	ASP.ACULEATUS
CT:	NEUTRAL, PEPTIDE, ECHINOCANDIN T.
EA:	(C, 55) (H, 8) (N, 11)
MW:	1021
EW:	860
PC:	WH., CRYST.
OR:	(-47.4, MEOH)
UV:	MEOH: (278, 15.5,) (226, 145,)
SOL-GOOD:	MEOH, BUOH
SOL-FAIR:	ETOAC
SOL-POOR:	ACET, W, CHL, HEX
QUAL:	(PAULY, +) (BIURET, +) (NINH., -) (SAKA., -) (EHRL., -) (FECL3, -) (DNPH, -)
STAB:	(ACID, +) (HEAT, +) (BASE, -)
TO:	(FUNGI, .008)
LD50:	(350, IV) (600, IP)

REFERENCES:

Belg. P 866095

43130-6234

NAME:	ACULEACIN-D G"
PO:	ASP.ACULEATUS
CT:	NEUTRAL, PEPTIDE, ECHINOCANDIN T.
EA:	(C, 58) (H, 8) (N, 9)
MW:	1265
EW:	555
PC:	WH., CRYST.
OR:	(-46.7, MEOH)
UV:	MEOH: (278, 17.0,) (226, 137,)
SOL-GOOD:	MEOH, BUOH
SOL-FAIR:	ETOAC
SOL-POOR:	ACET, W, CHL, HEX
QUAL:	(PAULY, +) (BIURET, +) (NINH., -) (SAKA., -) (EHRL., -) (FECL3, -) (DNPH, -)
STAB:	(ACID, +) (HEAT, +) (BASE, -)
TO:	(FUNGI, .002)
LD50:	(400|200, IM)

REFERENCES:

Belg. P 866095

4314
Bacillomycin Type

These antibiotics are long known substances; most of them were discovered in the 1950s. Recently it has been shown that almost all antifungal peptide-type substances isolated from various *B. subtilis* or closely related species (about 12 known examples) are identical either with iturin A, bacillomycin L, or mycosubtilin.

These cyclic peptidolipidic antibiotics consists of seven or eight molecules of D and L common amino acids and a branched-chain C_{14} to C_{16} β-amino acid, forming a large homodetic peptide ring with the long alkyl side chain of the β-amino acid (iturinic acids). All of these antibiotics are mixtures of homolog lipopeptides. Their amino acid composition is summarized in the following table:

		asp		asn		ser					
Antibiotic	**β-Amino acid**	D	L	D	L	D	L	L-gln	L-pro	D-tyr	L-thr
Iturin A	3-NH_2-*iso*-C_{14} 3-NH_2-*anteiso*-C_{14}			2	1	1		1	1	1	
Bacillomycin L	3-NH_2-*iso*-C_{14} 3-NH_2-*anteiso*-C_{15} 3-NH_2-*iso*-C_{16}	1	1			1	1	1		1	1
Mycosubtilin	3-NH_2-*iso*-C_{16} 3-NH_2-*normal*-C_{16} 3-NH_2-*anteiso*-C_{17}			2	2	1		1	1	1	
Iturin C (inactive)	3-NH_2-*iso*-C_{14} 3-NH_2-*anteiso*-C_{15}		1	2		1		1	1	1	

Antibiotic	**β-Amino acid**	D, L-asp	L-glu	D-ser	L-pro	D-tyr	ala	val
Subsporin A	C_{19}-acid	6(3)	2(1)	2(1)	2(1)	2(1)		
Subsporin B	C_{19}-acid	3	1		1	1	1	
Subsporin C	C_{19}-acid	4	2	1	1	1		
Polcillin	?	4	1	1	1	1		
"Raubitschek substance"	3-NH_2-C_{15} 3-NH_2-C_{14}	3	1	1	1	1		
Bacillomycin C	?	+	+			+	+	+
Antibiotic B_7	?	+	+	+	+	+		+
Antibiotic AL	?	+	+		+	+	+	
Bacillocin	?	+	+		+	+		+

The bacillomycins have strong antifungal activity against yeasts and fungi and are active against only very few bacteria. Clinical trials show that iturin is a valuable antifungal drug against dermatomycoses because of its low toxicity and low allergenic effects.

Moreover, the group of lipopeptides covers longicatenamycins (4315) with unique amino acid composition and some other lipopeptides (431).

REFERENCES

1. *Biochem. Soc. Trans.*, 5, 1122, 1977.
2. *JA*, 29, 1043, 1976; 31, 284, 1978.

Structures
43140

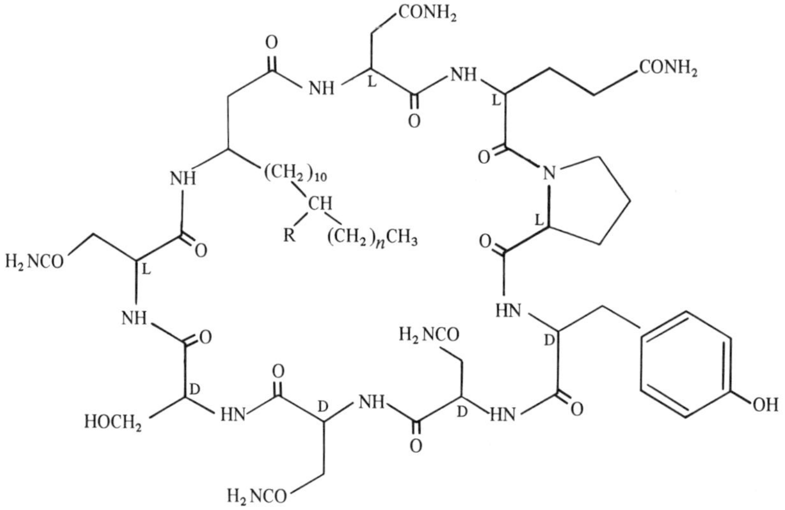

βNC$_{16,17}$ → L—asn → L—gln → L—pro → D—tyr → D—asn → D—asn → D—ser → L—asn → βNC$_{16,17}$

mycosubtilin R = H, CH_3, n = 0, 1

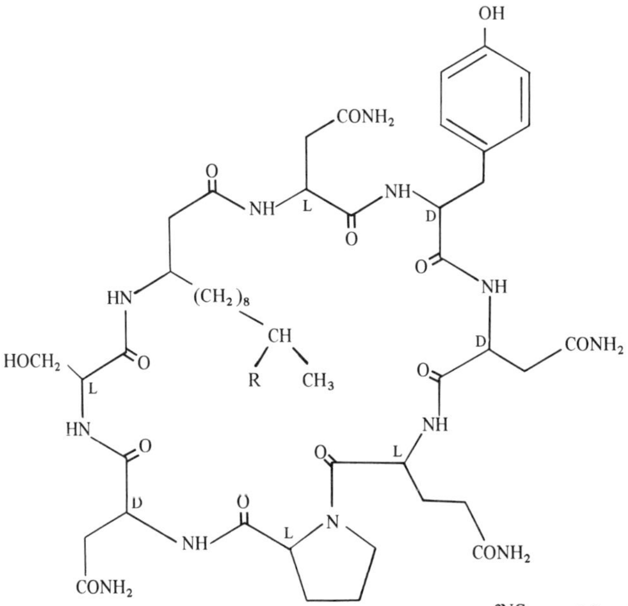

βNC$_{14,15}$ → L—asn → D—tyr → D—asn → L—gln → L—pro → D—asn → L—ser → βNC$_{14,15}$

iturin A R = CH_3, C_2H_5

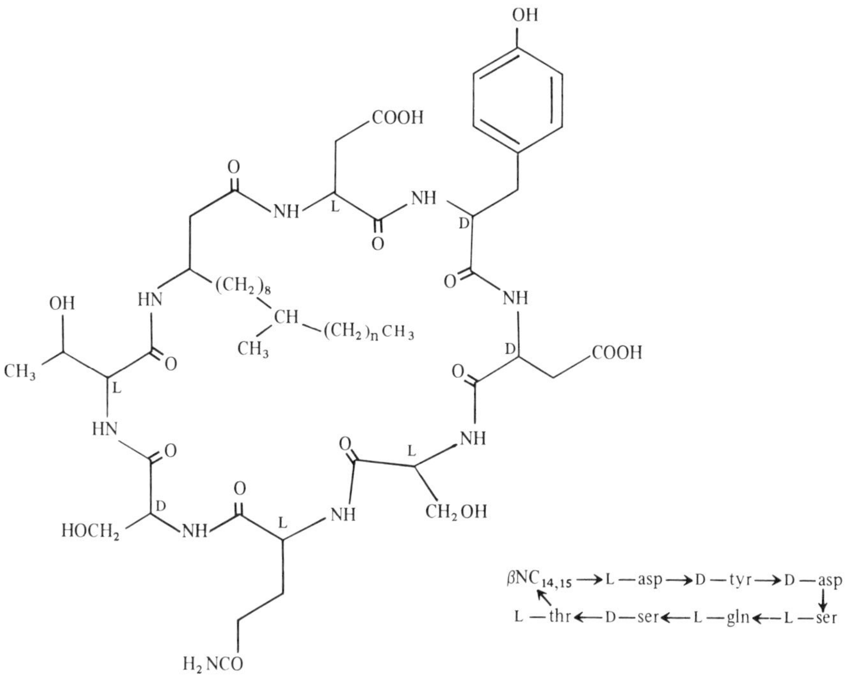

bacillomycin L n = 0, 1

43150

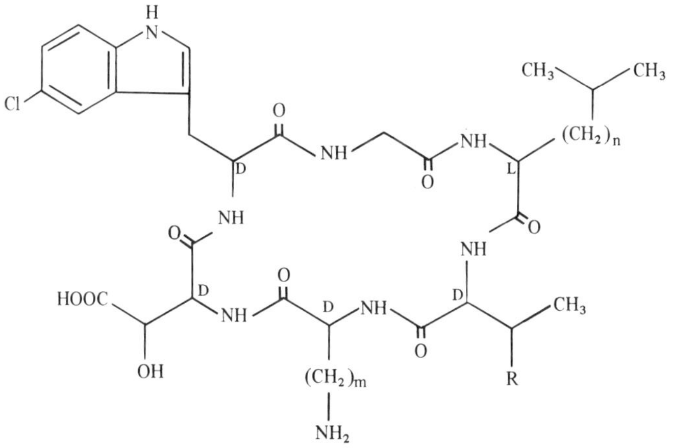

longicatenamycin complex

R = CH_3, C_2H_5
n = 3, 4, 5
m = 2, 3

43140-1644

NAME: BACILLOMYCIN
IDENTICAL: FUNGOCIN, EUMYCIN, BACILLOMYCIN-R, ITURIN-A
PO: B.SUBTILIS
CT: BACILLOMYCIN T., PEPTIDE, ACIDIC, AMPHOTER
FORMULA: C49H75N12O14
EA: (C, 53) (H, 7) (N, 12)
MW: 950, 1100
EW: 940|65
PC: WH., CRYST.
OR: (0, ETOH)
UV: ETOH: (276, , 1400)
UV: ETOH-NAOH: (296, , 2200)
SOL-GOOD: MEOH, ACET, BASE, DMFA
SOL-POOR: W, ACID, ETOAC, HEX, ACET, PYR
QUAL: (PAULY, +) (NINH., -) (BIURET, +)
STAB: (ACID, +) (HEAT, +) (BASE, -)
TO: (C.ALB., 25) (FUNGI, 2) (K.PNEUM., 20)
LD50: (75, IP)
IS-CHR: (IRC-50-H, NH4OH) (SEPHADEX LH-20, HEX-CHL-MEOH)
IS-CRY: (PREC., FILT., HCL)
REFERENCES:

Proc. Soc. Exp. B.M., 67, 539, 1948; *J. Bact.*, 54, 24, 1947; *J. Biol. Chem.*, 190, 133, 1951; *ABB*, 60, 364, 1956; *Nature*, 170, 618, 1953; 174, 1190, 1954; *Rev. Argent. Agron.*, 18, 33, 1951; *Rev. Invest. Agric.*, 4, 325, 1950; 13, 225, 1959; *JA*, 29, 1043, 1976; *Eur. J. Bioch.*, 77, 61, 1977

43140-1645

NAME: BACILLOMYCIN-B
IDENTICAL: ITURIN-A
PO: B.SUBTILIS
CT: BACILLOMYCIN T., PEPTIDE, ACIDIC, AMPHOTER
FORMULA: C45H76N12O14
EA: (N, 11)
MW: 2000
PC: YELLOW, POW.
SOL-GOOD: MEOH, ETOAC, BASE, DMFA
SOL-FAIR: ACET
SOL-POOR: ET2O, BENZ, HEX, W, ACET, PYR
QUAL: (PAULY, +) (NINH., -) (FECL3, -) (FEHL., -) (BIURET, +)
STAB: (ACID, +) (HEAT, +) (BASE, -)
TO: (FUNGI, 5) (S.CEREV., 20)
IS-CHR: (SEPHADEX LH-20, HEX-CHL-MEOH)
REFERENCES:

J. Ferm. Techn., 31, 339, 1953; *BBA*, 13, 553, 1954; *CA*, 48, 2832

43140-1646

NAME: BACILLOMYCIN-C
PO: B.SUBTILIS
CT: BACILLOMYCIN T., PEPTIDE, ACIDIC, AMPHOTER
EA: (N, 9)
SOL-GOOD: MEOH, ETOAC, BASE
SOL-POOR: W, CHL, HEX
QUAL: (BIURET, +) (NINH., -) (FECL3, -) (FEHL., -)
STAB: (HEAT, +)
TO: (S.CEREV., 12) (C.ALB., 100) (FUNGI, 5)
IS-ABS: (CAHPO4, MEOH) (CARBON, ACET-NH4OH)
REFERENCES:
J. Ferm. Techn., 32, 115, 1954; *CA*, 48, 12886

43140-1647

NAME: TOXIMYCIN
PO: B.SUBTILIS
CT: BACILLOMYCIN T., PEPTIDE, ACIDIC, AMPHOTER
EA: (N,)
PC: WH., POW.
SOL-GOOD: BASE, MEOH
SOL-FAIR: W, ETOH, BUOH, DIOXAN
SOL-POOR: ACID, ACET, HEX
QUAL: (BIURET, +) (NINH., +) (FEHL., -)
STAB: (ACID, +) (HEAT, +) (BASE, -)
TO: (S.AUREUS, 50) (PHYT.FUNGI, 5) (S.CEREV., 50)
LD50: (45,)
TV: PLANT V
IS-FIL: 9
IS-CRY: (PREC., FILT., HCL)
REFERENCES:
Nature, 170, 618, 1951; 174, 1190, 1952; *Phytopath.*, 42, 20, 23, 1952; 43, 23, 1953; *CA*, 44, 10797; 47, 4948

43140-1648

PO: B.SUBTILIS
CT: BACILLOMYCIN T., PEPTIDE, ACIDIC, AMPHOTER
EA: (N,)
PC: BROWN, POW.
UV: (275, ,)
SOL-GOOD: MEOH
SOL-POOR: W
TO: (NEUROSPORA CRASSA,) (FUNGI,)
REFERENCES:
Exp., 20, 504, 1964

43140-1649

NAME: FUNGOCIN
IDENTICAL: BACILLOMYCIN-A, ITURIN-A
PO: B.SUBTILIS
CT: BACILLOMYCIN T., PEPTIDE, ACIDIC, AMPHOTER
EA: (N, 12)
EW: 1100
PC: YELLOW, POW.
SOL-GOOD: BASE, MEOH, ETOH, ACOH
SOL-POOR: W, ACET, HEX
QUAL: (NINH., +)
STAB: (HEAT, +)
TO: (C.ALB., 25) (K.PNEUM., 25) (B.SUBT., 100) (FUNGI, 10)
IS-ABS: (CARBON,)
REFERENCES:
Rev. Invest. Agric., 4, 325, 1950; *CA*, 45, 6698; 46, 2616; 47, 7060

43140-1650

NAME: "RAUBITSCHEK SUBSTANCE"
PO: B.SUBTILIS
CT: BACILLOMYCIN T., PEPTIDE, ACIDIC, AMPHOTER
PC: WH., POW.
SOL-GOOD: BASE, MEOH
SOL-FAIR: W
SOL-POOR: ACET, HEX, CHL, ET2O, ACOH
STAB: (HEAT, +)
TO: (TRICHOPHYTON SP., 20)
IS-ABS: (CARBON, MEOH)
IS-CRY: (DRY,)
REFERENCES:
Dermatologica, 100, 45, 1950

43140-1651

NAME:	<u>BACILLOCIN</u>
PO:	B.SUBTILIS-ANTIBLASTI
CT:	BACILLOMYCIN T., PEPTIDE, ACIDIC, AMPHOTER
EA:	(C, 52) (H, 8) (N, 12) (S, 1) (O, 28)
MW:	1000
PC:	WH., POW.
OR:	(+32, MEOH)
UV:	(278, ,)
SOL-GOOD:	MEOH, BUOH, PYR, BASE
SOL-FAIR:	W
SOL-POOR:	ACID, CHL, HEX
QUAL:	(BIURET, +) (NINH., -)
STAB:	(HEAT, +)
TO:	(PHYT.FUNGI, 5)
IS-FIL:	4
IS-EXT:	(MEOH, 4, MIC.)
IS-CRY:	(PREC., MEOH, ETOH)

REFERENCES:

JP 61/1149; *CA*, 55, 21474

43140-1652

NAME:	<u>AL-ANTIBIOTIC</u>
PO:	B.SUBTILIS
CT:	BACILLOMYCIN T., PEPTIDE, ACIDIC, AMPHOTER
EA:	(N, 12)
PC:	YELLOW, WH., POW.
SOL-GOOD:	MEOH, W, PYR, BUOH-W, ACET-W
SOL-POOR:	ETOH, HEX
QUAL:	(BIURET, +) (NINH., -) (EHRL., -) (FECL3, -)
STAB:	(HEAT, +) (BASE, +)
TO:	(S.CEREV., 100) (FUNGI, 50) (B.SUBT., 200)
IS-EXT:	(BUOH, 7, WB.)
IS-CRY:	(PREC., BUOH, ET2O)

REFERENCES:

Kuchne Archiv., 74, 19, 1960

43140-1653

NAME:	"NANDY SUBSTANCE", ASPERGILLUS FACTOR-II
PO:	B.SUBTILIS
CT:	BACILLOMYCIN T., PEPTIDE, ACIDIC, AMPHOTER
EA:	(N,)
SOL-GOOD:	MEOH, ETOH, BASE
SOL-FAIR:	W
SOL-POOR:	ACID, ACET, HEX
QUAL:	(BIURET, +) (NINH., +) (FEHL., -) (DNPH, -) (FECL3, -) (EHRL., -)
STAB:	(HEAT, +) (BASE, -)
TO:	(FUNGI, 12) (B.SUBT., 500)
LD50:	(200, SC)
IS-EXT:	(BUOH, ,)
IS-CRY:	(PREC., FILT., HCL) (PREC., MEOH, ET2O)

REFERENCES:

Nature, 172, 871, 1954

43140-1654

NAME:	POLCILLIN
PO:	B.SUBTILIS
CT:	BACILLOMYCIN T., PEPTIDE, ACIDIC, AMPHOTER
EA:	(C, 52) (H, 8) (N, 14)
MW:	7300
PC:	WH., POW.
UV:	MEOH: (278, 12.8,)
SOL-GOOD:	MEOH, BUOH, PYR, BASE
SOL-POOR:	ACET, HEX
QUAL:	(BIURET, +) (PAULY, +) (NINH., -) (EHRL., -) (FEHL., -) (FECL3, -)
STAB:	(ACID, +) (HEAT, +)
TO:	(C.ALB., 25) (S.CEREV., 6.25) (FUNGI, 6)
LD50:	(38, IV) (49, IP) (1200, PEROS)

REFERENCES:

Agr. Biol. Ch., 29, 548, 1968; Swiss P 446615; JP 61/1149

43140-1655

NAME: <u>B7-I</u>
PO: B.SUBTILIS
CT: BACILLOMYCIN T., PEPTIDE, ACIDIC, AMPHOTER
EA: (N,)
PC: BROWN, RED, POW.
UV: ETOH: (276, ,)
SOL-GOOD: MEOH, BUOH, PYR, BASE
SOL-POOR: ET2O, BENZ, HEX, ACID, W
QUAL: (NINH., +) (FEHL., -)
STAB: (HEAT, +) (ACID, -)
TO: (FUNGI, 2) (S.AUREUS,)
IS-CRY: (PREC., FILT., HCL)
REFERENCES:
J. Appl. Bacteriol., 23, 114, 1960

43140-1656

NAME: <u>SUBSPORIN-A</u>
PO: B.SUBTILIS
CT: BACILLOMYCIN T., PEPTIDE, ACIDIC, AMPHOTER
FORMULA: C88H148N20O26, C88H125N20O33
EA: (N, 15)
MW: 1766, 1168
EW: 957, 1859
PC: WH., CRYST.
OR: (+20.5, PYR)
UV: ETOH-W: (278, 12.6,)
SOL-GOOD: MEOH, PYR, DIOXAN, BASE
SOL-POOR: W, ACET, HEX
QUAL: (BIURET, +) (NINH., -)
STAB: (HEAT, +)
TO: (C.ALB., 5) (FUNGI, 5) (K.PNEUM., 50) (SHYG., 100) (E.COLI, 100) (B.SUBT., 50) (S.AUREUS, 50) (S.LUTEA, 50)
LD50: (73, IP)
IS-FIL: 2.5
IS-EXT: (ETOH, 2.5, MIC.)
IS-CHR: (SILG, CHL-MEOH-ETOH-W)
IS-CRY: (PREC., ETOH, W) (CRYST., CHL-MEOH-ETOH-W)
REFERENCES:
JA, 22, 467, 1969; JP 71/40195

43140-1657

NAME:	SUBSPORIN-B
PO:	B.SUBTILIS
CT:	BACILLOMYCIN T., PEPTIDE, ACIDIC, AMPHOTER
FORMULA:	C88H148N20O24, C88H121N23O28
EA:	(N, 14)
EW:	971, 1150
PC:	WH., CRYST.
OR:	(+16.8, PYR)
UV:	ETOH-W: (278, 12.6,)
SOL-GOOD:	MEOH, DIOXAN, PYR, BASE
SOL-POOR:	W, ACET, HEX, ACID
QUAL:	(BIURET, +) (NINH., -)
STAB:	(HEAT, +)
TO:	(FUNGI, 2) (C.ALB., 30) (B.SUBT., 50) (S.AUREUS, 50) (S.LUTEA, 50) (E.COLI, 50) (SHYG., 50) (K.PNEUM., 50)
IS-CHR:	(SILG,)

REFERENCES:

JA, 22, 467, 1969; JP 71/40195

43140-1658

NAME:	SUBSPORIN-C
PO:	B.SUBTILIS
CT:	BACILLOMYCIN T., PEPTIDE, ACIDIC, AMPHOTER
FORMULA:	C90H147N21O26
EA:	(N, 14)
EW:	1140, 1230
PC:	WH., CRYST.
OR:	(+13, PYR)
UV:	ETOH-W: (278, 12.8,)
SOL-GOOD:	MEOH, PYR, DIOXAN, BASE
SOL-POOR:	W, ACET, HEX
QUAL:	(BIURET, +) (NINH., -)
STAB:	(HEAT, +)
TO:	(FUNGI, 10)
IS-CHR:	(SILG,)

REFERENCES:

JA, 22, 467, 1969; JP 71/40195

43140-1659

NAME: B7-II, A SUBST.
PO: B.SUBTILIS
CT: PEPTIDE, ACIDIC, AMPHOTER, BACILLOMYCIN T.
EA: (N,)
PC: YELLOW, WH., POW.
SOL-GOOD: MEOH, ETOH, PYR
SOL-POOR: W, ET2O, HEX
QUAL: (NINH., +) (FEHL., -)
STAB: (HEAT, -) (ACID, -)
TO: (FUNGI, 8)
IS-EXT: (BUOH, ,)
IS-CRY: (PREC., FILT., HCL)
REFERENCES:
J. Appl. Bact., 23, 114, 1960

43140-1660

NAME: B7-IV
PO: B.SUBTILIS
CT: PEPTIDE, AMPHOTER, BACILLOMYCIN T.
EA: (N,)
TO: (FUNGI,)
IS-ION: (IR-120-H, ACOH)
REFERENCES:
J. Appl. Bact., 23, 114, 1960

43140-1663

NAME:	MYCOSUBTILIN
PO:	B.SUBTILIS, B.SUBTILIS-NIGER
CT:	BACILLOMYCIN T., PEPTIDE, ACIDIC, AMPHOTER
FORMULA:	C55H85N14O16
EA:	(C, 55) (H, 7) (N, 15)
EW:	1980
PC:	WH., CRYST.
UV:	ETOH-W: (277, 14.58,)
SOL-GOOD:	BASE, MEOH, PYR
SOL-POOR:	ETOH, HEX, W
QUAL:	(BIURET, +) (NINH., -) (FECL3, -) (DNPH, -) (FEHL., -)
STAB:	(HEAT, +)
TO:	(FUNGI, 1.5) (S.CEREV., 3) (C.ALB., 100)
LD50:	(20, SC)
IS-FIL:	2.5
IS-EXT:	(ETOH, 2.5, MIC.)
IS-CRY:	(CRYST., ETOH-W)

REFERENCES:

JA, 8, 189, 1955; *J. Clin. Invest.*, 28, 974, 1949; *Eur. J. Bioch.*, 63, 391, 1976; USP 2602767

43140-1750

NAME:	ITURIN-A
IDENTICAL:	BACILLOMYCIN-B, EUMYCIN, BACILLOMYCIN-R, BACILLOMYCIN, FUNGOCIN
PO:	B.SUBTILIS-ITURIENSIS
CT:	BACILLOMYCIN T., PEPTIDE, AMPHOTER
FORMULA:	C49H75N12O14
EA:	(C,) (H,) (N, 14)
MW:	923, 1002, 1315
PC:	WH., POW.
OR:	(-60, W)
UV:	NAOH: (294, ,)
UV:	W: (277, 15.8,)
SOL-GOOD:	MEOH, ETOH, PYR, ACID, BASE, DMFA
SOL-POOR:	W, ACET, HEX, DMFA, ACET, PYR
QUAL:	(PAULY, +) (NINH., -) (BIURET, +) (FECL3, -) (FEHL., -) (SAKA., -)
STAB:	(HEAT, +)
TO:	(S.LUTEA, 8) (S.CEREV., 16) (C.ALB., 69) (PHYT.FUNGI, 8)
LD50:	(65, IV) (157, SC)
IS-FIL:	ORIG.
IS-CHR:	(SILG, CHL-MEOH-W) (SEPHADEX LH-20, HEX-CHL-MEOH)
IS-CRY:	(PREC., FILT., HCL)
UTILITY:	ON CLINICAL TRIAL

REFERENCES:

CR Soc. Biol., 144, 1431; 1950; 146, 789, 1808; 1952; *Arch. Int. Physiol.*, 60, 554, 1952; *Bull. Soc. Chim. Belg.*, 74, 315, 329, 1965; *Arch. Belges Derm. Syph.*, 12, 224, 1956; 14, 63, 1958; *Bioch. Soc. Trans.*, 5, 1122, 1977; *Tetr.*, 29, 3455, 1973; *JA*, 29, 1043, 1976; 31, 284, 1978; *BBRC*, 81, 297, 1978

43140-5639

NAME:	BACILLOMYCIN-L
IDENTICAL:	"LANDY SUBSTANCE"
PO:	B.SUBTILIS
CT:	BACILLOMYCIN T., PEPTIDE, ACIDIC, AMPHOTER
FORMULA:	C46H71N9017
EA:	(N, 12)
MW:	993|40, 1021
PC:	WH., POW.
UV:	MEOH: (201, , 14400) (275, , 1310)
SOL-GOOD:	MEOH, PYR, DMFA
SOL-POOR:	CHL, BENZ, ETOAC, BUOH, THF, W
QUAL:	(BIURET, +) (PAULY, +) (NINH., -)
TO:	(FUNGI,)
IS-EXT:	(BUOH-ACET, 3, PREC.)
IS-CHR:	(AL, ACET-W) (SEPHADEX LH-20, HEX-CHL-MEOH)
IS-CRY:	(PREC., FILT., HCL) (PREC., BUOH, ACET-ET20)

REFERENCES:

J. Bact., 54, 74, 1947; *ABB*, 60, 364, 1956; *Eur. J. Bioch.*, 77, 61, 1977; *Biochem. Soc. Trans.*, 5, 1122, 1977

43140-6074

NAME:	ITURIN-C
PO:	B.SUBTILIS
CT:	PEPTIDE, BACILLOMYCIN T., ACIDIC, AMPHOTER
FORMULA:	C49H74N11016
EA:	(N,)
PC:	WH., POW.

REFERENCES:

Tetr., 34, 1147, 1978; *Biochem.*, 17, 3992, 1978

43140-6076

NAME:	BACILLOMYCIN-S
PO:	B.SUBTILIS
CT:	PEPTIDE, BACILLOMYCIN T.
EA:	(N,)
PC:	WH., POW.
SOL-POOR:	ACID
TO:	(HELMINTHOSPORIUM TURCICUM, .03)
IS-CHR:	(SEPHADEX G-75,)

REFERENCES:

Mycol., 69, 975, 1977; *Arzn. Forsch.*, 28, 1067, 1978; *CA*, 88, 115751

43150-1751

NAME: LONGICATENAMYCIN, S-520
PO: S.DIASTATICUS
CT: PEPTIDE, AMPHOTER
FORMULA: C37|2H54|2N8O9CL
EA: (N, 14) (CL, 8)
MW: 985
EW: 900
PC: WH., POW.
OR: (+13.2, MEOH)
UV: ETOH: (227, 416,) (283.5, 59.4,) (290, 61.8,) (299.5, 43.5,)
UV: MEOH: (226, ,) (282, ,) (259, ,) (298, ,)
SOL-GOOD: MEOH, ACID
SOL-POOR: W, BUOH, HEX
QUAL: (NINH., +) (EHRL., +)
TO: (B.SUBT., 6.25) (S.AUREUS, 6.25) (S.LUTEA, 10) (K.PNEUM., 100) (SHYG., 100)
LD50: (130, IP)
IS-FIL: 2
IS-EXT: (MEOH, 2, MIC.)
IS-CHR: (SEPHADEX LH-20, MEOH)
IS-CRY: (PREC., MEOH, ETOAC)
REFERENCES:

JA, 23, 418, 429, 432, 519, 1970; 28, 561, 1975; *Bull. Ch. Soc. Jap.*, 48, 1902, 1975; *TL*, 3085, 1974; JP 70/27800

43100-2099

NAME: KUWAITIMYCIN
PO: S.KUWAITINENSIS
CT: LIPOPEPTIDE, BASIC, AMPHOTER
EA: (C, 66) (H, 8) (N, 6) (O, 20)
PC: YELLOW, CRYST.
OR: (+60, ETOH)
UV: MEOH: (254, 225,) (278, 165,)
SOL-GOOD: MEOH, ETOH, BUOH, ACET, ETOAC
SOL-FAIR: BENZ
SOL-POOR: W, ET2O, HEX
QUAL: (NINH., +) (BIURET, +) (SAKA., +) (FECL3, -) (FEHL., -)
TO: (B.SUBT., .7) (S.AUREUS, .1) (S.LUTEA, 6.25) (E.COLI, 25) (SHYG., 50)
LD50: (342, IM)
IS-EXT: (ETOAC, 8.5, FILT.)
IS-CHR: (SILG, BENZ-ACET)
IS-CRY: (PREC., ACET, ET2O)
REFERENCES:

JA, 26, 593, 1973; 30, 749, 1977

43100-2127

NAME: SAIHOCHIN-A
PO: PS.SP.
CT: LIPOPEPTIDE, AMPHOTER, NEUTRAL
FORMULA: C50H85N11O25
EA: (C, 49) (H, 7) (N, 13)
EW: 1243
PC: YELLOW, WH., POW.
UV: HCL: (288, 105,)
UV: NAOH: (248, 85,) (330, 60,)
SOL-GOOD: DMSO
SOL-FAIR: BASE
SOL-POOR: BUOH, HEX
QUAL: (BIURET, +) (NINH., -) (PAULY, +)
STAB: (ACID, +) (HEAT, +) (BASE, -)
TO: (C.ALB., 1) (S.CEREV., .78) (FUNGI, .78) (PHYT.FUNGI, .39)
LD50: (4.5, IP)
IS-EXT: (ACET, , MIC.)
REFERENCES:

Jap. Med. Gaz., 4, 7, 1972; JP 74/45596

43100-2128

NAME:	<u>SAIHOCHIN-B</u>
PO:	PS.SP.
CT:	LIPOPEPTIDE, NEUTRAL
FORMULA:	C53H89N11O26
EA:	(C, 48) (H, 7) (N, 12)
EW:	1298
PC:	YELLOW, WH., POW.
UV:	NAOH: (244, 85,) (330, 60,)
SOL-GOOD:	DMSO
SOL-POOR:	MEOH, HEX
STAB:	(ACID, +) (HEAT, +)
TO:	(S.CEREV., 1.56) (C.ALB., 3.12) (PHYT.FUNGI, 1.50)

REFERENCES:
Jap. Med. Gaz., 4, 7, 1972; JP 74/45596

43100-5279

NAME:	<u>339-29</u>
PO:	B.PUMILUS
CT:	LIPOPEPTIDE, PEPTIDE, BASIC
EA:	(C, 56) (H, 9) (N, 13)
MW:	1700
PC:	WH., POW.
OR:	(-27.1, MEOH)
UV:	MEOH: (225, 1258,) (278, 9.6,)
SOL-GOOD:	MEOH, BUOH-W
SOL-FAIR:	W
SOL-POOR:	ACET, HEX
QUAL:	(NINH., +) (SAKA., +) (PAULY, +)
TO:	(B.SUBT., 3.13) (S.AUREUS, 3.13) (K.PNEUM., 50)
LD50:	(7.5|2.5, IP)
IS-EXT:	(ACET-W, 8, MIC.) (BUOH, 8.5, FILT.) (W, 2, BUOH-ETOAC)
IS-CHR:	(SILG, CHL-ETOH-NH4OH)
IS-CRY:	(PREC., BUOH, ET2O)

REFERENCES:
JA, 29, 810, 1976

43100-5638

NAME: 340-19-I
PO: B.LATEROSPORUS
CT: BASIC, LIPOPEPTIDE
SOL-GOOD: W
TO: (E.COLI,) (G.POS.,) (G.NEG.,)
IS-FIL: 5
IS-EXT: (BUOH, 7.8, W)
IS-ION: (IRC-50-NA, HCL)
IS-ABS: (CARBON, ACET-W-HCL)
REFERENCES:
JA, 29, 390, 1976

43100-5994

NAME: TRICHOPOLIN-A
PO: TRICHODERMA POLYSPORUM
CT: LIPOPEPTIDE, BASIC
EA: (N,)
MW: 2000
PC: WH., POW.
TO: (S.AUREUS, 6.2) (B.SUBT., 6.2) (S.LUTEA, 1.56) (S.CEREV., 25) (C.ALB., 6.2) (FUNGI, .78) (PHYT.FUNGI, .78)
LD50: (10|5, IP)
IS-EXT: (ET2O, , EVAP.FILT.)
IS-CHR: (SILG, ACET-MEOH)
REFERENCES:
Exp., 34, 238, 1978

43100-5995

NAME: TRICHOPOLIN-B
PO: TRICHODERMA POLYSPORUM
CT: LIPOPEPTIDE, BASIC
EA: (N,)
MW: 2000
PC: WH., POW.
TO: (S.AUREUS, 6.2) (B.SUBT., 6.2) (S.LUTEA, 1.56) (S.CEREV., 12) (C.ALB., 3.1) (FUNGI, .78) (PHYT.FUNGI, .78)
IS-EXT: (ET2O, , EVAP.FILT.)
IS-CHR: (SILG, ACET-MEOH)
REFERENCES:
Exp., 34, 238, 1978

432
Thiapeptides

Introduction

In this group some sulfur-containing, highly modified peptide antibiotics are listed. The sulfur is within the molecule of these compounds present in the thiazole or other heterocyclic ring containing amino acid-like constituents.

The common feature of these antibiotics is their high oxidation level, i.e., strong heteroaromatic character. They are distributed into the so-called thiazolyl-peptide type (4321) containing compounds usually with a large peptide or peptide-lactone ring with inserted thiazolyl fragments; the bottromycin (4322), berninamycin (4323), and leucinamycin type (4324) thiapeptides with cyclic character; and into other less known sulfur-containing peptide-type antibiotics (432).

The thiazole-containing bleomycin-type glycopeptide antibiotics, owing to their chelate-forming ability and for several other reasons (e.g., their linear peptide-type structure), are listed elsewhere in the group of chelate-forming peptides (433). The simple oligopeptide (tripeptide) althiomycins are listed in this group due to the very close structural and biogenetic relationships to larger molecular thiazolyl peptides. Thiostreptons and micrococcins, because they also contain a peptide-lactone ring, are chemically related to peptolide antibiotics (44), especially to the highly modified ostreogrycin A type compounds.

These compounds — except the micrococcin subtype (bacterial metabolites) — all are of *Actinomycetales* origin. Several newly isolated antibiotics are produced by *Micromonospora, Actinoplanes,* or *Pseudonocardia* species.

4321
Thiazolyl Peptides

This type of compound covers numerous *Actinomycetales* metabolites — thiostrepton, althiomycin, and saramycetin (43211, 43212, and 43213, respectively) subtypes — as well as the bacterial micrococcin subtype (43214). The close chemical and biogenetic relationship between thiostrepton and micrococcin type of compounds is very remarkable, especially in the similarity of actinomycetal and bacterial metabolism. They represent the second example — besides the butirosin and ribostamycin pair — for the production of such complicated closely related chemical structures by two distinctly different taxa.

Apart from althiomycin-type compounds which are relatively simple molecules (and which will be discussed separately), these antibiotics are one of the most complicated and most unique compounds ever isolated from natural sources. The antibiotics with known chemical structures (thiostrepton, siomycin, nosiheptid, micrococcins P_1 and P_2) are constructed from common amino acids (thr, val, ileu, cyst), dehydroamino acids (dehydroalanine, dehydrobutyrine), heterocyclic thiazol-containing complicated amino acid-like compounds, and various other heterocyclic fragments (pyridine, indole, quinoline derivatives). These compounds possess multiple macrocyclic structures. Thiostrepton, siomycin, and nosiheptid have a large peptide and an attached peptide-lactone ring (thioester-linked lactone in the case of nosipheptid) and a peptide side chain. In the structure of micrococcins only a peptide ring and the peptide side chain occur. It is interesting that the framework of the peptide macro ring is identical in all of these compounds.

The arrangement of the constituents and the structures of these corresponding building stones are summarized in the following tables:

CONSTITUENTS OF THE PEPTIDE RING

A Thiostreptonic acid ($C_{19}H_{19}N_4O_5S_3$) (thiostrepton, siomycin, thiopeptin)

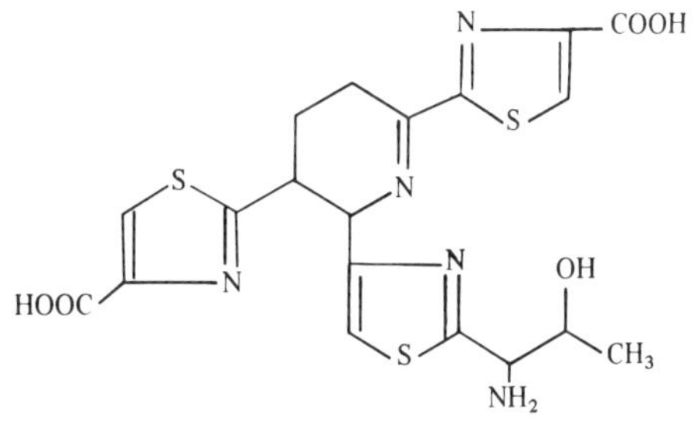

"Fragment A" ($C_{18}H_{10}N_4O_6S_3$) (nosiheptid)

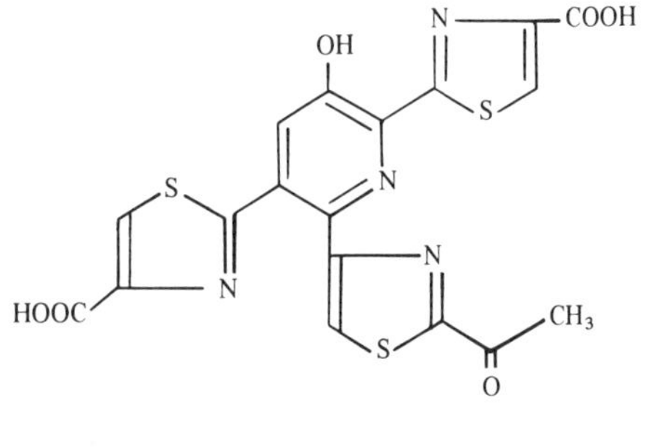

Micrococcinic acid ($C_{22}H_{13}N_5O_5S_4$) (micrococcin P_1, P_2)

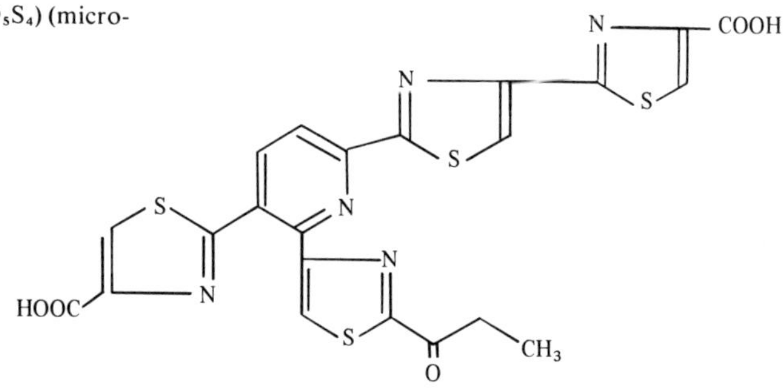

B Thiostreptin ($C_9H_{14}N_2O_4S$) (thiostrepton, siomycin, thiopeptin)

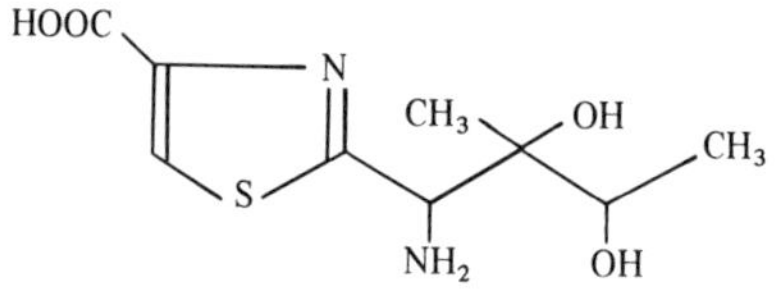

"Fragment D" ($C_8H_{10}N_2O_5S$) (nosiheptid)

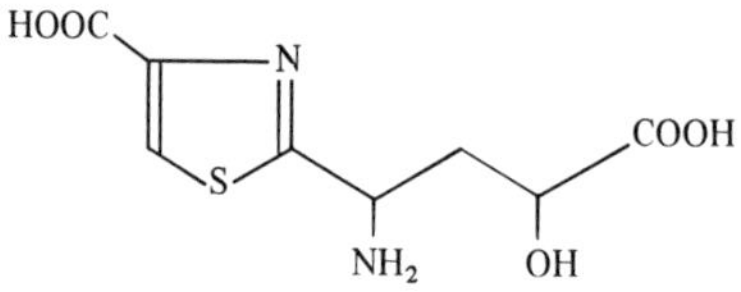

"Subunit D" ($C_8H_{12}N_2O_2S$) (micrococcin P_1, P_2)

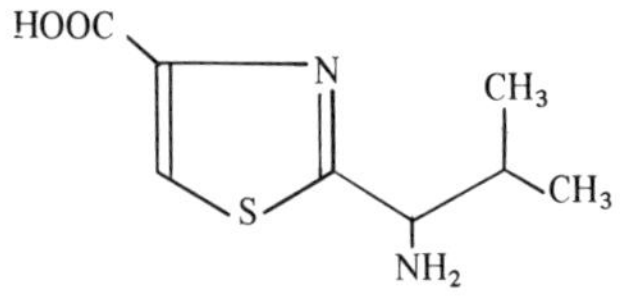

C 2(1-Aminoacetonyl)-thiazole-4-carboxylic acid **(1)** or 2(1-amino-2-carboxyethyl)-thiazole-4-carboxylic acid **(2)** or 2-aminomethyl-thiazole-4-carboxylic acid **(3)** (thiostrepton, siomycin)

2-Propionyl-thiazol-4-carboxylic acid **(4)** (nosiheptid, "fragment C"; micrococcins, "subunit C")

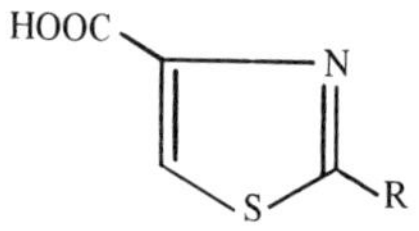

(1) R =

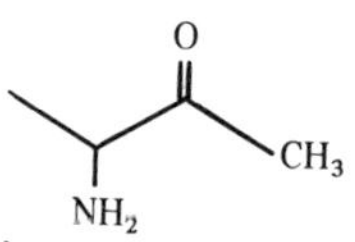

(2) R =

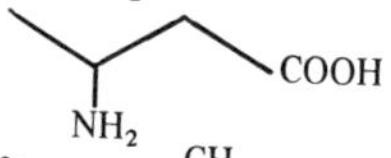

(3) R =

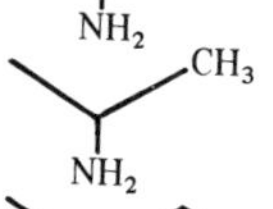

(4) R =

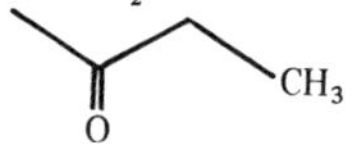

D Threonine (thiostrepton, siomycin, thiopeptin, nosiheptid, micrococcins)

C Cysteine, butyrine (thiostrepton, siomycin)

CONSTITUENTS OF THE PEPTIDE-LACTONE RING

E Alanine, dehydroalanine (thiostrepton, siomycin, thiopeptin) isoleucine (thiostrepton) valine (siomycin, thiopeptin)

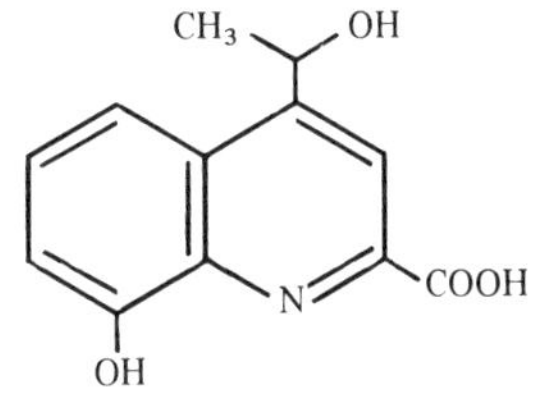

F 4-α-Hydroxyethyl-8-hydroxyquinaldinic acid $C_{12}H_{11}NO_4$ (thiostrepton, siomycin, thiopeptin)
2-Carboxy-3-methyl-5-hydroxymethyl-indole ("fragment E") $C_{10}H_{11}NO_3$ (nosiheptid)

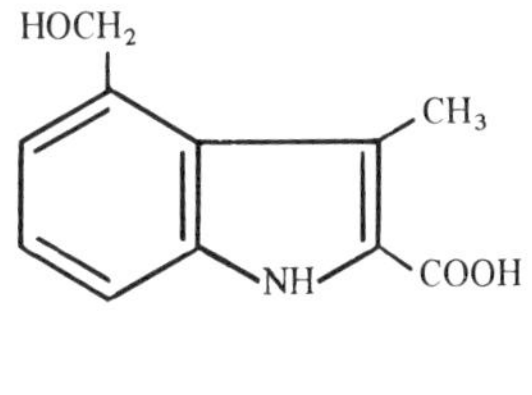

CONSTITUENTS OF THE PEPTIDE SIDE CHAIN

G Dehydroalanine (thiostrepton, siomycin, nosiheptid)

Dehydrobutyrine (or threonine); 2-hydroxypropylamine, aminoacetone (micrococcins)

The thiazolyl peptides are easily crystallizable, relatively stable, neutral antibiotics. They are insoluble in water, acids, bases, and in all organic solvents, except chlorinated hydrocarbons and some polar solvents such as pyridine, dimethylformamide, or dimethylsulfoxide. They have strong UV absorption between 220 and 300 nm, without definite absorption maxima, generally showing several inflections only. Their high melting points (above 220°C) are not typical; thus the optical rotation value is the only characteristic physical property of these compounds. Their molecular weight is about 1700 (thiostrepton, siomycin) or about 1200 (nosiheptid, micrococcin).

Although thiostrepton was discovered in 1952, its structural determination was achieved by X-ray analysis in 1970. This proposed structure (with certain obscurity) and those of the other congeners of this type were confirmed and established by chemical degradation and primarily by extensive use of NMR only recently.

Thiostrepton- and micrococcin-type thiazolyl peptides inhibit Gram-positive bacteria including primarily streptococci and pneumococci, but they are not active against Gram-negative and eucaryotic organisms. They are fairly toxic compounds. These low toxicity values may be due to their low solubility. Clinical studies with thiostrepton (after topical and oral administration) were also found to produce no toxic effects; however, these antibiotics have not found a place in clinical medicine. Their therapeutic effects are rather poor because they are not absorbed from the injection site or from the intestinal tract. Thiostrepton is used in veterinary medicine in the treatment of bovine mastitis, while thiopeptin, siomycin, and nosiheptin are used as animal feed additives.

Thiostrepton and micrococcin inhibit protein synthesis. They bind to the 50S ribosomal subunit and inhibit aminoacyl-tRNA binding and translocation reactions which require several elongation factors.

Biogenetically these compounds represent highly modified peptides. The skeleton of these antibiotics was derived by intense enzymatic oxidations or dehydrogenations as well as by cyclization and oxidative deamination reactions from precursor peptides composed of cysteine, threonine, and other amino acids, such as α-aminobutyric and β-aminoadipic acids. Thiazole residues formally can be derived from D-cysteine via dehydrocysteine residues. The dehydroamino acid residues are derived from serine and threonine, and the pyridine ring is also derived from two dehydroalanaine residues.

Alamethicin-type antibiotics (43212) are simple analogs of thiostrepton-type compounds, containing thiazoline, thiazole systems, and pyrrolinone **(1)** and oxime fragments. They are acid-labile substances active against both Gram-positive and Gram-negative bacteria, with low toxicity. They show characteristic UV absorption at 225 and 286 nm and may be considered highly modified dipeptides.

Saramycetin (43213) is a polypeptide-type antibiotic with a molecular weight of about 2200. This peptide, for which only a partial structure — representing about half of the total molecule — was proposed, contains several thiazole-II and benzthiazole-containing amino acid-like fragments, such as saramycetic acid I **(2)** and saramycetic acid II (saramycetoic acid) **(3)**. It is a clinically effective, less toxic antifungal agent having specific activity against *Cryptococcus, Blastomyces,* and *Histoplasma* species (yeast-like fungi).

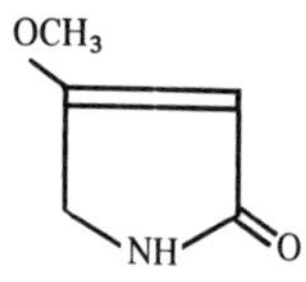

(1)

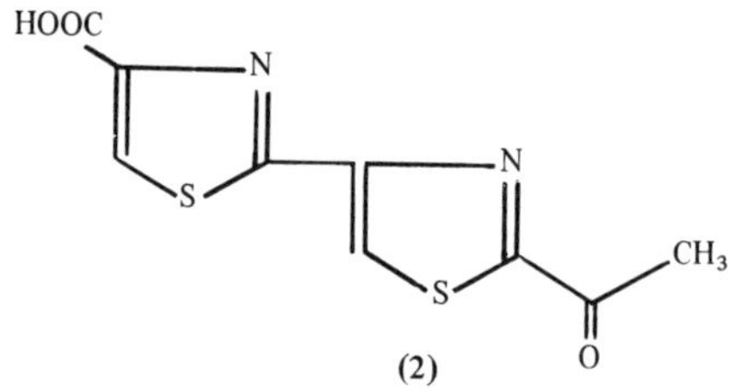

(2)

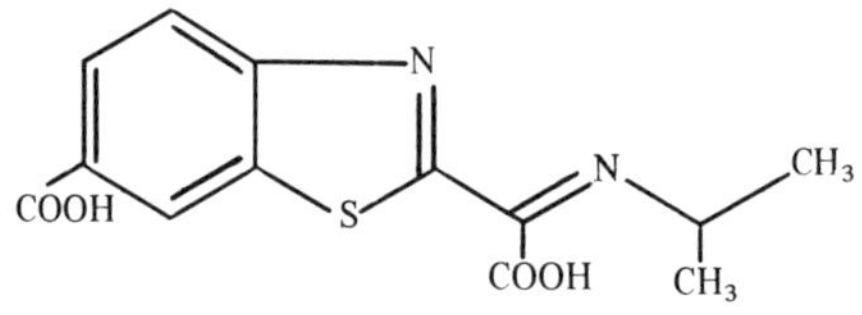

(3)

Structures

43211

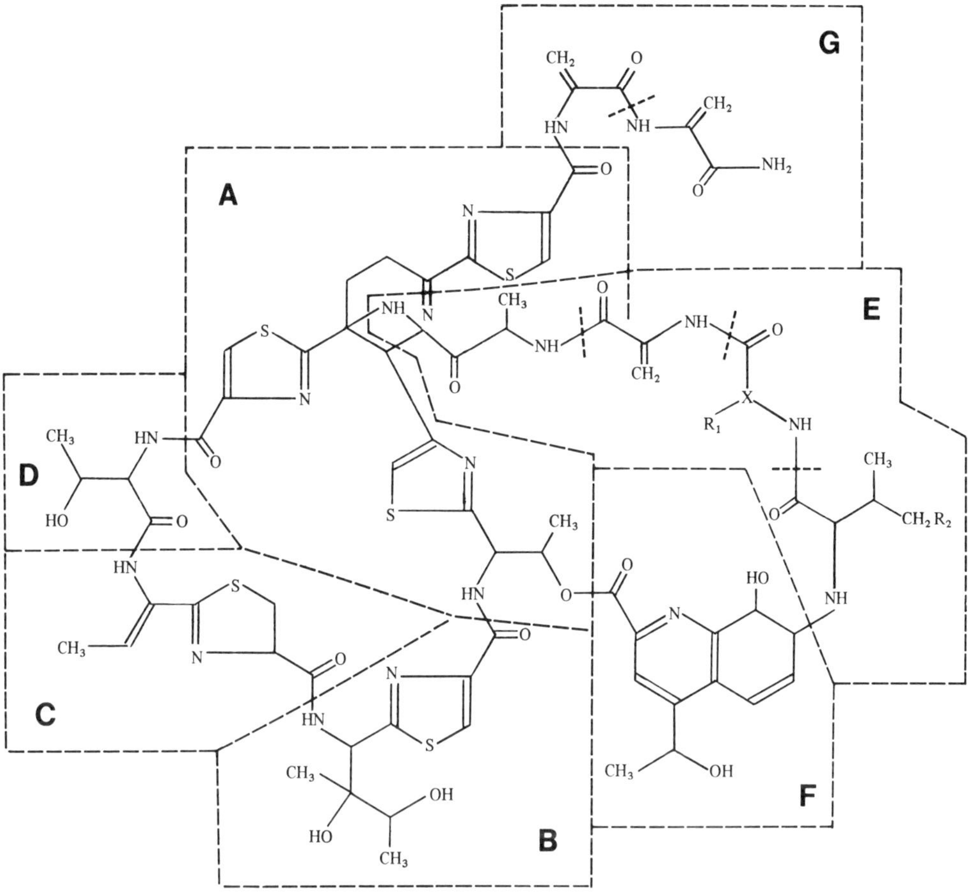

Antibiotic	X	R_1	R_2
Thiostrepton	–CH–	$-CH_3$	CH_3
Siomycin A	>C=	$=CH_2$	H

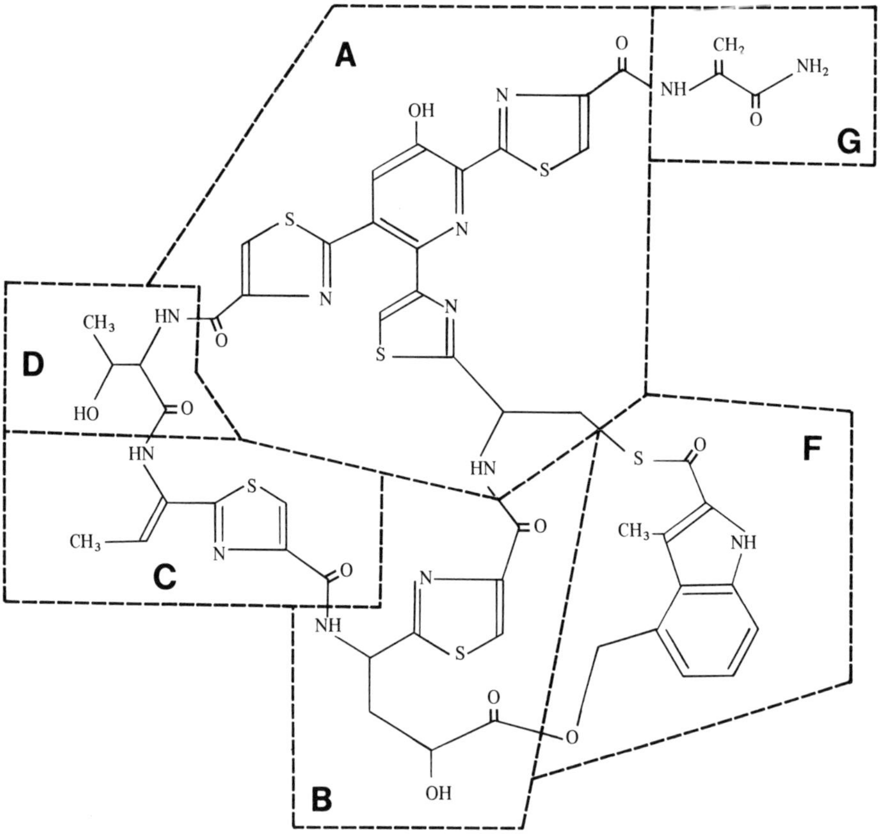

43212

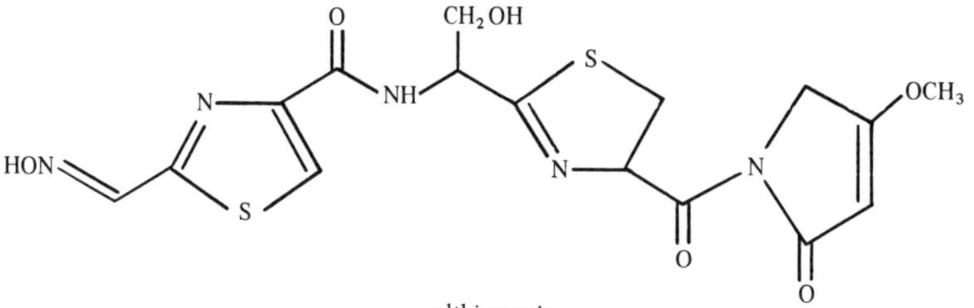

althiomycin

43213

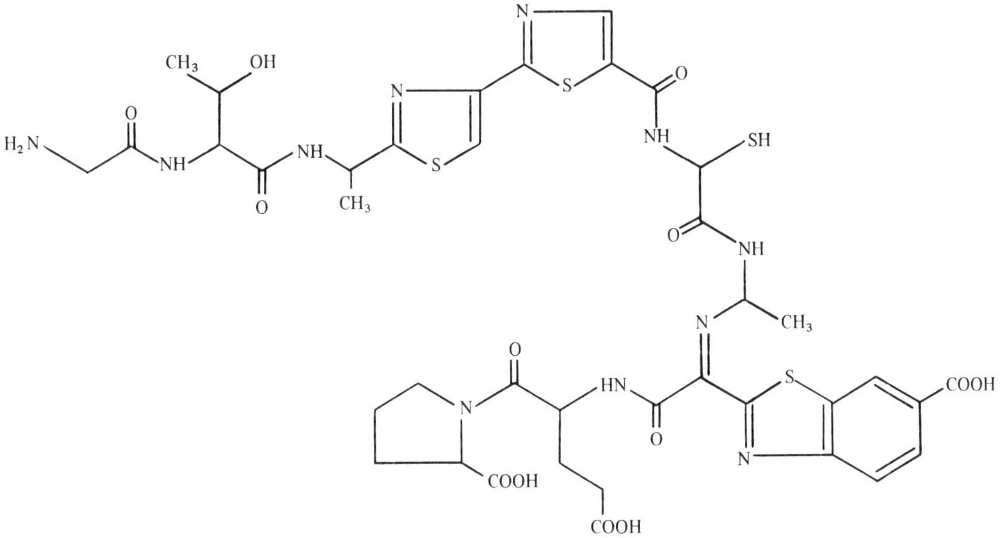

saramycetin
(partial structure)

43214

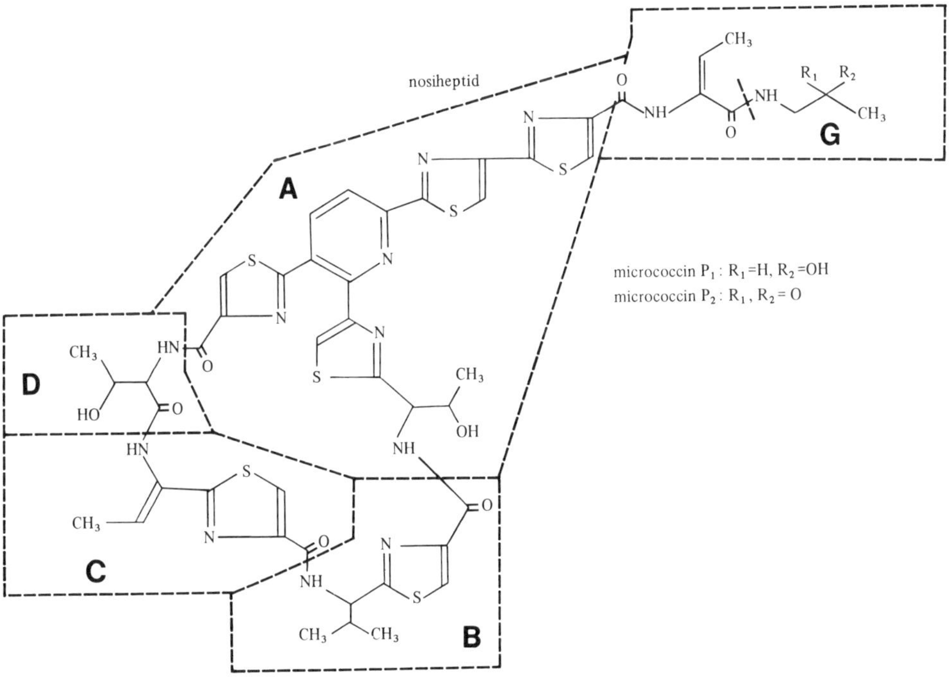

43211-1752

NAME:	THIOSTREPTON, A-8506, X-146
IDENTICAL:	BRYAMYCIN, THIACTIN, 6761-31
PO:	S.AZUREUS, S.SP., S.LAURENTII
CT:	THIAZOLYL-PEPTIDE, THIOSTREPTON T., AMPHOTER
FORMULA:	C72H85N19018S5
EA:	(N, 16) (S, 9)
MW:	1650, 1613
EW:	390|20
PC:	WH., CRYST.
OR:	(-98.5, ACOH) (-61, DIOXAN) (-20, PYR) (-69, CHL)
UV:	(200, ,)
UV:	ETOH: (225, ,) (250, ,) (280, ,)
UV:	MEOH: (225, 520,) (250, 280,) (280, 225,) (305, 120,)
UV:	MEOH-HCL: (240, ,) (280, ,) (305, ,)
SOL-GOOD:	CHL, PYR, DIOXAN, ACOH, DMFA, ACID
SOL-POOR:	W, ETOH, HEX, BASE
QUAL:	(EHRL., +) (BIURET, +) (SAKA., -) (NINH., -)
STAB:	(HEAT, -) (BASE, -) (ACID, -)
TO:	(S.AUREUS, .005) (B.SUBT., .03) (SHYG., 50) (K.PNEUM., 30) (E.COLI, 100) (PS.AER., 100) (P.VULG., 100) (C.ALB., 6.25)
LD50:	(41.2, IV) (2000, IP)
IS-EXT:	(CHL, , MIC.) (ME.I.BU.KETON, 5.8, FILT.)
IS-CHR:	(AL, DIOXAN) (AL, CHL-MEOH)
IS-CRY:	(PREC., CHL, HEX) (CRYST., CHL-DIOXAN)
UTILITY:	VETERINARY DRUG

REFERENCES:

Ant. An., 554, 560, 1955—56; *JACS*, 83, 3906, 1961; 84, 2003, 1962; 86, 2478, 1964; 91, 4934; *JCS*, 2143, 1963; *JCSC*, 2115, 1966; *JA*, 16, 76, 1973; 22, 287, 1969; 30, 639, 1977; *AAC*, 1, 192, 1972; *An. Rep. Shionogi*, 11, 137, 1965; *Nature*, 225, 233, 1970; *Acta Cryst.*, 25, 200, 1969; *TL*, 185, 1976; *BBRC*, 44, 912, 1971; USP 2982689, 2982698, 4064013

43211-1753

NAME: BRYAMYCIN
IDENTICAL: THIOSTREPTON, THIACTIN
PO: S.HAWAIIENSIS
CT: THIAZOLYL-PEPTIDE, THIOSTREPTON T., AMPHOTER
EA: (C, 52) (H, 6) (N, 16) (S, 10)
MW: 1675|75
PC: WH., CRYST.
OR: (-69, CHL)
UV: (250, ,) (310, 125,)
SOL-POOR: W
TO: (G.POS., .1) (C.ALB.,)
LD50: (2000, IP) (1000, IM)
IS-EXT: (BUOH, , WB.)
REFERENCES:
JA, 16, 76, 1963; *Ant. & Chem.*, 6, 63, 1956; 8, 387, 1958; *Hakko Kyokai Shr.*, 19, 140, 1961; BP 790521

43211-1754

NAME: SIOMYCIN-A, SIOMYCIN, A-59-A, 21-31, 6741-21
IDENTICAL: SPORANGIOMYCIN, MUTABILLICIN
PO: S.SIOYAENSIS
CT: THIAZOLYL-PEPTIDE, THIOSTREPTON T., AMPHOTER
FORMULA: C71H81N19018S5
EA: (N, 16) (S, 9)
MW: 1750|100
EW: 1740
PC: WH., YELLOW, CRYST.
OR: (-90.9, DIOXAN) (-95.3, DIOXAN)
UV: MEOH: (240, ,) (270, ,) (280, ,)
SOL-GOOD: CHL, ACOH, DMFA, DIOXAN
SOL-FAIR: MEOH, ETOH, BUOH, ACET
SOL-POOR: BENZ, HEX, W, ACID, BASE
QUAL: (BIURET, +) (FEHL., +) (NINH., -) (FECL3, -) (EHRL., -)
STAB: (ACID, +) (BASE, -)
TO: (B.SUBT., .05) (S.AUREUS, .05)
LD50: (100, IV)
IS-FIL: 5
IS-EXT: (CHL, , MIC.)
IS-CHR: (AL, CHL) (SILG, CHL-MEOH)
IS-CRY: (PREC., CHL, HEX) (CRYST., CHL-MEOH)
UTILITY: FEED ADDITIVE
REFERENCES:
JA, 14, 255, 1961; 22, 364, 423, 434, 451, 506, 1969; *An. Rep. Shionogi*, 11, 137, 141, 1961; *TL*, 185, 1976; *CC*, 577, 1978; DT 1178172; USP 3082153

43211-1755

NAME: <u>SPORANGIOMYCIN</u>
IDENTICAL: MUTABILLICIN, SIOMYCIN-A
PO: PLANOMONOSPORA PARONTOSPORA
CT: THIAZOLYL-PEPTIDE, THIOSTREPTON T., AMPHOTER
FORMULA: C78H103N20O21S6
EA: (N, 16) (S, 10)
MW: 1800
PC: WH., CRYST.
OR: (-100, CHL)
UV: (200, ,)
SOL-GOOD: DMFA, DMSO, ACOH
SOL-FAIR: CHL
SOL-POOR: W, MEOH, HEX
QUAL: (BIURET, +) (FEHL., +) (FECL3, -)
TO: (S.AUREUS, .07) (B.SUBT., .03) (S.LUTEA, .015)
LD50: (2000, IP)
IS-EXT: (ETOAC, , MIC.)
IS-CRY: (CRYST., CHL)
REFERENCES:
JA, 21, 525, 1968; *Antib.*, 204, 1971

43211-1756

NAME: <u>MUTABILLICIN</u>, 21-31, 6741-21
IDENTICAL: SIOMYCIN-A, SPORANGIOMYCIN
PO: ACT.MUTABILIS, S.MUTABILIS
CT: THIAZOLYL-PEPTIDE, THIOSTREPTON T., AMPHOTER
FORMULA: C42H53N11O12S3
EA: (N, 15) (S, 9)
PC: WH., CRYST.
OR: (-91.5, CHL) (-94.6, DIOXAN)
UV: (200, ,)
SOL-GOOD: CHL, DMFA, DIOXAN, ACOH
SOL-FAIR: MEOH
SOL-POOR: ETOH, HEX, ACID, W
QUAL: (NINH., -)
TO: (S.AUREUS, .01) (B.SUBT., .01) (E.COLI, 50) (SHYG., 50)
IS-EXT: (MEOH, , MIC.)
IS-CRY: (PREC., CHL, ACET)
REFERENCES:
Antib., 410, 887, 1966; 204, 1971

43211-1757

NAME:	SIOMYCIN-C
PO:	S.SIOYAENSIS
CT:	THIAZOLYL-PEPTIDE, THIOSTREPTON T., AMPHOTER
FORMULA:	C69H87N14031S4.5
EA:	(N, 11) (S, 8)
MW:	1700
PC:	WH., CRYST.
OR:	(-84.6, DIOXAN)
UV:	MEOH: (200, ,)
SOL-GOOD:	CHL, DMFA, DIOXAN
SOL-FAIR:	ACET, MEOH
SOL-POOR:	W, ACID, BASE, ETOAC, HEX
QUAL:	(NINH., -) (FECL3, -) (EHRL., -)
TO:	(B.SUBT., 100) (S.AUREUS, .05) (S.LUTEA, .05)
IS-EXT:	(ACET, , MIC.)
IS-CHR:	(SILG, CHL-MEOH)

REFERENCES:

JA, 22, 364, 1969; JP 70/5034

43211-1758

NAME:	THIOPEPTIN-A1, THIOPEPTIN-A1A
TRADE NAMES:	TATEMYCIN-A1
PO:	S.TATEYAMENSIS+N-ACETYL-METHIONINE
CT:	THIAZOLYL-PEPTIDE, THIOSTREPTON T., AMPHOTER
FORMULA:	C72H86N18O18S6
EA:	(C, 49) (H, 5) (N, 14) (S, 12)
MW:	1637
PC:	YELLOW, CRYST.
OR:	(-71, CHL)
UV:	MEOH: (200, ,)
SOL-GOOD:	DMSO, DMFA, PYR, CHL, DIOXAN
SOL-FAIR:	MEOH, ACET, ETOAC
SOL-POOR:	BENZ, HEX, W
QUAL:	(NINH., -) (BIURET, -) (FEHL., -) (FECL3, -) (EHRL., -)
STAB:	(ACID, +) (HEAT, +)
TO:	(S.AUREUS, .1) (B.SUBT., .1) (S.LUTEA, .05)
LD50:	(500, IP)
IS-EXT:	(MEOH, , MIC.)
IS-CHR:	(SILG, CHL-MEOH)
IS-CRY:	(PREC., CHL, HEX)

REFERENCES:

JA, 23, 113, 1970; 25, 537, 1972; *AAC*, 1, 192, 496, 1972; DT 1929355

43211-1759

NAME: THIOPEPTIN-A2
PO: S.TATEYAMENSIS
CT: THIAZOLYL-PEPTIDE, THIOSTREPTON T., AMPHOTER
PC: YELLOW, CRYST.
UV: MEOH: (240|10, 760,) (305, 220,)
SOL-GOOD: DMFA, DMSO, DIOXAN, PYR, CHL
SOL-FAIR: MEOH, ACET, ETOAC
SOL-POOR: W, BENZ, HEX
TO: (G.POS., .01)
LD50: (1000, IP)
IS-CHR: (SILG, CHL-MEOH)
REFERENCES:
JA, 23, 113, 1970; 25, 537, 1972; *AAC*, 1, 192, 496, 1972; DT 1929355

43211-1760

NAME: THIOPEPTIN-A3, THIOPEPTIN-A3A
PO: S.TATEYAMENSIS
CT: THIAZOLYL-PEPTIDE, THIOSTREPTON T., AMPHOTER
FORMULA: C65H79N17O15S6
EA: (C, 48) (H, 5) (N, 14) (S, 12)
MW: 1972
PC: YELLOW, CRYST.
OR: (-10.8, CHL)
UV: MEOH: (200, ,)
SOL-GOOD: DMSO, THF, CHL, DIOXAN
SOL-FAIR: ETOAC, ACET
SOL-POOR: BENZ, HEX, W
QUAL: (FEHL., -) (FECL3, -) (BIURET, -) (NINH., -)
TO: (S.AUREUS, .25) (B.SUBT., .25) (S.LUTEA, 1)
LD50: (250, IP)
IS-CHR: (SILG, CHL-MEOH)
REFERENCES:
JA, 23, 113, 1970; 25, 537, 1972; *AAC*, 1, 192, 496, 1972; DT 1929355

43211-1761

NAME: THIOPEPTIN-A4, THIOPEPTIN-A4A
PO: S.TATEYAMENSIS
CT: THIAZOLYL-PEPTIDE, THIOSTREPTON T., AMPHOTER
FORMULA: C68H82N18O16S6
EA: (C, 50) (H, 5) (N, 15) (S, 12)
MW: 1700, 1854
PC: YELLOW, CRYST.
OR: (-81, CHL)
UV: MEOH: (200, ,)
SOL-GOOD: CHL, DIOXAN, DMFA, DMSO
SOL-FAIR: MEOH, ACET, ETOAC
SOL-POOR: BENZ, HEX, W
QUAL: (NINH., -) (BIURET, -) (FEHL., -) (FECL3, -)
STAB: (ACID, +) (BASE, -)
TO: (S.AUREUS, .03) (B.SUBT., .25) (S.LUTEA, .25)
LD50: (1000, IP)
REFERENCES:

JA, 23, 133, 1970; *AAC*, 1, 192, 1972; DT 2057033

43211-1762

NAME: THIOPEPTIN-B, THIOPEPTIN-BA
TRADE NAMES: TATEMYCIN
PO: S.TATEYAMENSIS
CT: THIAZOLYL-PEPTIDE, THIOSTREPTON T., AMPHOTER
FORMULA: C71H84N18O18S6
EA: (N, 14) (S, 11)
MW: 1942, 1782
PC: YELLOW, CRYST.
OR: (-80, CHL)
UV: MEOH: (248, 430,)
SOL-GOOD: DMFA, DMSO, DIOXAN, PYR, CHL, THF
SOL-FAIR: MEOH, ACET, ETOAC
SOL-POOR: BENZ, HEX, W
QUAL: (NINH., -) (BIURET, -) (FECL3, -) (EHRL., -)
STAB: (ACID, +) (BASE, -)
TO: (S.AUREUS, .19) (B.SUBT., .05) (S.LUTEA, .025)
LD50: (20|60, IP) (3600, SC)
IS-CHR: (SILG, CHL-MEOH)
IS-CRY: (CRYST., ACET)
UTILITY: FEED ADDITIVE
REFERENCES:

AAC, 1, 192, 496, 1972; *JA*, 25, 537, 1972; 30, 383, 1977; DT 1929355

43211-1763

NAME:	A-59-A
IDENTICAL:	SIOMYCIN-A
PO:	S.SP.
CT:	THIAZOLYL-PEPTIDE, THIOSTREPTON T., AMPHOTER
EA:	(C, 50) (H, 6) (N, 14) (S, 10)
MW:	2000
PC:	WH., CRYST.
OR:	(-92, DIOXAN) (-93, DMFA)
UV:	MEOH: (200, ,)
SOL-GOOD:	DMFA, PYR, ACOH, DIOXAN, CHL
SOL-FAIR:	ETOH, ACET, ETOAC
SOL-POOR:	MEOH, I.PROH, BENZ, HEX, W
QUAL:	(BIURET, +) (FEHL., +) (SAKA., -) (NINH., -) (FECL3, -)
STAB:	(HEAT, +)
TO:	(S.AUREUS, .02) (B.SUBT., .02) (S.LUTEA, .04)
LD50:	(150, IP)
IS-FIL:	4
IS-EXT:	(MEOH, 4, MIC.)
IS-CRY:	(CRYST., CHL-DIOXAN-MEOH)

REFERENCES:

JA, 14, 194, 1961

43211-1764

NAME:	1456, 2337
PO:	S.SP.
CT:	THIAZOLYL-PEPTIDE, THIOSTREPTON T., AMPHOTER
FORMULA:	C14H21N4O5S
EA:	(C, 47) (H, 6) (N, 18) (S, 9)
PC:	YELLOW, CRYST.
OR:	(-93|4, DMFA)
UV:	(200, ,)
SOL-GOOD:	CHL, DMFA, ACOH, THF
SOL-FAIR:	MEOH, BUOH
SOL-POOR:	ETOAC, HEX, W
QUAL:	(BIURET, +) (NINH., -)
TO:	(S.AUREUS, .02)
LD50:	(120, IP)

REFERENCES:

Med. and Chem., 6, 276, 1958

43211-1765

NAME: <u>SULFACTIN</u>
PO: ACT.ROSEUS, S.ROSEUS
CT: THIAZOLYL-PEPTIDE, THIOSTREPTON T., AMPHOTER
FORMULA: C38H55N11O7S4
EA: (C, 50) (H, 6) (N, 17) (S, 14)
MW: 670|20
PC: WH., CRYST.
SOL-GOOD: CHL, ETOAC, DIOXAN, BUOH
SOL-FAIR: MEOH
SOL-POOR: BENZ, HEX, W
QUAL: (FEHL., +) (SAKA., -) (BIURET, -) (FECL3, -)
STAB: (HEAT, +)
TO: (S.AUREUS, .03) (B.SUBT., .01)
LD50: (148, IP)
IS-FIL: 8.2
IS-EXT: (BUOH, 7, FILT.)
IS-CRY: (CRYST., ETOH)
REFERENCES:
J. Biol. Chem., 168, 765, 1947; *Proc. Soc. Exp. B.M.*, 66, 345, 1947; 69, 26, 1948; *CA*, 41, 5168; 42, 2642

43211-1982

NAME: <u>MULTHIOMYCIN</u>
IDENTICAL: NOSIHEPTID
PO: S.ANTIBIOTICUS
CT: THIAZOLYL-PEPTIDE, THIOSTREPTON T., ACIDIC
FORMULA: C51H43N13O12S6
EA: (N, 15) (S, 15)
MW: 1043
PC: YELLOW, CRYST.
OR: (0, DMFA)
UV: MEOH: (328, 220,) (420, 20,)
UV: MEOH-NAOH: (292, 255,) (406, 132,)
SOL-GOOD: DMFA, DMSO, PYR
SOL-FAIR: MEOH, ETOH, ETOAC, DIOXAN
SOL-POOR: BUOH, HEX
QUAL: (FECL3, +) (NINH., -) (BIURET, -) (FEHL., -)
STAB: (ACID, +) (BASE, -) (HEAT, +)
TO: (B.SUBT., .006) (S.LUTEA, .006) (S.AUREUS, .06) (SHYG., .06)
LD50: (20|10, IV)
IS-EXT: (MEOH, , MIC.) (ETOAC, , W)
IS-CHR: (SILG, ETOAC-DMFA)
IS-CRY: (CRYST.,)
REFERENCES:
JA, 23, 231, 1970; 31, 623, 1978; Belg. P 847684; JP 78/101593

43211-5534

NAME: NOSIHEPTID, RP-9671
IDENTICAL: MULTHIOMYCIN, TAITOMYCIN
PO: S.ACTUOSUS
CT: THIOSTREPTON T., NEUTRAL, THIAZOLYL-PEPTIDE
FORMULA: C51H43N13O12S6
EA: (N, 14) (S, 15)
MW: 1222
PC: YELLOW, WH., CRYST.
OR: (+38, PYR)
SOL-GOOD: DMSO, DMFA, PYR, CHL-MEOH
SOL-POOR: W, MEOH
TO: (S.AUREUS,) (B.SUBT.,)
UTILITY: FEED ADDITIVE
REFERENCES:

Nature, 265, 189, 1977; *TL*, 1395, 1399, 1403, 1406, 1977; *JA*, 31, 623, 1978; *JACS*, 99, 6418, 1977

43211-5572

NAME: SCH-18640, 68-1147-I
PO: MIC.ARBORENSIS
CT: THIOSTREPTON T., THIAZOLYL PEPTIDE, NEUTRAL
EA: (N, 15) (S, 10)
PC: WH., YELLOW, POW.
OR: (-87.5, DIOXAN)
UV: ETOH: (202, 535,) (247, 325,) (308, 107,)
SOL-FAIR: BUOH
SOL-POOR: HEX, W
TO: (S.AUREUS, .003) (B.SUBT., .03)
LD50: NONTOXIC
IS-EXT: (ETOAC, , MIC.)
IS-CHR: (SILG, BENZ-ACET)
IS-CRY: (PREC., ACET, ET2O-HEX)
REFERENCES:

Abst. AAC, 16, 36, 1976; USP 4078056

43211-5828

NAME:	CP-41043, 41043
PO:	PSEUDONOCARDIA FASTIDIOSA
CT:	THIOSTREPTON T., THIAZOLYL-PEPTIDE, NEUTRAL
EA:	(C, 50) (H, 5) (N, 9) (S, 8) (O, 27)
PC:	WH., POW.
OR:	(+77, ACET)
UV:	ETOH: (225, 444,) (270, 217,) (350, 91,)
SOL-GOOD:	ACET, CHL, ETOAC, ETOH, DMSO, DMFA
SOL-POOR:	ET2O, HEX, W
TO:	(S.AUREUS, .2) (B.SUBT., .05) (E.COLI, 200) (PS.AER., 200) (K.PNEUM., 200)
IS-EXT:	(ME.I.BU.KETON, 7, FILT.) (MEOH, , MIC.)
IS-CHR:	(SILG, CHL-ETOH)
IS-CRY:	(DRY,)

REFERENCES:

USP 4031206

43211-5829

NAME:	CP-41494, 41494
PO:	PSEUDONOCARDIA FASTIDIOSA
CT:	THIAZOLYL-PEPTIDE, THIOSTREPTON T., NEUTRAL
EA:	(C, 50) (H, 5) (N, 9) (S, 8) (O, 28)
PC:	WH., POW.
OR:	(+29, ACET)
UV:	ETOH: (270, 241,) (350, 114,)
SOL-GOOD:	ACET, CHL, ETOAC, ETOH, DMSO, DMFA
SOL-POOR:	ET2O, HEX, W
TO:	(S.AUREUS, .78) (B.SUBT., 2) (E.COLI, 200) (PS.AER., 200) (K.PNEUM., 200)

REFERENCES:

USP 4031206

43211-5879

NAME: A-7413-A
PO: ACTINOPLANES SP.
CT: THIAZOLYL-PEPTIDE, ACIDIC, THIOSTREPTON T.
FORMULA: C72H87N12O23S5
EA: (N, 10) (S, 10)
EW: 1308
PC: WH., YELLOW, CRYST.
OR: (+54.5, CHL)
UV: ETOH: (215, 485,) (260, 240,) (300, 170,) (358, 112,)
UV: ETOH-HCL: (217, 440,) (265, 227,) (293, 210,) (358, 95,)
UV: ETOH-NAOH: (278, 255,) (408, 80,)
SOL-GOOD: MEOH, DMFA, DMSO, CHL, CH4CL2
SOL-FAIR: ETOH
SOL-POOR: ACET, BENZ, CCL4, CH2CL2, ETOAC, W, ET2O
TO: (S.AUREUS, .06) (B.SUBT., 1) (S.LUTEA, .1)
LD50: (1000|600, IP)
IS-FIL: 4|1
IS-EXT: (MEOH, 4, MIC.) (CHL-MEOH, 4.3, W)
IS-CHR: (SILG, CHL-MEOH)
IS-CRY: (CRYST., ETOH) (PREC., CHL, HEX)
REFERENCES:
DT 2703938; Belg. P 850899

43211-6075

NAME: SCH-18640-B, 68-1147-II
PO: MIC.ARBORENSIS
CT: NEUTRAL, THIAZOLYL-PEPTIDE, THIOSTREPTON T.
EA: (C, 50) (H, 5) (N, 16) (S, 13)
PC: YELLOW, WH., POW.
OR: (-65.5, DIOXAN)
UV: ETOH: (240, 188,) (300, 54,)
SOL-GOOD: CHL, ETOAC
SOL-POOR: W, HEX, ET2O
TO: (S.AUREUS, .005) (B.SUBT., .005)
REFERENCES:
USP 4078056

43211-6124

NAME: CP-46192, 46192
PO: STREPTOSPORANGIUM ROSEUM-INCARNATUM
CT: NEUTRAL, THIAZOLYL-PEPTIDE, THIOSTREPTON T.
EA: (C, 49) (H, 5) (N, 13) (S, 11) (O, 23)
PC: WH., CRYST.
OR: (-129, CHL)
UV: MEOH: (238, 350,) (303|2, 80,)
SOL-GOOD: CHL, ETOAC
SOL-FAIR: MEOH
SOL-POOR: W, HEX
TO: (S.AUREUS, .1) (B.SUBT., .1)
IS-EXT: (ME.I.BU.KETONE, 5, WB)
IS-CHR: (SILG, CHL-MEOH)
IS-CRY: (CRYST., MEOH)
REFERENCES:
USP 4083963

43211-6235

NAME: THIOPEPTIN-BB
PO: S.TATEYAMAENSIS
CT: THIAZOLYL-PEPTIDE, THIOSTREPTON T., NEUTRAL
FORMULA: C71H82N18O18S6
EA: (N, 15) (S, 11)
MW: 1666
PC: WH., YELLOW, POW.
TO: (G.POS.,)
IS-CHR: (SILG,)
REFERENCES:
TL, 3649, 1978

43211-6236

NAME: THIOPEPTIN-A1B
PO: S.TATEYAMAENSIS
CT: THIAZOLYL-PEPTIDE, THIOSTREPTON T., NEUTRAL
FORMULA: C72H84N18O18S6
EA: (N, 15) (S, 11)
MW: 1680
PC: WH., YELLOW
SOL-GOOD: CHL
SOL-POOR: W
TO: (G.POS.,)
IS-CHR: (SILG,)
REFERENCES:
TL, 3649, 1978

43211-6237

NAME: THIOPEPTIN-A3B
PO: S.TATEYAMAENSIS
CT: THIAZOLYL-PEPTIDE, THIOSTREPTON T., NEUTRAL
FORMULA: C65H77N17O15S6
EA: (N, 15) (S, 12)
MW: 1527
PC: WH., YELLOW
SOL-GOOD: CHL
SOL-POOR: W
TO: (G.POS.,)
IS-CHR: (SILG,)
REFERENCES:
TL, 3649, 1978

43211-6238

NAME: THIOPEPTIN-A4B
PO: S.TATEYAMAENSIS
CT: THIAZOLYL-PEPTIDE, THIOSTREPTON T., NEUTRAL
FORMULA: C68H80N18O16S6
EA: (N, 15) (S, 11)
MW: 1596
PC: WH., YELLOW
SOL-GOOD: CHL
SOL-POOR: W
TO: (G.POS.,)
IS-CHR: (SILG,)
REFERENCES:
TL, 3649, 1978

43211-6614

NAME:	S-53210-A-1
PO:	MICROELLOBOSPORIA BRUNEA
CT:	NEUTRAL, THIAZOLYL-PEPTIDE, THIOSTREPTON T.
EA:	(C, 49) (H, 4) (N, 12) (O, 19) (S, 14)
PC:	YELLOW, POW.
OR:	(+104, CHL)
UV:	ACCN: (215, ,) (305|5, ,) (355|5, ,)
SOL-GOOD:	DMFA, DMSO, DIOXAN, ACCN
SOL-FAIR:	CHL, MEOH, ETOH
SOL-POOR:	W, HEX
QUAL:	(NINH., -)
TO:	(S.AUREUS, .01) (B.SUBT., .3) (S.LUTEA, .01)
IS-EXT:	(BUOH, , FILT.) (MEOH, , MIC.) (CH2CL2, I.PROH, , W)
IS-CHR:	(SILG, CH2CL2-MEOH) (SEPHADEX LH-20, MEOH)
IS-CRY:	(DRY,)

REFERENCES:

BP 2000120; DT 2825618

43211-6615

NAME:	S-53210-A-II
PO:	MICROELLOBOSPORIA BRUNEA
CT:	NEUTRAL, THIAZOLYL-PEPTIDE, THIOSTREPTON T.
EA:	(C, 52) (H, 5) (N, 12) (O, 19) (S, 12)
PC:	YELLOW, POW.
OR:	(+107, CHL)
UV:	ACCN: (215, ,) (305|5, ,) (355|5, ,)
SOL-GOOD:	CHL, DMFA, DMSO, ACCN, DIOXAN
SOL-FAIR:	MEOH, ETOH
SOL-POOR:	W, HEX
QUAL:	(NINH., -)
TO:	(S.AUREUS, .01) (B.SUBT., .1) (S.LUTEA, .01)

REFERENCES:

BP 2000120; DT 2825618

43211-6616

NAME: S-53210-A-III
PO: MICROELLOBOSPORIA BRUNEA
CT: NEUTRAL, THIAZOLYL-PEPTIDE, THIOSTREPTON T.
EA: (C, 52) (H, 5) (N, 12) (O, 20) (S, 11)
PC: YELLOW, POW.
OR: (+67.2, CHL)
UV: ACCN: (215, ,) (300, ,) (350, ,)
SOL-GOOD: CHL, DMFA, DMSO, ACCN, DIOXAN
SOL-FAIR: MEOH, ETOH
SOL-POOR: W, HEX
QUAL: (NINH., -)
TO: (S.AUREUS, .01) (B.SUBT., 1) (S.LUTEA, .3)
REFERENCES:
BP2000120; DT 2825618

43211-6617

NAME: AB-97
PO: ACTINOMADURA HELVATA-ANTIBIOTICA
CT: THIAZOLYL-PEPTIDE, THIOSTREPTON T.
EA: (C, 49) (H, 4) (N, 11) (S, 10)
PC: YELLOW, POW.
OR: (+764, DMSO)
SOL-GOOD: ETOAC, MEOH, DMSO, BASE
SOL-POOR: ACID, HEX
QUAL: (FEHL., +) (NINH., -)
TO: (S.AUREUS, .025)
IS-EXT: (ETOAC, , FILT.)
IS-CHR: (SILG, CHL-MEOH) (SILG, CHL-MEOH-PHENOL-ACOH)
REFERENCES:
JP 78/101301

43212-1767

NAME: <u>ALTHIOMYCIN</u>, 116-A
IDENTICAL: MATAMYCIN
PO: S.ALTHIOTICUS
CT: THIAZOLYL-PEPTIDE, ALTHIOMYCIN T., NEUTRAL
FORMULA: C16H17N5O6S2
EA: (N, 14) (S, 13)
MW: 439, 708
EW: 256
PC: WH., CRYST.
OR: (+37.8, ETOH-CH2CL2) (+20.3, METILCELLOSOLVE)
UV: ETOH: (223, , 60000) (286, , 14000)
UV: ETOH-NAOH: (238, , 36000) (310, , 2000)
UV: H2SO4: (224, , 57000)
SOL-GOOD: PYR, DIOXAN, DMFA
SOL-FAIR: MEOH, BUOH, ACET, ETOAC
SOL-POOR: BENZ, HEX, W
QUAL: (FECL3, -) (FEHL., -) (SAKA., -) (BIURET, -) (NINH., -)
STAB: (ACID, -) (BASE, -)
TO: (S.AUREUS, 5) (B.SUBT., 2) (E.COLI, 6) (SHYG., 6) (C.ALB., 100)
LD50: (720, IP)
IS-FIL: 6
IS-EXT: (BUOAC, 6, FILT.) (ETOH, , MIC.)
IS-CRY: (CRYST., METILCELLOSOLVE)
REFERENCES:

JA, 10, 195, 1957; 23, 271, 1970; 27, 897, 1974; 28, 286, 1975; *JACS*, 85, 1430, 1963; *CC*, 121, 1975; JP 59/6248

43212-1768

NAME:	MATAMYCIN
IDENTICAL:	ALTHIOMYCIN
PO:	S.MATENSIS, S.BELLUS
CT:	THIAZOLYL-PEPTIDE, ALTHIOMYCIN T., NEUTRAL
FORMULA:	C16H17N5O6S2
EA:	(N, 14) (S, 14)
PC:	WH., CRYST.
OR:	(+36.6, MEOH) (+25, METILCELLOSOLVE)
UV:	MEOH: (210, 900,) (255, 190,)
UV:	MEOH-NAOH: (237, 550,) (306, 270,)
SOL-FAIR:	MEOH, BUOH, ACET, ETOAC
SOL-POOR:	W, BENZ, HEX
QUAL:	(FEHL., +) (DNPH, +) (FECL3, -) (BIURET, -) (SAKA., -) (PAULY, -)
STAB:	(ACID, -)
TO:	(S.LUTEA, .5) (S.AUREUS, 5) (B.SUBT., 5) (E.COLI, 50) (K.PNEUM., 5) (P.VULG., 50)
IS-EXT:	(ETOAC, 7, FILT.)
IS-CRY:	(CRYST., ETOAC)

REFERENCES:

Ant. & Chem., 9, 76, 1959

43212-1769

NAME:	RP-10206
PO:	S.SP.
CT:	THIAZOLYL-PEPTIDE, ALTHIOMYCIN T., NEUTRAL
FORMULA:	C16H17N7O7S2
EA:	(N, 14) (S, 14)
PC:	WH., CRYST.
OR:	(+41, METILCELLOSOLVE)
UV:	MEOH: (224, ,) (285, ,)
TO:	(G.POS.,)
IS-EXT:	(ETOAC, , FILT.)

REFERENCES:

Abst. IUPAC Congr. Nat. Prod., 307, 1963.

43212-1770

NAME: GARLANDOSUS, U-9279
PO: S.ALTHIOTICUS.
CT: THIAZOLYL-PEPTIDE, ALTHIOMYCIN T., NEUTRAL
FORMULA: C27H28N8O10S3
EA: (N, 15) (S, 13)
MW: 708
PC: WH., CRYST.
OR: (+37.8, MEOH-CHL)
UV: MEOH: (240, ,) (282, ,)
SOL-POOR: W, MEOH, HEX
QUAL: (NINH., -) (BIURET, -) (SAKA., -) (FECL3, -) (FEHL., +)
TO: (S.AUREUS, 5) (B.SUBT., 20) (K.PNEUM., 50) (P.VULG., 50)
REFERENCES:
USP 3642984

43212-1771

NAME: ACTINOTHIOCIN
PO: ACTINOMADURA PUSILLA
CT: THIAZOLYL-PEPTIDE, ALTHIOMYCIN T., NEUTRAL
FORMULA: C49H54N13O10S5
EA: (N, 16) (S, 14)
MW: 1057
PC: WH., CRYST.
OR: (+164, DIOXAN)
UV: MEOH: (310, , 29500)
UV: MEOH-HCL: (304, 200,)
SOL-GOOD: DMFA, DMSO, DIOXAN, CHL-MEOH
SOL-FAIR: MEOH, CHL
SOL-POOR: BENZ, HEX, W
QUAL: (NINH., -)
STAB: (BASE, +) (ACID, -)
TO: (S.AUREUS, .03) (B.SUBT., .1)
LD50: (1000, IP)
IS-FIL: 8.4
IS-EXT: (ACET, , MIC.)
IS-CHR: (SILG, CHL-MEOH)
IS-CRY: (CRYST., MEOH)
REFERENCES:
JA, 26, 343, 1973; *J. Ferm. Techn.*, 49, 904, 1971; JP 73/78692

43213-1772

NAME:	SARAMYCETIN, X-5079-C, RO-2-7758, NSC-100844
PO:	S.SARACETICUS
CT:	THIAZOLYL-PEPTIDE, ACIDIC, AMPHOTER
EA:	(C, 46) (H, 5) (N, 16) (S, 14)
MW:	2100, 14000|2000
PC:	WH., POW.
OR:	(-28.4, W)
UV:	ETOH: (222, 510,) (273, 245,)
UV:	W: (227.5, 440,) (270, 275,)
SOL-GOOD:	MEOH, PYR, ETOH, ACID, ACOH, W
SOL-FAIR:	ACET, BUOH
SOL-POOR:	ETOAC, HEX
QUAL:	(BIURET, +) (NINH., -) (DNPH, -)
TO:	(FUNGI, .01) (CRYPTOCOCCUS SP., .01)
LD50:	(375, IV) (650, IP)
IS-FIL:	4
IS-EXT:	(BUOH, , MIC.)
IS-CHR:	(AL, MEOH)
UTILITY:	ON CLINICAL TRIAL

REFERENCES:

JA, 22, 577, 1969; *AAC 1961*, 436; *AAC 1967*,456; *Am. Rev. Resp. Dis.*, 84, 504; *Helv.*, 47, 661, 1964; *J. Pharm. Sci.*, 56, 410, 1967; *J. Colloid Interface Sci.*, 33, 439, 1970; *J. Bact.*, 85, 833, 1962; *Naturwiss.*, 55, 344, 1968; *Am. Rev. Resp. Dis.*, 84, 504, 507, 514, 529, 1961; USP 3118813

43214-1766

NAME: MICROCOCCIN-P1, MICROCOCCIN, MICROCOCCIN-P
PO: MICROCOCCUS SP., B.PUMILUS
CT: THIAZOLYL-PEPTIDE, NEUTRAL, MICROCOCCIN T.
FORMULA: C48H49N13O9S6
EA: (N, 14) (S, 16)
MW: 1143
PC: WH., CRYST.
OR: (+116, ETOH) (+63.7, ETOH)
UV: ETOH: (346, 210,)
UV: HCL: (320, , 57500)
SOL-GOOD: MEOH, ETOH, PYR, ACET, CHL, ETOH
SOL-POOR: W, BENZ, ET2O, HEX, ETOAC
QUAL: (NINH., -) (FECL3, -)
STAB: (ACID, +) (BASE, +) (HEAT, +) (LIGHT, -)
TO: (B.SUBT., .01) (S.AUREUS, .02)
LD50: (1500, SC)
IS-FIL: ORIG.
IS-ABS: (CARBON, PYR)
IS-CHR: (AL, CHL)
IS-CRY: (CRYST., ETOH-W) (PREC., FILT., ACID)
REFERENCES:

Brit. J. Exp. Path., 29, 473, 1948; 32, 106, 353, 1951; 33, 105, 1952; *Nature*, 175, 722, 1955; 178, 44, 1956; *J. Gen. Micr.*, 6, 30, 41, 1953; *Bioch. J.*, 50, 247, 1951; 61, 534, 1955; *JCS*, 689, 1957; 909, 916, 925, 1960; 3381, 1961; *JCSC*, 1354, 1357, 1361, 1966; *CC*, 706, 1977; 256, 1978; *CA*, 49, 14884

43214-4872

NAME: MICROCOCCIN-M, MICROCOCCIN-M1
PO: STAPHYLOCOCCUS AUREUS, STAPHYLOCOCCUS EPIDERMIDIS
CT: BASIC, THIAZOLYL-PEPTIDE, MICROCOCCIN T.
FORMULA: C48H50N12O11S6
EA: (N, 14) (S, 16)
MW: 1500|300
PC: WH., CRYST.
OR: (+66.6, ETOH)
UV: ETOH: (216, 750,) (345, 198,)
SOL-GOOD: MEOH, CHL
SOL-FAIR: ET2O
SOL-POOR: HEX, W
TO: (S.AUREUS, .001) (S.LUTEA, .01)
IS-EXT: (CH2CL2, 2, WB.)
IS-CHR: (SILG, CHL-MEOH)
IS-CRY: (CRYST., ETOH)
REFERENCES:

Arzn. Forsch., 25, 1004, 1244, 1365, 1975; *CC*, 706, 1977

43214-5194

NAME: THIOCILLIN-I, G-15-II
PO: B.CEREUS, B.MEGATHERIUM
CT: NEUTRAL, THIAZOLYL-PEPTIDE, MICROCOCCIN T.
FORMULA: C50H59N13O12S6
EA: (N, 15) (S, 16)
MW: 1292
PC: WH., CRYST.
OR: (+97.7, ETOH)
UV: MEOH: (217, 734,) (275, 326,) (348, 199,)
SOL-GOOD: DMFA, DMSO, THF, CHL-MEOH
SOL-FAIR: MEOH, ETOH, ACET, CHL
SOL-POOR: ETOAC, BENZ, ET2O, W, ACID
QUAL: (PAULY, +) (NINH., -)
TO: (S.AUREUS, .2) (B.SUBT., 1.56)
LD50: (1000|500, IP)
IS-EXT: (BUOH, 8, FILT.) (BUOH-MEOH, 7, MIC.)
IS-CHR: (SILG, CHL-MEOH)
IS-CRY: (PREC., CHL-MEOH, ET2O)
REFERENCES:
JA, 29, 366, 1976; JP 76/79789; *CA*, 86, 25489

43214-5195

NAME: THIOCILLIN-II, G-15-I
PO: B.CEREUS, B.BADIUS, B.MEGATHERIUM
CT: NEUTRAL, THIAZOLYL-PEPTIDE, THIOSTREPTON T., MICROCOCCIN T.
EA: (C, 49) (H, 5) (N, 15) (S, 16) (O, 14)
MW: 1392
PC: WH., CRYST.
OR: (+93.4, ETOH)
UV: MEOH: (217, 705,) (278, 291,) (348, 202,)
SOL-GOOD: DMSO, DMFA, THF, CHL-MEOH
SOL-FAIR: MEOH, ETOH, ACET, CHL
SOL-POOR: ETOAC, BENZ, ET2O, W, ACID
QUAL: (PAULY, +) (NINH., -)
TO: (S.AUREUS, .1) (B.SUBT., .39)
LD50: (100|500, IP)
REFERENCES:
JA, 29, 366, 1976; JP 76/79789; *CA*, 86, 25489

43214-5196

NAME: THIOCILLIN-III
PO: B.BADIUS
CT: NEUTRAL, THIAZOLYL-PEPTIDE, THIOSTREPTON T., MICROCOCCIN T.
EA: (C, 50) (H, 5) (N, 15) (S, 16) (O, 13)
PC: WH., POW.
OR: (+88, ETOH)
UV: MEOH: (217, 729,) (275, 302,) (347, 208,)
SOL-GOOD: DMFA, DMSO, THF, CHL-MEOH
SOL-FAIR: MEOH, ETOH, ACET, CHL
SOL-POOR: ETOAC, BENZ, ET2O, W, ACID
QUAL: (PAULY, +) (NINH., -)
TO: (S.AUREUS, .2)
REFERENCES:
JA, 29, 366, 1976; JP 76/79789; *CA*, 86, 25489

43214-6077

NAME: MICROCOCCIN-P2
PO: MICROCOCCUS SP.
CT: NEUTRAL, THIAZOLYL-PEPTIDE, MICROCOCCIN T.
FORMULA: C48H47N13O9S6
EA: (N,) (S,)
MW: 1141
PC: WH., POW.
UV: ETOH: (345, ,)
TO: (G.POS.,)
REFERENCES:
CC, 706, 1977; 256, 1978

4322
Bottromycin Type

Bottromycins, according to recent results, are thiazole-containing branched-chain cyclic hexapeptides. They are basic substances because the terminal carboxy group of the side chain is methylated and one of the peptide bonds in the ring exists in an amidine form.

From the hydrolysate of these antibiotics the following uncommon amino acids were isolated:

(1) 3-(2-Thiazolyl)-β-alanine or β-thiazolyl-β-alanine
(2) 3-Methyl-3-phenyl-L-alanine (L-β-methylphenylalanine)
(3) 3,3-Dimethyl-2-aminobutyric acid (L-β,β-dimethyl-α-amino-butyric acid)
(4) *cis*-3-Methyl-L-proline

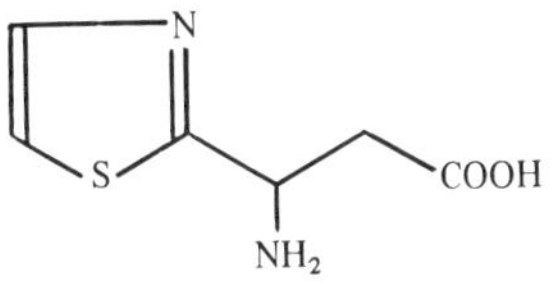

(1)

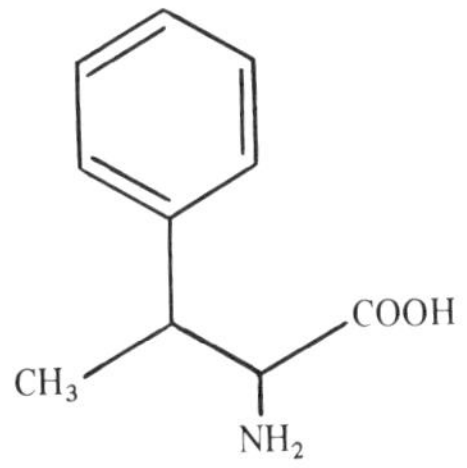

(2)

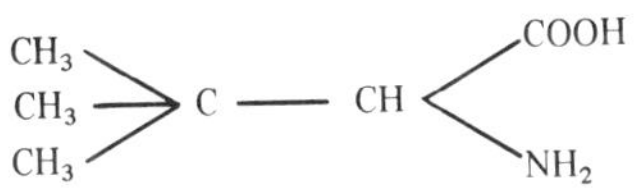

(3)

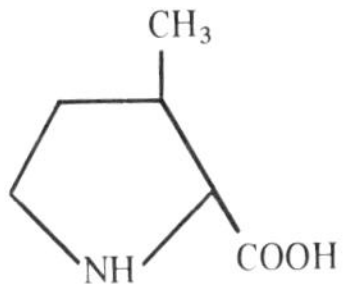

(4)

The bottromycins differ from each other in the proline residues. Proline or dimethyl/ethylproline instead of methylproline exists in the different congeners. These antibiotics are active against Gram-positive and mycobacteria and show high activity against *Mycoplasma* species.

Structure

43220

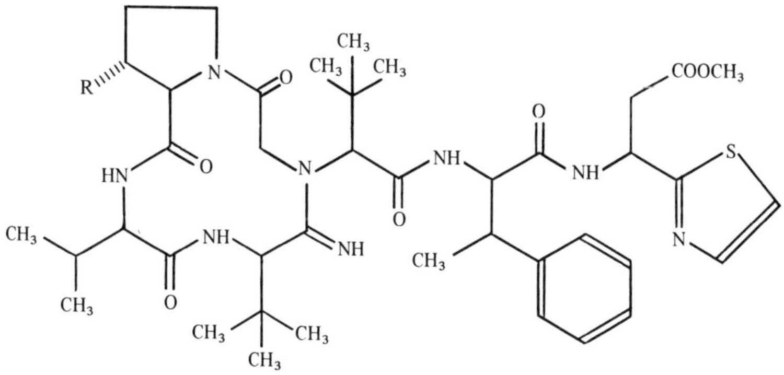

Bottromycin A_2	$R = CH_3$
Bottromycin B_2	$R = H$
Bottromycin C_2	$R = C_2H_5$? or two CH_3 on the proline residue

43220-1773

NAME:	BOTTROMYCIN-A, BOTTROMYCIN, B-MYCIN, BOTTRO-MYCIN-A
IDENTICAL:	METHOBOTTROMYCIN, 1-337-C
PO:	S.BOTTROPENSIS, KITASATOA KANAENSIS
CT:	BOTTROMYCIN T., PEPTIDE, BASIC
FORMULA:	C41H62N8O7S
EA:	(N, 13) (S, 4)
MW:	790|20, 770
PC:	WH., POW.
OR:	(-14.2, ETOH)
UV:	ETOH: (203, 1100,)
SOL-GOOD:	MEOH, ET2O
SOL-FAIR:	W
SOL-POOR:	HEX
QUAL:	(NINH., -)
STAB:	(HEAT, +) (BASE, -)
TO:	(S.AUREUS, .2) (B.SUBT., .1) (PS.AER., 100) (E.COLI, 50) (K.PNEUM., 50) (MYCOPLASMA SP., .0001)
LD50:	NONTOXIC
IS-FIL:	ORIG.
IS-EXT:	(ETOAC, 8, FILT.)
IS-CRY:	(DRY, ET2O)

REFERENCES:

JA, 19, 149, 1966; 20, 1, 162, 1967; 18, 47, 60, 1966; 29, 1120, 1976; 79, 4520, 4524, 1957; 80, 383, 1958; *Chem. Ph. Bull.*, 13, 599, 1965; 14, 981, 1966; *J. Med. Chem.*, 11, 746, 1968; *Bull. Ch. Soc. Jap.*, 51, 878, 1978; BP 762736; *AAC 1967*, 407

43220-1774

NAME:	BOTTROMYCIN-A2
PO:	S.SP.
CT:	BOTTROMYCIN T., PEPTIDE, BASIC
FORMULA:	C42H62N8O7S
EA:	(N, 13) (S, 4)
MW:	822
PC:	WH., POW.
OR:	(-25, MEOH)
UV:	MEOH: (208, 380,)
SOL-GOOD:	MEOH, ET2O
SOL-FAIR:	W
SOL-POOR:	HEX
TO:	(S.AUREUS, .1) (B.SUBT., .1) (S.LUTEA, .4) (K.PNEUM., 50) (SHYG., 12) (E.COLI, 3) (PS.AER., 50) (P.VULG., 12) (MYCOPLASMA SP., .0007)
LD50:	NONTOXIC
IS-CHR:	(PAP., BUOH-ACOH-W)

REFERENCES:

JA, 19, 149, 1966; 20, 1, 162, 1967; 18, 47, 60, 1966; 29, 1120, 1976; *JACS*, 79, 4520, 4524, 1957; 80, 383, 1958; *Chem. Ph. Bull.*, 13, 599, 1965; 14, 981, 1966; *J. Med. Chem.*, 11, 746, 1968; *Bull. Ch. Soc. Jap.*, 51, 878, 1978; BP 762736; *AAC 1967*, 407

43220-1775

NAME:	BOTTROMYCIN-B1
IDENTICAL:	AMETHOBOTTROMYCIN
PO:	S.BOTTROPENSIS, S.SP.
CT:	BOTTROMYCIN T., PEPTIDE, BASIC
FORMULA:	C40H60N8O7S
EA:	(N, 13) (S, 4)
MW:	785|15
PC:	WH., POW.
OR:	(-25, MEOH)
UV:	MEOH: (203, ,)
SOL-GOOD:	MEOH, ET2O
SOL-FAIR:	W
SOL-POOR:	HEX
QUAL:	(NINH., -)
STAB:	(HEAT, +) (ACID, +) (BASE, -)
TO:	(S.AUREUS, .8) (B.SUBT., .4) (E.COLI, 50) (K.PNEUM., 15)
LD50:	NONTOXIC

REFERENCES:

JA, 18, 47, 60, 1965; 20, 1, 162, 1967; *Bull. Ch. Soc. Jap.*, 51, 828, 1978

43220-1776

NAME: BOTTROMYCIN-B2
PO: S.SP.
CT: BOTTROMYCIN T., PEPTIDE, BASIC
FORMULA: C41H60N807S
EA: (N, 14) (S, 13)
MW: 808
PC: WH., POW.
UV: MEOH: (200, ,)
SOL-GOOD: MEOH, ET20
SOL-FAIR: W
SOL-POOR: HEX
TO: (S.AUREUS, .8) (B.SUBT., .2) (E.COLI, 5) (P.VULG., 100) (SHYG., 25) (MYCOPLASMA SP., .001)
LD50: NONTOXIC
REFERENCES:
JA, 18, 47, 60, 1965; 20, 1, 162, 1967; *Bull. Ch. Soc. Jap.*, 51, 828, 1978

43220-1777

NAME: BOTTROMYCIN-C2
PO: S.SP., S.BOTTROPENSIS
CT: BOTTROMYCIN T., PEPTIDE, BASIC
FORMULA: C43H64N807S
EA: (N, 19) (S, 13)
PC: WH., POW.
UV: MEOH: (200, ,)
SOL-GOOD: MEOH, ET20
SOL-FAIR: W
SOL-POOR: HEX
TO: (S.AUREUS, .1) (B.SUBT., .06) (S.LUTEA, .8) (E.COLI, 6) (P.VULG., 50) (MYCOPLASMA SP., .001)
LD50: NONTOXIC
REFERENCES:
JA, 20, 1, 162, 1967; *Chem. Ph. Bull.*, 14, 981, 1966

43220-1778

NAME:	AMETHOBOTTROMYCIN-B
IDENTICAL:	BOTTROMYCIN-B1
PO:	S.CANADENSIS
CT:	BOTTROMYCIN T., PEPTIDE, BASIC
FORMULA:	C40H60N807S
EA:	(N, 13) (S, 5)
MW:	800
PC:	WH., POW.
OR:	(-25, ETOH)
SOL-GOOD:	MEOH, ET20
SOL-FAIR:	W
SOL-POOR:	HEX
STAB:	(ACID, +) (BASE, -)
TO:	(S.AUREUS, .23) (MYCOPLASMA SP.,)
IS-FIL:	4.2
IS-ION:	(DX-50-NA, MEOH-NH4OH)

REFERENCES:

J. Med. Chem., 11, 746, 1968; *AAC, 1967,* 407; USP 3683072

43220-1779

NAME:	METHOBOTTROMYCIN-C
IDENTICAL:	BOTTROMYCIN-A1
PO:	S.CANADENSIS
CT:	BOTTROMYCIN T., PEPTIDE, BASIC
FORMULA:	C41H62N807S
EA:	(N, 14) (S, 4)
MW:	800
PC:	WH., POW.
OR:	(-15, ETOH)
SOL-GOOD:	MEOH, ET20
SOL-FAIR:	W
SOL-POOR:	HEX
TO:	(S.AUREUS, .04) (MYCOPLASMA SP.,)

REFERENCES:

J. Med. Chem., 11, 746, 1968; USP 3683073

4323, 4324, and 432
Berninamycin, Leucinamycin, and Less Known Types of Compounds

The berninamycin-type compounds are modified cyclopeptides containing several unusual heterocyclic fragments such as berninamycinic acid **(1)**, sulfomycinine **(2)**, sulfomycinamic acid **(3)**, and oxazole-containing amino acid derivatives called Oxa-A **(4)**, Oxa-B **(5)**, and sulfomycinic amide **(6)**. These compounds contain several dehydroamino acid residues and L-β-hydroxyvaline **(7)** also.

They are active against Gram-positive bacteria. Berninamycin is a potent inhibitor of bacterial protein synthesis, interfering with amino acid incorporation.

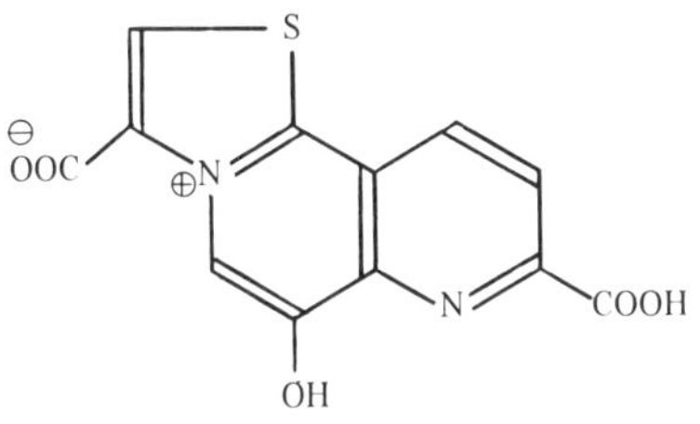

(1)

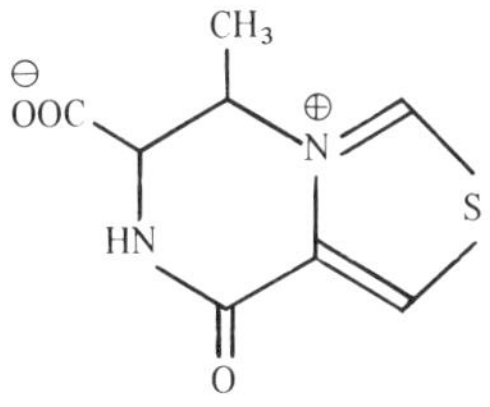

(2)

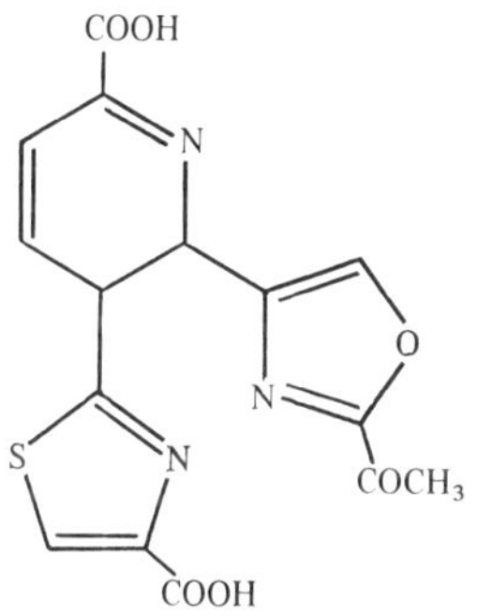

(3)

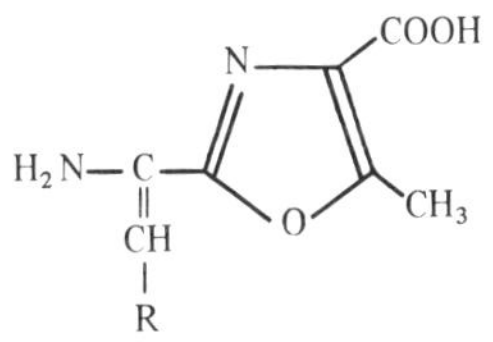

(4) R = H
(5) R = CH_3

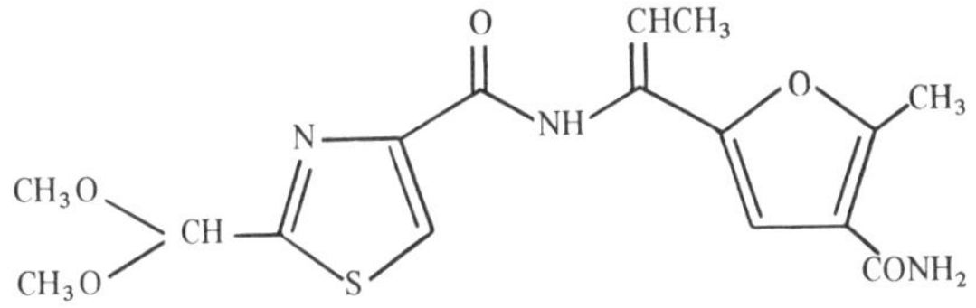

(6)

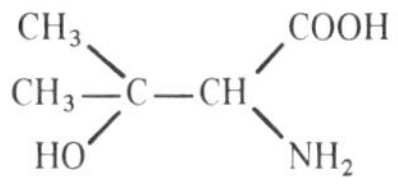

(7)

Structure

43230

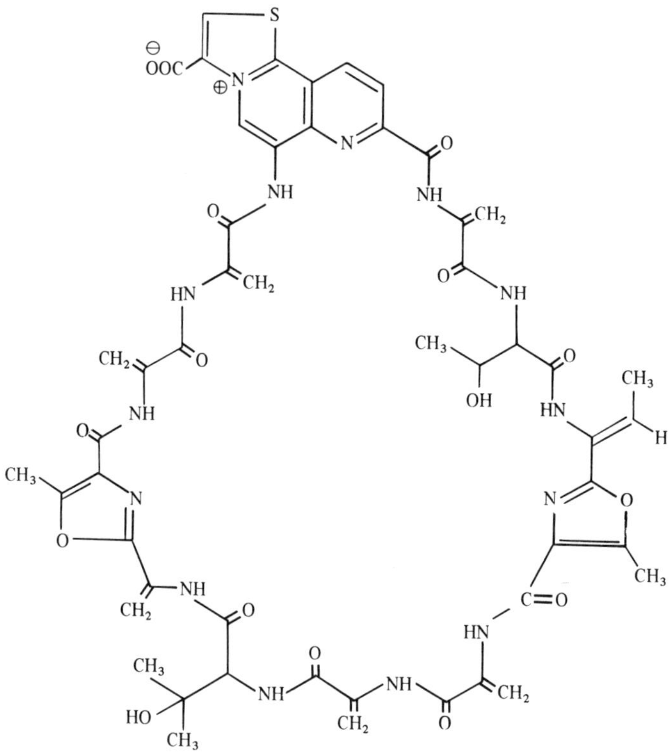

berninamycin A

43230-1782

NAME: SULFOMYCIN-I
PO: S.VIRIDOCHROMOGENES, S.CINEROVIRIDIS
CT: PEPTIDE, BERNINAMYCIN T.
FORMULA: C56N60N16O21S2
EA: (N, 17) (S, 5)
MW: 1222|4
PC: WH., POW.
OR: (-16, MEOH)
UV: MEOH: (252, 712,)
UV: MEOH-HCL: (252, 700,)
UV: MEOH-NAOH: (255, 629,) (330, 110,)
SOL-GOOD: MEOH, CHL, DMFA, ACOH, BASE
SOL-FAIR: W
SOL-POOR: BENZ, HEX
QUAL: (EHRL., +) (NINH., -) (BIURET, -) (FECL3, -)
(SAKA., -) (DNPH, -)
STAB: (ACID, +) (BASE, -)
TO: (S.AUREUS, .09) (B.SUBT., .07)
LD50: (600, IP)
IS-FIL: ORIG.
IS-EXT: (ACET, , MIC.) (ETOAC, 7, W)
IS-CHR: (AL, ETOAC) (SILG, CHL-MEOH)
IS-CRY: (PREC., CHL, ET2O)
REFERENCES:
JA, 22, 12, 1969; *Heterocycl.,* 8, 461, 1977; *TL,* 735, 1977; 2791, 1978; USP 4007090; JP 70/17599

43230-1783

NAME:	SULFOMYCIN-II
PO:	S.VIRIDOCHROMOGENES, S.CINEROVIRIDIS
CT:	PEPTIDE, ACIDIC, BERNINAMYCIN T.
FORMULA:	C46H47N13O16S2
EA:	(N, 17) (S, 6)
MW:	1138
PC:	WH., POW.
OR:	(-11.8, MEOH)
UV:	MEOH: (252, 630,)
UV:	MEOH-HCL: (252, ,)
UV:	MEOH-NAOH: (256, 549,) (328, 103,)
SOL-GOOD:	MEOH, CHL, DMFA, BASE, ACOH
SOL-FAIR:	W
SOL-POOR:	BENZ, HEX
QUAL:	(EHRL., +) (NINH., -) (BIURET, -) (FECL3, -) (SAKA., -)
STAB:	(ACID, +) (BASE, -)
TO:	(S.AUREUS, .19) (S.LUTEA,) (B.SUBT., .09)
LD50:	(120, IP)

REFERENCES:

JA, 22, 12, 1969; *Heterocycl.,* 8, 461, 1977; *TL,* 735, 1977; 2791, 1978; USP 4007090; JP 70/17599

43230-1784

NAME:	SULFOMYCIN-III
PO:	S.VIRIDOCHROMOGENES, S.CINEROVIRIDIS
CT:	PEPTIDE, ACIDIC, BERNINAMYCIN T.
FORMULA:	C51H52N14O17S2
EA:	(N, 17) (S, 5)
MW:	1233
PC:	WH., POW.
OR:	(+3.8, MEOH)
UV:	MEOH: (252, 672,)
UV:	MEOH-HCL: (252, ,)
UV:	MEOH-NAOH: (253, 571,) (328, 98,)
SOL-GOOD:	MEOH, CHL, DMFA, ACOH, BASE
SOL-FAIR:	W
SOL-POOR:	BENZ, HEX
QUAL:	(EHRL., +) (NINH., -) (BIURET, -) (FECL3, -) (SAKA., -)
STAB:	(ACID, +) (BASE, -)
TO:	(S.AUREUS, .19) (B.SUBT., .39)
LD50:	(500, IP)

REFERENCES:

JA, 22, 12, 1969; *Heterocycl.,* 8, 461, 1977; *TL,* 735, 1977; 2791, 1978; USP 4007090; JP 70/17599

43230-1785

NAME: BERNINAMYCIN-A, BERNINAMYCIN, U-27810
PO: S.BERNIENSIS
CT: PEPTIDE, NEUTRAL, BERNINAMYCIN T.
FORMULA: C51H50N14016S
EA: (N, 17) (S, 3)
MW: 1146
PC: WH., CRYST.
OR: (+149, DMFA)
UV: MEOH: (208, 624,) (236, 644,) (250|30, , 16000)
SOL-GOOD: MEOH, BUOH, DMFA
SOL-POOR: W, ACET, HEX
QUAL: (NINH., -)
TO: (S.AUREUS, .1) (B.SUBT., .5) (S.LUTEA, .1)
IS-EXT: (ME.ET.KETON, 7, FILT.)
IS-CHR: (DIATOM., DMFA-ETOAC-W-HEX) (SILG, CH2CL2-MEOH)
REFERENCES:

JACS, 98, 299, 8237, 1976; 99, 1645, 1977; *Biochem.*, 8, 3303, 1969; *Diss. Abst.*, 36, 4458, 1976; USP 3689639; *CA*, 77, 150582

43230-1786

NAME: THEIOMYCETIN, THERMOMYCETIN
PO: S.SP.
CT: PEPTIDE, NEUTRAL, BERNINAMYCIN T.
FORMULA: C55H60N15020S
EA: (N, 17) (S, 3)
PC: WH., GRAY, CRYST.
OR: (+179, MEOH)
UV: MEOH: (242, 621,) (258, 615,)
SOL-GOOD: MEOH, ETOAC
SOL-POOR: W, BENZ, HEX
QUAL: (FEHL., +) (NINH., -) (SAKA., -) (FECL3, -)
TO: (B.SUBT., .2) (S.LUTEA, .2) (S.AUREUS, 2) (MYCOB.TUB., .2)
LD50: (650, IP)
IS-EXT: (ETOAC, 7, FILT.)
IS-CRY: (DRY, ACET) (CRYST., ACET)
REFERENCES:

An. Rep. Takeda, 18, 44, 1959; JP 60/11599; *CA*, 54, 19840; 55, 11760

43230-1791

NAME: PHALAMYCIN
PO: S.NOURSEI
CT: PEPTIDE, NEUTRAL, BERNINAMYCIN T.
FORMULA: C36H41N9O14S
EA: (N, 14) (S, 5)
MW: 855
PC: WH., CRYST.
UV: (200, ,)
SOL-GOOD: MEOH, CHL
SOL-FAIR: BENZ, ET2O
SOL-POOR: W, HEX
QUAL: (BIURET, -) (NINH., -) (SAKA., -) (FECL3, -)
STAB: (BASE, -) (ACID, +)
TO: (B.SUBT., .05) (S.AUREUS, .1) (S.LUTEA, .05)
LD50: (29, IP)
IS-FIL: ORIG.
IS-EXT: (ETOAC, 8, W)
IS-CHR: (AL, ETOAC)
IS-CRY: (CRYST., ACET) (DRY, MEOH) (DRY, CHL)
REFERENCES:

Ant. & Chem., 3, 815, 1953; BP 790521; *CA*, 64, 1901; 48, 7686; 51, 16672

43230-5073

NAME: BERNINAMYCIN-B
PO: S.BERNIENSIS
CT: PEPTIDE, NEUTRAL, BERNINAMYCIN T.
FORMULA: C59H74N14O22S
EA: (N, 14) (S, 2)
MW: 1362
PC: WH., POW.
UV: MEOH: (245|35, ,)
SOL-GOOD: MEOH, ETOH, DMFA
SOL-POOR: ACET, HEX, W
TO: (G.POS.,)
REFERENCES:

JACS, 98, 299, 1976

43240-1787

NAME: ARSIMYCIN
PO: S.ARSITIENSIS, S.ROSEUS
CT: PEPTIDE, BASIC, AMPHOTER, LEUCINAMYCIN T.
FORMULA: C27H47N7O11S.N
EA: (N, 15) (S, 5)
EW: 1350, 1378
PC: WH., POW.
OR: (-58, W)
UV: W: (268|3, 5,)
SOL-GOOD: MEOH
QUAL: (NINH., +)
STAB: (BASE, +)
TO: (B.SUBT., .004) (S.AUREUS, 100) (S.LUTEA, 100) (P.VULG., 100) (E.COLI, 100) (FUNGI, 12)
IS-FIL: 2
IS-EXT: (BUOH, 6.3, FILT.) (HCL, , BUOH)
IS-ABS: (CARBON, MEOH-W)
IS-CRY: (LIOF.,)
REFERENCES:

DT 1090380

43240-1788

NAME: LEUCOPEPTIN
PO: S.HACHIJOENSIS-TAKAHAZIENSIS
CT: PEPTIDE, AMPHOTER, BASIC, LEUCINAMYCIN T.
EA: (C, 49) (H, 7) (N, 15) (S, 6) (O, 21)
MW: 990, 1125|75
PC: WH., CRYST.
OR: (-88, W) (-77, W-HCL)
UV: NAOH: (200, ,)
UV: W: (259, 4,)
SOL-GOOD: PYR, DMFA, ACOH, ACID
SOL-FAIR: W, MEOH, ETOAC, ETOH
SOL-POOR: ET2O, HEX
QUAL: (NINH., +) (BIURET, +) (SAKA., -) (EHRL., -) (FECL3, -)
STAB: (HEAT, +) (BASE, +)
TO: (B.SUBT., 1.25) (S.AUREUS, 1.25) (PHYT.FUNGI, 25)
LD50: (22, IV)
IS-FIL: ORIG.
IS-EXT: (BUOH, 2, FILT.)
IS-ION: (IRC-50-H, NH4OH)
REFERENCES:

JA, 17, 262, 1964

43240-1793

NAME:	LEUCINAMYCIN
PO:	S.CINNAMONEUS
CT:	PEPTIDE, BASIC, AMPHOTER, LEUCINAMYCIN T.
EA:	(C, 49) (H, 7) (N, 16) (S, 5) (O, 22)
MW:	2000
PC:	WH., CRYST.
OR:	(-82, HCL)
UV:	HCL: (252, , 200) (257, , 158) (265, , 40)
SOL-GOOD:	ACID, ACOH, PYR, DMSO
SOL-FAIR:	W, MEOH, BUOH
SOL-POOR:	ACET, HEX
QUAL:	(NINH., +) (SAKA., +) (BIURET, +) (EHRL., -) (FECL3, -)
TO:	(B.SUBT., .25) (PS.AER., 100) (FUNGI, .78) (PIRICULARIA ORYZAE, 6.25) (PHYT.BACT., 3)
LD50:	(23, IP)
IS-EXT:	(BUOH, 7.4, FILT.)
IS-CHR:	(AL, MEOH-W)
IS-CRY:	(CRYST., MEOH-W)

REFERENCES:

JA, 20, 194, 1967; JP 74/35085

43240-1794

NAME:	KOBENOMYCIN
PO:	S.KOBENENSIS
CT:	PEPTIDE, BASIC, AMPHOTER, LEUCINAMYCIN T.
FORMULA:	$C_{84}H_{126}N_{22}O_{25}S_3$
EA:	(N, 16) (S, 5)
PC:	WH., CRYST.
OR:	(-87.5, ACOH)
UV:	HCL: (280, 260,)
UV:	NAOH: (222, 253,) (275, ,)
UV:	W: (280, 221,)
SOL-GOOD:	PYR, DMSO, ACOH
SOL-FAIR:	W, MEOH, ETOH
SOL-POOR:	ACET, HEX
QUAL:	(NINH., +) (BIURET, +) (EHRL., +) (SAKA., -) (FEHL., -) (PAULY, -)
STAB:	(ACID, +) (HEAT, +) (BASE, -)
TO:	(B.SUBT., 5)
LD50:	(15, IV) (25, IP)
IS-FIL:	ORIG.
IS-ABS:	(CARBON, ACET-W)
IS-CRY:	(CRYST., MEOH-W)

REFERENCES:

JA, 21, 320, 1968; JP 70/14878

43240-4787

NAME:	NEGINAMYCIN
PO:	STV.CINNAMONEUM
CT:	BASIC, PEPTIDE, LEUCINAMYCIN T.
EA:	(C, 47) (H, 7) (N, 14) (S, 4)
MW:	3300
EW:	1400
PC:	WH., POW.
OR:	(-61.5, HCL)
UV:	W: (200, ,)
SOL-GOOD:	W, BASE
SOL-POOR:	MEOH, ETOH, HEX
QUAL:	(NINH., +) (DNPH, +)
STAB:	(ACID, +) (HEAT, +) (BASE, -)
TO:	(B.SUBT., 12.5) (PS.AER., 50) (K.PNEUM., 100) (C.ALB., 50) (PIRICULARIA ORYZAE,)
LD50:	(1816, IV)
IS-FIL:	ORIG.
IS-ION:	(CG-50-H, NH4OH)
IS-ABS:	(CARBON, ACET-HCL)
IS-CHR:	(CG-50-H, NH4OAC) (AL, MEOH-W)
IS-CRY:	(PREC., W, ACET)

REFERENCES:

An. Rep. Sankyo, 26, 64, 1974; *CA,* 83, 41414

43240-4790

NAME:	KM-8
PO:	STV.TAITOENSIS
CT:	PEPTIDE, BASIC, LEUCINAMYCIN T.
EA:	(C, 48) (H, 6) (N, 15)
PC:	WH., POW.
OR:	(-91.7, W)
UV:	W: (252, 5.13,) (258, 5.2,) (264, 4.51,) (268, 3.79,)
SOL-GOOD:	W
SOL-FAIR:	MEOH, ETOH
SOL-POOR:	ACET, HEX
QUAL:	(NINH., +) (PAULY, +) (BIURET, +) (SAKA., -) (EHRL., -)
TO:	(B.SUBT., .78) (S.AUREUS,) (E.COLI, 200) (SHYG., 200) (C.ALB., 100) (PHYT.FUNGI, 25)
LD50:	(22, IV)
IS-FIL:	ORIG.
IS-ION:	(XAD-2, ACET-W) (XAD-7, ACET-W)
IS-CHR:	(SILG, ETOH-W)
IS-CRY:	(LIOF.,)

REFERENCES:

JA, 28, 819, 1975; JP 76/115994

43200-1780

NAME:	PEPTHIOMYCIN-A
PO:	S.ROSEOSPINUS
CT:	PEPTIDE, AMPHOTER
EA:	(C, 59) (H, 6) (N, 11) (S, 4) (O, 21)
PC:	YELLOW, POW.
OR:	(+35, DMFA)
UV:	MEOH: (230, 510,) (310, 87,)
SOL-GOOD:	ACOH, PYR, DMSO, DMFA
SOL-FAIR:	MEOH, ETOAC
SOL-POOR:	CHL, HEX, W
QUAL:	(BIURET, +) (NINH., +) (SAKA., -) (FECL3, -) (EHRL., -)
TO:	(S.AUREUS, 3.12) (S.LUTEA, .78) (B.SUBT., .3.12) (PHYT.BACT., 3)
IS-FIL:	4
IS-EXT:	(ACET, , MIC.) (BUOH, 4, FILT.)
IS-CRY:	(PREC., BUOH, HEX)

REFERENCES:

JA, 21, 429, 1968; *J. Agr. Chem. Soc. Jap.*, 38, 334, 1964

43200-1781

NAME:	PEPTHIOMYCIN-B
PO:	S.ROSEOSPINUS
CT:	PEPTIDE, AMPHOTER
EA:	(C, 51) (H, 5) (N, 15) (O, 23) (S, 4)
PC:	YELLOW, POW.
OR:	(-30, DMFA)
UV:	MEOH: (240, 872,) (310, 220,)
SOL-GOOD:	ACOH, PYR, DMFA
SOL-FAIR:	MEOH, ETOAC
SOL-POOR:	CHL, HEX, W
QUAL:	(NINH., +) (BIURET, +) (EHRL., +) (SAKA., -) (FECL3, -)
TO:	(S.AUREUS, .39) (S.LUTEA, .2) (B.SUBT., .39) (PHYT.BACT., 12)

REFERENCES:

JA, 21, 429, 1968; *J. Agr. Chem. Soc. Jap.*, 38, 334, 1964

43200-1789

NAME:	MICROPOLYSPORIN-AB, 55-AB
PO:	MICROPOLYSPORA CAESIA, THERMOMONOSPORA VIRIDIS
CT:	PEPTIDE, AMPHOTER
EA:	(N,) (S,)
PC:	GRAY, WH., POW.
UV:	MEOH: (200, ,)
SOL-GOOD:	DMFA, ACOH, PYR
SOL-FAIR:	MEOH
SOL-POOR:	W, ETOH, HEX
STAB:	(ACID, +) (HEAT, +) (BASE, -)
TO:	(S.LUTEA, 5) (S.AUREUS, 50) (MYCOB.SP., 5)

REFERENCES:

Antib., 587, 1966; *Mikrob.*, 33, 858, 1964

43200-1790

NAME:	THERMOTHIOCIN
PO:	THERMOACTINOPOLYSPORA COREMIALIS, NOC.MADURAE
CT:	PEPTIDE, AMPHOTER
FORMULA:	C60H110N16O25S3
EA:	(N, 14) (S, 6)
MW:	1500
PC:	YELLOW, POW.
OR:	(+29.4, DMFA)
UV:	DMFA: (200, ,)
SOL-GOOD:	PYR, DIOXAN, DMFA
SOL-FAIR:	BASE, MEOH, BUOH
SOL-POOR:	ACID, W, ACET, HEX
QUAL:	(FECL3, +) (NINH., -)
STAB:	(ACID, -) (BASE, -)
TO:	(S.AUREUS, .2) (B.SUBT., 1)
LD50:	(600, IP)
IS-EXT:	(ETOAC, , FILT.)

REFERENCES:

Ann. Micr. Enzym., 13, 125, 1963; USP 3697646; *CA*, 62, 9481

43200-1792

NAME:	CHALCIDINES, 845
PO:	MIC.CHALCEA
CT:	PEPTIDE, AMPHOTER
EA:	(N, 12) (S,)
PC:	WH., POW.
SOL-GOOD:	MEOH, BENZ
TO:	(S.AUREUS, .3) (S.LUTEA, .1) (B.SUBT., 4) (E.COLI, 50) (K.PNEUM., 50) (C.ALB., 50)
IS-FIL:	ORIG.
IS-EXT:	(CHL, 7, FILT.)
IS-CHR:	(SILG, BENZ-ACET)
IS-CRY:	(PREC., CHL, HEX) (CRYST., ETOH)

REFERENCES:

Antib., 483, 1970

43200-5336

NAME:	MC-902 COMPLEX
PO:	S.PLATENSIS
CT:	AMPHOTER, PEPTIDE
EA:	(C, 51) (H, 7) (N, 15) (S, 4) (O, 22)
PC:	WH., POW.
OR:	(-80, PROH-HCL)
UV:	PROH-NH4OH: (220, ,)
SOL-GOOD:	DMSO, DMFA, ACOH
SOL-POOR:	W, MEOH, HEX
QUAL:	(NINH., +) (SAKA., +)
TO:	(PELLICULARIA SASAKII,) (INSECTICID,) (PIRICULARIA ORYZAE, 1.56)
LD50:	(2000|500, IP)
IS-EXT:	(BUOH, 2, FILT.)
IS-ION:	(IRC-50-H, MEOH-W-PH11)
IS-ABS:	(CARBON, MEOH-W-HCL)
IS-CHR:	(SILG, BUOH-ACOH-W)
IS-CRY:	(DRY, PROH-W)

REFERENCES:

JP 77/102201, 76/76492; *CA*, 88, 20528; 85, 190723

43200-5880

NAME: A-7413-B
PO: ACTINOPLANES SP.
CT: THIAZOLYL-PEPTIDE
EA: (C, 66) (H, 9) (N, 3) (S, 3) (O, 19)
PC: WH., YELLOW, POW.
OR: (-26.2, DMSO)
UV: ETOH: (268, 104,) (357, 30,)
UV: ETOH-HCL: (268, 108,) (357, 35,)
UV: ETOH-NAOH: (268, 179,)
SOL-GOOD: MEOH, DMFA, CHL, DMSO, C2H4CL2
SOL-FAIR: ETOH
SOL-POOR: ACET, CCL4, BENZ, W, ET2O, HEX
TO: (B.SUBT.,) (S.AUREUS,) (S.LUTEA,)
REFERENCES:
USP 4147390; DT 2703938

43200-5881

NAME: A-7413-C
PO: ACTINOPLANES SP.
CT: THIAZOLYL-PEPTIDE
EA: (C, 69) (H, 10) (N, 2) (S, 2) (O, 17)
PC: WH., YELLOW, POW.
UV: ETOH: (205, 356,) (235, 180,) (260, 127,) (290, 104,)
UV: ETOH-HCL: (205, 356,) (235, 180,) (260, 127,) (290, 103,) (355, 40,)
UV: ETOH-NAOH: (260, 268,) (325, 189,)
SOL-GOOD: MEOH, DMFA, CHL, DMSO, CH4CL2
SOL-FAIR: ETOH
SOL-POOR: ACET, CCL4, BENZ, ET2O, W, HEX
TO: (B.SUBT.,) (S.AUREUS,) (S.LUTEA,)
REFERENCES:
USP 4174390; DT 2703938

43200-5990

NAME: MC-902-I
PO: S.SP.
CT: PEPTIDE
EA: (C, 50) (H, 7) (N, 16) (O, 22) (S, 4)
PC: WH., POW.
OR: (-121, PROH-NH4OH)
UV: PROH-NH4OH: (218, 370,)
SOL-GOOD: DMSO, DMFA, ACOH
SOL-POOR: W, MEOH, HEX
QUAL: (SAKA., +) (NINH., -)
TO: (G.POS.,) (PHYT.BACT.,)
REFERENCES:
JP 76/76492, 77/102201; *CA*, 85, 190723; 88, 20518

43200-6079

NAME: L-13365
PO: ACTINOPLANES SARVEPARENSIS
CT: ACIDIC, PEPTIDE
EA: (C, 51) (H, 5) (N, 10) (S, 11)
EW: 1400
PC: YELLOW, CRYST.
OR: (+125, MEOH-CHL)
UV: 7.5: (237, 326,) (378, 67,)
UV: 9: (238, 336,) (408, 99,)
UV: HCL: (237, 326,) (360, 103,)
SOL-GOOD: DMSO, DMFA, CHL-MEOH
SOL-FAIR: CHL-MEOH, ACOH
SOL-POOR: ETOH, HEX, W
QUAL: (FEHL., +) (FECL3, +) (NINH., -)
TO: (S.AUREUS, .025)
LD50: (1500|500, IP)
REFERENCES:
Belg. P 856273; DT 2724090; USP 4100273

43200-6127

NAME: MC-902-I′
PO: S.PLATENSIS
CT: PEPTIDE
EA: (C, 49) (H, 7) (N, 15) (O, 21) (S, 3.5)
OR: (-59,)
UV: MEOH: (218, 408,)
TO: (S.AUREUS, 6.25) (S.LUTEA, 6.25) (E.COLI, 100) (PS.AER., 100) (PHYT.FUNGI, 12.5)
REFERENCES:

433
Chelate-Forming Peptides

4331
Sideromycins

The trihydroxamic acid iron chelates or siderochromes exhibit a number of interesting biological properties. The term "siderochrome" refers to natural compounds in which three bidentate hydroxamate ligands coordinate octahedrally with the ferric ion, forming three five-membered chelate rings. The trivalent Fe ion, which is rather selectively bound, may be removed by treating the complexes with 8-hydroxyquinoline. These compounds are either long-chain or large-ring containing trihydroxamates in a linear sequence of constituents (ferrioxamine and ferrichrome types).

The growth-promoting siderochromes are called sideramines, whereas those having strong antibiotic activity are known as sideromycins. Sideramines antagonize the antibacterial action of sideromycins. In a few instances, however, a sideramine may be inhibitory to several microorganisms also, and curiously in certain circumstances a sideromycin may antagonize another sideromycin.

Sideromycins usually contain, besides the hydroxamic acids and ferric ions, several simple amino acids and other constituents such as aromatic acids, pyrimidine bases, etc. Sideromycins with known structure cover a group of linear and cyclic hexapeptides. The cyclic albomycin subtype (43311) consists of compounds containing three molecules of N-acetylated N^5-hydroxyornithine (hydroxamic acid part) **(1)** or N-acetylated serine. The iron-binding center is the cyclic hexapeptide of these six constituents. The N-acetyl residues of **(1)** were found to contribute in the iron binding together with the hydroxamate function. In addition, the albomycins were disclosed to contain a pyrimidine nucleus (3-methyluracyl derivatives) **(2)** attached via a sulfone bridge to a serine hydroxyl giving rise to a sulfamate. Because the main component of the albomycin complex — the δ_2 component — is extremely labile, the other congeners which vary only in the pyrimidine nucleus may be artefacts formed during the isolation of the active materials. According to some recent results, doubt arose against the proposed structure of albomycins. Namely, only one serine (and three molecules of ornithine) was found in the hydrolysate of albomycins, and the CD results suggest the binding of a pyrimidine nucleus to an asymmetric carbon atom.

The iron binding center of ferrimycin A_1, which is a prototype of linear sideromycins (43312), is ferrioxamine B. This sideramine contains acetic acid, succinic acid, and 1-amino-5-hydroxylamino-pentane **(3)** in a molar ratio of 1:2:3. In the linear peptide consisting of these six units, the terminal amino group is acylated with a 3-N-substituted 3-amino-5-hydroxybenzoic acid derivative **(4)**. Ferrimycin A_1 contains a cyclic iminoether-type constituent also, which is essential for bioactivity.

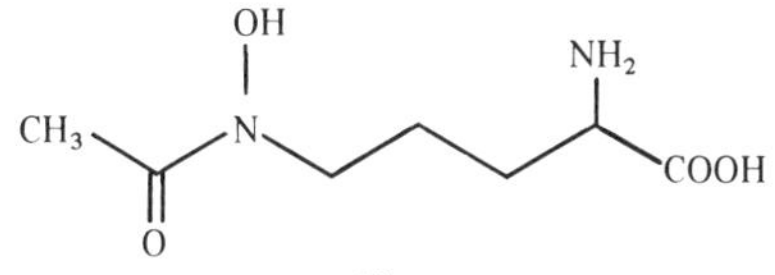

(1)

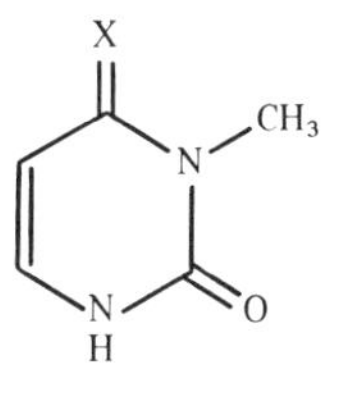

(2)

(3)

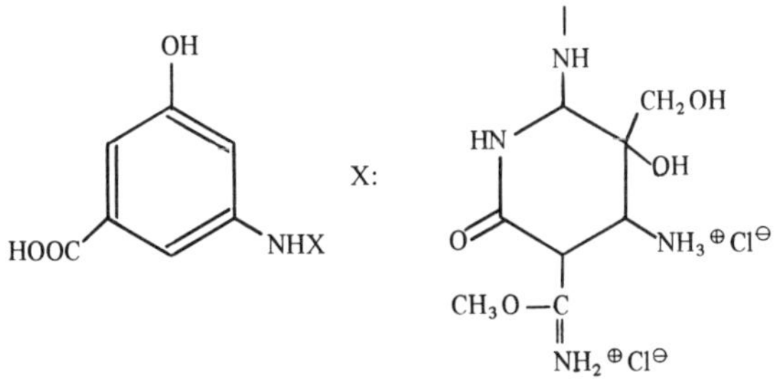

(4)

The other types of sideromycins — succinimycin (43313) and pseudosideromycin (43314) subtypes — contain various amino acids, diamines such as 1,5-diaminopentane, succinic acid, glutaric acid, etc. as products of their hydrolytic cleavage.

Sideromycins are red to orange or reddish-brown amorphous substances soluble only in water and strongly polar organic solvents such as phenol, dimethyl sulfoxide, or formamide. All siderochromes exhibit absorption maxima between 420 and 450 nm and one or two additional maxima at a lower wavelength according to special substituents. They are at 270 to 290 nm in albomycins and about 230 and 320 nm in the other subtypes.

Sideromycins are produced exclusively by *Streptomyces* species, but sideramines have been found in fungal and bacterial cultures also.

Sideromycins are generally strong anti-Gram-positive antibiotics, but albomycin exhibits some activity against Gram-negative organisms, too. Clinical trials proved its usefulness in the treatment of infections caused by penicillin-resistant cocci. Albomycin interferes with the transport of metabolic precursors through the bacterial membranes during protein and nucleic acid synthesis. It inhibits the respiratory function of cells. The iron is necessary for antibacterial activity, because the iron-free derivatives show only about 5 to 10% activity.

The in vitro very active sideromycins (apart from the very limited utilization of albomycin), because of their instability and the fast development of resistant strains, have found no clinical application. However, a medical use has been found for the iron-free complexing agent ferrioxamine B which has extremely high affinity for Fe^{+++} ions and a rather low affinity for all other cations. It can be used for treatment of hemosiderosis or hemochromatosis for removing pathological iron from the liver, spleen, pancreas, etc.

REFERENCES

1. *Forschr.*, 22, 279, 1964.
2. *Science*, 156, 1443, 1967.
3. *Pure Appl. Chem.*, 28, 603, 1971.
4. *JA*, 24, 830, 1971.

Structures

43311

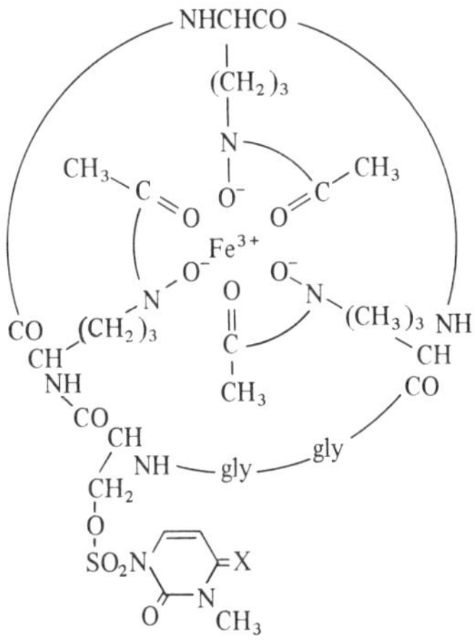

albomycin δ_2	$X = N{-}COCH_3$
albomycin δ_1	$X = O$
albomycin ϵ	$X = NH$

43312

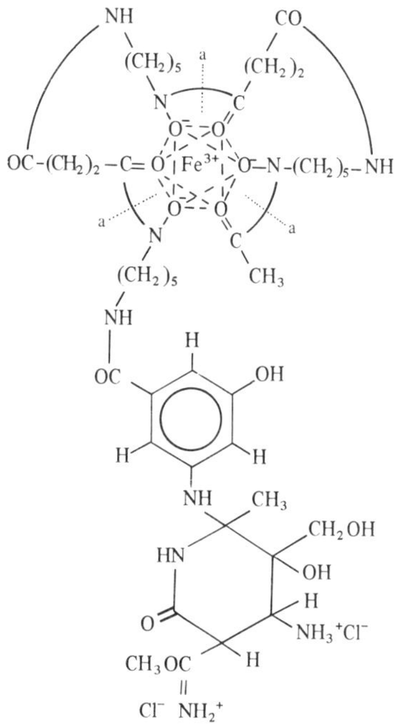

ferrimycin A_1

43315

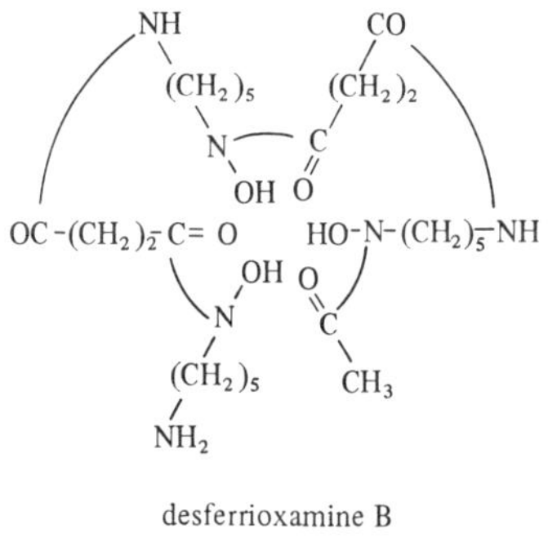

desferrioxamine B

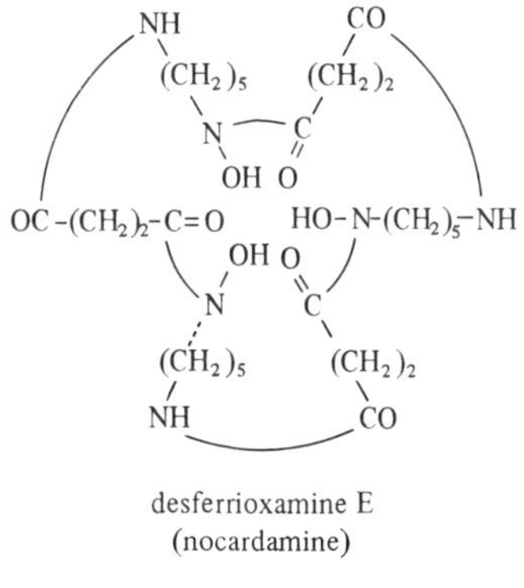

desferrioxamine E
(nocardamine)

43311-1795

NAME: GRISEIN
IDENTICAL: ALBOMYCIN, 3510, X-2455
PO: S.GRISEUS
CT: SIDEROMYCIN, ALBOMYCIN T., ACIDIC
FORMULA: C40H61N10O20SFE
EA: (N, 13) (S, 3) (FE, 5)
MW: 1090
PC: RED, POW.
UV: W: (265, 108,) (420, 28.9,)
SOL-GOOD: W, PHENOL
SOL-FAIR: MEOH, ACET, ETOH
SOL-POOR: BUOH, HEX
QUAL: (BIURET, +) (DNPH, -) (FEHL., -) (NINH., -)
STAB: (ACID, -) (HEAT, -)
TO: (B.SUBT., 1) (S.AUREUS, 1) (S.LUTEA, 1) (E.COLI, 1) (PS.AER., 1) (SHYG., 1) (K.PNEUM., 1)
LD50: (600, IP)
IS-FIL: 3
IS-ABS: (CARBON, PYR)
IS-CHR: (SILG, PHENOL-CHL)
REFERENCES:

J. Bact., 55, 739, 1948; *Sci.*, 125, 585, 591, 1957; *Proc. Soc. Exp. B.M.*, 55, 66, 1944; 64, 50, 1947; *Proc. Nat. Acad. Sci.*, 34, 232, 1948; *JACS*, 73, 1770, 1951; USP 2505053, 2546267; *Exp.*, 16, 129, 1960; *Jap. Med. J.*, 2, 79

43311-1796

NAME: ALBOMYCIN-A", ALBOMYCIN-A4
IDENTICAL: GRISEIN-4, GRISEIN-C
PO: S.SUBTROPICUS
CT: SIDEROMYCIN, ALBOMYCIN T., AMPHOTER
EA: (C,) (H,) (N,) (S,) (FE,)
PC: RED, POW.
UV: W: (260, 128,) (430|10, 32,)
STAB: (BASE, +)
TO: (G.POS.,) (G.NEG.,)
REFERENCES:

Coll., 31, 2444, 1966; *Dokl.*, 175, 480, 1967

43311-1797

NAME: ALBOMYCIN-E", ALBOMYCIN-A3
IDENTICAL: GRISEIN-3, GRISEIN-B, RO-7-7731
PO: S.SUBTROPICUS
CT: SIDEROMYCIN, ALBOMYCIN T., AMPHOTER
FORMULA: C37H60N12O19SFE
EA: (N, 14) (S, 3) (FE, 5)
MW: 1300
PC: RED, POW.
UV: W: (290, ,) (420, ,)
SOL-GOOD: W
SOL-FAIR: MEOH
SOL-POOR: BUOH, HEX
QUAL: (BIURET, +) (SAKA., -) (NINH., -)
TO: (S.AUREUS,) (B.SUBT.,) (E.COLI,) (K.PNEUM.,)
REFERENCES:
Coll., 31, 2444, 1966; *Dokl.*, 175, 480, 1967

43311-1798

NAME:	ALBOMYCIN-D"2, ALBOMYCIN-A1
IDENTICAL:	GRISEIN-1, RO-5-2667
PO:	S.SUBTROPICUS, S.SP.
CT:	SIDEROMYCIN, ALBOMYCIN T., AMPHOTER
FORMULA:	C39H62N12O20SFE
EA:	(N, 15) (S, 3) (FE, 5)
MW:	1300
EW:	1317|30
PC:	RED, POW.
UV:	W: (290, ,) (420, ,)
SOL-GOOD:	W
SOL-FAIR:	MEOH
SOL-POOR:	BUOH, HEX
QUAL:	(BIURET, +) (NINH., -) (SAKA., -) (PAULY, -)
STAB:	(HEAT, +)
TO:	(S.AUREUS, .001) (E.COLI, .001) (K.PNEUM., 1) (B.SUBT., 1) (SHYG., 1)
LD50:	NONTOXIC
IS-FIL:	3
IS-ION:	(IRC-50,)
IS-ABS:	(CARBON,)
IS-CHR:	(ZEOLIT 225, PH5.5 PUFF.)
IS-CRY:	(LIOF.,)
UTILITY:	ON CLINICAL TRIAL

REFERENCES:

Dokl., 96, 645, 1954; 99, 827, 1956; 108, 677, 1959; 175, 480, 1967; *Nov. Med. (Moscow)*, 23, 3, 1951; *Brit. Med. J.*, 2, 1177, 1955; *Coll.*, 27, 581, 591, 1962; 28, 1747, 1963; 29, 280, 1964; 30, 118, 1965; 31, 2444, 2454, 1966; *Zh. Obsch. Khim.*, 31, 3820, 1961; 32, 1005, 2102, 1962; 33, 1379, 1963; *JA*, 24, 830, 1971; *Antib.*, 1031, 1977; *Eur. J. Appl. Micr.*, 5, 51, 1978

43311-1799

NAME: ALBOMYCIN-D"1, ALBOMYCIN-A2
IDENTICAL: GRISEIN-2, GRISEIN-A, RO-7-7730
PO: S.SUBTROPICUS
CT: SIDEROMYCIN, ALBOMYCIN T., AMPHOTER
FORMULA: C37H59N11O20SFE
EA: (N, 14) (S, 3) (FE, 5)
PC: RED, POW.
UV: W: (290, ,) (420, ,)
SOL-GOOD: W
SOL-FAIR: MEOH
SOL-POOR: BUOH, HEX
QUAL: (BIURET, +) (NINH., -)
TO: (E.COLI,) (S.AUREUS,) (B.SUBT.,) (K.PNEUM.,)
REFERENCES:
Brit. Med. J., 2, 1177, 1955; *Coll.*, 27, 581, 591, 1962; 28, 1747, 1963; 29, 280, 1964; 30, 118, 1965; 31, 2444, 2454, 1966; *Zh. Obsch. Khim.*, 31, 3820, 1961; 32, 1005, 2102, 1962; 33, 1379, 1963; *JA*, 24, 830, 1971; *Antib.*, 1031, 1977; *Eur. J., Appl. Micr.*, 5, 51, 1978

43311-1800

NAME: RO-7-7730
IDENTICAL: ALBOMYCIN-D"1
PO: S.GRISEUS
CT: SIDEROMYCIN, ALBOMYCIN T., AMPHOTER
EA: (N,) (S,) (FE,)
PC: RED, BROWN, POW.
UV: 7: (265, 100,) (420, 22,)
UV: HCL: (265, 100,) (470, 16,)
SOL-GOOD: W, PHENOL
SOL-FAIR: MEOH, DMFA
SOL-POOR: ETOH, HEX
TO: (E.COLI, .01) (P.VULG., .01) (PS.AER., .01) (B.SUBT., .1) (S.AUREUS, .01) (S.LUTEA, 1)
REFERENCES:
Biotech. Bioeng., 11, 1111, 1969; *JA*, 24, 830, 1971

43311-1801

NAME: RO-7-7731
IDENTICAL: ALBOMYCIN-E"
PO: S.GRISEUS
CT: SIDEROMYCIN, ALBOMYCIN T., AMPHOTER
EA: (N,) (S,) (FE,)
PC: RED, BROWN, POW.
UV: 7: (278, 104,) (420, 22,)
UV: HCL: (276, 108,) (485|15, 18,)
SOL-GOOD: W, PHENOL
SOL-FAIR: MEOH, DMFA
SOL-POOR: ETOH, HEX
TO: (E.COLI, .01) (P.VULG., .01) (PS.AER., .1) (B.SUBT., .1) (S.LUTEA, 1) (S.AUREUS, 10)
REFERENCES:

Biotech. Bioeng., 11, 1111, 1969; *JA*, 24, 830, 1971

43311-1802

NAME: 3510
IDENTICAL: GRISEIN, ALBOMYCIN
PO: S.GRISEUS
CT: SIDEROMYCIN, ALBOMYCIN T., AMPHOTER
EA: (N,) (FE,)
PC: RED, POW.
SOL-GOOD: W, PHENOL
SOL-FAIR: ETOH-W
SOL-POOR: ACET, HEX
STAB: (HEAT, -)
TO: (E.COLI,) (SHYG.,) (S.AUREUS,) (B.SUBT.,)
IS-FIL: ORIG.
IS-ABS: (CARBON, ETOH-W)
IS-CRY: (PREC., W, ACET)
REFERENCES:

Proc. Nat. Acad. Sci., 34, 232, 1948

43311-1803

NAME: LA-5352
PO: S.SP.
CT: SIDEROMYCIN, ALBOMYCIN T., AMPHOTER
EA: (FE, 2)
PC: RED
QUAL: (BIURET, +)
TO: (S.AUREUS, 1) (S.LUTEA, 1) (B.SUBT., 1)
IS-FIL: 7.5
IS-EXT: (BENZYLALCOHOL, 7.5, FILT.+NACL) (H2SO4, , BENZYLALCOHOL)
IS-CRY: (PREC., , ET2O)
REFERENCES:

Ant. & Chem., 9, 160, 1959; *CA*, 53, 10367

43311-1804

NAME: A-418-Z4
PO: S.SP.
CT: SIDEROMYCIN, ALBOMYCIN T., AMPHOTER
EA: (FE,)
TO: (S.AUREUS, 1.56)
REFERENCES:
JA, 15, 227, 1962

43311-1805

NAME: ALVEOMYCIN
PO: S.SP.
CT: SIDEROMYCIN, ALBOMYCIN T., AMPHOTER
EA: (N,) (FE, 2)
PC: RED, POW.
UV: W: (277, 51,) (420, 11,)
SOL-GOOD: W
SOL-POOR: BUOH, HEX
STAB: (BASE, +) (HEAT, -) (ACID, -)
TO: (S.AUREUS, .01) (B.SUBT.,) (S.LUTEA,) (E.COLI,) (K.PNEUM.,)
LD50: (700, IV)
IS-ABS: (CARBON, ACET-NH4OH)
IS-CHR: (SILG, I.PROH-W)
IS-CRY: (LIOF.,)
REFERENCES:
Med. Chem., 7, 528, 1963; *CA*, 60, 1542; 55, 1542

43311-1806

NAME: A-1787
PO: S.SP.
CT: SIDEROMYCIN, ALBOMYCIN T., AMPHOTER
EA: (FE,)
MW: 1000
PC: ORANGE, RED, POW.
UV: W: (275, ,)
SOL-GOOD: W, PYR, DMFA, MEOH
SOL-FAIR: ACOH
SOL-POOR: BUOH, HEX
TO: (G.POS., .1) (G.NEG., .1)
IS-ION: (WOFATIT E, MEOH-W)
IS-CHR: (CEL, PROH-ACOH-W)
IS-CRY: (LIOF.,)
REFERENCES:
Naturwiss., 44, 561, 1957; *Sci.*, 125, 357, 1957

43311-1807

NAME: 1695
PO: S.SP.
CT: SIDEROMYCIN, ALBOMYCIN T., AMPHOTER
EA: (N,) (S,) (FE,)
PC: RED, POW.
SOL-GOOD: W, PHENOL
SOL-FAIR: MEOH
SOL-POOR: BUOH, HEX
QUAL: (NINH., -) (FEHL., -)
STAB: (HEAT, +)
TO: (S.AUREUS, .25) (B.SUBT., .25) (E.COLI, 10) (P.VULG., 10) (C.ALB., 100) (S.CEREV., 100)
LD50: (500, IP)
IS-FIL: 2.5
IS-ABS: (CARBON, BUOH-MEOH-W)
REFERENCES:
Riv. Biol., 53, 229, 195; *CA*, 57, 8997

43311-1808

NAME: LA-5937
PO: S.BOBILAE-SPORIFICANS
CT: SIDEROMYCIN, ALBOMYCIN T., BASIC
EA: (C, 48) (H, 6) (N, 15)
PC: WH., POW.
OR: (-24, HCL)
UV: W: (200, ,)
SOL-GOOD: ACID
SOL-FAIR: MEOH, BUOH
SOL-POOR: W
QUAL: (BIURET, +) (NINH., +) (FECL3, -) (FEHL., -) (SAKA., -)
TO: (S.AUREUS,) (S.LUTEA,) (B.SUBT.,)
LD50: (200, IV)
IS-FIL: 7
IS-EXT: (BENZYLALCOHOL, 8.5, FILT.+NACL)
REFERENCES:
Ant. & Chem., 9, 160, 1959; BP 920799; *CA*, 59, 2134

43311-1810

NAME:	RO-5-2667
IDENTICAL:	ALBOMYCIN-D"2, GRISEIN
PO:	S.GRISEUS
CT:	SIDEROMYCIN, ALBOMYCIN T.
EA:	(N,) (S,) (FE,)
PC:	RED, BROWN, POW.
UV:	7: (277, 122,) (420, 28,)
UV:	HCL: (305, 123,) (470, 20,)
SOL-GOOD:	W, PHENOL
SOL-FAIR:	MEOH, DMFA
SOL-POOR:	ETOH, HEX
TO:	(S.AUREUS, .01) (E.COLI, .01) (P.VULG., .01) (PS.AER., .01) (B.SUBT., .01) (S.LUTEA, .1)
IS-FIL:	4
IS-ABS:	(CARBON, ACET-W)
IS-CHR:	(CELIT, ETOH-W) (DX-50, NAH2PO4-NA2HPO4)

REFERENCES:

Biotech. Bioeng., 11, 1111, 1969; *JA*, 24, 830, 1971

43312-1809

NAME: FERRIMYCIN-A1, A-9578
IDENTICAL: PILOSOMYCIN-A
PO: S.GRISEOFLAVUS, S.GALILAEUS, S.LAVENDULAE, S.SP.
CT: SIDEROMYCIN, FERRIMYCIN T., BASIC
FORMULA: C41H65N10O14FE
EA: (N, 13) (FE, 5)
MW: 1106
EW: 1078
PC: RED, BROWN, POW.
UV: W: (229, 336,) (319, 37,) (428, 27.6,)
SOL-GOOD: W, MEOH, PHENOL, DMFA
SOL-FAIR: ACOH, ETOH, PROH, PYR
SOL-POOR: BUOH, HEX
QUAL: (NINH., +) (SAKA., -)
STAB: (ACID, +) (BASE, -) (HEAT, +)
TO: (S.AUREUS, .001) (B.SUBT., .01) (E.COLI,) (SHYG.,) (K.PNEUM.,)
IS-FIL: 4
IS-EXT: (CHL-PHENOL, , W)
IS-ION: (IRC-50-NA, MEOH-HCL)
IS-CHR: (CEL, BUOH-ACOH-W)
REFERENCES:

Exp., 16, 129, 1960; *Tetr.*, 8, Suppl. 171, 1966; *Helv.*, 43, 901, 1868, 2105, 1960; 44, 709, 1981, 1961; *Pure Appl. Chem.*, 6, 327, 1963; *JA*, 15, 227, 1962; USP 3093550; DT 1058216, 1157735

43312-1811

NAME: FERRIMYCIN-A2
IDENTICAL: PILOSOMYCIN-B1
PO: S.GRISEOFLAVUS
CT: SIDEROMYCIN, FERRIMYCIN T., BASIC
FORMULA: C41H68N10O15FE.2HCL
EA: (N, 13) (FE, 5)
MW: 1086
EW: 984
PC: RED, BROWN, POW.
UV: MEOH: (227, 332,) (319, 37,) (425, 25,)
UV: W: (231, 328,) (319, 30,) (435, 26.2,)
SOL-GOOD: MEOH, W
SOL-FAIR: ETOH
SOL-POOR: BUOH, HEX
QUAL: (NINH., +) (SAKA., -)
STAB: (BASE, -) (HEAT, -)
TO: (S.AUREUS, .01)
REFERENCES:

Helv., 43, 2105, 1960; Can. P 798312

43312-1812

NAME: FERRIMYCIN-B
PO: S.GRISEOFLAVUS
CT: SIDEROMYCIN, FERRIMYCIN T., BASIC
EA: (FE,)
PC: RED, POW.
TO: (S.AUREUS,)
REFERENCES:
Helv., 43, 901, 1868, 2105, 1960

43312-1813

NAME: PILOSOMYCIN, A-9578
IDENTICAL: FERRIMYCIN
PO: S.SP.
CT: SIDEROMYCIN, FERRIMYCIN T., BASIC
FORMULA: C42H69N10O15FE
EA: (N, 13) (FE, 4)
MW: 1025|25
PC: ORANGE, POW.
UV: W: (215, 312,) (315, 42,)
SOL-GOOD: MEOH, W, DMFA
SOL-FAIR: ETOAC
SOL-POOR: BUOH, HEX
QUAL: (FECL3, +) (NINH., +) (SAKA., -)
STAB: (BASE, -)
TO: (S.AUREUS,) (B.SUBT.,) (E.COLI,)
LD50: (1200, SC)
REFERENCES:
DT 1089122, 1058216; USP 3033760; JP 63/6595

43312-1814

NAME: GRISONOMYCIN, A-10073
PO: S.GRISEUS
CT: SIDEROMYCIN, FERRIMYCIN T., BASIC
EA: (FE,)
PC: YELLOW, POW.
UV: W: (280, 82,) (425, 16.4,)
SOL-GOOD: W, PHENOL
SOL-POOR: BUOH, HEX
QUAL: (SAKA., -) (BIURET, -)
TO: (S.AUREUS, 1) (B.SUBT., 1) (E.COLI, 1) (SHYG., 1) (PS.AER., 1) (K.PNEUM., 1)
IS-FIL: 7
IS-ABS: (CARBON, MEOH-HCL)
IS-CRY: (DRY, MEOH-W)
REFERENCES:
Exp., 16, 129, 1960; DT 1070782; Swiss P 366123; BP 876096; USP 3147184

43313-1815

NAME:	A-22765
PO:	S.AUREOFACIENS
CT:	SIDEROMYCIN, SUCCINIMYCIN T., BASIC
EA:	(C, 50) (H, 8) (N, 10) (FE, 2)
PC:	BROWN, POW.
OR:	(-17, W)
UV:	W: (225|5, ,) (330, ,) (430, ,)
SOL-GOOD:	W, MEOH, DMFA, PHENOL
SOL-POOR:	BUOH, HEX
STAB:	(ACID, -) (BASE, -)
TO:	(S.AUREUS, .05) (B.SUBT., .08)
LD50:	(1200, SC)
IS-ION:	(IRC-50-H,)
IS-ABS:	(CARBON, CHL-PHENOL)

REFERENCES:

Arch. Mikr., 68, 107, 1969; USP 3155578, 3211246; DT 1129259

43313-1816

NAME:	SUCCINIMYCIN
PO:	S.OLIVOCHROMOGENES
CT:	SIDEROMYCIN, SUCCINIMYCIN T., BASIC
EA:	(C, 46) (H, 7) (N, 10) (FE, 5)
PC:	ORANGE, POW.
OR:	(+76, W)
UV:	W: (430, 22.8,)
SOL-GOOD:	MEOH, W, DMFA
SOL-POOR:	BUOH, HEX
QUAL:	(EHRL., -) (NINH., -) (FEHL., -)
STAB:	(ACID, -) (BASE, -)
TO:	(S.AUREUS, .001) (B.SUBT., .001)
LD50:	(770, IV)
IS-ION:	(DX-50-NA, NA2SO4)
IS-ABS:	(CARBON, ACET-W)
IS-CRY:	(LIOF.,)

REFERENCES:

JA, 26, 67, 1963

43313-1817

NAME:	DANOMYCIN, 425
PO:	S.ALBADUNCUS
CT:	SIDEROMYCIN, SUCCINIMYCIN T., BASIC
FORMULA:	C73H125N10O37FE
EA:	(N, 8) (FE, 3)
MW:	1791
EW:	1800
PC:	RED, POW.
UV:	HCL: (325, 18,) (450|10, 13,)
UV:	NAOH: (325, 20,) (420|10, 25,)
UV:	W: (270, 48,) (325, 12.6,) (430, 15.6,)
SOL-GOOD:	W, PHENOL
SOL-FAIR:	MEOH, ETOH-W
SOL-POOR:	BUOH, HEX
QUAL:	(NINH., -) (FEHL., -)
STAB:	(ACID, -) (BASE, -)
TO:	(S.AUREUS, .01) (S.LUTEA, .01) (B.SUBT., .003) (E.COLI, 50) (K.PNEUM., 50) (SHYG., 25)
LD50:	(3250, IV)
IS-FIL:	6
IS-EXT:	(CHL-PHENOL, , W)
IS-ABS:	(CARBON, MEOH-W)
IS-CRY:	(LIOF.,)

REFERENCES:

JA, 17, 39, 45, 57, 1964; Belg. P 634041; BP 975492; JP 65/13796

43314-1818

NAME: GLUCONIMYCIN
PO: S.SP.
CT: PSEUDOSIDEROMYCIN
EA: (C, 56) (H, 7) (N, 11) (O, 25) (FE, 1.4)
PC: ORANGE, POW.
UV: W: (235, ,) (432|2, ,)
SOL-GOOD: MEOH, CHL, W
SOL-FAIR: ET2O
SOL-POOR: BENZ, HEX
QUAL: (NINH., -) (BIURET, -) (SAKA., -) (FECL3, -)
TO: (B.SUBT., .1) (S.AUREUS, .1) (S.LUTEA, .1) (E.COLI, 1) (SHYG., 1.2) (K.PNEUM., 1) (C.ALB., 5) (S.CEREV., 5)
LD50: (10, IV)
REFERENCES:
Arch. Mikr., 54, 246, 1966

43314-1819

NAME: FERRAMIDO-CHLOROMYCIN
PO: S.SP.
CT: PSEUDOSIDEROMYCIN
FORMULA: C127H201N24O70SCL2FE7
EA: (N, 10) (S, 1) (CL, 2) (FE, 4)
PC: BROWN, GRAY, CRYST.
UV: W: (200, ,)
SOL-GOOD: MEOH, ETOH, BUOH
SOL-POOR: ETOAC, HEX, W
QUAL: (NINH., +) (BIURET, +) (FEHL., -) (SAKA., -)
TO: (B.SUBT., 2) (S.AUREUS, 2) (E.COLI, 50) (K.PNEUM., 50) (C.ALB., 8) (S.CEREV., 50)
LD50: (50, IV)
REFERENCES:
JA, 19, 110, 250, 1966

43314-1820

NAME:	ASK-753
PO:	S.SP.
CT:	PSEUDOSIDEROMYCIN
EA:	(C, 55) (H, 7) (N, 7) (O, 29) (FE, 2.5)
PC:	BROWN, YELLOW, CRYST.
UV:	ETOH: (270, 120,)
UV:	ETOH-HCL: (270, 120,)
UV:	ETOH-NAOH: (287, 135,)
SOL-GOOD:	MEOH, CHL, ET2O
SOL-FAIR:	W, ETOAC
SOL-POOR:	BENZ, HEX
QUAL:	(NINH., -) (FEHL., -) (BIURET, -) (SAKA., -) (FECL3, -)
TO:	(B.SUBT., .75) (S.AUREUS, .35) (E.COLI, 3) (K.PNEUM., 6) (SHYG., 6) (PS.AER., .37) (S.CEREV., 3) (C.ALB., 6)
LD50:	(58, IP)
IS-EXT:	(CHL, 8, FILT.)
IS-CHR:	(SEPHADEX LH-20, CHL-ETOH)

REFERENCES:

JA, 21, 107, 1968; 27, 874, 1974; *Ind. J. Bioch.*, 8, 723, 1977; *CA*, 88, 45568

43314-1821

NAME:	NRCS-15
PO:	S.SP.
CT:	PSEUDOSIDEROMYCIN
EA:	(C, 56) (H, 6) (N, 8) (CL, 3) (FE, 2)
PC:	YELLOW, WH., POW.
UV:	ETOH: (210, 122.5,)
UV:	ETOH-HCL: (208, 112,)
UV:	ETOH-NAOH: (222, 12.2,)
SOL-GOOD:	W, MEOH, CHL
SOL-FAIR:	ET2O
SOL-POOR:	HEX
QUAL:	(NINH., +) (BIURET, +) (FEHL., -) (SAKA., -) (FECL3, -)
TO:	(B.SUBT., .008) (S.AUREUS, .8) (E.COLI, 12) (K.PNEUM., 6.3) (P.VULG., 25) (PS.AER., 100)
LD50:	(50, SC)
IS-FIL:	ORIG.
IS-EXT:	(ETOAC, 8.5, FILT.)
IS-ABS:	(CARBON, ETOH-W)
IS-CRY:	(PREC., CHL, HEX)

REFERENCES:

JA, 27, 1, 1974

43314-5382

NAME: AS-N-7A
PO: S.ERYTHROCHROMOGENES
CT: PSEUDOSIDEROMYCIN
TO: (S.AUREUS,)
LD50: (1.1, IM)
REFERENCES:

Antib., 13, 30, 1975; *CA*, 85, 171695

43315-1822

NAME: NOCARDAMIN, DESFERRI-FERRIOXAMIN-E, DESFERRI-FERRIOXAMIN-E
PO: ACT.BUCHANAN, NOC.SP., S.HYGROSCOPICUS-GELDANUS, S.SP.
CT: SIDERAMINE, ACIDIC
FORMULA: C27H48N6O9
EA: (N, 14)
MW: 545|55
PC: WH., CRYST.
OR: (0,)
SOL-GOOD: MEOH, W, BASE
QUAL: (FECL3, +) (FEHL., +)
TO: (MYCOB.SP., .1)
IS-EXT: (BUOH, , FILT.)
IS-CRY: (CRYST., W)
REFERENCES:
Schw. Z. Allg. Path. Bakt., 14, 225, 1951; *J. Ph. Soc. Jap.*, 81, 1216, 1493, 1497, 1961; *Helv.*, 43, 1868, 1959; 34, 862, 1951; 44, 1981, 1961; *Z. Naturforsch. Ser. B*, 32, 937, 1977

43315-1823

NAME: FERRICHROCIN
PO: ASP.SP.
CT: SIDERAMINE
FORMULA: C28H44N9O13FE
EA: (N, 16) (FE, 7)
PC: ORANGE, CRYST.
UV: (214, 175,) (230, 33,)
SOL-GOOD: MEOH, W
TO: (G.POS.,)
REFERENCES:
Helv., 46, 1907, 1963; *Eur. J. Appl. Micr.*, 5, 51, 1978; *Arch. Mikr.*, 106, 191, 1975

43315-1824

NAME: FERRICHRYSIN
PO: ASP.SP.
CT: SIDERAMINE
FORMULA: C29H49N9O14FE
EA: (N, 17) (FE, 7)
PC: RED, CRYST.
UV: W: (415, ,)
SOL-GOOD: MEOH, W
SOL-POOR: ETOH
REFERENCES:
Helv., 46, 1385, 1963; *JACS*, 83, 1626, 1961; Belg. P 625235

43315-5448

NAME:	<u>TRIACETYLDESFERRIFUSIGEN</u>
PO:	ASP.DEFLECTUS
CT:	SIDERAMINE, NEUTRAL
FORMULA:	C39H60N6O15
MW:	852
TO:	(B.SUBT., 1) (S.LUTEA, 50) (E.COLI, 5) (P.VULG., 5) (S.AUREUS, 10)
IS-EXT:	(ETOAC, 7, EVAP.FILT.)
IS-CHR:	(SEPHADEX LH-20, MEOH) (SEPHADEX G-10, W)
IS-CRY:	(LIOF.,)

REFERENCES:

JA, 30, 125, 1977; *Arch. Mikr.*, 106, 191, 1975; *Biochem.*, 15, 2719, 1976; *CA*, 86, 153890

43315-5774

NAME:	<u>DESFERRIOXAMIN-B</u>
PO:	S.SP.
CT:	SIDERAMINE
FORMULA:	C25H48N6O8
EA:	(N, 12)
PC:	WH., CRYST.
SOL-GOOD:	W
TO:	(P.VULG., 50) (E.COLI,)

REFERENCES:

AAC, 7, 377, 1975; *Helv.*, 43, 2118, 1960; 46, 1385, 1963

4332
Bleomycin Type

These antibiotics are copper-chelated glycopeptide-type compounds with significant antibacterial and antitumor effects. They contain unique amino acids, sugars, and aliphatic amines. The skeleton of these antibiotics is a linear hexapeptide chain, and attached to it is a glycosidically linked disaccharide fragment. The peptide part is terminated in the carboxyl end with the so-called "terminal amine".

These antibiotics are a mine of collection of unique amino acid-type constituents and unusual molecular fragments. They contain a L-α-aminocarboxamide group, pyrimidine chromophore, β-hydroxyhistidine/valine, various γ-amino carboxylic acids, a bithiazole- or thiazolyl-thiazine-containing amino acid, rare sugars (gulose, tallose), and a variety of (poly)amine fragments. The L-β-aminoalanine amide links to the pyrimidine chromophore **(2)**. This unique structural element is depicted as **(1)**. According to very recent results, bleomycin-type compounds do not contain a β-lactam group. The amino acid-type compounds and sugar moieties occurring in these antibiotics are listed below:

(2) β-Amino-β-(4-amino-6-carboxy-5-methylpyrimidin-2-yl)propionic acid [obtained from **(1)**]
(3) *erythro*-β-Hydroxy-L-histidine
(4) 4-Amino-3-hydroxy-2-methylpentanoic acid
(5) 4-Amino-3,6-dihydroxy-2-methylhexanoic acid
(6) 4-Amino-3-hydroxy-*erythro*-pentanoic acid
(7) 4-Amino-*n*-butyric acid
(8) L-Threonine
(9) β-Hydroxy-L-valine (β-methylthreonine)
(10) 2′-(2-Aminoethyl)-2,4′-bithiazole-4-carboxylic acid
(11) 2′-[2-(2- Aminoethyl)-Δ^2-thiazolin-4-yl]-thiazole-4-carboxylic acid
(12) 2′-(2- Amino-3,4-dihydroxyethyl)-2,4′-bithiazole-4-carboxylic acid
(13) L-β-Lysine
(14) L-Gulose
(15) 6-Deoxy-L-gulose
(16) 3-O-Carbamoyl-D-mannose
(17) 4-Amino-4,6-dideoxy-L-tallose

The congeners of the antibiotic mixtures produced by the microorganisms vary only in the terminal amine moiety. The structures of these fragments will be included in the chemical structures of the individual antibiotics.

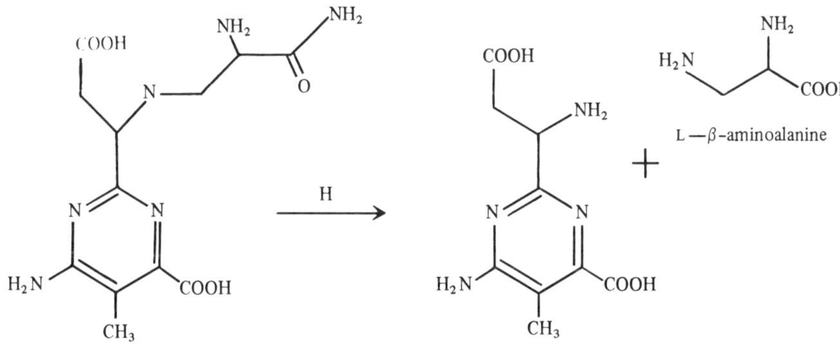

(1) (2)

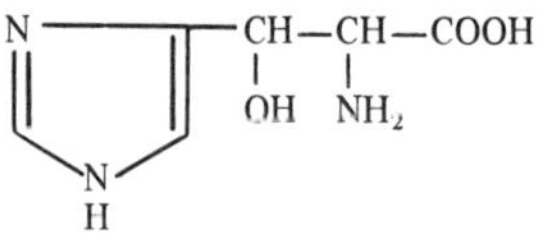

(3)

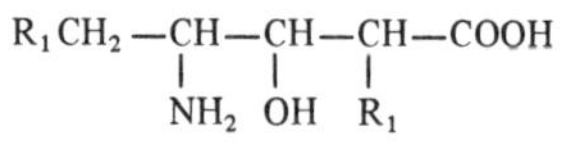

	R_1	R_2
(4)	H	CH_3
(5)	CH_2OH	CH_3
(6)	H	H

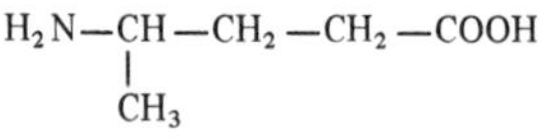

(7)

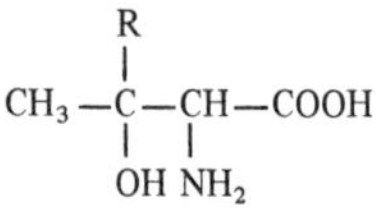

(8) R = H
(9) R = CH_3

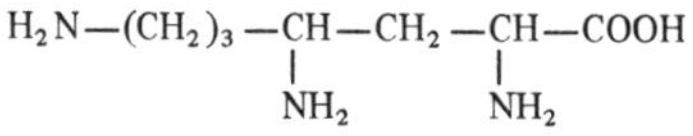

(13)

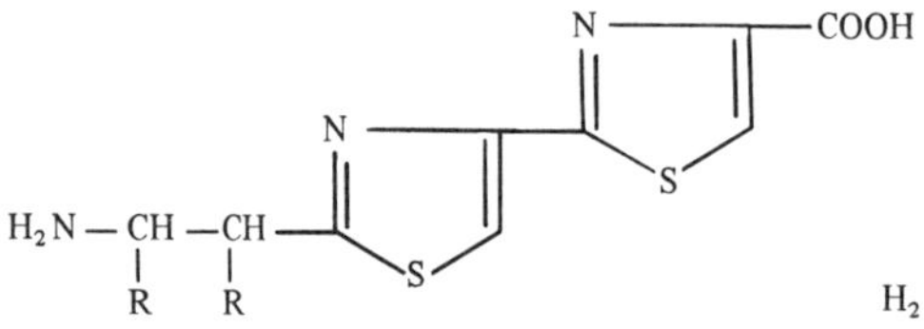

(10) R = H
(12) R = OH

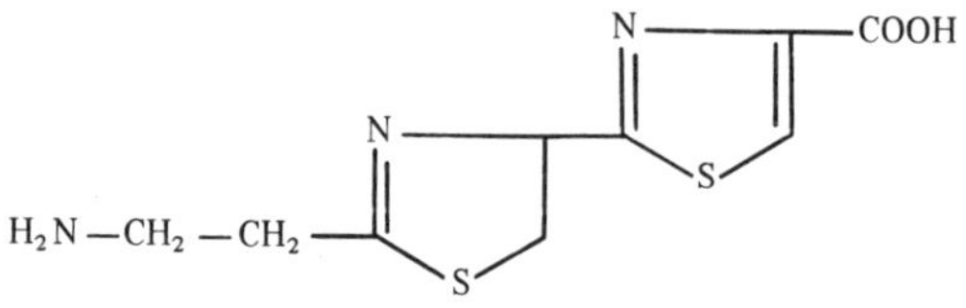

(11)

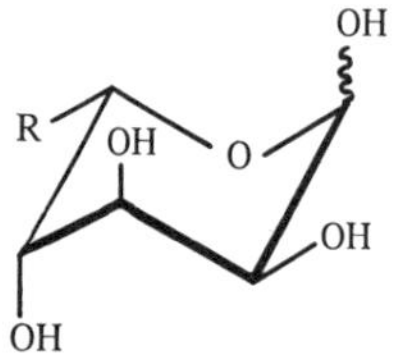

(14) R = CH_2OH
(15) R = CH_3

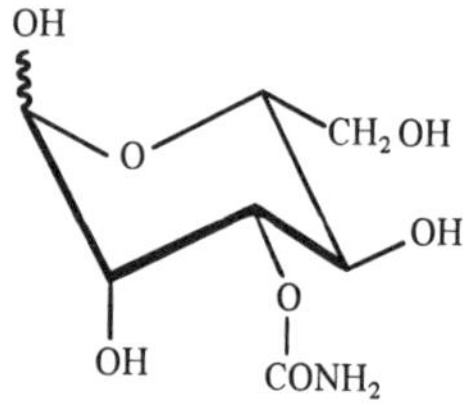

(16)

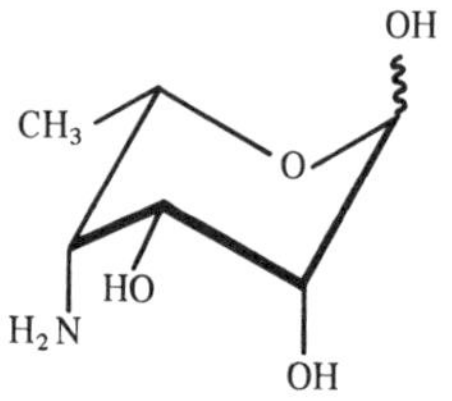

(17)

The structural fragments occurring in and characteristic of a given bleomycin-type antibiotic are summarized in the following scheme:

$$\begin{array}{ccccccccccccc}
(1) & \longrightarrow & (3) & \longrightarrow & X_1 & \longrightarrow & X_2 & \longrightarrow & X_3 & \longrightarrow & [X_4] & \longrightarrow & \mathrm{TA} \\
 & & & & {\scriptstyle O}| & & & & | & & & & \\
 & & & & Y_1 & \overset{O}{—} & (16) & & [Y_2] & & & &
\end{array}$$

general structure

Antibiotic	Structural units					
	X_1	X_2	X_3	X_4	Y_1	Y_2
Bleomycins	**(4)**	**(8)**	**(10)**	—	**(14)**	—
Phleomycins	**(4)**	**(8)**	**(11)**	—	**(14)**	—
Zorbamycin (YA-56X)	**(5)**	**(9)**	**(11)**	—	**(15)**	—
Zorbamycin B	**(5)**	**(8)**	**(10)**	—	?	—
YA-56Y	**(7)**	**(9)**	**(11)**	—	**(15)**	—
Tallysomycin A	**(6)**	**(8)**	**(12)**	**(13)**	**(14)**	**(17)**
Tallysomycin B	**(6)**	**(8)**	**(12)**	—	**(14)**	**(17)**
Platomycins	?	?	?	—	**(14)**	—

Note: TA, terminal amine; X, amino acids; Y, sugars.

As can be seen from this scheme, the first two amino acid fragments and the carbamoyl-mannose moiety are the same in each compound. The disaccharide fragment links to the hydroxyl group of the β-hydroxyhistidine residue through an α-glycosidic linkage. The third sugar in both tallysomycins is linked to the β-hydroxyl of bithiazole acid. Tallysomycins are chemically somewhat different compounds because of (a) the additional amino sugar unit, (b) the carbinolamine-type new thiazole acid, (c) the additional β-lysine in the tallysomycin A (heptapeptide), and (d) spermidine as the sole terminal amine moiety.

The presence of copper is a common feature of most isolated glycopeptide compounds, and they contain equimolar complexed Cu^{++} ions. In the chelation of Cu^{++} the amino group of the α-carboxamide, one of the nitrogen atom of the pyrimidine chromophore and of the imidazole moiety, and the carbamoyl group of mannose are involved. The complexing ability of copper is selective. Contrary to the sideromycins, the copper-free antibiotics show equal bioactivity both in vitro and in vivo.

These antibiotics are basic water-soluble substances. The copper complexes are blue amorphous powders, while the copper-free compounds are white materials. Their molecular weight ranges from about 1500 to 1600. They show characteristic UV absorption due to the pyrimidine and thiazole chromophores. Bleomycins show maxima around 244 and 293 nm with an absorption ratio of about 1.1 to 1.3. Phleomycins and similar antibiotics containing **(11)** instead of **(10)** show corresponding maxima at 244 to 246 and 295 to 300 nm with an absorption ratio of about 2.7 to 3.0. The copper complexes show absorption in the visible region at 450 and 580 to 620 nm.

These antibiotics were isolated by successive cation-exchange resin absorption processes and carbon or alumina chromatography. Their separation into individual components was achieved by ion-exchange chromatography. Phleomycin, the first antibiotic of this group, was discovered in 1956, but it has never found practical application because of its high renal toxicity. As a result of successive work of Umezawa's group in 1966, bleomycin, the more favorable member of this group, was discovered. Its structure was determined in 1972 and it soon became one of the most important antitumor drugs with fewer side effects but a rather narrow antitumor spectrum.

All compounds in this type are actinomycetales products. Some novel antibiotics are produced by *Streptosporangium* or *Streptoalloteichus* species. From the fermentation broth of a *Streptomyces verticillatus* strain 16 natural bleomycins, in which bleomycin A_2 is representative and is the principal (55 to 70%) component, have so far been isolated, and from another *S. verticillatus* strain about 15 natural phleomycins were isolated.

After addition of various amine-type precursors (usually aliphatic mono-, di-, or triamines) to the fermentation, more than 200 artificial bleomycins and 20 artificial phleomycins have been isolated. From the natural bleomycins both enzymatic and chemical methods led to the preparation of terminal amine-free bleomycinic acid from which further new semisynthetic bleomycins can be derived. By chemical methods more than 200 additional semisynthetic bleomycins have been prepared. These derivatives are all different from one another in their terminal amine moiety.

Bleomycins are broad-spectrum antibiotics with moderate acute toxicity. They are strongly active against Gram-positive and mycobacteria and show strong activity against certain Gram-negative bacteria and fungi also.

The antitumor effect of bleomycin has some special features. It exhibits wide-ranging antitumor activity in experimental animal systems, including Ehrlich ascites carcinoma, S-180 sarcoma, murine mammary carcinomas, and Rous sarcoma virus, but cytotoxic activity on cell lines is relatively low.

Clinical studies confirmed the therapeutic effect of bleomycin in the pallitative treatment of human squamous cell carcinoma of the head and neck. It is slightly active on testicular carcinomas, some soft tissue sarcomas, and Hodgkin's disease. Objective responses have been obtained with malignant lymphoma and reticulosarcoma, but bleomycin was ineffective in many other tumors. It also inhibits replication of vaccinia virus and protects mice against the effects of vaccinia infection.

Bleomycin shows reversible hepatotoxicity but no renal toxicity in dogs, and it damages the lung. Pulmonary toxicity — from pneumonitis to fatal pulmonary fibrosis — occurs in about 10% of patients and is toxic to the skin and mucous membranes. A large dose causes hardening of skin and hair loss. On the other hand, bleomycin even in high doses does not cause leukopenia, thrombocytopenia, or any abnormal blood picture or immunosuppression. The lack of bone marrow and myelosuppressive toxicities indicates that bleomycin has a cytoselectivity that could not be achieved by any other antitumor antibiotic. These results indicate that bleomycin should be a very useful addition to a combination formulation for cancer therapy.

The individual bleomycins were found to differ in their degree of renal and lung toxicity. These untoward effects are dependent on terminal amines in the compounds. Substances containing two or more guanidine groups or an amidine group (bleomycins B_2, B_4, zorbamycin) cause irreversible renal toxicity. Some new bleomycin derivatives exhibit a two- to fourfold decrease of acute and chronic toxicity and their pulmonary toxicity is also lower. PEP-bleomycin (pepleomycin or 3-[(S)-1′-phenylethylamino]-aminopropylamino-bleomycin) inhibits rat stomach adenocarcinoma. The observed therapeutic effectiveness predicts its activity against human stomach cancer. Some other data also suggest the possibility that the new bleomycins will have a wider antitumor spectrum.

The antineoplastic effect of bleomycin can be attributed (in part) to its strand cleavage effects on DNA. Generally, bleomycin acts as a low molecular weight DNA-ase. Copper-free bleomycin, which escapes inactivations by bleomycin-hydrolase, binds and reacts with DNA and causes single-strand scission by a nonenzymatic reaction of native DNA. In the binding, the amino group of α-carboxamide and the carbamoyl groups are involved. Due to the chelation of these functions, Cu-bleomycins do not cause strand scission. In this reaction the terminal amine is indifferent, but its absence (bleomycinic acid) strongly reduces the binding ability of bleomycins.

The high therapeutic effect of bleomycin on squamous cell carcinoma is due to the low concentration of bleomycin-hydrolase and the high concentration of active bleomycin in this tumor. Bleomycin-hydrolase (aminopeptidase B), which is widely distributed in animal cells, hydrolyzes the amide group of copper-free bleomycins, thereby inactivating it (and not the Cu-bleomycin). After penetration into tumorous cells, the Cu^{++} ion in bleomycin is removed (after reduction to Cu^{+} ion) by sulfhydryl compounds and transferred to cellular proteins having the ability to bind Cu^{+}. The formed Cu-free bleomycin reaches the nucleus and inhibits the growth of cells, causing strand scission of DNA, inhibiting DNA-ligase resulting in DNA membrane breakage, inhibiting cell division, etc. As a result of the above outlined mechanism, the therapeutic action of bleomycin is enhanced by bestatin which is an aminopeptidase B inhibitor. The free radical producing or reducing agents (sulfhydryl compounds, H_2O_2, ascorbic acid) also enhance the activity of bleomycin.

The group of other chelate-forming antibiotics (4333) covers some different types of compounds. The antibacterial viridomycins are Fe^{+++} complexes of aromatic nitroso-formyl-phenols. These green pigments show absorption maxima in the visible region at 680 to 700 nm. Similarly to sideromycins, the antifungal trichostins are hydroxamic acid derivatives. Matchamycin is a Cu-chelated antibiotic.

REFERENCES

1. *Pure Appl. Chem.*, 28, 665, 1971.
2. *Biomedicine*, 18, 459, 1973.
3. *Fed. Proc.*, 33, 2296, 1974.
4. *Progr. Biochem. Pharmacol.*, 11, 18, 1976.
5. *Lloydia*, 40, 67, 1977.
6. *Jap. J. Ant.*, 30, S-41, 1977.

Structures

43320

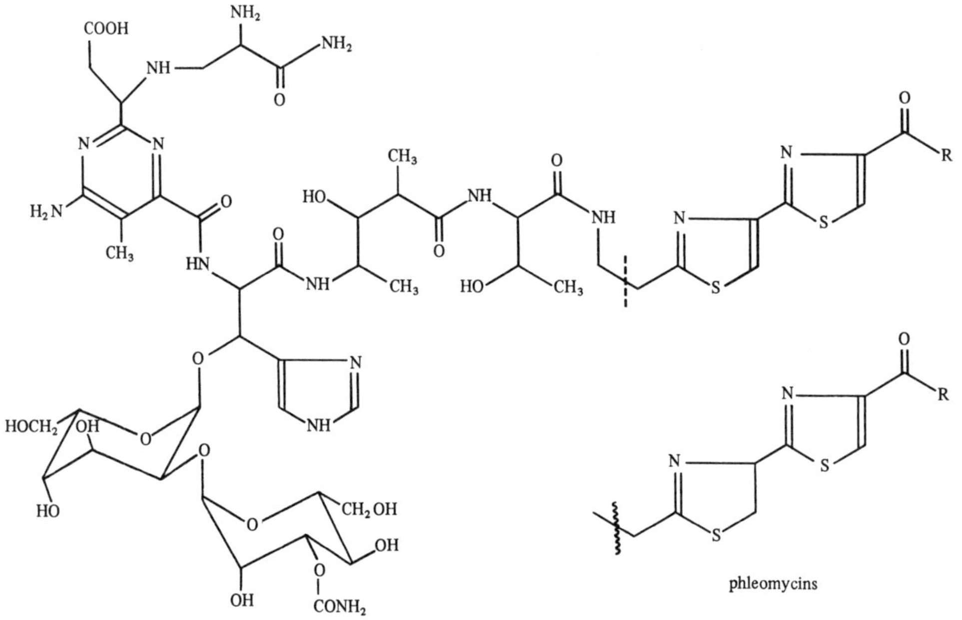

bleomycins   phleomycins

R = terminal amine

Bleomycins (phleomycins)	R
A_1	$NH(CH_2)_3SOCH_3$
A_2	$NH(CH_2)_3S^+(CH_3)_2$
A_2'-a	$NH(CH_2)_4NH_2$
A_2'-b	$NH(CH_2)_3NH_2$
A_2'-c	—NH(CH)$_2$— 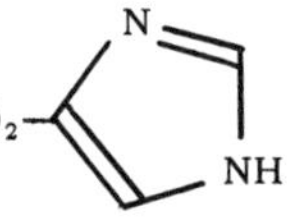
Demethyl A_2	$NH(CH_2)_2SCH_3$
A_5	$NH(CH_2)_3NH(CH_2)_4NH_2$
A_6	$NH(CH_2)_3NH(CH_2)_4NH(CH_2)_3NH_2$
B_1	$NHCH(COOH)(CH_2)_3NHC(NH)NH_2$
B_1	NH_2
$B_2(D_1)$	$NH(CH_2)_4NHC(NH)NH_2$
$B_4(E_1)$	$NH(CH_2)_4NHC(NH)NH(CH_2)_4NHC(NH)NH_2$

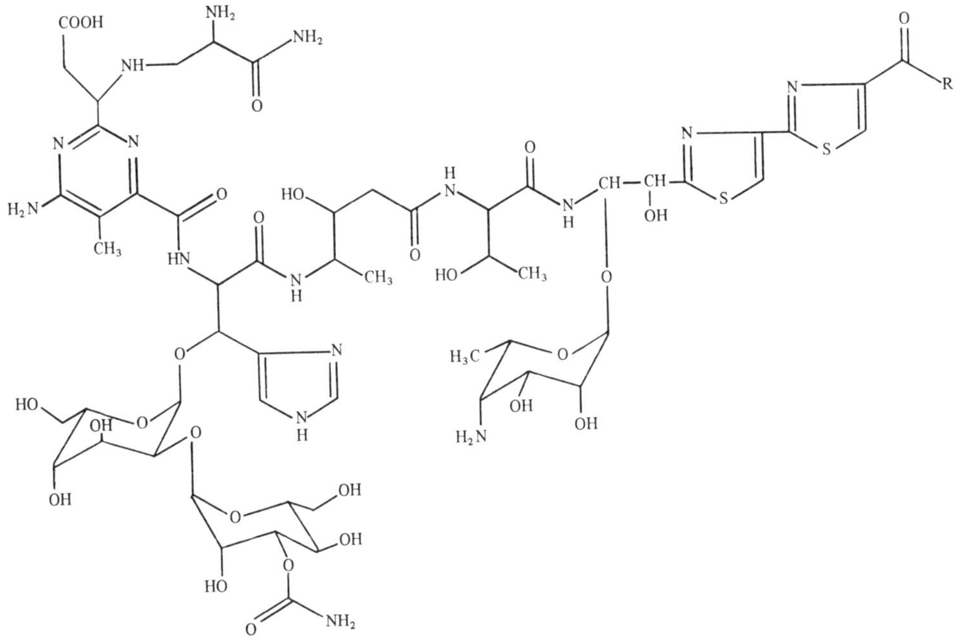

tallysomycin A R =

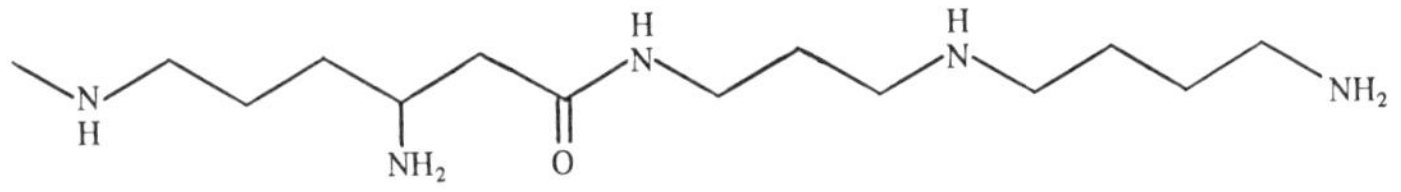

tallysomycin B R =

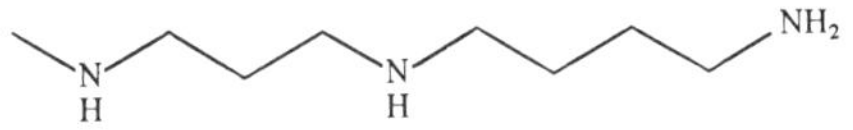

Tentative structures of some bleomycin-type antibiotics according to their degradation products:

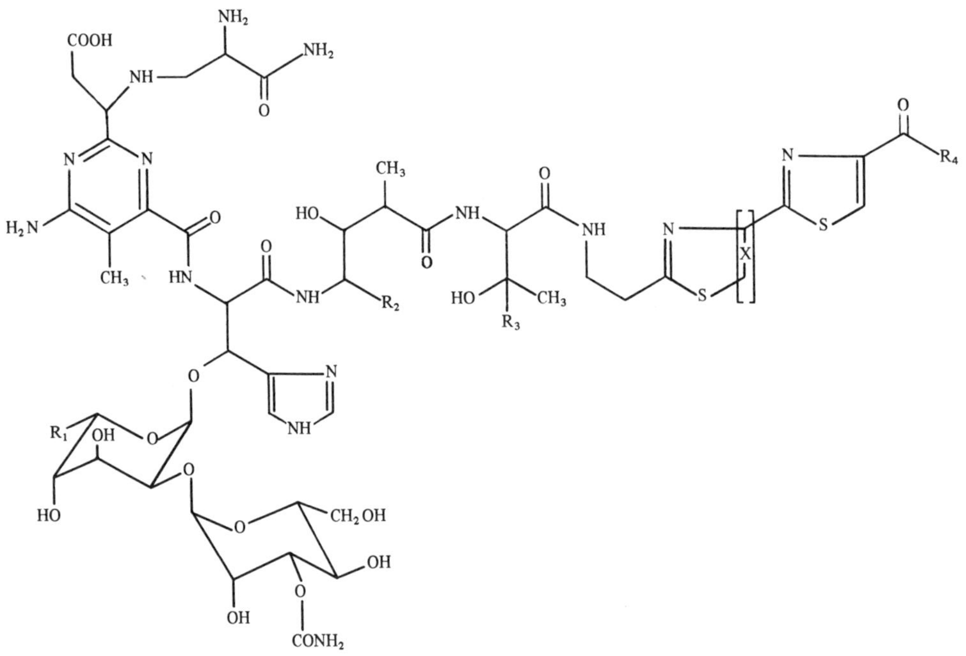

Antibiotic	R_1	R_2	R_3	R_4	X
Zorbamycin (YA-56X)	CH_3	CH_2CH_2OH	CH_3	$NHCH_2CH_2C(NH)NH_2$	$-CH_2-CH_2-$
Zorbamycin B	?	CH_2CH_2OH	H	$NHCH_2CH_2C(NH)NH_2$	$-CH=CH-$
YA-56-Y	CH_3	H	CH_3	$NHCH_2CH_2C(NH)NH_2$	$-CH_2-CH_2-$
Platomycin	CH_2OH	?	?	Guanidine	$-CH=CH-$
Bleomycins	CH_2OH	CH_3	H	Different groups	$-CH=CH-$
Phleomycins	CH_2OH	CH_3	H	Different groups	$-CH_2-CH_2-$
Tallysomycin B	CH_2OH	CH_3	H	Spermidine	$-CH=CH-$

43330

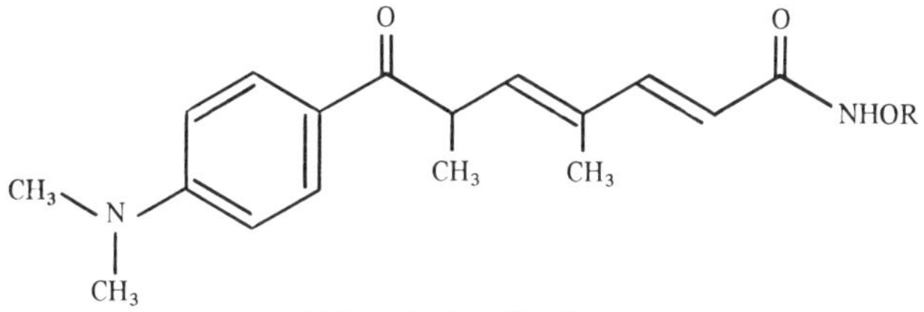

trichostatin A R = H
trichostatin B R = 1/3 Fe^{++}

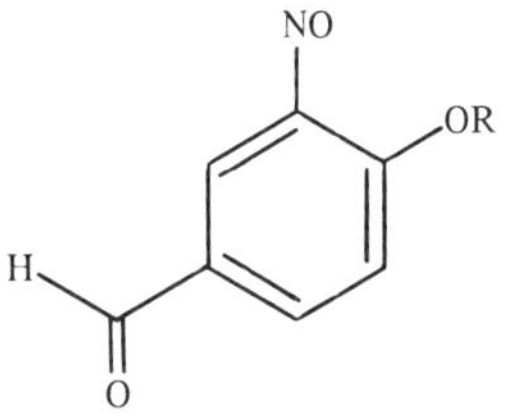

viridomycin A R = 1/2 Fe^{++}

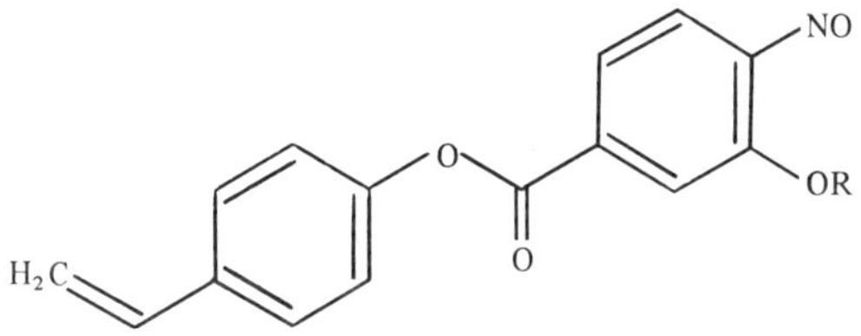

ferroverdin R = 1/2 Fe^{++}

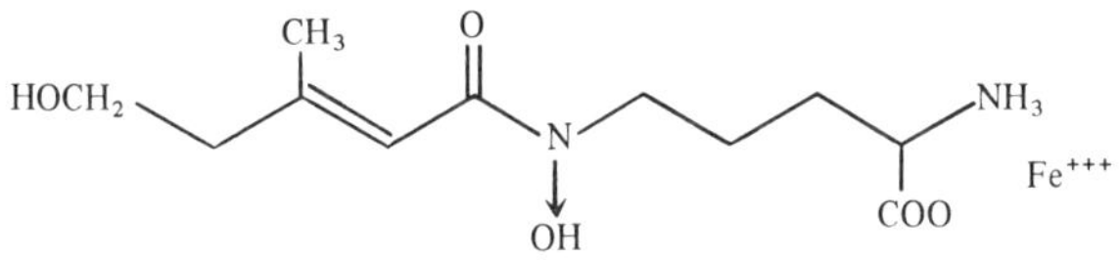

fusarinin

43320-1826

NAME:	BLEOMYCIN COMPLEX
TRADE NAMES:	BLEO, BLENOXANE
PO:	S.VERTICILLUS
CT:	BLEOMYCIN T., BASIC, GLYCOPEPTIDE
EA:	(C, 45) (H, 7) (N, 16) (S, 5) (O, 22) (CU, 5)
MW:	1600|200
PC:	BLUE, POW.
UV:	W: (244, ,) (295, ,) (620, ,)
SOL-GOOD:	MEOH, W
SOL-FAIR:	ETOH, BUOH
SOL-POOR:	ACET, HEX
QUAL:	(NINH., +) (PAULY, +) (EHRL., +) (SAKA., -) (BIURET, -) (FEHL., -) (FECL3, -)
STAB:	(ACID, +) (BASE, +)
TO:	(B.SUBT., 1.6) (S.AUREUS, .1) (S.LUTEA, .4) (E.COLI, .4) (K.PNEUM., .4) (SHYG., .4) (PS.AER., .4) (MYCOB.SP., .0004) (S.CEREV., 25) (FUNGI, 6) (PHYT.BACT., .4)
LD50:	(125, IV)
TV:	EHRLICH, S-180, L-1210, HELA, VACCINIA
IS-FIL:	3
IS-ION:	(IRC-50-H, HCL)
IS-CHR:	(SEPHADEX G-25, W)
IS-CRY:	(LIOF.,)
UTILITY:	ANTITUMOR DRUG

REFERENCES:

JA, 19, 200, 210, 1966; 20, 15, 149, 1967; 21, 79, 592, 1968; 23, 473, 1970; 25, 185, 197, 755, 1972; 26, 400, 521, 109, 1973; 27, 73, 1974; 29, 762, 1976; 30, 861, 870, 1977; *TL*, 4635, 1968; *Asian Med. J.*, 13, 190, 1970; *Appl. Micr.*, 22, 564, 1971; *Chem. Ph. Bull.*, 25, 1725, 1977; *Mutat. Res.*, 28, 107, 1975; *Cancer Res.*, 33, 2849, 1973; *JACS*, 99, 5078, 1977; *Biochem.*, 16, 2731, 1977; DT 2307986, 1217549; JP 65/8117

43320-1827

NAME: BLEOMYCIN-A1, NSC-125066
PO: S.VERTICILLUS
CT: BLEOMYCIN T., BASIC, GLYCOPEPTIDE
FORMULA: C54H77N16O22S3
EA: (N, 15) (S, 5) (O, 29)
PC: WH., POW.
UV: (244, 110,) (295, 85,)
SOL-GOOD: MEOH, W
SOL-FAIR: ETOH
SOL-POOR: ACET, HEX
QUAL: (PAULY, +) (EHRL., +) (NINH., -) (SAKA., -) (FECL3, -) (FEHL., -)
STAB: (ACID, +) (BASE, +)
TO: (S.AUREUS, 3) (S.LUTEA, 1.2) (B.SUBT., .1) (K.PNEUM., .6) (E.COLI, 2.5) (SHYG., .6) (MYCOB.SP., .04)
TV: ANTITUMOR
IS-CHR: (CM-SEPHADEX C-25, NH4-FORMIAT)
REFERENCES:

JA, 19, 200, 210, 1966; 20, 15, 149, 1967; 21, 79, 592, 1968; 23, 473, 1970; 25, 185, 197, 755, 1972; 26, 400, 521, 109, 1973; 27, 73, 1974; 29, 762, 1976; 30, 861, 870, 1977; *TL*, 4635, 1968; *Asian Med. J.*, 13, 190, 1970; *Appl. Micr.*, 22, 564, 1971; *Chem. Ph. Bull.*, 25, 1725, 1977; *Mutat. Res.*, 28, 107, 1975; *Cancer Res.*, 33, 2849, 1973; *JACS*, 99, 5078, 1977; *Biochem.*, 16, 2731, 1977; DT 2307986, 1217549; JP 65/8117

43320-1828

NAME: BLEOMYCIN-A2, NSC-146842
PO: S.VERTICILLUS
CT: BLEOMYCIN T., BASIC, GLYCOPEPTIDE
FORMULA: C55H80N16021S3
EA: (N, 15) (S, 6)
MW: 1550
PC: WH., BLUE, POW.
UV: W: (290, 120,) (243, 86,)
SOL-GOOD: MEOH, W
SOL-FAIR: ETOH
SOL-POOR: ACET, HEX
QUAL: (PAULY, +) (EHRL., +) (SAKA., -) (NINH., -) (FECL3, -) (FEHL., -)
STAB: (ACID, +) (BASE, +)
TO: (S.AUREUS, .1) (B.SUBT., .025) (S.LUTEA, .2) (MYCOB.SP., .0004) (E.COLI, .4) (K.PNEUM., .01) (SHYG., .1) (PS.AER., 50) (P.VULG., 1) (FUNGI, .2) (C.ALB., 100) (S.CEREV., 25)
LD50: (120, IV)
TV: S-180, EHRLICH, HELA
UTILITY: ANTITUMOR DRUG
REFERENCES:

JA, 19, 200, 210, 1966; 20, 15, 149, 1967; 21, 79, 592, 1968; 23, 473, 1970; 25, 185, 197, 755, 1972; 26, 400, 521, 109, 1973; 27, 73, 1974; 29, 762, 1976; 30, 861, 870, 1977; *TL*, 4635, 1968; *Asian Med. J.*, 13, 190, 1970; *Appl. Micr.*, 22, 564, 1971; *Chem. Ph. Bull.*, 25, 1725, 1977; *Mutat. Res.*, 28, 107, 1975; *Cancer Res.*, 33, 2849, 1973; JACS, 99, 5078, 1977; *Biochem.*, 16, 2731, 1977; DT 2307986, 1217549; JP 65/8117

43320-1829

NAME: BLEOMYCIN-A2′-B
PO: S.VERTICILLUS
CT: BLEOMYCIN T., BASIC, GLYCOPEPTIDE
FORMULA: C53H77N17021S2
EA: (N, 17) (S, 4)
MW: 1600
PC: WH., POW.
UV: W: (244, ,) (295, ,)
SOL-GOOD: MEOH, W
SOL-FAIR: ETOH
SOL-POOR: ACET, HEX
QUAL: (PAULY, +) (EHRL., +) (NINH., +) (SAKA., -) (FECL3, -) (FEHL., -)
STAB: (ACID, +) (BASE, +)
TO: (G.POS., .01) (G.NEG., .1) (MYCOB.SP., .001)
TV: ANTITUMOR
REFERENCES:

JA, 26, 396, 1973; 27, 73, 1974; *Pure Appl. Chem.*, 28, 665, 1971

43320-1830

NAME: BLEOMYCIN-A2′-A
PO: S.VERTICILLUS
CT: BLEOMYCIN T., BASIC, GLYCOPEPTIDE
FORMULA: C54H79N17O21S2
EA: (N,) (S,)
PC: WH., POW.
UV: W: (243, ,) (293, ,)
SOL-GOOD: MEOH, W
SOL-FAIR: ETOH
SOL-POOR: ACET, HEX
QUAL: (EHRL., +) (SAKA., -)
STAB: (ACID, +) (BASE, +)
TO: (G.POS., .01) (G.NEG., .1) (MYCOB.SP., .01)
TV: ANTITUMOR
REFERENCES:
JA, 26, 396, 1973; 27, 73, 1974; *Pure Appl. Chem.*, 28, 665, 1971

43320-1831

NAME: BLEOMYCIN-A2′-C
PO: S.VERTICILLUS
CT: BLEOMYCIN T., BASIC, GLYCOPEPTIDE
FORMULA: C55H77N18O21S2
EA: (N,) (S,)
PC: WH., POW.
UV: W: (243, ,) (295, ,)
SOL-GOOD: MEOH, W
SOL-FAIR: ETOH
SOL-POOR: ACET, HEX
QUAL: (EHRL., +) (SAKA., -)
STAB: (ACID, +) (BASE, +)
TO: (G.POS.,) (G.NEG.,)
TV: ANTITUMOR
REFERENCES:
JA, 26, 396, 1973; 27, 73, 1974; *Pure Appl. Chem.*, 28, 665, 1971

43320-1832

NAME:	DEMETHYLBLEOMYCIN-A2
PO:	S.VERTICILLUS
CT:	BLEOMYCIN T., BASIC, GLYCOPEPTIDE
FORMULA:	C54H78N16021S3
EA:	(N, 16) (S, 7)
PC:	WH., POW.
UV:	W: (243, ,) (293, ,)
SOL-GOOD:	MEOH, W
SOL-FAIR:	ETOH
SOL-POOR:	ACET, HEX
QUAL:	(EHRL., +) (SAKA., -)
STAB:	(ACID, +) (BASE, +)
TO:	(G.POS.,) (G.NEG.,)
TV:	ANTITUMOR

REFERENCES:

JA, 26, 396, 1973; 27, 73, 1974; *Pure Appl. Chem.*, 28, 665, 1971

43320-1833

NAME:	BLEOMYCIN-A3
PO:	S.VERTICILLUS
CT:	BLEOMYCIN T., BASIC, GLYCOPEPTIDE
EA:	(C,) (H,) (N,) (S,)
PC:	WH., POW.
UV:	W: (244, ,) (295, ,)
SOL-GOOD:	MEOH, W
SOL-FAIR:	ETOH
SOL-POOR:	ACET, HEX
QUAL:	(PAULY, +) (EHRL., +) (NINH., -) (SAKA., -) (FECL3, -) (FEHL., -)
STAB:	(ACID, +) (BASE, +)
TO:	(S.AUREUS, .1) (B.SUBT., .1) (S.LUTEA, .2) (E.COLI, .1) (K.PNEUM., .2) (SHYG., .05) (MYCOB.SP., .012)
TV:	ANTITUMOR

REFERENCES:

JA, 26, 396, 1973; 27, 73, 1974; *Pure Appl. Chem.*, 28, 665, 1971

43320-1834

NAME:	BLEOMYCIN-A4
PO:	S.VERTICILLUS
CT:	BLEOMYCIN T., BASIC, GLYCOPEPTIDE
EA:	(N,) (S,)
PC:	WH., POW.
UV:	W: (244, ,) (295, ,)
SOL-GOOD:	MEOH, W
SOL-FAIR:	ETOH
SOL-POOR:	ACET, HEX
QUAL:	(NINH., +) (PAULY, +) (EHRL., +) (SAKA., -) (FECL3, -) (FEHL., -)
STAB:	(ACID, +) (BASE, +)
TO:	(S.AUREUS, .4) (S.LUTEA, .4) (B.SUBT., .05) (E.COLI, .4) (K.PNEUM., .4) (SHYG., .4) (MYCOB.SP., .04)
TV:	ANTITUMOR

REFERENCES:

JA, 26, 396, 1973; 27, 73, 1974; *Pure Appl. Chem.*, 28, 665, 1971

43320-1835

NAME:	BLEOMYCIN-A5
PO:	S.VERTICILLUS
CT:	BLEOMYCIN T., BASIC, GLYCOPEPTIDE
FORMULA:	$C_{57}H_{86}N_{18}O_{21}S_2$
EA:	(N, 17) (S, 4)
PC:	WH., POW.
UV:	W: (244, ,) (295, ,)
SOL-GOOD:	MEOH, W
SOL-FAIR:	ETOH
SOL-POOR:	ACET, HEX
QUAL:	(NINH., +) (PAULY, +) (EHRL., +) (SAKA., -) (FEHL., -) (FECL3, -)
STAB:	(ACID, +) (BASE, +)
TO:	(S.AUREUS, .2) (S.LUTEA, .2) (B.SUBT., .05) (E.COLI, .02) (K.PNEUM., .02) (MYCOB.SP., .012)
TV:	ANTITUMOR

REFERENCES:

JA, 26, 396, 1973; 27, 73, 1974; *Pure Appl. Chem.*, 28, 665, 1971

43320-1836

NAME:	BLEOMYCIN-A6
PO:	S.VERTICILLUS
CT:	BLEOMYCIN T., BASIC, GLYCOPEPTIDE
FORMULA:	C60H93N19O21S2
EA:	(N, 17) (S, 4)
PC:	WH., POW.
UV:	W: (244, ,) (295, ,)
SOL-GOOD:	MEOH, W
SOL-FAIR:	ETOH
SOL-POOR:	ACET, HEX
QUAL:	(NINH., +) (PAULY, +) (EHRL., +) (SAKA., -) (FECL3, -) (FEHL., -)
STAB:	(ACID, +) (BASE, +)
TO:	(S.AUREUS, .2) (S.LUTEA, .2) (B.SUBT., .003) (E.COLI, .025) (K.PNEUM., .025) (SHYG., .012) (MYCOB.SP., .006)
TV:	ANTITUMOR

REFERENCES:

JA, 26, 396, 1973; 27, 73, 1974; *Pure Appl. Chem.*, 28, 665, 1971

43320-1837

NAME:	BLEOMYCIN-B1
IDENTICAL:	PHLEOMYCIN-D1
PO:	S.VERTICILLUS
CT:	BLEOMYCIN T., BASIC, GLYCOPEPTIDE
FORMULA:	C56H81N19O23S2
EA:	(N, 15) (S, 3)
PC:	WH., POW.
UV:	W: (244, ,) (296, ,)
SOL-GOOD:	MEOH, W
SOL-FAIR:	ETOH
SOL-POOR:	ACET, HEX
QUAL:	(SAKA., -)
STAB:	(ACID, +) (BASE, +)
TO:	(G.POS.,) (G.NEG.,)

REFERENCES:

JA, 26, 396, 1973; 27, 73, 1974; *Pure Appl. Chem.*, 28, 665, 1971

43320-1838

NAME:	BLEOMYCIN-B2, DEHYDROPHLEOMYCIN-D1
IDENTICAL:	PHLEOMYCIN-D2
PO:	S.VERTICILLUS
CT:	BLEOMYCIN T., BASIC, GLYCOPEPTIDE
FORMULA:	C55H81N19O21S2
EA:	(N, 16) (S, 5)
EW:	1540
PC:	WH., POW., BLUE
UV:	W: (244, 140,) (295, 110,)
SOL-GOOD:	MEOH, W
SOL-FAIR:	ETOH
SOL-POOR:	ACET, HEX
QUAL:	(BIURET, -) (SAKA., +) (FEHL., -) (EHRL., +) (PAULY, +) (FECL3, -) (NINH., -)
STAB:	(ACID, +) (BASE, +)
TO:	(S.AUREUS, .1) (S.LUTEA, 20) (B.SUBT., 1) (E.COLI, .1) (K.PNEUM., .1) (P.VULG., 1) (SHYG., 1) (PS.AER., 20) (MYCOB.SP., .01) (C.ALB., 100) (S.CEREV., 20) (PHYT.FUNGI, 1)
TV:	S-180, EHRLICH, HELA

REFERENCES:

JA, 26, 396, 1973; 27, 73, 1974; *Pure Appl. Chem.*, 28, 665, 1971

43320-1839

NAME:	BLEOMYCIN-B3
PO:	S.VERTICILLUS
CT:	BLEOMYCIN T., BASIC, GLYCOPEPTIDE
EA:	(N,) (S,)
PC:	WH., POW.
UV:	W: (244, ,) (295, ,)
SOL-GOOD:	MEOH, W
SOL-FAIR:	ETOH
SOL-POOR:	ACET, HEX
QUAL:	(SAKA., +) (EHRL., +) (PAULY, +) (NINH., -) (FECL3, -) (FEHL., -)
STAB:	(ACID, +) (BASE, +)
TO:	(S.AUREUS, .2) (S.LUTEA, .2) (B.SUBT., .025) (E.COLI, .4) (K.PNEUM., 1.5) (SHYG., .4) (MYCOB.SP., .01)
TV:	ANTITUMOR

REFERENCES:

JA, 26, 396, 1973; 27, 73, 1974; *Pure Appl. Chem.*, 28, 665, 1971

43320-1840

NAME: BLEOMYCIN-B4, DEHYDROPHLEOMYCIN-E
IDENTICAL: PHLEOMYCIN-F
PO: S.VERTICILLUS
CT: BLEOMYCIN T., BASIC, GLYCOPEPTIDE
FORMULA: C60H94N22O21S2
EA: (N, 18) (S, 4)
PC: WH., POW.
UV: W: (244, ,) (295, ,)
SOL-GOOD: MEOH, W
SOL-FAIR: ETOH
SOL-POOR: ACET, HEX
QUAL: (SAKA., +) (PAULY, +) (EHRL., +) (NINH., -) (FEHL., -) (FECL3, -)
STAB: (ACID, +) (BASE, +)
TO: (S.AUREUS, .1) (S.LUTEA, .1) (B.SUBT., .05) (K.PNEUM., 3.1) (E.COLI, .5) (SHYG., .1) (MYCOB.SP., .06)
TV: ANTITUMOR
REFERENCES:
JA, 26, 396, 1973; 27, 73, 1974; *Pure Appl. Chem.*, 28, 665, 1971

43320-1841

NAME: BLEOMYCIN-B6
IDENTICAL: PHLEOMYCIN-G′
PO: S.VERTICILLUS
CT: BLEOMYCIN T., BASIC, GLYCOPEPTIDE
EA: (N,) (S,)
PC: WH., POW.
UV: W: (244, ,) (295, ,)
SOL-GOOD: MEOH, W
SOL-FAIR: ETOH
SOL-POOR: ACET, HEX
QUAL: (SAKA., +) (PAULY, +) (EHRL., +) (NINH., -) (FECL3, -) (FEHL., -)
STAB: (ACID, +) (BASE, +)
TO: (G.POS.,) (MYCOB.SP.,)
REFERENCES:
JA, 26, 396, 1973; 27, 73, 1974; *Pure Appl. Chem.*, 28, 665, 1971

43320-1842

NAME: PHLEOMYCIN, CU-PHLEOMYCIN COMPLEX, NSC-61586
PO: S.VERTICILLUS
CT: BLEOMYCIN T., BASIC, GLYCOPEPTIDE
FORMULA: C53H91N17O32CU
EA: (N, 16) (CU, 4)
MW: 1500
PC: BLUE, POW.
UV: W: (244, 135,) (297.5|2.5, 47,)
QUAL: (NINH., +) (PAULY, +) (SAKA., +) (FEHL., -) (BIURET, -) (FECL3, -) (EHRL., +)
STAB: (ACID, -) (BASE, +)
TO: (B.SUBT., .3) (S.AUREUS, .5) (K.PNEUM., .5) (E.COLI, .2) (SHYG, .2) (PS.AER., 4) (P.VULG., 4) (MYCOB.SP., .05)
LD50: (45|5, IV) (150, IV)
TV: ANTITUMOR
IS-FIL: 3
IS-ION: (IRC-50-NA, NACL) (IRC-50-H, HCL)
IS-CHR: (AL, MEOH-W) (CM-SEPHADEX C-25, NH4-FORMIAT)
IS-CRY: (PREC., W, ACET)
REFERENCES:

JA, 9, 82, 1956; 12, 111, 285, 1957; 15, 274, 1962; 16, 86, 1963; 17, 194, 1964; 19, 260, 1960; *AAC, 1962,* 740; Cancer Res., 29, 912, 1969; *Nature,* 196, 652, 783, 1962; *An. N.Y. Acad. Sci.,* 76, 20, 1958; *JA,* 25, 752, 755, 1972; JP 59/2595, 61/10697

43320-1843

NAME: PHLEOMYCIN-C
PO: S.VERTICILLUS
CT: BLEOMYCIN T., BASIC, GLYCOPEPTIDE
EA: (N,) (S,) (CU,)
PC: BLUE, POW.
UV: MEOH: (245, 121,) (295, 90,)
SOL-GOOD: W
SOL-FAIR: MEOH
SOL-POOR: BUOH, HEX
QUAL: (SAKA., +) (PAULY, +) (EHRL., +) (NINH., -) (FEHL., -) (FECL3, -)
STAB: (ACID, -) (BASE, +)
TO: (S.AUREUS, .8) (B.SUBT., .05) (S.LUTEA, .8) (E.COLI, .8) (K.PNEUM., 1.5) (SHYG., .2) (MYCOB.SP., .025)
TV: EHRLICH, HELA
REFERENCES:

JA, 9, 82, 1956; 12, 111, 285, 1957; 15, 274, 1962; 16, 86, 1963; 17, 194, 1964; 19, 260, 1960; *AAC, 1962,* 740; *Cancer Res.,* 29, 912, 1969; *Nature,* 196, 652, 783, 1962; *An. N.Y. Acad. Sci.,* 76, 20, 1958; *JA,* 25, 752, 755, 1972; JP 59/2595, 61/1069

43320-1844

NAME:	PHLEOMYCIN-D1, DIHYDROBLEOMYCIN-B2
PO:	S.VERTICILLUS
CT:	BLEOMYCIN T., BASIC, GLYCOPEPTIDE
FORMULA:	C55H83N19O21S2CU
EA:	(N, 17) (S, 3) (CU, 3)
EW:	1415
PC:	BLUE, POW.
OR:	(+,)
UV:	MEOH: (244, 128,) (301, 46.8,)
SOL-GOOD:	W
SOL-FAIR:	MEOH
SOL-POOR:	BUOH, HEX
QUAL:	(EHRL., +) (SAKA., +) (NINH., -) (BIURET, -) (FEHL., -) (FECL3, -)
STAB:	(ACID, -) (BASE, +)
TO:	(B.SUBT., .1) (S.AUREUS, .8) (E.COLI, .8) (MYCOB.SP., .0001)
LD50:	(37.5|12.5, IV)
TV:	HELA, EHRLICH, S-180, CA-755
IS-CHR:	(CM-SEPHADEX C-25, NH4-FORMIAT)

REFERENCES:

JA, 9, 82, 1956; 12, 111, 285, 1957; 15, 274, 1962; 16, 86, 1963; 17, 194, 1964; 19, 260, 1960; *AAC, 1962,* 740; *Cancer Res.*, 29, 912, 1969; *Nature*, 196, 652, 783, 1962; *An. N.Y. Acad. Sci.*, 76, 20, 1958; *JA*, 25, 752, 755, 1972; JP 59/2595, 61/10697

43320-1845

NAME:	PHLEOMYCIN-D2
IDENTICAL:	BLEOMYCIN-B2
PO:	S.VERTICILLUS
CT:	BLEOMYCIN T., BASIC, GLYCOPEPTIDE
EA:	(N, 16) (S, 3)
PC:	BLUE, POW.
UV:	MEOH: (244, 120,) (295, 89.5,)
SOL-GOOD:	W
SOL-FAIR:	MEOH
SOL-POOR:	BUOH, HEX
QUAL:	(SAKA., -)
STAB:	(ACID, -) (BASE, +)
TO:	(B.SUBT., .1) (S.AUREUS, .8) (E.COLI, .8) (MYCOB.SP., .0055)
TV:	ANTITUMOR

REFERENCES:

JA, 9, 82, 1956; 12, 111, 285, 1957; 15, 274, 1962; 16, 86, 1963; 17, 194, 1964; 19, 260, 1960; *AAC, 1962,* 740; *Cancer Res.*, 29, 912, 1969; *Nature*, 196, 652, 783, 1962; *An. N.Y. Acad. Sci.*, 76, 20, 1958; *JA*, 25, 752, 755, 1972; JP 59/2595, 61/10697

43320-1846

NAME: PHLEOMYCIN-E, DIHYDROBLEOMYCIN-B4
PO: S.VERTICILLUS
CT: BLEOMYCIN T., BASIC, GLYCOPEPTIDE
FORMULA: C60H96N22O21S2
EA: (N, 18) (S, 3)
EW: 1171
PC: BLUE, POW.
OR: (+68, W)
UV: MEOH: (244, 128,) (301, 41.8,)
SOL-GOOD: W
SOL-FAIR: MEOH
SOL-POOR: BUOH, HEX
QUAL: (EHRL., +) (SAKA., +) (NINH., -) (BIURET, -) (FEHL., -) (FECL3, -)
STAB: (ACID, -) (BASE, +)
TO: (S.AUREUS, .04) (B.SUBT., .0008) (E.COLI, .8) (MYCOB.SP., .0015)
LD50: (37.5|12.5, IV)
TV: EHRLICH, HELA
REFERENCES:

JA, 9, 82, 1956; 12, 111, 285, 1957; 15, 274, 1962; 16, 86, 1963; 17, 194, 1964; 19, 260, 1960; *AAC, 1962*, 740; *Cancer Res.*, 29, 912, 1969; *Nature*, 196, 652, 783, 1962; *An. N.Y. Acad. Sci.*, 76, 20, 1958; *JA*, 25, 752, 755, 1972; JP 59/2595, 61/10697

43320-1847

NAME: PHLEOMYCIN-F, BLEOMYCIN-B5, CU-BT-5
IDENTICAL: BLEOMYCIN-B4
PO: S.VERTICILLUS
CT: BLEOMYCIN T., BASIC, GLYCOPEPTIDE
EA: (C, 41) (H, 6) (N, 17) (S, 3) (CU, 3)
UV: MEOH: (244, 122,) (295, 95.4,)
SOL-GOOD: W
SOL-FAIR: MEOH
SOL-POOR: BUOH, HEX
QUAL: (EHRL., +) (SAKA., +) (PAULY, +) (NINH., -) (BIURET, -) (FECL3, -) (FEHL., -)
STAB: (ACID, -) (BASE, +)
TO: (S.AUREUS, .1) (B.SUBT., .012) (S.LUTEA, .2) (E.COLI, .8) (K.PNEUM., 1.5) (SHYG., .2) (MYCOB.SP., .0008)
TV: EHRLICH, HELA
REFERENCES:

JA, 9, 82, 1956; 12, 111, 285, 1957; 15, 274, 1962; 16, 86, 1963, 17, 194, 1964; 19, 260, 1960; *AAC, 1962*, 740; *Cancer Res.*, 29, 912, 1969; *Nature*, 196, 652, 783, 1962; *An. N.Y. Acad. Sci.*, 76, 20, 1958; *JA*, 25, 752, 755, 1972; JP 59/2595, 61/10697

43320-1848

NAME: PHLEOMYCIN-G, DIHYDROBLEOMYCIN-B6
PO: S.VERTICILLUS
CT: BLEOMYCIN T., BASIC, GLYCOPEPTIDE
FORMULA: C26H49N9012SCU
EA: (N, 15) (S, 4) (CU, 7)
EW: 808
PC: BLUE, POW.
OR: (+84, W)
UV: MEOH: (244, 138,) (301, 49,)
SOL-GOOD: W
SOL-FAIR: MEOH
SOL-POOR: BUOH, HEX
QUAL: (EHRL., +) (SAKA., -) (NINH., -) (BIURET, -) (FEHL., -) (FECL3, -)
STAB: (ACID, -) (BASE, +)
TO: (S.AUREUS, 6.25) (B.SUBT., .8) (E.COLI, 50) (MYCOB.SP., .1)
LD50: (200, IV)
REFERENCES:

JA, 9, 82, 1956; 12, 111, 285, 1957; 15, 274, 1962; 16, 86, 1963; 17, 194, 1964; 19, 260, 1960; *AAC, 1962*, 740; *Cancer Res.*, 29, 912, 1969; *Nature*, 196, 652, 783, 1962; *An. N.Y. Acad. Sci.*, 76, 20, 1958; *JA*, 25, 752, 755, 1972; JP 59/2595, 61/10697

43320-1849

NAME: PHLEOMYCIN-H
PO: S.VERTICILLUS
CT: BLEOMYCIN T., BASIC, GLYCOPEPTIDE
FORMULA: C42H72N16018SCU2
EA: (N, 17) (S, 2) (CU, 5)
EW: 1250
PC: BLUE, POW.
OR: (+75, W)
UV: MEOH: (244, 120,) (301, 43.7,)
SOL-GOOD: W
SOL-FAIR: MEOH
SOL-POOR: BUOH, HEX
QUAL: (EHRL., +) (SAKA., +) (NINH., -) (BIURET, -) (FEHL., -) (FECL3, -)
STAB: (ACID, -) (BASE, +)
TO: (S.AUREUS, 25) (B.SUBT., .4) (E.COLI, 50) (MYCOB.SP., .05)
LD50: (200, IV)
TV: EHRLICH
REFERENCES:

JA, 9, 82, 1956; 12, 111, 285, 1957; 15, 274, 1962; 16, 86, 1963; 17, 194, 1964; 19, 260, 1960; *AAC, 1962*, 740; *Cancer Res.*, 29, 912, 1969; *Nature*, 196, 652, 783, 1962; *An. N.Y. Acad. Sci.*, 76, 20, 1958; *JA*, 25, 752, 755, 1972; JP 59/2595, 61/10697

43320-1850

NAME: PHLEOMYCIN-I
PO: S.VERTICILLUS
CT: BLEOMYCIN T., BASIC, GLYCOPEPTIDE
FORMULA: C59H111N21O32S2CU
EA: (N, 16) (S, 3) (CU, 4)
PC: BLUE, POW.
UV: MEOH: (244, 121,) (301, 44.2,)
SOL-GOOD: W
SOL-FAIR: MEOH
SOL-POOR: BUOH, HEX
QUAL: (EHRL., +) (SAKA., +) (NINH., -) (BIURET, -) (FEHL., -) (FECL3, -)
STAB: (ACID, -) (BASE, +)
TO: (S.AUREUS, 60) (B.SUBT., .2) (E.COLI, 50) (MYCOB.SP., .006)
LD50: (800, IV)
TV: EHRLICH
REFERENCES:
JA, 9, 82, 1956; 12, 111, 285, 1957; 15, 274, 1962; 16, 86, 1963; 17, 194, 1964; 19, 260, 1960; *AAC, 1962,* 740; *Cancer Res.,* 29, 912, 1969; *Nature,* 196, 652, 783, 1962; *An. N.Y. Acad. Sci.,* 76, 20, 1958; *JA,* 25, 752, 755, 1972; JP 59/2595, 61/10697

43320-1851

NAME: ZORBAMYCIN, ZORBONAMYCIN, U-30604, NSC-146208
IDENTICAL: YA-56-X
PO: S.BIKINIENSIS
CT: BLEOMYCIN T., BASIC, GLYCOPEPTIDE
PC: BLUE, POW.
OR: (+,)
UV: (244, ,) (295, ,)
SOL-GOOD: W, MEOH
SOL-POOR: BUOH, HEX
TO: (S.AUREUS, 1) (B.SUBT., 10) (E.COLI, 1) (SHYG., 1) (K.PNEUM., 1) (PS.AER., 50) (MYCOB.SP., .1) (FUNGI,)
TV: ANTITUMOR, EHRLICH, HELA, S-180
REFERENCES:
J. Bact., 105, 880, 1971; *JA,* 24, 543, 1971; BP 1277150

43320-1852

NAME: YA-56-X
IDENTICAL: ZORBAMYCIN
PO: S.HUMIDUS-ANTITUMORIS
CT: BLEOMYCIN T., BASIC, GLYCOPEPTIDE
EA: (C, 45) (H, 6) (N, 18) (S, 5)
MW: 559, 1800|200
PC: WH., POW.
OR: (+20, W)
UV: W: (234, 155.9,) (295, 36.9,)
SOL-GOOD: W, MEOH, DMFA, DMSO
SOL-FAIR: ETOH
SOL-POOR: BUOH, HEX
QUAL: (NINH., -) (EHRL., +) (PAULY, +) (SAKA., -) (BIURET, -)
STAB: (BASE, +)
TO: (S.AUREUS, .5) (B.SUBT., .1) (E.COLI, .4) (K.PNEUM., .5) (SHYG., 1) (P.VULG.,) (MYCOB.SP.,)
TV: EHRLICH
IS-FIL: 6.8
IS-ION: (DUOLIT-S-30, ACET-HCL)
IS-CHR: (AL, W) (SEPHADEX LH-20, MEOH)
REFERENCES:
Agr. Biol. Ch., 37, 2277—2387, 1973

43320-1853

NAME: ZORBAMYCIN-B, U-32166-E
PO: S.BIKINIENSIS
CT: BLEOMYCIN T., BASIC, GLYCOPEPTIDE
FORMULA: C58H94N19015
EA: (N, 16) (S, 4)
EW: 660
PC: WH., POW.
UV: W: (235, 64,) (293, 48,)
SOL-GOOD: W, MEOH
SOL-POOR: BUOH, HEX
TO: (S.AUREUS, .2) (E.COLI, .1) (SHYG., .1) (K.PNEUM., .01) (S.LUTEA, 25) (P.VULG., .2)
TV: ANTITUMOR
REFERENCES:
JA, 24, 543, 1971; DT 2124711

43320-1854

NAME: ZORBAMYCIN-C
PO: S.BIKINIENSIS
CT: BLEOMYCIN T., BASIC, GLYCOPEPTIDE
EA: (N,) (S,) (CU,)
PC: BLUE, POW.
UV: W: (243, ,) (293, ,)
SOL-GOOD: MEOH, W
SOL-POOR: BUOH, HEX
TO: (S.AUREUS, .1) (S.LUTEA, 20) (E.COLI, .1) (K.PNEUM., .1) (SHYG.,)
REFERENCES:
JA, 24, 543, 1971; DT 2124711

43320-1855

NAME: PLATOMYCIN-A, XK-78-1
PO: STREPTOSPORANGIUM VIOLACEOCHROMOGENES-GLOBOPHILUM
CT: BLEOMYCIN T., BASIC, GLYCOPEPTIDE
EA: (C, 40) (H, 6) (N, 15) (S, 2) (CU, 4)
PC: BLUE, POW.
OR: (-100, W)
UV: W: (244, 110,) (293, 84,)
SOL-GOOD: MEOH, W
SOL-FAIR: ETOH
SOL-POOR: BUOH, HEX
QUAL: (EHRL., +) (SAKA., +) (PAULY, +) (NINH., -) (FECL3, -)
STAB: (ACID, +) (BASE, -)
TO: (S.AUREUS, .014) (B.SUBT., .007) (E.COLI, .007) (SHYG., .053) (K.PNEUM., .027)
LD50: (25, IV) (40, IP)
TV: S-180, EHRLICH, HELA
IS-FIL: 6.8
IS-ION: (IRC-50-H, HCL)
IS-CHR: (CM-SEPHADEX C-25, NH4-FORMIAT)
IS-CRY: (LIOF.,)
REFERENCES:
Abst. AAC, 14, 193, 1974; *JA*, 28, 656, 662, 1975; DT 2408121; Belg. P 811311

43320-1856

NAME:	PLATOMYCIN-B, XK-78-2
PO:	STREPTOSPORANGIUM VIOLACEOCHROMOGENES-GLOBOPHILUM
CT:	BLEOMYCIN T., BASIC, GLYCOPEPTIDE
EA:	(C, 40) (H, 6) (N, 15) (S, 3) (CU, 5)
PC:	BLUE, POW.
OR:	(+112, W)
UV:	W: (244, 102,) (293, 83,)
SOL-GOOD:	W, MEOH
SOL-FAIR:	ETOH
SOL-POOR:	BUOH, HEX
QUAL:	(SAKA., +) (EHRL., +) (PAULY, +) (NINH., -)
STAB:	(ACID, +) (BASE, -)
TO:	(S.AUREUS, .001) (B.SUBT., .001) (E.COLI, .004) (P.VULG., .21) (SHYG., .014) (K.PNEUM., .014)
LD50:	(12.5, IV) (35, IP)
TV:	S-180, EHRLICH, HELA

REFERENCES:

Abst. AAC, 14, 193, 1974; *JA,* 28, 656, 662, 1975; DT 2408121; Belg. P 811311

43320-1857

NAME:	YA-56-Y
PO:	S.HUMIDUS-ANTITUMORIS
CT:	BLEOMYCIN T., BASIC, GLYCOPEPTIDE
EA:	(C, 43) (H, 6) (N, 15) (S, 4)
MW:	1500
PC:	WH., POW.
OR:	(+134.8, W)
UV:	W: (241, 117.5,) (297, 36.4,)
SOL-GOOD:	MEOH, W, DMFA
SOL-FAIR:	ETOH
SOL-POOR:	BUOH, HEX
QUAL:	(EHRL., +) (PAULY, +) (SAKA., -) (BIURET, -) (NINH., -)
STAB:	(BASE, +) (ACID, +)
TO:	(S.AUREUS, .01) (B.SUBT., .01) (E.COLI, .4) (SHYG., .1) (K.PNEUM., .4) (MYCOB.SP., .2)
LD50:	(52, IV)
TV:	ANTITUMOR

REFERENCES:

Agr. Biol. Ch., 37, 2277, 2287, 2383, 1973; *JA,* 24, 727, 1971; 25, 356, 543, 1972; 26, 77, 83, 1973; DT 2206637; JP 72/2557

43320-1858

NAME: VICTOMYCIN, XK-49-1-B-2
PO: STREPTOSPORANGIUM VIOLACEOCHROMOGENES
CT: BLEOMYCIN T., BASIC, GLYCOPEPTIDE
EA: (C, 32) (H, 6) (N, 14) (CU, 3)
PC: BLUE, POW.
UV: W: (244, 134,) (293, 100,)
SOL-GOOD: MEOH, W
SOL-FAIR: ETOH
SOL-POOR: BUOH, HEX
QUAL: (SAKA., +) (PAULY, +) (EHRL., +) (NINH., -)
TO: (S.AUREUS, .06) (B.SUBT., .011) (E.COLI, .04) (K.PNEUM., .03) (PS.AER., 10.4) (P.VULG., 1.32) (SHYG., .005)
TV: EHRLICH, S-180, HELA
IS-ION: (IRC-50-H, HCL)
IS-CHR: (SEPHADEX LH-20, MEOH-W)
IS-CRY: (LIOF.,)
REFERENCES:
JA, 28, 358, 366, 1975; Belg. P 804529; DT 2344780

43320-5076

NAME: SS-70-A
PO: S.OLIVOGRISEUS
CT: BASIC, BLEOMYCIN T., GLYCOPEPTIDE
EA: (C, 41) (H, 6) (N, 16) (S, 5) (CU, 4)
MW: 1781
PC: BLUE, POW.
UV: W: (243, 124,) (298, 42,)
SOL-GOOD: W
SOL-FAIR: MEOH
SOL-POOR: BUOH, HEX
QUAL: (EHRL., +) (NINH., -)
STAB: (ACID, -) (BASE, +)
TO: (S.AUREUS, 1.56) (B.SUBT., .39) (S.LUTEA, .19) (E.COLI, 19) (K.PNEUM., .56)
TV: ANTITUMOR
IS-ABS: (XAD-2, MEOH-HCL)
IS-CHR: (XAD-2, MEOH-W) (CM-SEPHADEX C-25-H, NACL)
REFERENCES:
Sci. Rep. Meiji, 16, 29, 1976; JP 76/15694

43320-5077

NAME: SS-70-B
PO: S.OLIVOGRISEUS
CT: BASIC, BLEOMYCIN T., GLYCOPEPTIDE
EA: (C, 42) (H, 6) (N, 17) (S, 4) (CU, 3)
MW: 1830
PC: BLUE, POW.
UV: W: (243, 130,) (298, 46.4,)
SOL-GOOD: W
SOL-FAIR: MEOH
SOL-POOR: BUOH, HEX
QUAL: (EHRL., +) (NINH., -)
STAB: (BASE, +) (ACID, -)
TO: (S.AUREUS, 3) (B.SUBT., .78) (S.LUTEA, .19) (E.COLI,)
REFERENCES:
Sci. Rep. Meiji, 16, 29, 1976; JP 76/15694

43320-5431

NAME: TALLYSOMYCIN-A, BU-2231-A
PO: STREPTOALLOTEICHUS HINDUSTANUS
CT: BASIC, BLEOMYCIN T., GLYCOPEPTIDE
FORMULA: C68H107N21O27S2
EA: (N, 16) (S, 4)
MW: 1736
PC: WH., POW.
OR: (-21, W)
UV: W: (290, ,)
SOL-GOOD: W, MEOH, DMFA
SOL-FAIR: ETOH
SOL-POOR: BUOH, HEX
QUAL: (NINH., +) (FEHL., -) (SAKA., -)
TO: (S.AUREUS, .1) (B.SUBT., .2) (S.LUTEA,) (E.COLI, .025) (K.PNEUM., .0063) (P.VULG., .8) (PS.AER., .2) (C.ALB., .8) (S.CEREV., .4) (PIRICULARIA ORYZAE, 1.6)
LD50: (28, SC) (17, IV) (19, IP)
TV: WALKER-256, LEWIS, B-16, P-388, S-180, LEWIS, MELANOMA, P-388, S-180
IS-ION: (IRC-50-NH4, HCL)
IS-ABS: (CARBON, BUOH-HCL)
IS-CHR: (XAD-2, W) (CM-SEPHADEX C-25, AMMONIUMFORMIAT) (SEPHADEX LH-20, MEOH)
REFERENCES:
JA, 30, 779, 789, 1977; Belg. P 845513; USP 4051237

43320-5432

NAME:	BU-2231-B, TALLYSOMYCIN-B
PO:	STREPTOALLOTEICHUS HINDUSTANUS
CT:	BASIC, BLEOMYCIN T., GLYCOPEPTIDE
FORMULA:	C62H95N19026S2
EA:	(N, 16) (S, 4)
MW:	1608
PC:	WH., POW.
OR:	(-19, W)
UV:	W: (289.5, 77,)
SOL-GOOD:	W, MEOH, DMFA
SOL-FAIR:	ETOH
SOL-POOR:	BUOH, HEX
QUAL:	(NINH., +) (FEHL., -) (SAKA., -)
TO:	(S.AUREUS, .05) (B.SUBT., .2) (S.LUTEA,) (E.COLI, .05) (K.PNEUM., .025) (P.VULG., .2) (PS.AER., .2) (C.ALB., .8) (S.CEREV., .2) (PIRICULARIA ORYZAE, 1.6)
LD50:	(70|20, SC) (30, IV) (46, IP)
TV:	WALKER-256, LEWIS, B-16, P-388, S-180, LEWIS, MELANOMA, P-388, S-180

REFERENCES:

JA, 30, 779, 789, 1977; Belg. P 845513; USP 4051237

43320-5689

NAME:	SF-1771
PO:	S.TOYOCAENSIS
CT:	BLEOMYCIN T., BASIC, GLYCOPEPTIDE
EA:	(C, 30) (H, 6) (N, 13) (O, 30) (S, 4) (CU, 4)
MW:	1600
PC:	BLUE, POW.
UV:	W: (248, 146,) (283|1, 106,)
SOL-GOOD:	W
SOL-FAIR:	ETOH, BUOH
SOL-POOR:	ACET-HEX
QUAL:	(NINH., +) (EHRL., +) (SAKA., -)
STAB:	(ACID, +) (BASE, -)
TO:	(S.AUREUS, 3.12) (B.SUBT., 1.56) (PS.AER., 25) (E.COLI, .39) (C.ALB., 12.5) (S.CEREV., 12.5) (FUNGI, 1.56)
LD50:	(12.5, IV)
TV:	HELA, S-180
IS-ION:	(XAD-2, ACET-W-HCL)
IS-CHR:	(CM-SEPHADEX E-25-H, NACL) (SEPHADEX LH-20, BUOH-MEOH-W)

REFERENCES:

DT 2649604

43320-5690

NAME: SF-1771-B
PO: S.TOYOCAENSIS
CT: BLEOMYCIN T., BASIC, GLYCOPEPTIDE
EA: (C, 43) (H, 6) (N, 16) (O, 30) (S, 4)
MW: 1600
PC: WH., YELLOW, POW.
OR: (-18.4, W)
UV: W: (289, 84,)
SOL-GOOD: W, MEOH
SOL-FAIR: ETOH, BUOH
SOL-POOR: ACET, HEX
QUAL: (NINH., +) (EHRL., +) (SAKA., -)
STAB: (ACID, +) (BASE, -)
TO: (S.AUREUS, 6.25) (B.SUBT., 1.56) (PS.AER., 50) (E.COLI, .39)
LD50: (25, IV)
TV: HELA, S-180
REFERENCES:

DT 2649604

43320-5691

PO: S.BIKINIENSIS-ZORBONENSIS
CT: BLEOMYCIN T., GLYCOPEPTIDE
TO: (B.SUBT.,) (S.AUREUS,) (K.PNEUM.,)
REFERENCES:

J. Bact., 105, 880, 1971

43320-5692

NAME: 3-AMINOPROPYLAMINO-BLEOMYCIN
PO: S.VERTICILLUS+1.3-DIAMINOPROPANE
CT: BLEOMYCIN T., BASIC, GLYCOPEPTIDE
EA: (C, 43) (H, 6) (N, 17) (S, 4)
PC: BLUE, POW.
UV: W: (244, ,) (293, ,)
SOL-GOOD: W
SOL-POOR: ACET, HEX
QUAL: (NINH., +) (SAKA., -)
TO: (MYCOB.TUB., .1)
REFERENCES:

Belg. P 745926

43320-5693

NAME: 3-BUTYL-3-AMINOPROPYL-BLEOMYCIN
PO: S.VERTICILLUS+BUTYL-AMINOPROPANE
CT: BLEOMYCIN T., BASIC, GLYCOPEPTIDE
EA: (C, 43) (H, 6) (N, 16) (S, 4)
UV: W: (244, ,) (294, ,)
SOL-GOOD: W
SOL-POOR: ACET, HEX
QUAL: (NINH., -) (SAKA., -)
TO: (MYCOB.TUB., .05)
REFERENCES:
Belg. P 745926

43320-5694

NAME: 3-DIETILAMINOETILAMINO-BLEOMYCIN
PO: S.VERTICILLUS+NN-DIETIL-1.2-DIAMINOETAN
CT: BLEOMYCIN T., BASIC, GLYCOPEPTIDE
EA: (C, 45) (H, 6) (N, 10) (S, 4)
UV: W: (244, ,) (294, ,)
SOL-GOOD: W
SOL-POOR: ACET, HEX
QUAL: (NINH., -) (SAKA., -)
TO: (MYCOB.TUB., 1)
REFERENCES:
Belg. P 745926

43320-5695

NAME: 3-CYCLOHEXYLAMINOPROPYLAMINO-BLEOMYCIN
PO: S.VERTICILLUS+CYCLOHEXYLAMINOPROPYLAMINE
CT: BLEOMYCIN T., BASIC, GLYCOPEPTIDE
EA: (C, 44) (H, 7) (N, 16) (S, 4)
UV: W: (244, ,) (294, ,)
QUAL: (NINH., -) (SAKA., -)
TO: (MYCOB.TUB., 1)
REFERENCES:
Belg. P 745926

43320-5696

NAME:	<u>3-NN-DIMETILAMINOETILAMINO-BLEOMYCIN</u>
PO:	S.VERTICILLUS+NN-DIMETHYL-1.2-DIAMINOETHAN
CT:	BLEOMYCIN T., BASIC, GLYCOPEPTIDE
EA:	(C, 43) (H, 6) (N, 16) (S, 4)
QUAL:	(NINH., -) (SAKA., -)
TO:	(MYCOB.TUB., 2)

REFERENCES:
Belg. P 745926

43320-5697

NAME:	<u>3-1-METHYL-3-AMINOPROPYL-AMINOPROPYLAMINO-BLEOMYCIN</u>
PO:	S.VERTICILLUS+N-3-AMINO-1-METHYLPROPYL-1.3-DIAMINOPROPAN
CT:	BLEOMYCIN T., BASIC, GLYCOPEPTIDE
EA:	(C, 43) (H, 6) (N, 17) (S, 4)
UV:	W: (244, ,) (294, ,)
SOL-GOOD:	W
SOL-POOR:	ACET, HEX
QUAL:	(NINH., +) (SAKA., -)
TO:	(MYCOB.TUB., .5)

REFERENCES:
Belg. P 745926

43320-6239

NAME:	<u>C-11924 F-1</u>
PO:	STV.CINNAMONEUM
CT:	BASIC, GLYCOPEPTIDE, BLEOMYCIN T.
EA:	(C, 42) (H, 6) (N, 16) (S, 3.5) (CU, 3)
MW:	1800|50
PC:	BLUE, POW.
UV:	W: (243, 167,) (297, 55,)
SOL-GOOD:	W, MEOH
SOL-FAIR:	ETOH
SOL-POOR:	ETOAC, HEX
QUAL:	(SAKA., +) (NINH., +) (EHRL.,)
STAB:	(ACID, -)
TO:	(S.AUREUS, 2) (B.SUBT., 1) (E.COLI, .2)
LD50:	(200, IV)
TV:	S-180
IS-ION:	(DIAION HP-10, MEOH-W)
IS-CHR:	(SEPHADEX LH-20, MEOH-W) (CM-SEPHADEX C-25, NH4 FORMIAT)

REFERENCES:
DT 2802792

43320-6353

NAME: PEP-BLEOMYCIN
TRADE NAMES: PEPLEOMYCIN
PO: S.VERTICILLUS+N-2-B"-PYRIDYL-ETHYL-1.3-DIAMINOPROPANE
CT: BASIC, GLYCOPEPTIDE, BLEOMYCIN T.
FORMULA: C59H87N10O21S2
EA: (N, 16) (S, 4) (CU,)
PC: BLUE, POW.
UV: W: (244, ,) (292.5, ,)
SOL-GOOD: W
TO: (G.POS.,)
TV: ANTITUMOR
IS-ION: (IRC-50-H, HCL)
UTILITY: ANTITUMOR DRUG
REFERENCES:
JP 76/121598; *Jap. J. Ant.*, 30, 1977; *JA*, 31, 801, 1978

43320-6618

NAME: SF-1961-A
PO: S.FILAMENTOSUS
CT: BASIC, GLYCOPEPTIDE, BLEOMYCIN T.
EA: (C, 43) (H, 6) (O, 27) (N, 14) (S, 4) (CU, 3)
PC: BLUE, POW.
UV: W: (250, 173,) (291|1, , 126)
SOL-GOOD: W
QUAL: (NINH., +) (EHRL., +) (SAKA., -)
TO: (B.SUBT.,) (E.COLI,) (K.PNEUM.,) (P.VULG.,)
TV: ANTITUMOR
IS-ION: (DIAION HP-10, MEOH-W)
IS-CHR: (CM-SEPHADEX C-25-H, NACL)
REFERENCES:
JP 78/127895; *CA*, 90, 184892

43320-6619

NAME: SF-1961-B
PO: S.FILAMENTOSUS
CT: BASIC, GLYCOPEPTIDE, BLEOMYCIN T.
EA: (C, 43) (H, 6) (N, 13) (O, 31) (S, 4) (CU, 3)
PC: BLUE, POW.
UV: W: (250, 157.6,) (286|2, 111,)
SOL-GOOD: W
QUAL: (NINH., +) (EHRL., +) (SAKA., -)
TO: (B.SUBT.,) (E.COLI,) (K.PNEUM.,) (P.VULG.,)
TV: ANTITUMOR
REFERENCES:
JP 78/127895; *CA*, 90, 184892

43330-1825

NAME: FERROVERDIN
PO: S.SP.
CT: PEPTIDE L., CHELATE FORMING
FORMULA: C30H20N2O8FE
EA: (N,) (FE,)
REFERENCES:
Nature, 194, 769, 1961

43330-1859

NAME: MATCHAMYCIN
PO: S.AMAGASAKAENSIS
CT: CHELATE-FORMING, PEPTIDE L.
FORMULA: C26H13N3O6CU
EA: (N, 9) (CU, 14)
PC: GREEN, POW.
OR: (+33, DMSO)
UV: MEOH: (320, ,)
UV: MEOH-NAOH: (335, ,)
SOL-GOOD: MEOH, CHL
SOL-FAIR: BENZ, ET2O
SOL-POOR: W, HEX
QUAL: (NINH., -)
TO: (B.SUBT., 50) (S.AUREUS, 50) (S.LUTEA, 50) (SHYG., 50) (E.COLI, 50) (PS.AER., 50) (K.PNEUM., 50)
IS-EXT: (ACET, , MIC.) (ETOAC, , W)
IS-CHR: (SILG, MEOH)
REFERENCES:
JA, 23, 461, 1970; JP 70/14879

43330-1860

NAME: TRICHOSTATIN-B, A-300-II
PO: S.HYGROSCOPICUS
CT: CHELATE-FORMING, PEPTIDE L., NEUTRAL
FORMULA: C17H21N2O3.FE.3
EA: (N, 8) (FE, 6)
MW: 679
PC: RED, CRYST.
UV: ETOH: (277, 651,) (351, 918,) (450, 50,)
UV: MEOH: (262, 680,) (345, 920,)
SOL-GOOD: MEOH, ET2O
SOL-POOR: W
TO: (TRICHOPHYTON SP., 12.5)
REFERENCES:
JA, 29, 1, 1976; JP 74/14691; *CA*, 81, 48547

43330-1861

NAME:	<u>TRICHOSTATIN-A</u>, A-300-I
PO:	S.HYGROSCOPICUS
CT:	CHELATE-FORMING, PEPTIDE L., ACIDIC
FORMULA:	C17H22N2O3
EA:	(N, 9)
MW:	370
PC:	WH., POW.
OR:	(+62.8, MEOH)
UV:	ETOH: (265, 582,) (341, 648,)
UV:	MEOH: (253, 477,) (267, 495,) (341, 776,)
UV:	MEOH-NAOH: (249, 500,) (343, 800,)
SOL-GOOD:	MEOH, ET2O
SOL-POOR:	HEX, W
TO:	(TRICHOPHYTON SP., 3.1)
IS-EXT:	(ETOAC, , FILT.)
IS-CHR:	(POLYAMID, ETOAC)

REFERENCES:

JA, 29, 1, 1976; JP 74/14691; *CA*, 81, 48547

43330-1862

NAME:	<u>PROVIRIDOMYCIN</u>, 1876-1
PO:	ACT.VIRIDARIS, S.VIRIDARIS, S.ROSEOVIRIDIS, S.OLIVOVIRIDIS
CT:	CHELATE-FORMING, PEPTIDE L.
EA:	(N, 8)
PC:	YELLOW, POW.
UV:	MEOH: (298, ,) (430, ,)
SOL-GOOD:	W, MEOH, BUOH
SOL-FAIR:	ETOAC, ACET
SOL-POOR:	CHL, BENZ, HEX
QUAL:	(FECL3, +)
STAB:	(HEAT, -)
TO:	(S.AUREUS, 100) (B.SUBT., 100) (S.LUTEA, 100)

REFERENCES:

Z. Allg. Mikr., 8, 437, 1968

43330-1863

NAME:	VIRIDOMYCIN-A
PO:	ACT.VIRIDARIS, S.VIRIDARIS, S.ROSEOVIRIDIS, S.OLIVOVIRIDIS
CT:	CHELATE-FORMING, PEPTIDE L., NEUTRAL
FORMULA:	C14H8N2O4FE
EA:	(N, 7) (FE, 8)
PC:	GREEN, POW., CRYST.
UV:	ETOH: (219, ,) (294, ,) (432, ,) (680, ,)
UV:	ETOH-HCL: (293, ,) (430, ,) (680, ,)
UV:	ETOH-NAOH: (296, ,) (430, ,) (680, ,)
UV:	MEOH: (298, ,) (430, ,) (700, ,)
SOL-GOOD:	ETOAC, PYR, ACOH, DMFA
SOL-FAIR:	MEOH, ETOH, ACET, W
SOL-POOR:	CHL, HEX
QUAL:	(NINH., -)
TO:	(SHYG.,) (TRICHOPHYTON SP.,) (S.AUREUS, 1) (B.SUBT., 4) (S.LUTEA, 1)

REFERENCES:

Dokl., 215, 1493, 1974; 180, 978, 1968; *Antib.*, 511, 1966; *Khim. Prir. Soed.*, 490, 1975; *Bioorg. Khim.*, 2, 365, 1976

43330-1864

NAME:	IAQUIRIN-III
PO:	S.IAKYRUS
CT:	CHELATE-FORMING, PEPTIDE L., NEUTRAL
PC:	GREEN, POW.
UV:	ETOH: (264, 650,) (360, 100,)
UV:	ETOH-NAOH: (240, 430,) (295, 470,)
SOL-GOOD:	MEOH, ET2O
SOL-POOR:	W
TO:	(B.SUBT., .6) (S.LUTEA, 1) (S.AUREUS, 1) (E.COLI, 60) (K.PNEUM., 60) (PS.AER., 100) (SHYG., 60) (MYCOB.SP., 4)

REFERENCES:

Rev. Inst. Antib., 4, 33, 67, 1959

43330-1865

NAME: ACTINOMYCELLIN
PO: S.SP.
CT: CHELATE-FORMING, PEPTIDE L., NEUTRAL
PC: GREEN, YELLOW, POW.
SOL-GOOD: W, MEOH, ETOH
SOL-FAIR: ACET, ETOAC, CHL
SOL-POOR: BENZ, ET2O, HEX
STAB: (HEAT, -) (ACID, -) (BASE, -)
TO: (B.SUBT., 5) (S.AUREUS, 5)
IS-FIL: ORIG.
IS-EXT: (BUOH, , FILT.)
IS-CHR: (AL, MEOH-MEOAC)
IS-CRY: (DRY, BUOH)
REFERENCES:
Rev. Invest. Agric., 2, 147, 1948; *Inst. Fitotech. Pub. Tech.*, 16, 147, 1948; *JAMA*, 137, 901, 1948

43330-1866

NAME: 168-"GREEN PIGMENT"
PO: S.STREPTOMYCINI, ACT.STREPTOMYCINI
CT: CHELATE-FORMING, PEPTIDE L.
EA: (FE,)
PC: GREEN, POW.
UV: MEOH: (43, ,) (700, ,)
TO: (S.AUREUS,)
REFERENCES:
Antib., 963, 1964

43330-1867

NAME: 5066-"GREEN PIGMENT"
PO: ACT.MALACHITOFUSCUS, ACT.MALACHITORECTUS
CT: CHELATE-FORMING, PEPTIDE L.
EA: (FE,)
PC: GREEN, POW.
UV: MEOH: (430, ,) (700, ,)
TO: (S.AUREUS,)
REFERENCES:
Antib., 963, 1964

43330-1868

NAME: 7543- "GREEN PIGMENT", 15620, 5505, 12428
PO: ACT.ATROOLIVACEUS, ACT.ROSEOVIRIDIS, ACT.INTERMEDIUS
CT: CHELATE-FORMING, PEPTIDE L.
EA: (FE,)
PC: GREEN, POW.
UV: MEOH: (430, ,) (700, ,)
TO: (S.AUREUS,)
REFERENCES:
Antib., 963, 1964

43330-4788

NAME: VIRIDOMYCIN-B
PO: ACT.VIRIDARIS, ACT.SP.
CT: CHELATE-FORMING, PEPTIDE L.
EA: (N,) (FE,)
PC: GREEN, POW.
UV: ETOH: (222, ,) (294, ,) (435, ,) (680, ,)
UV: ETOH-HCL: (294, ,) (430, ,) (680, ,)
UV: ETOH-NAOH: (296, ,) (430, ,) (680, ,)
SOL-GOOD: PYR, ACOH, DMFA
SOL-FAIR: MEOH, ETOH, ACET, BUOH, W
SOL-POOR: ETOAC, HEX
TO: (S.AUREUS, 1) (B.SUBT., 1) (S.LUTEA, 1)
IS-EXT: (BUOH, , FILT.)
REFERENCES:
Khim. Prir. Soed., 490, 1975

43330-4789

NAME: VIRIDOMYCIN-C
PO: ACT.VIRIDARIS
CT: CHELATE-FORMING, PEPTIDE L.
EA: (N,) (FE,)
PC: CREEN, POW.
UV: ETOH: (228, ,) (294, ,) (435, ,) (680, ,)
UV: ETOH-HCL: (294, ,) (435, ,) (680, ,)
UV: ETOH-NAOH: (294, ,) (438, ,) (680, ,)
SOL-GOOD: ACOH, DMFA, PYR
SOL-FAIR: MEOH, ACET, W
SOL-POOR: ETOAC, HEX
TO: (S.AUREUS, 1) (B.SUBT., 1) (S.LUTEA, 1)
REFERENCES:
Khim. Prir. Soed., 490, 1975

43330-5698

NAME: <u>FUSARININ</u>
PO: FUS.ROSEUM, FUS.ARBENSE
FORMULA: C11H20N2O5
EA: (N, 11)
PC: SYRUP, WH.
UV: (215, ,)
TO: (ARTHROBACTER SP.,)
REFERENCES:
Eur. J. Bioch., 3, 213, 1967; *Biochem.*, 4, 1410, 1965; 7, 184, 1969

43330-6355

NAME: <u>TRICHOSTATIN-C</u>
PO: S.HYGROSCOPICUS
CT: PEPTIDE L., CHELATE FORMING
FORMULA: C23H32N2O8
EA: (N, 6)
MW: 454
PC: WH., CRYST.
OR: (+50.5, MEOH)
UV: MEOH: (268, , 14600) (344, , 14300)
SOL-GOOD: MEOH, ETOAC
SOL-FAIR: CHL, BENZ
SOL-POOR: W, HEX
QUAL: (FECL3, -)
TO: (FUNGI, 6.25)
IS-EXT: (BUOH, , W)
IS-ABS: (SEPHADEX HP-20, MEOH)
IS-CHR: (SILG, CHL-MEOH)
IS-CRY: (CRY, ETOAC)
REFERENCES:
JA, 31, 939, 1978

4
OTHER LESS KNOWN PEPTIDE ANTIBIOTICS

40000-1874

NAME: LILACININ
PO: P.LILACINUM
CT: PEPTIDE
EA: (C, 58) (H, 9) (N, 12)
MW: 748
PC: WH., CRYST.
OR: (-26, MEOH)
SOL-GOOD: MEOH, ACET
SOL-FAIR: W, ETOAC, CHL, ET2O
SOL-POOR: BENZ, HEX
STAB: (HEAT, +) (ACID, +) (BASE, -)
TO: (B.SUBT., 50) (S.AUREUS, 50) (E.COLI, 100) (P.VULG., 100) (PS.AER., 100) (C.ALB., 25) (S.CEREV., 50) (TRICHOPHYTON SP., .78)
IS-FIL: 5
IS-EXT: (ETOAC, 5, FILT.)
IS-CHR: (SILG, BENZ-ETOAC-MEOH)
IS-CRY: (CRYST., MEOH-W)
REFERENCES:

JP 71/22552; *CA*, 75, 108517

40000-1875

NAME: RAMIHYPHIN-A
PO: FUS.SP.
CT: PEPTIDE
EA: (C, 60) (H, 9) (N, 13)
MW: 1192
PC: WH., POW.
UV: MEOH: (210, ,)
SOL-GOOD: MEOH, CHL
SOL-POOR: W, BENZ, HEX
TO: (FUNGI, .1)
TV: HELA
IS-EXT: (ETOAC, , FILT.)
IS-CHR: (AL, CHL-ETOH)
IS-CRY: (DRY,)
REFERENCES:

Folia Micr., 19, 537, 1974; *CA*, 82, 153750, 153751; Cz. P 155753, 155754

40000-1876

NAME: MYRORHODIN, MYRORODIN
PO: MIROTHECIUM RORIDUM-MINUS
CT: PEPTIDE
FORMULA: C37H76N12O14
EA: (N, 18)
MW: 913
PC: WH., POW.
OR: (-3.65, MEOH)
UV: MEOH: (278, ,)
SOL-GOOD: MEOH, W
SOL-FAIR: ETOH
SOL-POOR: BUOH, HEX
QUAL: (NINH., +) (PAULY, +)
STAB: (BASE, -) (ACID, +)
TO: (C.ALB., .5) (S.CEREV., .1) (P.VULG., 20)
LD50: (250, IP)
TV: HELA
REFERENCES:
Tohoku J. Exp. Med., 122, 403, 1977; *CA*, 88, 4681; JP 70/12276

40000-1877

NAME: LEUCINOSTATIN
PO: P.LILACINUM
CT: PEPTIDE, ACIDIC, AMPHOTER
EA: (C, 57) (H, 9) (N, 12) (O, 22)
MW: 1568
PC: WH., CRYST.
UV: MEOH: (220, 128,)
SOL-GOOD: MEOH, CHL
SOL-FAIR: ET2O, BENZ
SOL-POOR: W, HEX
QUAL: (BIURET, +) (NINH., -)
STAB: (HEAT, +)
TO: (S.LUTEA, 2.5) (B.SUBT., 5) (S.AUREUS, 75)
(S.CEREV., 5) (C.ALB., 1) (FUNGI, .5)
TV: EHRLICH, HELA
IS-EXT: (ETOAC, 2, FILT.)
IS-CHR: (SILG, CHL-MEOH) (SEPHADEX LH-20, MEOH)
IS-CRY: (CRYST., ET2O-HEX)
REFERENCES:
JA, 26, 197, 1973; *AAC*, 9, 893, 1976; JP 74/41594; *CA*, 81, 134621

40000-1878

NAME:	LILACIN
PO:	P.LILACINUM
CT:	PEPTIDE
EA:	(C, 59) (H, 9) (N, 11)
PC:	WH., POW.
OR:	(-35, CHL)
SOL-GOOD:	MEOH, BUOH, CHL
SOL-FAIR:	ACET, BENZ
SOL-POOR:	ET2O, HEX, W
QUAL:	(BIURET, +)
STAB:	(ACID, +) (BASE, -)
TO:	(MYCOB.SP., .08) (S.AUREUS, 1) (SHYG., 1) (PS.AER., 100)
IS-EXT:	(CHL, 3, FILT.)
IS-ABS:	(CARBON, MEOH)
IS-CHR:	(AL, MEOH-BENZ)

REFERENCES:

Ph.D. thesis, ETH, Zurich; 1953; *Thorn. Landbuch,* 9, 39, 1953

40000-1880

PO:	SPOROCYTOPHAGA CAULIFORMIS
CT:	PEPTIDE, AMPHOTER
EA:	(N,)
PC:	WH., CRYST.
SOL-GOOD:	W
SOL-POOR:	MEOH, HEX
QUAL:	(NINH., +)
STAB:	(ACID, +) (HEAT, +) (BASE, +)
TO:	(S.AUREUS, 35) (S.LUTEA, 1.7) (E.COLI, 250) (SHYG., 250)
IS-EXT:	(W, , MIC.)
IS-CHR:	(PAP., BUOH-ACOH-W)
IS-CRY:	(LIOF.,)

REFERENCES:

DT 1467923

40000-1881

NAME:	ALMARCETIN
PO:	S.ALBUS
CT:	PEPTIDE, ACIDIC, AMPHOTER
EA:	(N,)
PC:	WH., POW.
UV:	W: (300, 450,)
SOL-GOOD:	MEOH-W, ACET-W
SOL-FAIR:	MEOH, ETOH
SOL-POOR:	BUOH, HEX
QUAL:	(NINH., -) (FECL3, -) (DNPH, -) (BIURET, +)
STAB:	(ACID, +) (BASE, +) (HEAT, +)
TO:	(B.SUBT., 10) (S.AUREUS, 100) (S.LUTEA, 100) (P.VULG., 100) (E.COLI, 10) (MYCOB.SP., 1) (S.CEREV., 10)
IS-ABS:	(CARBON, ACET-W)

REFERENCES:

AAC 1964, 53; USP 3332847; *CA*, 63, 3356

40000-1882

NAME:	HISTIDOMYCIN-A
PO:	NOC.HISTIDANS, S.MEDIOLANI
CT:	PEPTIDE, ACIDIC, AMPHOTER
FORMULA:	C25H36N9O10CL
EA:	(N, 19) (CL, 5)
PC:	WH., CRYST.
OR:	(-39.3, W) (-39.8, HCL) (-36.9, PH10 PUFF)
UV:	W: (200, ,)
SOL-GOOD:	W
SOL-FAIR:	MEOH, ETOH
SOL-POOR:	BUOH, HEX
TO:	(PHYT.BACT., .0016) (B.SUBT., 1) (S.AUREUS, 20) (E.COLI, 1)
LD50:	NONTOXIC
IS-FIL:	7.5
IS-ION:	(IR-120-H, NH4OH)
IS-CHR:	(CEL, BUOH-ACOH-W)
IS-CRY:	(CRYST., ETOH-W)

REFERENCES:

AAC 1966, 595, 603; *Exp.*, 25, 241, 1969

40000-1883

NAME:	<u>HISTIDOMYCIN-B</u>
PO:	NOC.HISTIDANS
CT:	PEPTIDE, AMPHOTER
EA:	(N,)
PC:	WH., POW.
UV:	W: (200, ,)
SOL-GOOD:	W
SOL-FAIR:	MEOH, ETOH
SOL-POOR:	BUOH, HEX
TO:	(E.COLI, 1) (B.SUBT., 1) (S.AUREUS, 100) (PHYT.BACT., .1)

REFERENCES:

AAC 1966, 595, 603

40000-1884

NAME:	<u>PRACTOMYCIN-C</u>
PO:	S.LAVENDULAE
CT:	PEPTIDE, BASIC
FORMULA:	C24H50N8016
EA:	(N, 16)
MW:	730
PC:	WH., POW., HYGROSCOPIC
OR:	(-19.2, W)
UV:	HCL: (251, 28,) (256, 30,) (262, 18,)
UV:	NAOH: (251, 20,) (256, 22,) (263, 16,)
UV:	W: (251, ,) (256, ,) (262, ,)
SOL-GOOD:	W, MEOH
SOL-POOR:	BUOH, HEX
QUAL:	(NINH., +) (BIURET, +) (SAKA., -) (EHRL., -) (FECL3, -)
STAB:	(ACID, +) (HEAT, +) (BASE, -)
TO:	(B.SUBT., .2) (S.LUTEA, .4) (S.AUREUS, .4) (E.COLI, .8) (PS.AER., .8) (P.VULG., 3) (K.PNEUM., .8) (C.ALB., 1.5) (S.CEREV., 1)
LD50:	(15, IV)
IS-FIL:	7
IS-ION:	(IRC-50-NA, HCL)
IS-CHR:	(CEL, PROH-PYR-ACOH-W)

REFERENCES:

JP 73/98094; *CA*, 80, 144390; *Jap. Med. Gaz.*, 5, 9, 1973

40000-1885

NAME: YEMENIMYCIN
PO: S.ALBUS
CT: PEPTIDE, AMPHOTER
FORMULA: C41H43N409CL
EA: (N, 7) (CL, 5)
PC: YELLOW, WH., CRYST.
OR: (-268, MEOH)
UV: ETOH: (230, 449,) (314, 626,)
UV: ETOH-NAOH: (235, 440,) (356, 558,)
UV: W: (232, 319,) (255, 308,) (318, 523,)
SOL-GOOD: ACET, ETOAC, CHL
SOL-FAIR: MEOH, ETOH, BUOH
SOL-POOR: W, HEX
QUAL: (NINH., -) (FEHL., -) (BIURET, -) (SAKA., -) (FECL3, -)
TO: (S.AUREUS, .06) (B.SUBT., .78) (S.LUTEA, .2) (E.COLI, 12) (P.VULG., 12) (PS.AER., 100) (SHYG., 12) (K.PNEUM., 100) (C.ALB., .01) (FUNGI, .01)
LD50: (2.3|1, IP)
TV: S-180, YOSHIDA
IS-EXT: (CHL, 7.5, FILT.) (ACET, , MIC.)
IS-ABS: (CARBON, MEOH)
IS-CRY: (DRY,) (CRYST., MEOH)
REFERENCES:
JA, 24, 283, 1971; USP 3839560

40000-1886

NAME: NRC-101
PO: S.SP.
CT: PEPTIDE, BASIC, AMPHOTER
FORMULA: C43H72N20O19
EA: (N, 24)
MW: 1172
PC: YELLOW, WH., POW.
UV: (210, ,)
SOL-GOOD: MEOH, CHL
SOL-FAIR: BENZ
SOL-POOR: W, HEX
QUAL: (NINH., +) (BIURET, -) (SAKA., -) (FECL3, -)
TO: (S.AUREUS, 12) (S.LUTEA, .5) (B.SUBT., .1) (E.COLI, 100) (SHYG., 50)
LD50: (20, IP)
IS-EXT: (ETOAC, 7, FILT.)
IS-CRY: (PREC., CHL, HEX)
REFERENCES:
Z. Allg. Mikr., 11, 475, 1971

40000-1887

NAME:	HODYDAMYCIN
PO:	S.SP.
CT:	PEPTIDE
FORMULA:	C40H50N3O14CL
EA:	(N, 5) (CL, 4)
PC:	WH., CRYST.
OR:	(+40, ETOH)
UV:	ETOH: (249, 358,)
UV:	ETOH-NAOH: (237, 400,)
SOL-GOOD:	MEOH, ET2O
SOL-POOR:	W, HCL, ACID
QUAL:	(NINH., +) (BIURET, +) (FECL3, -) (FEHL., -) (SAKA., -)
TO:	(B.SUBT., .25) (S.AUREUS, 1.5) (K.PNEUM., 6) (P.VULG., 6)
LD50:	(1000, IP)
IS-EXT:	(ETOAC-CHL, 7.5, FILT.)
IS-CRY:	(CRYST., ETOH)

REFERENCES:

JA, 23, 388, 1970

40000-1888

NAME:	BA-17039-A
PO:	S.LONGISPORUS-GRISEUS
CT:	PEPTIDE, NEUTRAL, ACIDIC
FORMULA:	C24H41N5O9
EA:	(N, 13)
MW:	517|20
PC:	WH., CRYST.
OR:	(+11.8, CHL)
UV:	MEOH: (200, ,)
SOL-GOOD:	MEOH, CHL, PYR, DMFA
SOL-FAIR:	BENZ
SOL-POOR:	W, HEX
QUAL:	(FECL3, +) (NINH., -)
TO:	(S.AUREUS, 10) (B.SUBT., 25) (C.ALB., 2.5)
TV:	HELA, S-180, CA-755
IS-EXT:	(BUOH, 4, FILT.)
IS-CHR:	(SILG, BENZ-CHL)
IS-CRY:	(CRYST., ACET)

REFERENCES:

AAC 1963, 73; USP 3148119; *CA*, 61, 9916

40000-1889

NAME: RHIZOMYCIN, SF-674
PO: S.NOVOVERTICILLUS
CT: PEPTIDE, NEUTRAL
FORMULA: C19H31N405
EA: (N, 15)
MW: 338, 390
PC: WH., POW.
OR: (+19, MEOH)
UV: MEOH: (200, ,)
SOL-GOOD: MEOH, ACET, W
SOL-FAIR: BUOH, ETOAC, DMFA
SOL-POOR: ET20, HEX
QUAL: (FEHL., +) (BIURET, +) (NINH., -) (EHRL., -)
STAB: (ACID, -) (BASE, +)
TO: (S.LUTEA, .2) (S.AUREUS, 22) (B.SUBT., 1)
(FUNGI, 1) (PHYT.BACT., .4) (C.ALB., 15)
LD50: (200|100, IV)
TV: ANTIPHAGE
IS-EXT: (ETOAC, 7.5, FILT.+NH4.SULPHATE)
REFERENCES:
JP 70/17155; *Sci. Rep. Meiji*, 11, 26, 1970; CA, 76, 23795

40000-1890

NAME: GATAVALIN
PO: B.POLYMYXA-COLISTINUS, AEROBACILLUS COLISTINUS
CT: PEPTIDE, NEUTRAL
EA: (C, 51) (H, 8) (N, 15)
MW: 2000
PC: WH., POW.
OR: (+19.7, W)
UV: W: (200, ,)
SOL-GOOD: DMSO, ACOH, MEOH, ETOH
SOL-FAIR: W
SOL-POOR: ACET, HEX
QUAL: (NINH., -) (BIURET, +) (FEHL., -)
STAB: (ACID, +) (HEAT, +) (BASE, -)
TO: (B.SUBT., 1.25) (S.LUTEA, .62) (S.AUREUS, .62)
(MYCOB.SP., .02) (C.ALB., .6) (S.CEREV., 5)
IS-FIL: 3
IS-EXT: (BUOH, 1, FILT.)
IS-CHR: (SEPHADEX LH-20, MEOH-W)
IS-CRY: (PREC., BUOH, ET20)
REFERENCES:
JA, 25, 243, 1972; DT 2251916; BP 1346972; USP 3923978

40000-1891

NAME:	<u>BOTROCIDIN</u>
PO:	BACTERIUM SP.
CT:	PEPTIDE, BASIC
EA:	(N,)
PC:	WH., POW.
UV:	HCL: (222, 9.8,)
UV:	NAOH: (233, 18.3,)
UV:	W: (222, 8.3,)
SOL-GOOD:	W, MEOH
SOL-FAIR:	ETOH
SOL-POOR:	ACET, HEX
QUAL:	(SAKA., +) (NINH., +) (BIURET, +) (FEHL., +)
TO:	(B.SUBT., 6.2) (S.CEREV., 6.2) (PHYT.FUNGI, 3.12)
IS-ION:	(IRC-50-NA,)
IS-ABS:	(CARBON,)
IS-CHR:	(SEPHADEX LH-20,)

REFERENCES:

Jap. Med. Gaz., 3, 7, 1971; Ann. Meet. Agr. Chem. Soc. Jap., 1970

40000-2084

NAME:	<u>N-44-A-21</u>
PO:	S.SP.
CT:	POLYPEPTIDE, ACIDIC
EA:	(C, 50) (H, 8) (N, 13)
PC:	BROWN, POW.
UV:	MEOH: (200, ,) (252, ,)
SOL-GOOD:	MEOH, BUOH, BASE
SOL-FAIR:	ACET, ET2O, BENZ
SOL-POOR:	ETOAC, HEX
QUAL:	(NINH., +)
TO:	(S.AUREUS, 2) (S.LUTEA, .3) (B.SUBT., 1)
LD50:	(600, IP) (600, SC)

REFERENCES:

JP 64/9444; *CA*, 62, 4577

40000-2100

NAME:	<u>ICI-13595</u>
PO:	PAECYLOMYCES SP.
CT:	PEPTIDE, BASIC, AMPHOTER
EA:	(N,)
PC:	WH., POW.
SOL-GOOD:	ETOAC
TO:	(TRYPANOSOMA CONGOLENSE,)
IS-EXT:	(ETOAC, ,)
IS-CHR:	(SILG,)

REFERENCES:

Nature, 181, 48, 1957

40000-2111

NAME:	<u>CRYOMYCIN-A</u>
PO:	S.GRISEUS-PSYCHROPHYLUS
CT:	PEPTIDE, AMPHOTER, ACIDIC
EA:	(C, 60) (H, 8) (N, 10) (S,)
PC:	WH., POW.
UV:	W: (269, 60,)
SOL-GOOD:	W
SOL-FAIR:	MEOH, ETOH
SOL-POOR:	BUOH, HEX
QUAL:	(NINH., +) (BIURET, +) (SAKA., +) (FECL3, -) (PAULY, -)
STAB:	(HEAT, +) (BASE, -)
TO:	(B.SUBT., .3) (S.AUREUS, 1) (S.LUTEA, .5)
LD50:	(150, IV)
IS-FIL:	2
IS-EXT:	(BUOH, 2, FILT.)
IS-CHR:	(DEAE-CEL, NACL)
IS-CRY:	(PREC., BUOH, ETOAC)

REFERENCES:

JA, 25, 546, 653, 1972; 27, 138, 1974

40000-3898

NAME:	<u>GALANTIN-II</u>
PO:	B.PULVIFACIENS
CT:	PEPTIDE, AMPHOTER, BASIC
EA:	(C, 50) (H, 8) (N, 19)
PC:	WH., POW.
OR:	(0, HCL) (+6.2, HCL)
UV:	W: (200, ,)
SOL-GOOD:	W, MEOH, ETOH
SOL-POOR:	ACET, HEX
QUAL:	(NINH., +) (PAULY, +) (SAKA., -)
TO:	(B.SUBT., 3.1) (S.AUREUS, 3.1) (K.PNEUM., 12.5)

REFERENCES:

JA, 28, 122, 1975

40000-3899

NAME:	GALANTIN-I
PO:	B.PULVIFACIENS
CT:	PEPTIDE, AMPHOTER, BASIC
FORMULA:	C50H98N16O17
EA:	(C, 51) (H, 8) (N, 19)
PC:	WH., POW.
OR:	(+4.5, W) (-2.3, HCL)
UV:	W: (200, ,)
SOL-GOOD:	W, MEOH
SOL-POOR:	ACET, HEX
QUAL:	(NINH., +) (PAULY, +) (SAKA., -)
TO:	(B.SUBT., 3.1) (S.AUREUS, 1.6) (K.PNEUM., 3.1) (MYCOB.TUB., 2.5)
LD50:	(50, IP)
IS-FIL:	2
IS-ION:	(IRC-50-NA, HCL)
IS-ABS:	(CARBON, ACET-HCL)
IS-CHR:	(CARBON, MEOH-HCL)
IS-CRY:	(LIOF.,)

REFERENCES:

JA, 28, 122, 1975

40000-3920

PO:	B.SP.
CT:	PEPTIDE
PC:	WH., POW.
SOL-GOOD:	W
SOL-POOR:	ETOH, HEX
QUAL:	(NINH., +) (FECL3, -) (FEHL., -)
STAB:	(HEAT, +)
TO:	(B.SUBT.,) (E.COLI,) (S.LUTEA,) (MYCOB.SP.,)
IS-FIL:	4

REFERENCES:

An. Univ. M. Sklodowska Ser. C, 28, 75, 1973

40000-4143

NAME: B-28963
PO: S.SP.
CT: BASIC, AMPHOTER, PEPTIDE
EA: (C, 41) (H, 6) (N, 15)
PC: WH., POW.
OR: (+49.6, W) (+58, HCL) (+46, NAOH)
UV: W: (200, ,)
SOL-GOOD: W
SOL-FAIR: MEOH
SOL-POOR: MEOH, HEX, PYR, ACOH, DMFA
QUAL: (NINH., +) (SAKA., -)
TO: (MICROCOCCUS SP.,) (B.SUBT., 20) (S.LUTEA, 20) (S.AUREUS, 10) (E.COLI, 30) (P.VULG., 50)
LD50: (500|100, IV)
IS-ION: (IRC-50-H, NH4OH) (IRA-68-OH, ACOH)
IS-CHR: (CARBON,) (AL, NH4OH)
REFERENCES:
JP 74/80294; *CA* 82, 56067

40000-4380

NAME: A-43
PO: MORAXELLA SP.
CT: PEPTIDE
MW: 900|100
SOL-GOOD: W
QUAL: (NINH., +)
STAB: (HEAT, -) (ACID, +)
TO: (CLOSTRIDIUM SP.,)
REFERENCES:
Appl. Micr., 27, 329, 1974

40000-4393

NAME: GALLERIN
PO: B.BREVIS
CT: PEPTIDE, BASIC, AMPHOTER
EA: (N, 16)
PC: WH., POW.
UV: W: (200, ,) (207, ,) (255, ,) (280, ,)
SOL-GOOD: W, ACID, MEOH
SOL-POOR: ACET, HEX
QUAL: (FECL3, -) (NINH., -) (BIURET, -) (SAKA., -)
STAB: (ACID, +) (BASE, -) (HEAT, +)
TO: (S.LUTEA, .09) (S.AUREUS, 1.2) (MYCOB.TUB., 111)
IS-ION: (CG-50-H, HCL)
IS-CHR: (CM-CEL, NACL) (SEPHADEX G-25, W)
REFERENCES:
An. Univ. M. Sklodowska Ser. C, 25, 67, 1970; *CA,* 75, 18545

40000-4796

NAME:	BN-1512
PO:	B.CEREUS-MYCOIDES
CT:	PEPTIDE, BASIC
FORMULA:	C19H23N6O7
EA:	(N, 18)
EW:	475|25
PC:	WH., CRYST.
OR:	(-251, HCL)
UV:	HCL: (270, ,) (310, ,)
UV:	NAOH: (270, ,) (330, ,)
SOL-GOOD:	W, ACID, BASE
SOL-POOR:	MEOH, ETOH, ACET, ETOAC, BENZ, HEX
QUAL:	(NINH., -) (SAKA., -)
STAB:	(ACID, +) (BASE, +) (LIGHT, -) (BASE, -)
TO:	(B.SUBT.,) (PIRICULARIA ORYZAE, 1)
IS-FIL:	2
IS-ION:	(DX-50-H, NH4OH) (DX-1-AC, W)
IS-CHR:	(SEPHADEX G-10, W)
IS-CRY:	(CRYST., W)

REFERENCES:

Sci. Rep. Meiji, 14, 14, 1975; JP 75/5597; *CA,* 83, 26280, 204759

40000-4875

NAME:	CRYOMYCIN-B
PO:	S.SP.+PARAFFIN
CT:	PEPTIDE, ACIDIC, AMPHOTER
EA:	(N,)
MW:	1500|200
PC:	WH., POW.
UV:	HCL: (220, 60,)
SOL-GOOD:	MEOH-ETOH, BASE, PYR-ACOH
SOL-FAIR:	W, ACID, ACET, BUOH, PHENOL
SOL-POOR:	ETOAC, HEX
QUAL:	(NINH., +) (BIURET, +) (SAKA., +) (PAULY, +)
STAB:	(ACID, +) (BASE, -)
TO:	(B.SUBT., .1) (S.AUREUS, 1) (S.LUTEA, .5)
IS-EXT:	(BUOH, 2, FILT.)
IS-CHR:	(SEPHADEX G-10, W)

REFERENCES:

Agr. Biol. Ch., 35, 79, 1970; *JA,* 27, 138, 1974

40000-5059

NAME:	GARDIMYCIN
PO:	ACTINOPLANES GARBADINENSIS, ACTINOPLANES LIGURIAE
CT:	ACIDIC, AMPHOTER, PEPTIDE
FORMULA:	C84H138N13O34S3NA
EA:	(C, 49) (H, 7) (N, 12) (S, 5)
MW:	2080|80
EW:	2100|100
PC:	WH., POW.
OR:	(-44, DMFA)
UV:	HCL: (279, 26,) (288, 22,)
UV:	MEOH: (280, 26,) (299, 24,)
UV:	NAOH: (279, 26,) (288, 22,)
SOL-GOOD:	W, BASE, DMFA, ACOH, DMSO
SOL-FAIR:	MEOH
SOL-POOR:	ACID, ACET, ETOH, BUOH, BENZ, CHL, CCL4, THF
QUAL:	(FEHL., +) (NINH., -) (FECL3, -)
STAB:	(ACID, +) (BASE, -)
TO:	(S.AUREUS, 50) (S.LUTEA,)
LD50:	(1000, IP) (2000, IV)
IS-EXT:	(BUOH, 8, FILT.)
IS-CRY:	(PREC., BUOH, HEX)

REFERENCES:

JA, 29, 501, 507, 511, 1976; *AAC*, 11, 396, 1977; Belg. P 831743; DT 2533447

40000-5090

PO:	B.POLYMYXA-ROSS
CT:	BASIC, PEPTIDE, MACROMOLECULAR
QUAL:	(NINH., +)
TO:	(P.VULG.,)
IS-CHR:	(SEPHADEX G-25, W)

REFERENCES:

Mikrob., 43, 307, 1974

40000-5091

PO:	S.DOKKI
CT:	PEPTIDE
TO:	ANTIMICROBIAL

REFERENCES:

Ind. J. Exp. Biol., 11, 250, 1973

40000-5197

NAME: FR-3383
PO: S.ADAINENSIS
CT: PEPTIDE, AMPHOTER
FORMULA: C43H58N9O15S, C44H60N9O15S
EA: (N, 13) (S, 3)
MW: 950
PC: WH., YELLOW, CRYST.
UV: HCL: (212, 360,) (240, 300,)
UV: MEOH: (215, 340,) (258, 210,)
UV: W: (215, 340,) (258, 210,)
SOL-GOOD: W
SOL-POOR: MEOH, ACET, ETOAC, CHL
QUAL: (BIURET, +)
TO: (E.COLI,) (P.VULG.,) (PS.AER.,) (SHYG.,)
LD50: (1500|500, IP)
IS-ION: (DIAION HP-20, MEOH-W) (DUOLIT-A-6-OH, NAOH)
IS-CHR: (CEL, BUOH-W)
IS-CRY: (CRYST., BUOH)
REFERENCES:

JP 76/54988, 77/93701; *CA*, 85, 121791; 87, 121791

40000-5198

NAME: NRC-501
PO: S.SP.
CT: BASIC, PEPTIDE
FORMULA: C90H127N22O29S
EA: (N, 15) (S, 1.5)
EW: 414
PC: BROWN, WH., POW.
OR: (+56, MEOH)
UV: MEOH: (210, ,) (280, ,)
SOL-GOOD: MEOH, ETOH, CHL, ACET, ETOAC, BUOH
SOL-FAIR: W, TOL
SOL-POOR: HEX, ET2O, BENZ
QUAL: (BIURET, +) (NINH., +) (SAKA., +) (FECL3, -)
TO: (S.AUREUS, 12.5) (B.SUBT., 50)
LD50: (200, SC)
IS-FIL: 9
IS-EXT: (CHL, 9, FILT.)
IS-CRY: (PREC., CHL, HEX)
REFERENCES:

Z. Allg. Mikr., 16, 337, 1976

40000-5335

NAME: H-3787
PO: S.GRAMINOFACIENS
CT: AMPHOTER, PEPTIDE
EA: (C, 31) (H, 6) (N, 17) (O, 47)
MW: 1230|280
PC: WH., CRYST.
OR: (+53.7, HCL)
SOL-GOOD: ACID, BASE
SOL-POOR: MEOH, HEX, W
QUAL: (NINH., +) (BIURET, +)
TO: (S.AUREUS, 125)
LD50: (2000|1000, IP)
IS-ION: (AMB.PK-208-H, NH4OH)
IS-CRY: (CRYST., NH4OH)
REFERENCES:
JP 76/76493; *CA*, 85, 190724

40000-5337

PO: STAPHYLOCOCCUS SP.
CT: PEPTIDE
MW: 800
SOL-GOOD: W, MEOH
QUAL: (NINH., +)
STAB: (ACID, +) (BASE, +) (HEAT, +)
TO: (S.AUREUS,) (E.COLI,) (K.PNEUM.,) (PS.AER.,) (C.ALB.,)
IS-EXT: (W, , MIC.)
IS-CHR: (SEPHADEX G-10, W)
REFERENCES:
Abst. 9th Int. Congr. Chemoth., 1975, 391

40000-5455

NAME:	S-19
PO:	S.SP.
CT:	AMPHOTER, PEPTIDE
EA:	(C, 40) (H, 5) (N, 16)
PC:	WH., CRYST.
OR:	(-33.8, W)
UV:	W: (198, 152,)
SOL-GOOD:	W
SOL-FAIR:	ACET
SOL-POOR:	CHL, HEX
QUAL:	(NINH., +) (SAKA., -)
TO:	(PHYT.FUNGI,)
LD50:	(200|100, IP)
IS-ION:	(DX-50-H, PYR-ACOH)
IS-ABS:	(CARBON, ACET-W)
IS-CHR:	(SE-SEPHADEX,) (DX-AG-50,)
IS-CRY:	(PREC., W, ACET)

REFERENCES:

JP 77/12993; *CA*, 87, 4025

40000-5536

NAME:	SC-4
PO:	S.SP.
CT:	PEPTIDE

REFERENCES:

Proc. Nat. Sci. Council Taiwan Part 2, 9, 49, 1976; *CA*, 86, 153878

40000-5573

NAME: <u>BN-175</u>
PO: B.SP.
CT: BASIC, PEPTIDE
EA: (C, 47) (H, 7) (N, 19)
MW: 390, 320
PC: BLACK, POW.
OR: (+2.9, W)
UV: HCL: (228, ,) (275, ,)
UV: NAOH: (242, ,) (292, ,)
UV: W: (225, ,) (275, ,)
SOL-GOOD: W
SOL-FAIR: MEOH
SOL-POOR: ACET, ETOAC, CHL
QUAL: (NINH., +) (SAKA., +) (BIURET, +) (FEHL., -)
TO: (S.AUREUS, 50) (B.SUBT., 100) (S.LUTEA, 50)
(E.COLI, 100) (K.PNEUM., 100) (C.ALB., 50)
LD50: (50|20, IV)
IS-ION: (IRC-50-NH4, NH4OH)
IS-CHR: (DEAE-SEPHADEX,) (SEPHADEX G-10, W)
REFERENCES:
JP 76/18894; *CA*, 87, 20611

40000-5574

NAME: <u>MONOKETOORGANOMYCIN</u>, MKOM
PO: S.SP.
CT: PEPTIDE
EA: (N,)
TO: (S.AUREUS, 10) (B.SUBT., 1.5) (E.COLI, .1)
(K.PNEUM., 1.2) (PS.AER., 10) (SHYG., 100)
REFERENCES:
Proc. Egypt Acad. Sci., 27, 137, 1976; *JA*, 30, 314, 1977

40000-5680

NAME: <u>GEMINIMYCINS</u>
PO: S.SP.
CT: PEPTIDE
EA: (C, 72) (H, 8) (N, 8)
PC: WH., CRYST.
UV: (245, ,)
SOL-GOOD: BUOH
STAB: (HEAT, -)
TO: (B.SUBT.,) (S.AUREUS,) (E.COLI,)
REFERENCES:
AAC 1960, 72; *CA*, 56, 15960

40000-5703
PO: S.SP.
CT: PEPTIDE
EA: (N,)
TO: (G.POS.,)
REFERENCES:
Zbl. Bakt. Parasit., 127, 429, 1972; *CA*, 78, 41496

40000-5704
NAME: NIFUNGIN, 18894
PO: ASP.GIGANTEUS
CT: POLYPEPTIDE
EA: (N,)
TO: ANTIFUNGAL
REFERENCES:
JAMA, 212, 2246, 1970; *Diss. Abst.*, 34, 5879, 1974

40000-5720
PO: B.SUBTILIS
CT: POLYPEPTIDE
MW: 1200
SOL-GOOD: W
TO: (E.COLI,) (P.VULG.,) (SHYG.,) (K.PNEUM.,) (C.ALB.,) (S.CEREV.,)
IS-CHR: (SEPHADEX G-15, W)
REFERENCES:
AAC, 11, 1084, 1977

40000-5877
NAME: BN-165
PO: PS.SP.
CT: PEPTIDE, BASIC, AMPHOTER
EA: (C, 52) (H,) (N, 15) (O, 25)
MW: 1100|100
PC: WH., POW.
OR: (-68, MEOH)
SOL-GOOD: MEOH, ETOH
SOL-FAIR: W
SOL-POOR: ACET, ET2O, CHL, ETOAC
QUAL: (SAKA., +) (BIURET, +) (NINH., -) (FEHL., -)
TO: (B.SUBT.,) (S.AUREUS,)
LD50: (100, IP)
IS-EXT: (BUOH, , W)
IS-ION: (XAD-2, MEOH-W)
IS-CHR: (SILG,) (SEPHADEX LH-20,)
REFERENCES:
JP 77/72892; *CA*, 87, 199147

40000-5993

NAME:	AM-2504
PO:	S.SP.
CT:	PEPTIDE, BASIC
EA:	(C, 57) (H, 6) (N, 9)
MW:	1225
PC:	YELLOW, POW.
OR:	(-5.4, MEOH)
UV:	MEOH: (280, 70,) (300, 57,)
UV:	MEOH-HCL: (287, 73,) (305, 75,)
UV:	MEOH-NAOH: (280, ,)
SOL-GOOD:	MEOH, CHL
SOL-FAIR:	BENZ
SOL-POOR:	W, HEX
QUAL:	(NINH., +)
TO:	(B.SUBT., 6.25)
LD50:	(200|100, IV) (400|200, IP)
IS-EXT:	(BUOAC, 10, WB.) (W, 1, BUOAC) (ETOAC, 10, W)
IS-CHR:	(SILG, CHL-MEOH) (SILG, ETOAC)
IS-CRY:	(DRY, ETOAC)

REFERENCES:

Agr. Biol. Ch., 41, 1827, 1977

40000-5996

NAME:	FR-900012
PO:	S.CARNOSUS
CT:	PEPTIDE, AMPHOTER
EA:	(C, 45) (H, 5) (N, 17)
PC:	WH., CRYST.
OR:	(-28, W)
UV:	HCL: (215, ,)
UV:	NAOH: (215, ,) (272, ,)
SOL-GOOD:	W
SOL-FAIR:	MEOH, DMSO, DMFA, PYR
SOL-POOR:	ACET, HEX
QUAL:	(NINH., +) (EHRL., +) (FECL3, +)
TO:	(B.SUBT.,) (P.VULG.,) (E.COLI,)
IS-ION:	(DUOLIT C-20-H, HCL)
IS-CHR:	(CEL, PROH-W)

REFERENCES:

JP 77/118402; *CA*, 88, 61133

40000-6078

NAME: <u>SF-1919</u>
PO: MIC.SP.
CT: NEUTRAL, PEPTIDE
EA: (C, 58) (H, 7) (N, 12) (S, 3) (CL, 3)
MW: 820
PC: WH., POW.
OR: (-95,)
UV: MEOH: (200, ,)
SOL-GOOD: MEOH, CHL
SOL-POOR: W
TO: (B.SUBT., .09) (S.AUREUS, .39) (S.LUTEA, 1.56) (E.COLI, 100) (SHYG., 25) (MYCOPLASMA, .003)
IS-EXT: (ACET, , MIC.) (ETOAC, , FILT.)
REFERENCES:
JP 77/136995; *CA*, 88, 150591

40000-6125

NAME: <u>BN-192</u>
PO: B.CEREUS
CT: PEPTIDE
EA: (C, 53) (H, 8) (N, 14) (O, 25)
QUAL: (NINH., +) (BIURET, +) (FEHL., -) (FECL3, -)
REFERENCES:
JP 77/133903

40000-6217

PO: SACCHAROMYCES CEREVISIAE
CT: AMPHOTER, PEPTIDE
EA: (N,)
TO: (FUNGI,) (PHYT.FUNGI,)
REFERENCES:
JP 78/31663; *CA*, 89, 105879

40000-6219

NAME: <u>SYRINGOTOXIN</u>
PO: PS.SYRINGAE
CT: PEPTIDE
EA: (N,)
MW: 1000|200
TO: (GEOTHRICIUM CANDIDUM,)
LD50: PHYTOTOXIC
IS-EXT: (BUOH, , W)
REFERENCES:
J. Appl. Bact., 43, 453, 1977

40000-6220

NAME:	SF-1908
PO:	STV.CINNAMONEUM
CT:	PEPTIDE, AMPHOTER, NEUTRAL
EA:	(C, 48) (H, 6) (N, 14) (O, 26) (S, 5)
MW:	2500
PC:	WH., POW.
OR:	(-89.1, W)
UV:	W: (250, 2.2,) (256, 2.3,) (263, 2.66,) (266, 1.4,)
SOL-GOOD:	W
SOL-FAIR:	MEOH, ETOH
SOL-POOR:	ACET, HEX
QUAL:	(NINH., +) (BIURET, +) (SAKA., -) (EHRL., -) (FECL3, -)
STAB:	(ACID, +) (BASE, +)
TO:	(B.SUBT., .1) (C.ALB., 100) (FUNGI, .1) (PHYT.FUNGI, 12.5)
LD50:	(23,)
IS-ION:	(DX-50-4, HCL)
IS-CHR:	(SEPHADEX G-10, W)

REFERENCES:

JP 78/82701

40000-6620

NAME:	U-53946, CC-1014
PO:	PAECYLOMYCES ABRUPTUS
CT:	NEUTRAL, PEPTIDE
FORMULA:	C61H107N11O14
EA:	(N, 12)
MW:	1218
PC:	WH., POW.
OR:	(-26, ETOH)
UV:	ETOH: (245, , 1500)
SOL-GOOD:	MEOH, CHL, W
SOL-POOR:	HEX
TO:	(S.LUTEA,) (S.AUREUS,) (B.SUBT.,)
TV:	L-1210
IS-EXT:	(ETOAC, 10, FILT.)
IS-CHR:	(SILG, CHL-MEOH-NH4OH)
IS-CRY:	(DRY,)

REFERENCES:

USP 4123521

40000-6623

NAME:	B-843
PO:	FLAVOBACTERIUM ANTIBIOTICUM
CT:	AMPHOTER, POLYPEPTIDE
EA:	(C, 49) (H, 7) (N, 12)
MW:	6000|1000
PC:	WH., POW.
OR:	(+.15, MEOH)
UV:	MEOH: (200, ,)
SOL-GOOD:	MEOH, BUOH
SOL-POOR:	ACET, HEX, W
QUAL:	(SAKA., +) (NINH., -) (EHRL., -)
TO:	(G.POS.,)
LD50:	(800|400, IP)
IS-EXT:	(ACET, 7, WB.) (BUOH, 3, W)
IS-ION:	(DX-1X2-OH, NAOAC-MEOH-W)
IS-CHR:	(CEL,) (SEPHADEX LH-20, MEOH)

REFERENCES:

JP 78/130601; *CA*, 90, 119756

Indices

SEQUENCE OF ALPHABETIZING

These indices are computer-generated, and the following order represents the sequence used in alphabetizing characters within an entry:

SPACE	
“	(quote)
’	(apostrophe)
(	(open paren)
)	(close paren)
+	(plus)
,	(comma)
–	(minus or hyphen)
.	(period)
/	(slash)
:	(colon)
		(vertical bar)
A to Z	(letters)
0 to 9	(numbers)

Numbers are sequenced by digit from left to right. For example:

1		
1	2	
1	3	0
2		
2	1	
2	2	0
3		

Also, please note that unnamed compounds do not appear in the *Index of Names of Antibiotics* or the *Index of Antibiotic Numbers and Names.*

INDEX OF NAMES OF ANTIBIOTICS

"COMP.IA", 41214-6223
"COMP.IB", 41214-6224
"COMP.II B", 41214-6226
"COMP.IIA", 41214-6225
"LANDY SUBSTANCE", 43140-5639
"NANDY SUBSTANCE", 43140-1653
"RAUBITSCHEK SUBSTANCE", 43140-1650
A SUBST., 43140-1659
A"-AMINO-3-CHLORO-2-ISOOXAZOLYNYL-5-ACETIC ACID, A"-S-5-S--, 41124-1488
A"-AMINO-3-CHLORO-4-HYDROXY-4.5-DIHYDRO-5-ISOOXAZOLE ACETIC ACID, A"-S-4-S-5-R--, 41124-3893
A"-DEHYDROBIOTIN, 41230-1534
A"-MB, 41230-1535
A"-MDB, 41230-1536
A"-METHYL-DETHIOBIOTIN, 41230-1536
A"-METHYLBIOTIN, 41230-1535
A"-S-4-S-5-R-A"-AMINO-3-CHLORO-4-HYDROXY-4.5-DIHYDRO-5-ISOOXAZOLE ACETIC ACID, 41124-3893
A"-S-5-S-A"-AMINO-3-CHLORO-2-ISOOXAZOLYNYL-5-ACETIC ACID, 41124-1488
A-10073, 43312-1814
A-16884, 41212-1514
A-16886-I, 41212-1513
41212-1515
A-16886-II, 41212-1516
A-1787, 43311-1806
A-19009, 42120-1615
A-19427, 41123-1484
A-21101-II, 41321-1553
A-21101-III, 41321-1550
A-21101-IV, 41321-1552
A-22082, 43130-5685
A-22765, 43313-1815
A-250-II, 42330-1680
A-26771-A, 41324-1573
A-26771-C, 41324-1574
A-287-A, 42300-1709
A-287-B, 42300-1710
A-300-I, 43330-1861
A-300-II, 43330-1860
A-30641, 41326-4785
A-30912-A, 43130-5685
A-30912-B, 43130-5686
A-30912-C, 43130-5687
A-30912-D, 43130-5688
A-32204-A, 43130-5075
A-32204-B, 43130-1749
A-418-Z4, 43311-1804
A-43, 40000-4380
A-4993-A, 42113-1604
A-4993-B, 42113-1605
A-59-A, 43211-1754
43211-1763
A-6786-52, 43110-1714
A-7413-A, 43211-5879
A-7413-B, 43200-5880
A-7413-C, 43200-5881
A-8, 41212-1516
A-8506, 43211-1752
A-8999, 43110-1718
A-9578, 43312-1809
43312-1813
AA-1, 41123-1484
AB-1, 43122-5427
AB-2, 43123-5428
AB-97, 43211-6617
ACETOPYRROTHIN, 41220-1525
ACETYL-ARANOTIN, 41321-1551
ACETYLARANOTIN, 41321-1553
ACIDOMYCIN, 41230-1533
ACTINOMYCELLIN, 43330-1865
ACTINONIN, 42120-1611
ACTINOTHIOCIN, 43212-1771
ACTITHIAZIC ACID, 41230-1533
ACULEACIN COMPLEX, 43130-3902
ACULEACIN-A, 43130-5066
ACULEACIN-A A", 43130-6231
ACULEACIN-A G", 43130-6233
ACULEACIN-B, 43130-5067
ACULEACIN-C, 43130-5068
ACULEACIN-D, 43130-5069
ACULEACIN-D A", 43130-6232
ACULEACIN-D G", 43130-6234
ACULEACIN-E, 43130-5070
ACULEACIN-F, 43130-5071
ACULEACIN-G, 43130-5072
AEROSPORIN, 43121-1722
AIZUMYCIN, 42130-1627
42130-1628
AK-PS, 41220-6222
AL-ANTIBIOTIC, 43140-1652
ALAMETHICIN, 42250-1697
ALAMETHICIN-I, 42250-1697
ALAMETHICIN-II, 42250-5986
ALANOSINE, 41121-1460
ALAZOPEPTIN, 41110-1458
41110-1459
ALBOMYCIN, 43311-1795
43311-1802
ALBOMYCIN-A", 43311-1796
ALBOMYCIN-A1, 43311-1798
ALBOMYCIN-A2, 43311-1799
ALBOMYCIN-A3, 43311-1797
ALBOMYCIN-A4, 43311-1796
ALBOMYCIN-D"1, 43311-1799
43311-1800
ALBOMYCIN-D"2, 43311-1798
43311-1810
ALBOMYCIN-E", 43311-1797
43311-1801
ALBONOURSIN, 41310-1537
ALBOVERTICILLIN, 42300-1707
ALLYLMERCAPTOMETILPENICILLIN, 41211-1505
ALMARCETIN, 40000-1881

ALTHIOMYCIN, 43212-1767
43212-1768
ALVEOMYCIN, 43311-1805
AM-2504, 40000-5993
AMB, 41121-1474
AMBOMYCIN, 41110-1458
41110-1459
AMETHOBOTTROMYCIN, 43220-1775
AMETHOBOTTROMYCIN-B, 43220-1778
AMIDINOMYCIN, 42112-1601
AMPHOMYCIN, 43110-1714
43110-1718
43110-1721
AMYCLENOMYCIN, 41123-1481
AMYLPENICILLIN, 41211-1503
ANTHELVENCIN-A, 42111-1595
ANTHELVENCIN-B, 42111-1596
ANTIAMOEBIN, 42250-1747
42250-1748
ANTIAMOEBIN-I, 42250-1748
ANTIAMOEBIN-II, 42250-6071
ANTICAPSIN, 41123-1484
AO-3, 41330-1587
APOARANOTIN, 41321-1552
AR-110, 43124-5426
ARANOTIN, 41321-1550
ARANOTIN, ACETYL-, 41321-1553
ARANOTIN, APO-, 41321-1552
ARGINYL-D-ALLOTHREONYL-L-PHENYL-ALANINE, L--, 42120-1621
ARGLECIN, 41310-1542
ARIOTIN, 41321-1550
ARMENTOMYCIN, 41121-1464
ARSIMYCIN, 43240-1787
AS-N-136, 42300-5058
AS-N-7A, 43314-5382
ASK-753, 43314-1820
ASPARTOCIN, 43110-1714
43110-1718
43110-1721
ASPERGILIN, 41321-1543
ASPERGILLIC ACID, 41330-1582
ASPERGILLIC ACID, HYDROXY-, 41330-1583
ASPERGILLIC ACID, MUTA-, 41330-1585
ASPERGILLIC ACID, NEO-, 41330-1584
ASPERGILLIC ACID, NEOHYDROXY-, 41330-1586
ASPERGILLOMARASMIN-A, 41130-1493
ASPERGILLOMARASMIN-B, 41130-1494
ASPERGILLUS FACTOR-II, 43140-1653
ASPOCHRACIN, 42300-1713
AT-125, 41124-1488
ATHLESTAIN, 43130-5017
AUREOTHRICIN, 41220-1523
AYFIVIN, 42320-1673
AZASERIN, 41110-1454
AZIRINOMYCIN, 41124-1487
AZOMULTIN, 42113-1606
AZOTOMYCIN, 41110-1457
B"-5-HYDROXY-2-PYRIDILALANINE, L--, 41124-4057
B-MYCIN, 43220-1773
B-28963, 40000-4143
B-344-A, 42300-1661
B-344-B, 42300-1662
B-43, 43123-5280
B-456, 42310-1671
B-73, 41310-1537
B-843, 40000-6623
B-870, 41220-1527
BA-17039-A, 40000-1888
BA-8509-A, 41110-1456
BA-8509-B, 41110-1457
BA-8509-C, 41110-1458
BACILLIN, 42120-1617
42120-1618
42120-2109
BACILLOCIN, 43140-1651
BACILLOMYCIN, 43140-1644
43140-1750
BACILLOMYCIN-A, 43140-1649
BACILLOMYCIN-B, 43140-1645
43140-1750
BACILLOMYCIN-C, 43140-1646
BACILLOMYCIN-L, 43140-5639
BACILLOMYCIN-R, 43140-1644
43140-1750
BACILLOMYCIN-S, 43140-6076
BACILYSIN, 42120-1617
42120-1618
42120-2109
BACITRACIN-A, 42320-1673
BACITRACIN-B, 42320-1674
BACITRACIN-C, 42320-1675
BACITRACIN-F, 42320-1676
BACITRACIN-G, 42320-1676
BACITRACIN-X, 42320-1676
BACTERICID-4205-A, 43123-1736
BELCOMYCIN, 43121-1731
BENZYLPENICILLIN, 41211-1498
BERNINAMYCIN, 43230-1785
BERNINAMYCIN-A, 43230-1785
BERNINAMYCIN-B, 43230-5073
BESTATIN, 42120-5989
BICYCLOMYCIN, 42130-1627
42130-1628
BLENOXANE, 43320-1826
BLEO, 43320-1826
BLEOMYCIN COMPLEX, 43320-1826
BLEOMYCIN, 3-AMINOPROPYLAMINO--, 43320-5692
BLEOMYCIN, 3-BUTYL-3-AMINOPROPYL--, 43320-5693
BLEOMYCIN, 3-CYCLOHEXYLAMINOPROPYL-AMINO--, 43320-5695
BLEOMYCIN, 3-DIETILAMINOETILAMINO--, 43320-5694
BLEOMYCIN, 3-NN-DIMETILAMINOETIL-AMINO--, 43320-5696
BLEOMYCIN, 3-1-METHYL-3-AMINOPROPYL-AMINOPROPYLAMINO--, 43320-5697
BLEOMYCIN-A1, 43320-1827
BLEOMYCIN-A2, 43320-1828
BLEOMYCIN-A2'-A, 43320-1830
BLEOMYCIN-A2'-B, 43320-1829
BLEOMYCIN-A2'-C, 43320-1831
BLEOMYCIN-A2, DEMETHYL-, 43320-1832
BLEOMYCIN-A3, 43320-1833

BLEOMYCIN-A4, 43320-1834
BLEOMYCIN-A5, 43320-1835
BLEOMYCIN-A6, 43320-1836
BLEOMYCIN-B1, 43320-1837
BLEOMYCIN-B2, 43320-1838
43320-1845
BLEOMYCIN-B2, DIHYDRO-, 43320-1844
BLEOMYCIN-B3, 43320-1839
BLEOMYCIN-B4, 43320-1840
43320-1847
BLEOMYCIN-B4, DIHYDRO-, 43320-1846
BLEOMYCIN-B5, 43320-1847
BLEOMYCIN-B6, 43320-1841
BLEOMYCIN-B6, DIHYDRO-, 43320-1848
BN-109, 43124-3903
BN-1512, 40000-4796
BN-165, 40000-5877
BN-175, 40000-5573
BN-192, 40000-6125
BN-7, 43123-1741
BOTROCIDIN, 40000-1891
BOTTRO-MYCIN-A, 43220-1773
BOTTROMYCIN, 43220-1773
BOTTROMYCIN-A, 43220-1773
BOTTROMYCIN-A1, 43220-1779
BOTTROMYCIN-A2, 43220-1774
BOTTROMYCIN-B1, 43220-1775
43220-1778
BOTTROMYCIN-B2, 43220-1776
BOTTROMYCIN-C2, 43220-1777
BRESEIN, 42310-1672
BRL-14151, 41215-5057
BRYAMYCIN, 43211-1752
43211-1753
BSA, 42120-5188
BU-1880, 43122-3904
BU-1975-B, 43122-3904
BU-2231-A, 43320-5431
BU-2231-B, 43320-5432
B7-I, 43140-1655
B7-II, 43140-1659
B7-IV, 43140-1660
C-11924 F-1, 43320-6239
C-1778B, 41212-5333
C-1778C, 41212-5334
C-17781A, 41212-5332
C-2801-X, 41212-3894
C-43-219, 41212-5331
CAIROMYCIN-B, 42130-5422
CAPREOMYCIN-I-A, 42330-1680
CAPREOMYCIN-I-B, 42330-1682
CAPREOMYCIN-II-A, 42330-1681
CAPREOMYCIN-II-B, 42330-1683
CAPROMYCIN, 42330-1680
CAPSTAT, 42330-1680
CARBAMYL-D-SERINE, O--, 41121-1490
CC-1014, 40000-6620
CEPHALOSPORIN-C, 41212-1508
CEPHALOSPORIN-C, DESACETOXY-,
41212-1509
CEPHALOSPORIN-C, DESACETYL-, 41212-1510
CEPHALOSPORIN-C, N-ACETYLDEACETOXY-,
41212-4784
CEPHALOSPORIN-C, 7-MEHOXY-, 41212-1514
CEPHALOSPORIN-C, 7-METHOXYDEACETYL-,
41212-5054
CEPHALOSPORIN-N, 41211-1506
CEPHALOSPORIN-R, 41211-1506
CEPHAMYCIN-A, 41212-1511
CEPHAMYCIN-B, 41212-1512
CEPHAMYCIN-C, 41212-1513
41212-1515
41212-1520
CEPHEMIMYCIN, 41212-1513
41212-1520
CEREIN-B2, 42300-1705
CEREXIN-A, 42260-3905
CEREXIN-B, 42260-3906
CEREXIN-C, 42260-5424
CEREXIN-D, 42260-5425
CH-777-A, 42111-1590
CHAETOCIN, 41322-1554
CHAETOCIN, 11.11-DIHYDROXY-,
41322-1555
41322-1562
CHAETOMIN, 41322-1563
CHALCIDINES, 43200-1792
CHLAMYDOCIN, 42300-1698
CINNAMONIN, 41230-1533
CINNAMYCIN, 42230-1642
CIRCULIN-A, 43121-1734
CIRCULIN-B, 43121-1735
CLAVAM, FORMYLOXYMETHYL-, 41215-6610
CLAVAM, 2-HYDROXYMETHYL-, 41215-6213
CLAVAM-2-CARBOXYLIC ACID, 41215-6611
CLAVULANIC ACID, 41215-5057
41215-5369
CLAVULAVIC ACID, 1-B"-HYDROXYPROPIONYL-,
41215-5081
COLIMYCIN, 43121-1728
43121-1731
COLISAN, 42210-1637
COLISTIN, 43121-1728
COLISTIN-A, 43121-1731
COLISTIN-B, 43121-1732
COLISTIN-C, 43121-1733
COLISTINAT, 43121-1731
CONGOCIDIN, 42111-1591
CP-41012, 43110-5423
CP-41043, 43211-5828
CP-41494, 43211-5829
CP-46192, 43211-6124
CRYOMYCIN-A, 40000-2111
CRYOMYCIN-B, 40000-4875
CRYSTALLOMYCIN, 43110-1720
CU-BT-5, 43320-1847
CU-PHLEOMYCIN COMPLEX, 43320-1842
CYCLO-L-LEU-L-PRO, 41310-4049
CYCLO-VAL-PRO, 41310-5097
CYCLOHEXENYL-1-GLYCINE, 41123-1480
CYCLOMYCIN, 41124-1491
CYCLOSERINE, 41124-1491
CYCLOSPORIN-A, 42350-4873
CYCLOSPORIN-B, 42350-4874
CYCLOSPORIN-C, 42350-5060
CYCLOSPORIN-D, 42350-5575
CYCLOSPORIN-E, 42350-5576
CYL-?, 42300-6123

C2, 41212-1508
41212-5531
C3, 41212-1509
C4, 41212-5532
C6, 41212-5533
D"-HYDROXY-G"-OXO-NORVALINE, L--, 41121-1468
D"-N-HYDROXY-L-ARGININE, 41121-1472
41121-1473
D-4-AMINO-ISOOXAZOLIDONE, 41124-1491
DANOMYCIN, 43313-1817
DCS, 41310-1539
DEHYDROGLIOTOXIN, 41321-1547
DEHYDROLEUCIN, 41121-1467
DEHYDROPHLEOMYCIN-D1, 43320-1838
DEHYDROPHLEOMYCIN-E, 43320-1840
DEMETHYLBLEOMYCIN-A2, 43320-1832
DES-N-METHYLTHIOLUTIN, 41220-1524
DESACETOXYCEPHALOSPORIN-C, 41212-1509
41212-1517
DESACETYLCEPHALOSPORIN-C, 41212-1510
DESFERRI-FERRIOXAMIN-E, 43315-1822
43315-1822
DESFERRIOXAMIN-B, 43315-5774
DESLYSIL-VIOMYCIN, 42330-1679
DIAZOACETYL-L-SERINE, O--, 41110-1454
DIAZOMYCIN-A, 41110-1456
DIAZOMYCIN-B, 41110-1457
DIAZOMYCIN-C, 41110-1458
DIHY-DROPHENYLALANINE, 41123-1483
DIHYDROBLEOMYCIN-B2, 43320-1844
DIHYDROBLEOMYCIN-B4, 43320-1846
DIHYDROBLEOMYCIN-B6, 43320-1848
DIHYDROPENICILLIN-F, 41211-1503
DISTAMYCIN, 42111-1598
DISTAMYCIN-A, 42111-1598
DON, 41110-1455
DON, N-ACETYL--, 41110-1456
DUAZOMYCIN-A, 41110-1456
DUAZOMYCIN-B, 41110-1457
DUAZOMYCIN-C, 41110-1458
41110-1459
DURAMYCIN, 42230-1643
E-49-A", 43122-1742
E-49-B", 43122-1743
E-49-D", 43122-1745
E-49-G", 43122-1744
E-64, 42120-4940
E-733-A, 41124-1491
E-733-B, 41121-1490
ECHINOCANDIN-A, 43130-5075
ECHINOCANDIN-B, 43130-1749
43130-5063
ECHINOCANDIN-C, 43130-5064
ECHINOCANDIN-D, 43130-5065
EDEIN-A1, 42220-1639
EDEIN-A1, GUANYL--, 42220-1640
EDEIN-B1, 42220-1640
EDEIN-D, 42220-1641
EDEIN-F, 42220-6122
EM-2, 42250-1869
EM-3, 42250-1870
EM-4, 42250-1871
EM-98, 42111-1593
EMERICELLOPSINS, 41212-1522
EMERIMICIN-II, 42250-1869
EMERIMICIN-III, 42250-1870
EMERIMICIN-IV, 42250-1871
ENVIOMYCIN, 42330-1685
EPICORAZINE-A, 41321-5295
EPIDERMIDINS-A1, 42300-1704
EPIDERMIDINS-A2, 42300-1704
EPIDERMIDINS-B1, 42300-1704
EPIDERMIDINS-B2, 42300-1704
ESEIN, 42210-1638
EUMYCIN, 43140-1644
43140-1750
F-1, 41212-1521
F-10-C, 41220-1532
F-17-B, 42230-1643
F-30, 42250-1697
F-50, 42250-1697
F-6, 42111-1590
FARCINICIN, 41220-1523
FELDAMYCIN, 42120-5249
FERRAMIDO-CHLOROMYCIN, 43314-1819
FERRICHROCIN, 43315-1823
FERRICHRYSIN, 43315-1824
FERRIMYCIN, 43312-1813
FERRIMYCIN-A1, 43312-1809
FERRIMYCIN-A2, 43312-1811
FERRIMYCIN-B, 43312-1812
FERROVERDIN, 43330-1825
FICELLOMYCIN, 42120-5112
FLAVACIDIN, 41211-1504
FLAVACIN, 41211-1504
FLAVICIDIN, 41211-1500
FLAVICIN, 41211-1504
FLORIMYCIN, 42330-1677
FN-1636, 41123-1483
FORMYLOXYMETHYLCLAVAM, 41215-6610
FORPHENICINE, 41125-6119
FR-1923, 41213-4025
FR-1923-C, 41213-5186
FR-2458, 41213-5186
41213-5187
FR-29038, 41213-5875
FR-29055, 41213-5876
FR-29644, 41213-5980
FR-3383, 40000-5197
FR-900012, 40000-5996
FUMARYL-ALANINE, 42120-1622
FUMARYLCARBOXAMIDO-L-2.3-DIAMINO PROIONYL-L-ALANINE, 42120-1615
FUNGOCIN, 43140-1644
43140-1649
43140-1750
FURANOMYCIN, 41124-1492
FUSARININ, 43330-5698
FWH-775, 41000-1495
F1, 41212-1510
F2, 41212-1508
F3, 41212-1509
G-15-I, 43214-5195
G-15-II, 43214-5194
GALANTIN-I, 40000-3899
GALANTIN-II, 40000-3898
GALLERIN, 40000-4393

GANCIDIN-W, 41310-4049
GARDIMYCIN, 40000-5059
GARLANDOSUS, 43212-1770
GATAVALIN, 40000-1890
GEMINIMYCINS, 40000-5680
GIGANTIC ACID, 41211-1503
GK-340, 41212-6070
GLIOTOXIN, 41321-1543
GLIOTOXIN, DEHYDRO-, 41321-1547
GLIOTOXIN-B, 41321-1546
GLIOTOXIN-MONOACETATE, 41321-1544
GLUCONIMYCIN, 43314-1818
GLUMAMYCIN, 43110-1714
43110-1718
43110-1721
GP-3, 42260-3906
GRACEILLIN, 42300-5446
GRAMICIDIN LIKE SUBST., 42210-1636
GRAMICIDIN-A, 42210-1632
GRAMICIDIN-B, 42210-1633
GRAMICIDIN-C, 42210-1634
GRAMICIDIN-D, 42210-1635
GRAMICIDIN-J, 42310-1669
42310-1670
GRAMICIDIN-S, 42310-1669
42310-1670
GRAMINIC ACID, 42310-1664
GRANEGILLIN, 41330-1582
GRATIZIN, 42310-1706
GRISEIN, 43311-1795
43311-1802
43311-1810
GRISEIN-A, 43311-1799
GRISEIN-B, 43311-1797
GRISEIN-C, 43311-1796
GRISEIN-1, 43311-1798
GRISEIN-2, 43311-1799
GRISEIN-3, 43311-1797
GRISEIN-4, 43311-1796
GRISEOCOCCIN, 42110-1607
GRISEOCOCCIN-D, 42110-1608
GRISONOMYCIN, 43312-1814
GUANYL-EDEIN-A1, 42220-1640
H-3787, 40000-5335
H-899, 41121-1468
HA-9, 41220-1527
HADACIDIN, 41130-1462
HEPTYLPENICILLIN, 41211-1502
HISTIDOMYCIN-A, 40000-1882
HISTIDOMYCIN-B, 40000-1883
HODYDAMYCIN, 40000-1887
HOLOMYCIN, 41220-1524
HON, 41121-1468
HYALODENDRIN, 41324-1571
HYALODENDRIN-II, 41324-1572
HYALODENDRIN-III, 41324-5679
HYDROXYASPARTIC ACID, 41121-4781
HYDROXYASPERGILLIC ACID, 41330-1583
HYDROXYBENXYLPENICILLIN, 41211-1501
HYDROXYVIOMYCIN, 42330-1684
I-1, 42300-1702
I-1431, 41124-1491
I-2, 42300-1703
IA-887, 42111-1590
IAQUIRIN-III, 43330-1864
ICI-13595, 40000-2100
IKARUGAMYCIN, 42130-1626
ILAMYCIN, 42340-1688
ILAMYCIN-A, 42340-1688
42340-1692
ILAMYCIN-B, 42340-1689
ILAMYCIN-B1, 42340-1694
ILAMYCIN-B1+ILAMYCIN-B2, 42340-1689
ILAMYCIN-B2, 42340-1695
ILAMYCIN-C1, 42340-1690
ILAMYCIN-C2, 42340-1691
ILEUMYCIN, 40000-6126
ISOBUTYROPYRROTHIN, 41220-1528
ISOCEPHALOSPORIN-N, 41211-1507
ISOPENICILLIN-N, 41211-1507
ISOTENTOXINE, 42300-6072
ITURIN-A, 43140-1644
43140-1645
43140-1649
43140-1750
ITURIN-C, 43140-6074
JOLIPEPTIN, 43123-1746
K-117, 42111-1590
K-16, 42120-1612
K-300, 41124-1491
K-73, 41310-5097
KIKUMYCIN-A, 42113-1602
KIKUMYCIN-B, 42113-1603
KM-208, 42120-1617
42120-2109
KM-8, 43240-4790
KOBENOMYCIN, 43240-1794
KOLUOPTHISIN, 42330-1677
KPN, 41211-5330
KT-151, 41121-5981
KUWAITIMYCIN, 43100-2099
L-ARGINYL-D-ALLOTHREONYL-L-PHENYL-ALANINE, 42120-1621
L-B"-3-HYDROXYUREIDOALANINE, 41121-5004
L-B"-5-HYDROXY-2-PYRIDILALANINE, 41124-4057
L-D"-HYDROXY-G"-OXO-NORVALINE, 41121-1468
L-DIHYDROPHENYLALANINE, 41123-1483
L-N5-HYDROXYARGININE, 41121-1472
41121-1473
L-N5-PHOSPHONO-METHIONINE-S-SULPHOXY-MINYL-ALANYL-ALANINE, 42120-1625
L-N5-1-IMINOETHYLORNITHINE, 41121-1471
L-THREO-B"-HYDROXYASPARTIC ACID, 41121-4781
L-1.4-CYCLOHEX-ADIEN-1-ALANINE, 41123-1483
L-13365, 43200-6079
L-2-AMINO-PENTYNOIC ACID, 41121-1469
L-2-AMINO-3.4-DIHYDROXYBUTYRIC ACID, 41121-1470
L-2-AMINO-4-METHOXY-TRANS-3-BUTENOIC ACID, 41121-1474

L-2-AMINO-4-2-AMINOETHOXY-3-BUTENOIC ACID, 41122-1466
L-2.5-DIHYDRO-PHENYLALANINE, 41123-1483
L-4-AZALEUCIN, 41121-1465
L-4-OXALYSINE, 41122-1477
LA-5352, 43311-1803
LA-5937, 43311-1808
LASPARTOMYCIN, 43110-1716
LEUCINAMYCIN, 43240-1793
LEUCINOSTATIN, 40000-1877
LEUCOPEPTIN, 43240-1788
LEUCYL-3-EPIDEOXYNEGAMYCIN, 42120-5985
LEUCYLNEGAMYCIN, 42120-1610
LIA-0832-D, 42113-5681
LILACIN, 40000-1878
LILACININ, 40000-1874
LL-BB-547-B", 42330-5682
LL-BL-869-B", 42113-3895
LL-BM-547A", 42330-1679
LL-S-88-A", 41321-1551
41321-1553
LONGICATENAMYCIN, 43150-1751
LYCOMARASMIN, 41130-1494
LYDIMYCIN, 41230-1534
M-141, 42112-1601
M-22380, 41214-6223
M-22381, 41214-6224
M-22382, 41214-6225
M-22383, 41214-6226
M-4214, 43130-3902
M-6-62A, 41220-1523
MALFORMIN-A1, 42300-1699
MALFORMIN-B1, 42300-1700
MALFORMIN-B2, 42300-5445
MALFORMIN-C, 42300-5191
MALONOMYCIN, 42120-1612
MATAMYCIN, 43212-1767
43212-1768
MATCHAMYCIN, 43330-1859
MC-902 COMPLEX, 43200-5336
MC-902-I, 43200-5990
MC-902-I′, 43200-6127
MC696-SY2-A, 41214-2262
41214-4253
MELINACIDIN, 41322-1559
MELINACIDIN-II, 41322-1560
MELINACIDIN-III, 41322-1561
MELINACIDIN-IV, 41322-1555
41322-1562
METHOBOTTROMYCIN, 43220-1773
METHOBOTTROMYCIN-C, 43220-1779
MICROCOCCIN, 43214-1766
MICROCOCCIN-M, 43214-4872
MICROCOCCIN-M1, 43214-4872
MICROCOCCIN-P, 43214-1766
MICROCOCCIN-P1, 43214-1766
MICROCOCCIN-P2, 43214-6077
MICROPOLYSPORIN-AB, 43200-1789
MK-61, 42112-1600
MKOM, 40000-5574
MM-13902, 41214-4800
MM-14151, 41215-5057
MM-17880, 41214-5370
41214-6121
MM-27, 41123-1479
MM-4550, 41214-2262
41214-4253
MONOKETOORGANOMYCIN, 40000-5574
MORIMYCIN, 42120-1631
MSD-235-S2, 42120-1613
MSD-235-S3, 42120-1614
MULTHIOMYCIN, 43211-1982
43211-5534
MUTAASPERGILLIC ACID, 41330-1585
MUTABILLICIN, 43211-1754
43211-1755
43211-1756
MX-A, 43122-5074
MYCELIANAMIDE, 41310-1538
MYCOBACIDIN, 41230-1533
MYCOBACILLIN, 42300-1696
MYCOSUBTILIN, 43140-1663
MYRORHODIN, 40000-1876
MYRORODIN, 40000-1876
MYXOVIROMYCIN, 42112-1601
N-ACETYL-DEHYDROTHIENAMYCIN, 41214-6568
N-ACETYL-DON, 41110-1456
N-ACETYL-EPI-THIENAMYCIN-A, 41214-4902
41214-6223
N-ACETYL-EPI-THIENAMYCIN-B, 41214-5982
41214-6225
N-ACETYL-EPI-THIENAMYCIN-D, 41214-5983
41214-6226
N-ACETYL-THIENAMYCIN, 41214-5677
N-ACETYL-TYRAMINE, 41124-1489
N-ACETYL-8-EPI-THIENAMYCIN-C, 41214-6224
41214-6265
N-ACETYLDEACETOXYCEPHALOSPORIN-C, 41212-4784
N-NITROGLICIN, 41121-3728
N-PROPIONYLHOLOTHIN, 41220-5419
N-1409, 42120-5421
N-44-A-21, 40000-2084
NEGAMYCIN, 42120-1609
NEGAMYCIN, LEUCYL-, 42120-1610
NEGAMYCIN, LEUCYL-3-EPIDEOXY-, 42120-5985
NEGAMYCIN, 3-EPIDEOXY-, 42120-5984
NEGINAMYCIN, 43240-4787
NEOASPERGILLIC ACID, 41330-1584
NEOHYDROXYASPERGILLIC ACID, 41330-1586
NETROPSIN, 42111-1590
NFHAA, 41130-1462
NIFUNGIN, 40000-5704
NIKKOMYCIN, 41123-1480
41123-5055
NITRAMINOACETIC ACID, 41121-3728
NITROGLICIN, N--, 41121-3728

NJ-21, 41124-1491
NOCARDAMIN, 43315-1822
NOCARDICIN-A, 41213-5186
NOCARDICIN-B, 41213-5187
NOCARDICIN-C, 41213-5875
NOCARDICIN-COMPLEX, 41213-4025
NOCARDICIN-D, 41213-5876
NOCARDICIN-E, 41213-5675
NOCARDICIN-F, 41213-5676
NOCARDICIN-G, 41213-5980
NOFORMICIN, 42112-1600
NORVALYL-5-ISOUREA, O-L--, 41121-1475
NOSIHEPTID, 43211-1982
43211-5534
NRC-101, 40000-1886
NRC-501, 40000-5198
NRCS-15, 43314-1821
NSC-100844, 43213-1772
NSC-10270, 41110-1458
NSC-102866, 41321-1543
NSC-116328, 41124-1492
NSC-125066, 43320-1827
NSC-135758, 41310-1540
NSC-143647, 41121-1460
NSC-146208, 43320-1851
NSC-146842, 43320-1828
NSC-163501, 41124-1488
NSC-176324, 41124-3893
NSC-51097, 41110-1456
NSC-521778, 41130-1462
NSC-5664, 41110-1457
NSC-61586, 43320-1842
NSC-71935, 42230-1643
NSC-71936, 42230-1642
NSC-7365, 41110-1455
NSC-742, 41110-1454
N5-HYDROXYARGININE, L--, 41121-1472
N5-PHOSPHONO-METHIONINE-S-SULPHOXYMINYL-ALANYL-ALANINE, L--, 42120-1625
N5-1-IMINOETHYLORNITHINE, L--, 41121-1471
O-CARBAMYL-D-SERINE, 41121-1490
O-DIAZOACETYL-L-SERINE, 41110-1454
O-L-NORVALYL-5-ISOUREA, 41121-1475
O-2867-A", 41000-4006
O-2867-B", 41000-4005
OCTAPEPTIN, 43122-3904
43122-4786
OCTAPEPTIN-A1, 43122-1743
OCTAPEPTIN-A2, 43122-1742
OCTAPEPTIN-A3, 43122-1742
OCTAPEPTIN-B1, 43122-1745
OCTAPEPTIN-B2, 43122-1744
OCTAPEPTIN-B3, 43122-1744
OCTAPEPTIN-C1, 43122-5192
ORIENTMYCIN, 41124-1491
OROSOMYCIN, 41220-1527
ORYZACHLORIN, 41326-1581
OS-3256-B, 41110-1461
OXAMYCIN, 41124-1491
OXYMYCIN, 41124-1491
P-42-2, 41310-1537
P-6621, 41212-1513
PA-94, 41124-1491
PA-95, 41230-1533
PARASTICIN, 41211-1498
PARVULIN, 43110-1717
PARVULIN-A, 43110-1717
PENICILLANIC ACID, 6-AMINO-, 41211-1497
PENICILLIN F+DIHYDROPENICILLIN, 41211-1504
PENICILLIN NUCLEUS, 41211-1497
PENICILLIN, ALLYLMERCAPTOMETIL-, 41211-1505
PENICILLIN, AMYL-, 41211-1503
PENICILLIN, BENZYL-, 41211-1498
PENICILLIN, HEPTYL-, 41211-1502
PENICILLIN, HYDROXYBENXYL-, 41211-1501
PENICILLIN, PHENOXYMETHYL-, 41211-1499
PENICILLIN, 2-PENTENYL-, 41211-1500
PENICILLIN-F, 41211-1500
PENICILLIN-F, DIHYDRO-, 41211-1503
PENICILLIN-G, 41211-1498
PENICILLIN-I, 41211-1500
PENICILLIN-II, 41211-1498
PENICILLIN-III, 41211-1501
PENICILLIN-IV, 41211-1502
PENICILLIN-K, 41211-1502
PENICILLIN-N, 41211-1506
PENICILLIN-O, 41211-1505
PENICILLIN-V, 41211-1499
PENICILLIN-X, 41211-1501
PEP-BLEOMYCIN, 43320-6353
PEPTHIOMYCIN-A, 43200-1780
PEPTHIOMYCIN-B, 43200-1781
PHALAMYCIN, 43230-1791
PHENOXYMETHYLPENICILLIN, 41211-1499
PHLEOMYCIN, 43320-1842
PHLEOMYCIN-C, 43320-1843
PHLEOMYCIN-D1, 43320-1837
43320-1844
PHLEOMYCIN-D1, DEHYDRO-, 43320-1838
PHLEOMYCIN-D2, 43320-1838
43320-1845
PHLEOMYCIN-E, 43320-1846
PHLEOMYCIN-E, DEHYDRO-, 43320-1840
PHLEOMYCIN-F, 43320-1840
43320-1847
PHLEOMYCIN-G, 43320-1848
PHLEOMYCIN-G', 43320-1841
PHLEOMYCIN-H, 43320-1849
PHLEOMYCIN-I, 43320-1850
PHOSPHOTHRYCINYL-ALANYL-ALANINE, 42120-1623
42120-1624
PHTIOMYCIN, 42330-1677
42330-1678
PILOSOMYCIN, 43312-1813
PILOSOMYCIN-A, 43312-1809
PILOSOMYCIN-B1, 43312-1811
PIPERAZIDONE, 41310-1540
PIPERAZINEDIONE, 41310-1540
PLATOMYCIN-A, 43320-1855
PLATOMYCIN-B, 43320-1856

PLUMBEMYCIN-A, 42120-5420
PLUMBEMYCIN-B, 42120-5421
POLCILLIN, 43140-1654
POLYMYXIN-A, 43121-1722
43121-1723
POLYMYXIN-B1, 43121-1724
POLYMYXIN-B2, 43121-1725
POLYMYXIN-C, 43121-1726
POLYMYXIN-D1, 43121-1727
POLYMYXIN-E, 43121-1728
POLYMYXIN-E1, 43121-1731
POLYMYXIN-E2, 43121-1732
POLYMYXIN-F1, 43121-5991
POLYMYXIN-F2, 43121-5992
POLYMYXIN-K, 43121-6073
POLYMYXIN-M, 43121-1722
43121-1723
POLYMYXIN-P1, 43121-1729
POLYMYXIN-P2, 43121-1730
POLYMYXIN-S1, 43121-5683
POLYMYXIN-T1, 43121-5684
POLYPEPTIN-A, 43123-1739
PRACTOMYCIN-C, 40000-1884
PRIMOCARCIN, 41130-1463
PROPARGYLGLYCINE, 41121-1469
PROPYONYLPYRROTHIN, 41220-1523
PROVIRIDOMYCIN, 43330-1862
PS-5, 41214-6080
PULCHERRIMIN, 41330-1589
PULCHERRIMINIC ACID, 41330-1588
PULCHERRIMINIC ACID-FE-SALT,
41330-1589
PYRROTHIN, ACETO-, 41220-1525
PYRROTHIN, ISOBUTYRO-, 41220-1528
PYRROTHIN, PROPYONYL-, 41220-1523
R-719, 42113-1602
RADICICOLIN, 42350-1879
RAMIHYPHIN-A, 40000-1875
RB-103, 42210-1637
REUMYCIN, 42300-1712
RHIZOBITOXIN, 41122-1476
RHIZOMYCIN, 40000-1889
RIT-D-2214, 41211-5418
RO-1-9213, 41124-1491
RO-2-7758, 43213-1772
RO-5-2667, 43311-1798
43311-1810
RO-7-7730, 43311-1799
43311-1800
RO-7-7731, 43311-1797
43311-1801
RP-10206, 43212-1769
RP-9671, 43211-5534
RUFOMYCIN-A, 42340-1688
42340-1692
RUFOMYCIN-B, 42340-1689
42340-1693
RUFOMYCIN-B1, 42340-1694
RUFOMYCIN-B2, 42340-1695
RUFOMYCIN-I, 42340-1693
RUFOMYCIN-III, 42340-1692
S-ALANYL-3-A"-S-CHLORO-3-S-HYDROXY-2-
OXO-3-AZETIDINYLMETHYL-S-ALANINE,
42120-3896
S-19, 40000-5455
S-2.3-DICARBOXY-AZIRIDINE, 41124-4782
S-300, 42330-1677
S-31794-F-1, 43130-5429
S-520, 43150-1751
S-53210-A-II, 43211-6615
S-53210-A-III, 43211-6616
S-53210-A-1, 43211-6614
S-685, 42111-1599
S-7481-F1, 42350-4873
S-7481-F2, 42350-4874
S-82, 41321-1543
SAIHOCHIN-A, 43100-2127
SAIHOCHIN-B, 43100-2128
SALMOTIN, 41211-1506
SAMAROSPORIN, 42250-5193
SARAMYCETIN, 43213-1772
SC-4, 40000-5536
SCH-18640, 43211-5572
SCH-18640-B, 43211-6075
SEROMYCIN, 41124-1491
SF-1293, 42120-1623
42120-1624
SF-1293-B, 41121-5004
SF-1346, 41124-4057
SF-1623, 41212-4783
SF-1771, 43320-5689
SF-1771-B, 43320-5690
SF-1836, 41124-6221
SF-1908, 40000-6220
SF-1917, 40000-6218
SF-1919, 40000-6078
SF-1961-A, 43320-6618
SF-1961-B, 43320-6619
SF-674, 40000-1889
SF-7810-F, 43130-1749
SINANOMYCIN, 42111-1590
SIOMYCIN, 43211-1754
SIOMYCIN-A, 43211-1754
43211-1755
43211-1756
43211-1763
SIOMYCIN-C, 43211-1757
SIRODESMIN-A, 41325-1575
SIRODESMIN-B, 41325-1576
SIRODESMIN-C, 41325-1579
SIRODESMIN-D, 41325-1580
SIRODESMIN-F, 41325-1579
41325-1580
SIRODESMIN-G, 41325-1577
SIRODESMIN-J, 41325-1578
SL-3440, 42300-1698
SL-7810-F, 43130-5063
SL-7810-FII, 43130-5064
SL-7810-FIII, 43130-5065
SPORANGIOMYCIN, 43211-1754
43211-1755
43211-1756
SPORIDESMIN, 41323-1564
SPORIDESMIN-A, 41323-1564
SPORIDESMIN-B, 41323-1565
SPORIDESMIN-C, 41323-1566
SPORIDESMIN-D, 41323-1567
SPORIDESMIN-E, 41323-1568

SPORIDESMIN-F, 41323-1569
SPORIDESMIN-G, 41323-1570
SPORIDESMIN-H, 41323-6495
SS-70-A, 43320-5076
SS-70-B, 43320-5077
STALLIMYCIN, 42111-1598
STENOTHRICIN, 42240-2101
STENOTHRICIN COMPLEX, 42240-2101
STILBELLIN, 42250-1747
42250-1748
STRAVIDIN-S2, 42120-1613
STRAVIDIN-S3, 42120-1614
SUBSPORIN-A, 43140-1656
SUBSPORIN-B, 43140-1657
SUBSPORIN-C, 43140-1658
SUCCINIMYCIN, 43313-1816
SULFACTIN, 43211-1765
SULFOMYCIN-I, 43230-1782
SULFOMYCIN-II, 43230-1783
SULFOMYCIN-III, 43230-1784
SUZUKACILLIN-A, 42250-2081
SUZUKACILLIN-B, 42250-2082
SYNNEMATIN-B, 41211-1506
SYRINGOTOXIN, 40000-6219
T-1384, 42111-1590
T-3910, 43110-1718
TABTOXIN, 42120-3897
TAITOMYCIN, 43211-5534
TALLYSOMYCIN-A, 43320-5431
TALLYSOMYCIN-B, 43320-5432
TATEMYCIN, 43211-1762
TATEMYCIN-A1, 43211-1758
TETAINE, 42120-1617
42120-1618
42120-2109
THEIOMYCETIN, 43230-1786
THERMOMYCETIN, 43230-1786
THERMOTHIOCIN, 43200-1790
THIACTIN, 43211-1752
43211-1753
THIANOSINE, 43121-1740
THIAZOLIDOMYCIN, 41230-1533
THIAZOLIDONE ANTIBIOTIC, 41230-1533
THIENAMYCIN, 41214-5056
THIENAMYCIN, N-ACETYL--, 41214-5677
THIENAMYCIN-A, N-ACETYL-EPI--,
41214-4902
41214-6223
THIENAMYCIN-B, N-ACETYL-EPI--,
41214-5982
41214-6225
THIENAMYCIN-C, N-ACETYL-8-EPI--,
41214-6224
41214-6265
THIENAMYCIN-D, N-ACETYL-EPI--,
41214-5983
41214-6226
THIOAURIN, 41220-1527
41220-1530
THIOCILLIN-I, 43214-5194
THIOCILLIN-II, 43214-5195
THIOCILLIN-III, 43214-5196
THIOLUTIN, 41220-1525
THIOLUTIN, DES-N-METHYL-, 41220-1524
THIOMYCIN, 41220-1526
THIOPEPTIN-A1, 43211-1758
THIOPEPTIN-A1A, 43211-1758
THIOPEPTIN-A1B, 43211-6236
THIOPEPTIN-A2, 43211-1759
THIOPEPTIN-A3, 43211-1760
THIOPEPTIN-A3A, 43211-1760
THIOPEPTIN-A3B, 43211-6237
THIOPEPTIN-A4, 43211-1761
THIOPEPTIN-A4A, 43211-1761
THIOPEPTIN-A4B, 43211-6238
THIOPEPTIN-B, 43211-1762
THIOPEPTIN-BA, 43211-1762
THIOPEPTIN-BB, 43211-6235
THIOSTREPTON, 43211-1752
43211-1753
THREOMYCIN, 41124-1492
TM-743, 43122-5061
TOXIMYCIN, 43140-1647
TRIACETYLDESFERRIFUSIGEN, 43315-5448
TRICHOPOLIN-A, 43100-5994
TRICHOPOLIN-B, 43100-5995
TRICHORIN-A, 41326-5678
TRICHOSTATIN-A, 43330-1861
TRICHOSTATIN-B, 43330-1860
TRICHOSTATIN-C, 43330-6355
TRICHOTOXIN-A, 42250-1701
TRICHOTOXIN-A-40, 42250-1701
TRICULAMIN, 42300-1708
TRIDECAAPTIN-C, 43124-6230
TRIDECAPTIN-A, 43124-5426
TRIDECAPTIN-B, 43124-6229
TSUSHIMYCIN, 43110-1715
TUBERACTIN, 42330-1684
TUBERACTINOMYCIN-A, 42330-1684
TUBERACTINOMYCIN-B, 42330-1677
TUBERACTINOMYCIN-N, 42330-1685
TUBERACTINOMYCIN-O, 42330-1686
TYROCIDINE-A, 42310-1664
TYROCIDINE-B, 42310-1665
TYROCIDINE-C, 42310-1666
TYROCIDINE-D, 42310-1667
TYROCIDINE-E, 42310-1668
U-10923, 41121-1464
U-15738, 41123-1483
U-15965, 41230-1534
U-22324, 42250-1697
U-26362, 41322-1559
U-27810, 43230-1785
U-30116, 41121-1467
U-30604, 43320-1851
U-32166-E, 43320-1853
U-40588, 42250-1869
U-40589, 42250-1870
U-40590, 42250-1871
U-42126, 41124-1488
U-43795, 41124-3893
U-47929, 42120-5112
U-48266, 42120-5249
U-51738, 41123-1483
U-53946, 40000-6620
U-9279, 43212-1770

VALINE-MALFORMIN, 42300-5445
VALYL-GRAMICIDIN-A, 42210-1632
VALYL-GRAMICIDIN-B, 42210-1633
VALYL-GRAMICIDIN-C, 42210-1634
VD-844, 41220-1527
41220-1530
VD-846-B, 41220-1529
VERTICILLIN-A, 41322-1556
VERTICILLIN-A, 11-HYDROXY-, 41322-1557
VERTICILLIN-B, 41322-1557
VERTICILLIN-C, 41322-1558
VICTOMYCIN, 43320-1858
VINACTANE, 42330-1677
VINACTIN, 42330-1677
VIOCIN, 42330-1677
VIOLACETIN, 42111-1592
VIOMYCIN, 42330-1677
42330-1678
VIOMYCIN, DESLYSIL--, 42330-1679
VIOMYCIN, HYDROXY-, 42330-1684
VIRIDOMYCIN-A, 43330-1863
VIRIDOMYCIN-B, 43330-4788
VIRIDOMYCIN-C, 43330-4789
VIROCYTIN, 41321-1549
WILDFIRE TOXIN, 42120-3897
WS-1921, 41220-1531
WS-3442-A, 41212-1509
41212-1517
WS-3442-B, 41212-1516
WS-3442-C, 41212-1513
WS-3442-D, 41212-1518
WS-3442-E, 41212-1519
WS-4545, 42130-1627
X-1092, 42120-1482
X-11085, 41122-1466
X-11837, 41121-5053
X-13185, 41123-1483
X-146, 43211-1752
X-2455, 43311-1795
X-372-A, 42120-3896
X-5079-C, 43213-1772
X-73, 43130-2083
XK-33-F-2, 42330-1687
XK-49-1-B-2, 43320-1858
XK-78-1, 43320-1855
XK-78-2, 43320-1856
Y-G19Z-D3, 41212-5054
41212-5278
Y-8495, 43122-4786
YA-56-X, 43320-1851
43320-1852
YA-56-Y, 43320-1857
YEMENIMYCIN, 40000-1885
YG-19Z-D2, 41212-5874
ZAOMYCIN, 43110-1719
ZERVACIN-1, 42250-1872
ZERVACIN-2, 42250-1873
ZERVAMICIN-I, 42250-1872
ZERVAMICIN-II, 42250-1873
ZORBAMYCIN, 43320-1851
43320-1852
ZORBAMYCIN-B, 43320-1853
ZORBAMYCIN-C, 43320-1854
ZORBONAMYCIN, 43320-1851
1-AMINO-2-NITROCYCLOPENTANE CARBOXYLIC ACID, 41123-1479
1-B"-HYDROXYPROPIONYLCLAVULAVIC ACID, 41215-5081
1-S-HYDROXY-2.5.5-VALYLAMIDO-CYCLOBUTANE-1-ACETIC ACID, 42120-1482
1-337-C, 43220-1773
1.4-CYCLOHEX-ADIEN-1-ALANINE, L--, 41123-1483
102804, 42120-5417
1037, 42250-5878
106-7, 41124-1491
11-HYDROXYVERTICILLIN-A, 41322-1557
11.11-DIHYDROXYCHAETOCIN, 41322-1555
41322-1562
116-A, 43212-1767
122110, 42120-5298
12428, 43330-1868
12782, 42111-1590
42111-1597
13, 41321-1543
41321-1549
1456, 43211-1764
15620, 43330-1868
168-"GREEN PIGMENT", 43330-1866
1695, 43311-1807
1719, 41110-1457
17452, 41124-1491
17927-A1, 41214-6227
17927-A2, 41214-6228
1876-1, 43330-1862
18894, 40000-5704
2-AMINO-PENTYNOIC ACID, L--, 41121-1469
2-AMINO-3-DIMETHYLAMINO-PROPIONIC ACID, 41121-1465
2-AMINO-3.4-DIHYDROXYBUTYRIC ACID, L--, 41121-1470
2-AMINO-4-KETO-3-METHYLPENTANOIC ACID, 41121-5297
2-AMINO-4-METHYL-5-HEXENOIC ACID,
2-AMINO-4-METHOXY-TRANS-3-BUTENOIC ACID, L--, 41121-1474
41121-1467
2-AMINO-4.4-DICHLORO-BUTYRIC ACID, 41121-1464
2-HYDROXYMETHYLCLAVAM, 41215-6213
2-METHYLARGININE, 41121-5053
2-PENTENYLPENICILLIN, 41211-1500
2.3-DIAMINOSUCCINATE, 41130-1496
2.3-DICARBOXY-AZIRIDINE, S--, 41124-4782
2.5-BIS-AMINOOXYMETHYL-3.6-DIKETOPIPERAZINE, 41310-1539
2.5-DIHYDRO-PHENYLALANINE, L--, 41123-1483
2ND COMP.PHALAMYCIN, 41310-1537
21-31, 43211-1754
43211-1756
2337, 43211-1764

2814-A, 42111-1590
29275, 42330-1680
3-AMINOPROPYLAMINO-BLEOMYCIN,
43320-5692
3-BENZYL-6-HYDROXYMETHYL-1.4-DIMETHYL-3.6-EPITETRATHIOPIPERAZINE-2.6-DIONE, 41324-5679
3-BUTYL-3-AMINOPROPYL-BLEOMYCIN,
43320-5693
3-CYCLOHEXENYLGLICIN, 41123-5055
3-CYCLOHEXYLAMINOPROPYLAMINO-BLEOMYCIN,
43320-5695
3-DIETILAMINOETILAMINO-BLEOMYCIN,
43320-5694
3-EPIDEOXYNEGAMYCIN, 42120-5984
3-ISOPROPYL-2.5-DIOXO-1.4-DIAZABI-CYCLO-4.3.0-NONANE, 41310-5097
3-NN-DIMETILAMINOETILAMINO-BLEOMYCIN,
3-1-METHYL-3-AMINOPROPYL-AMINOPROPYLAMINO-BLEOMYCIN,
43320-5696
43320-5697
3.6-DIBENZYL-2.5-DIOXOPIPERAZINE,
41310-1541
300-A-B-C. 42300-1711
3008-B, 41215-5057
41215-5369
3016, 41212-1513
333-25, 43122-5192
339-29, 43100-5279
340-19-I, 43100-5638
3510, 43311-1795
43311-1802
4-AMINO-ISOOXAZOLIDONE, D--,
41124-1491
4-FORMYL-3-HYDROXYPHENYLGLYCINE,
41125-6119
4-KETO-ISOLEUCIN, 41121-5297
4-OXALYSINE, L--, 41122-1477
41012, 43110-5423
41043, 43211-5828
41494, 43211-5829
4204-A, 43123-1736
4205-A, 43123-1736
4205-B, 43123-1738
4205-C, 43123-1737
425, 43313-1817
439-A, 41121-5297
46192, 43211-6124
4738-A, 41220-1523
5066-"GREEN PIGMENT", 43330-1867
55-AB, 43200-1789
5505, 43330-1868
583, 42111-1594
5879, 42130-1627
42130-1628
5915, 41124-1491
593-A, 41310-1540
6-AMINOPENICILLANIC ACID, 41211-1497
6-APA, 41211-1497
6-DIAZO-5-OXO-L-NORLEUCIN,
60-6, 42260-3905
6604-4, 41230-1533
6741-21, 43211-1754
43211-1756
6761-31, 43211-1752
68-1147-I, 43211-5572
68-1147-II, 43211-6075
681-17, 43121-6613
41110-1455
7-B"-4-CARBOXYBUTANAMIDO-3-ACETOXY-METHYL-3-CEPHEM-4-CARBOXYLIC ACID, 41212-5334
7-B"-4-CARBOXYBUTANAMIDO-3-HYDROXY-METHYL-3-CEPHEM-4-CARBOXYLIC ACID, 41212-5333
7-B"-4CARBOXYBUTANAMIDO-3-METHYL-3-CEPHEM-4-CARBOXYLIC ACID,
41212-5332
7-GLUTARYLAMIDO-CEPHALOSPORANIC ACID,
41212-6070
7-MEHOXYCEPHALOSPORIN-C, 41212-1514
7-METHOXYDEACETYLCEPHALOSPORIN-C,
41212-5054
7-5-AMINO-5-CARBOXYPENTAMIDO-3-METHYLTHIOMETHYL-3-CEPHEM-4-CARBOXYLIC ACID, 41212-1521
7-5-AMINO-5-CARBOXYVALERAMIDO-3-METHYL-3-CEPHEM-4-CARBOXYLIC ACID. 41212-1517
7-5-AMINO-5-CARBOXYVALERAMIDO-7-METHOXY-3-HYDROXYMETHYL-3-CEPHEM-4-CARBOXYLIC ACID,
41212-5278
7543-"GREEN PIGMENT", 43330-1868
810-A, 41212-1511
810-B, 41212-1512
8217, 41124-1491
842-A, 41212-1513
845, 43200-1792
890-A1, 41214-4902
41214-6223
890-A10, 41214-5370
41214-6121
890-A2, 41214-5982
41214-6225
890-A3, 41214-6224
41214-6265
890-A5, 41214-5983
41214-6226
890-A9, 41214-4800
41214-6120
924-A1, 41214-5677

INDEX OF ANTIBIOTIC NUMBERS AND NAMES

40000 PEPTIDE/POLYPEPTIDE

40000-1874 LILACININ
40000-1875 RAMIHYPHIN-A
40000-1876 MYRORHODIN
MYRORODIN
40000-1877 LEUCINOSTATIN
40000-1878 LILACIN
40000-1881 ALMARCETIN
40000-1882 HISTIDOMYCIN-A
40000-1883 HISTIDOMYCIN-B
40000-1884 PRACTOMYCIN-C
40000-1885 YEMENIMYCIN
40000-1886 NRC-101
40000-1887 HODYDAMYCIN
40000-1888 BA-17039-A
40000-1889 RHIZOMYCIN
SF-674
40000-1890 GATAVALIN
40000-1891 BOTROCIDIN
40000-2084 N-44-A-21
40000-2100 ICI-13595
40000-2111 CRYOMYCIN-A
40000-3898 GALANTIN-II
40000-3899 GALANTIN-I
40000-4143 B-28963
40000-4380 A-43
40000-4393 GALLERIN
40000-4796 BN-1512
40000-4875 CRYOMYCIN-B
40000-5059 GARDIMYCIN
40000-5197 FR-3383
40000-5198 NRC-501
40000-5335 H-3787
40000-5455 S-19
40000-5536 SC-4
40000-5573 BN-175
40000-5574 MKOM
MONOKETOORGANOMYCIN
40000-5680 GEMINIMYCINS
40000-5704 NIFUNGIN
18894
40000-5877 BN-165
40000-5993 AM-2504
40000-5996 FR-900012
40000-6078 SF-1919
40000-6125 BN-192
40000-6126 ILEUMYCIN
40000-6218 SF-1917
40000-6219 SYRINGOTOXIN
40000-6220 SF-1908
40000-6620 CC-1014
U-53946
40000-6623 B-843

41000 AMINO ACID DERIVATIVES

41000-1495 FWH-775
41000-4005 O-2867-B"
41000-4006 O-2867-A"

41110 AZAAMINO ACID

41110-1454 AZASERIN
NSC-742
O-DIAZOACETYL-L-SERINE
41110-1455 DON
NSC-7365
6-DIAZO-5-OXO-L-NORLEUCIN
41110-1456 BA-8509-A
DIAZOMYCIN-A
DUAZOMYCIN-A
N-ACETYL-DON
NSC-51097
41110-1457 AZOTOMYCIN
BA-8509-B
DIAZOMYCIN-B
DUAZOMYCIN-B
NSC-5664
1719
41110-1458 ALAZOPEPTIN
AMBOMYCIN
BA-8509-C
DIAZOMYCIN-C
DUAZOMYCIN-C
NSC-10270
41110-1459 ALAZOPEPTIN
AMBOMYCIN
DUAZOMYCIN-C
41110-1461 OS-3256-B

41121 AMINO ACID

41121-1460 ALANOSINE
NSC-143647
41121-1464 ARMENTOMYCIN
U-10923
2-AMINO-4.4-
DICHLORO-BUTYRIC ACID
41121-1465 L-4-AZALEUCIN
2-AMINO-3-DIMETHYLAMINO-
PROPIONIC ACID
41121-1467 DEHYDROLEUCIN
U-30116
2-AMINO-4-METHYL-5-
HEXENOIC ACID
41121-1468 H-899
HON
L-D"-HYDROXY-G"-OXO-
NORVALINE
41121-1469 L-2-AMINO-PENTYNOIC ACID
PROPARGYLGLYCINE
41121-1470 L-2-AMINO-3.4-
DIHYDROXYBUTYRIC ACID
41121-1471 L-N5-1-IMINOETHYLORNITHINE
41121-1472 D"-N-HYDROXY-L-ARGININE

L-N5-HYDROXYARGININE
41121-1473 D"-N-HYDROXY-L-ARGININE
L-N5-HYDROXYARGININE
41121-1474 AMB
L-2-AMINO-4-METHOXY-
TRANS-3-BUTENOIC ACID
41121-1475 O-L-NORVALYL-5-ISOUREA
41121-1490 E-733-B
O-CARBAMYL-D-SERINE
41121-3728 N-NITROGLICIN
NITRAMINOACETIC ACID
41121-4781 HYDROXYASPARTIC ACID
L-THREO-B"-
HYDROXYASPARTIC ACID
41121-5004 L-B"-3-HYDROXYUREIDOALANINE
SF-1293-B
41121-5053 X-11837
2-METHYLARGININE
41121-5297 2-AMINO-4-KETO-3-
METHYLPENTANOIC ACID
4-KETO-ISOLEUCIN
439-A
41121-5981 KT-151

41122 AMINO ACID

41122-1466 L-2-AMINO-4-2-AMINOETHOXY-
3-BUTENOIC ACID
X-11085
41122-1476 RHIZOBITOXIN
41122-1477 L-4-OXALYSINE

41123 AMINO ACID

41123-1479 MM-27
1-AMINO-2-NITROCYCLOPENTANE
CARBOXYLIC ACID
41123-1480 CYCLOHEXENYL-1-GLYCINE
NIKKOMYCIN
41123-1481 AMYCLENOMYCIN
41123-1483 DIHY-DROPHENYLALANINE
FN-1636
L-DIHYDROPHENYLALANINE'
L-1.4-CYCLOHEX-ADIEN-
1-ALANINE
L-2.5-DIHYDRO-
PHENYLALANINE
U-15738
U-51738
X-13185
41123-1484 A-19427
AA-1
ANTICAPSIN
41123-5055 NIKKOMYCIN
3-CYCLOHEXENYLGLICIN

41124 AMINO ACID

41124-1487 AZIRINOMYCIN
41124-1488 A"-S-5-S-A"-AMINO-3-
CHLORO-2-ISOOXAZOLYNYL-5-
ACETIC ACID
AT-125
NSC-163501
U-42126
41124-1489 N-ACETYL-TYRAMINE
41124-1491 CYCLOMYCIN
CYCLOSERINE
D-4-AMINO-ISOOXAZOLIDONE
E-733-A
I-1431
K-300
NJ-21
ORIENTMYCIN
OXAMYCIN
OXYMYCIN
PA-94
RO-1-9213
SEROMYCIN
106-7
17452
5915
8217
41124-1492 FURANOMYCIN
NSC-116328
THREOMYCIN
41124-3893 A"-S-4-S-5-R-A"-AMINO-
3-CHLORO-4-HYDROXY-4.5-
DIHYDRO-5-ISOOXAZOLE
ACETIC ACID
NSC-176324
U-43795
41124-4057 L-B"-5-HYDROXY-2-
PYRIDILALANINE
SF-1346
41124-4782 S-2.3-DICARBOXY-AZIRIDINE
41124-6221 SF-1836

41125 AMINO ACID

41125-6119 FORPHENICINE
4-FORMYL-3-
HYDROXYPHENYLGLYCINE

41130 AMINO ACID ANALOG

41130-1462 HADACIDIN
NFHAA
NSC-521778
41130-1463 PRIMOCARCIN
41130-1493 ASPERGILLOMARASMIN-A
41130-1494 ASPERGILLOMARASMIN-B
LYCOMARASMIN
41130-1496 2.3-DIAMINOSUCCINATE

41211 BETA LACTAM, PENICILLIN-TYPE

41211-1497 PENICILLIN NUCLEUS
6-AMINOPENICILLANIC ACID
6-APA

41211-1498 BENZYLPENICILLIN
PARASTICIN
PENICILLIN-G
PENICILLIN-II
41211-1499 PENICILLIN-V
PHENOXYMETHYLPENICILLIN
41211-1500 FLAVICIDIN
PENICILLIN-F
PENICILLIN-I
2-PENTENYLPENICILLIN
41211-1501 HYDROXYBENXYLPENICILLIN
PENICILLIN-III
PENICILLIN-X
41211-1502 HEPTYLPENICILLIN
PENICILLIN-IV
PENICILLIN-K
41211-1503 AMYLPENICILLIN
DIHYDROPENICILLIN-F
GIGANTIC ACID
41211-1504 FLAVACIDIN
FLAVACIN
FLAVICIN
PENICILLIN
F+DIHYDROPENICILLIN
41211-1505 ALLYLMERCAPTOMETIL-
PENICILLIN
PENICILLIN-O
41211-1506 CEPHALOSPORIN-N
CEPHALOSPORIN-R
PENICILLIN-N
SALMOTIN
SYNNEMATIN-B
41211-1507 ISOCEPHALOSPORIN-N
ISOPENICILLIN-N
41211-5330 KPN
41211-5418 RIT-D-2214

41212 BETA LACTAM, CEPHALOSPORIN-TYPE

41212-1508 CEPHALOSPORIN-C
C2
F2
41212-1509 C3
DESACETOXYCEPHALOSPORIN-C
F3
WS-3442-A
41212-1510 DESACETYLCEPHALOSPORIN-C
F1
41212-1511 CEPHAMYCIN-A
810-A
41212-1512 CEPHAMYCIN-B
810-B
41212-1513 A-16886-I
CEPHAMYCIN-C
CEPHEMIMYCIN
P-6621
WS-3442-C
3016
842-A
41212-1514 A-16884
7-MEHOXYCEPHALOSPORIN-C
41212-1515 A-16886-I
CEPHAMYCIN-C
41212-1516 A-16886-II
A-8
WS-3442-B
41212-1517 DESACETOXYCEPHALOSPORIN-C
WS-3442-A
7-5-AMINO-5-
CARBOXYVALERAMIDO-3-METHYL-
3-CEPHEM-4-CARBOXYLIC ACID
41212-1518 WS-3442-D
41212-1519 WS-3442-E
41212-1520 CEPHAMYCIN-C
CEPHEMIMYCIN
41212-1521 F-1
7-5-AMINO-5-
CARBOXYPENTAMIDO-3-
METHYLTHIOMETHYL-3-CEPHEM-
4-CARBOXYLIC ACID
41212-1522 EMERICELLOPSINS
41212-3894 C-2801-X
41212-4783 SF-1623
41212-4784 N-ACETYLDEACETOXY
CEPHALOSPORIN-C
41212-5054 Y-G19Z-D3
7-METHOXYDEACETYL
CEPHALOSPORIN-C
41212-5278 Y-G19Z-D3
7-5-AMINO-5-
CARBOXYVALERAMIDO-7-
METHOXY-3-HYDROXYMETHYL-3-
CEPHEM-4-CARBOXYLIC ACID
41212-5331 C-43-219
41212-5332 C-17781A
7-B"-4CARBOXYBUTANAMIDO-
3-METHYL-3-CEPHEM-4-
CARBOXYLIC ACID
41212-5333 C-1778B
7-B"-4-CARBOXYBUTANAMIDO-
3-HYDROXY-METHYL-3-CEPHEM-
4-CARBOXYLIC ACID
41212-5531 C2
41212-5532 C4
41212-5533 C6
41212-5874 YG-19Z-D2
41212-6070 GK-340
7-GLUTARYLAMIDO-
3-ACETOXY-METHYL-3-
CEPHEM-4-CARBOXYLIC ACID
41212-5334 C-1778C
7-B"-4-CARBOXYBUTANAMIDO-
CEPHALOSPORANIC ACID

41213 BETA LACTAM, NOCARDICIN-TYPE

41213-4025 FR-1923
NOCARDICIN-COMPLEX
41213-5186 FR-1923-C
FR-2458
NOCARDICIN-A
41213-5187 FR-2458
NOCARDICIN-B
41213-5675 NOCARDICIN-E

41213-5676 NOCARDICIN-F
41213-5875 FR-29038
NOCARDICIN-C
41213-5876 FR-29055
NOCARDICIN-D
41213-5980 FR-29644
NOCARDICIN-G

41214 BETA LACTAM, THIENAMYCIN-TYPE

41214-2262 MC696-SY2-A
MM-4550
41214-4253 MC696-SY2-A
MM-4550
41214-4800 MM-13902
890-A9
41214-4902 N-ACETYL-EPI-THIENAMYCIN-A
890-A1
41214-5056 THIENAMYCIN
41214-5370 MM-17880
890-A10
41214-5677 N-ACETYL-THIENAMYCIN
924-A1
41214-5982 N-ACETYL-EPI-THIENAMYCIN-B
890-A2
41214-5983 N-ACETYL-EPI-THIENAMYCIN-D
890-A5
41214-6080 PS-5
41214-6120 890-A9
41214-6121 MM-17880
890-A10
41214-6223 "COMP.IA"
M-22380
N-ACETYL-EPI-THIENAMYCIN-A
890-A1
41214-6224 "COMP.IB"
M-22381
N-ACETYL-8-
EPI-THIENAMYCIN-C
890-A3
41214-6225 "COMP.IIA"
M-22382
N-ACETYL-EPI-THIENAMYCIN-B
890-A2
41214-6226 "COMP.II B"
M-22383
N-ACETYL-EPI-THIENAMYCIN-D
890-A5
41214-6227 17927-A1
41214-6228 17927-A2
41214-6265 N-ACETYL-8-
EPI-THIENAMYCIN-C
890-A3
41214-6568 N-ACETYL-DEHYDROTHIENAMYCIN

41215 BETA LACTAM, CLAVULANIC ACID-TYPE

41215-5057 BRL-14151
CLAVULANIC ACID
MM-14151
3008-B
41215-5081 1-B"-HYDROXYPROPIONYL-
CLAVULAVIC ACID
41215-5369 CLAVULANIC ACID
3008-B
41215-6213 2-HYDROXYMETHYLCLAVAM
41215-6610 FORMYLOXYMETHYLCLAVAM
41215-6611 CLAVAM-2-CARBOXYLIC ACID

41220 PYRROTHINE-TYPE

41220-1523 AUREOTHRICIN
FARCINICIN
M-6-62A
PROPYONYLPYRROTHIN
4738-A
41220-1524 DES-N-METHYLTHIOLUTIN
HOLOMYCIN
41220-1525 ACETOPYRROTHIN
THIOLUTIN
41220-1526 THIOMYCIN
41220-1527 B-870
HA-9
OROSOMYCIN
THIOAURIN
VD-844
41220-1528 ISOBUTYROPYRROTHIN
41220-1529 VD-846-B
41220-1530 THIOAURIN
VD-844
41220-1531 WS-1921
41220-1532 F-10-C
41220-5419 N-PROPIONYLHOLOTHIN
41220-6222 AK-PS

41230 ACTITHIAZIC ACID-TYPE

41230-1533 ACIDOMYCIN
ACTITHIAZIC ACID
CINNAMONIN
MYCOBACIDIN
PA-95
THIAZOLIDOMYCIN
THIAZOLIDONE ANTIBIOTIC
6604-4
41230-1534 A"-DEHYDROBIOTIN
LYDIMYCIN
U-15965
41230-1535 A"-MB
A"-METHYLBIOTIN
41230-1536 A"-MDB
A"-METHYL-DETHIOBIOTIN

41310 DIKETOPIPERAZINE DERIVATIVES

41310-1537 ALBONOURSIN
B-73
P-42-2
2ND COMP.PHALAMYCIN
41310-1538 MYCELIANAMIDE
41310-1539 DCS
2.5-BIS-AMINOOXYMETHYL-
3.6-DIKETOPIPERAZINE

41310-1540 NSC-135758
PIPERAZIDONE
PIPERAZINEDIONE
593-A
41310-1541 3.6-DIBENZYL-2.5-DIOXOPIPERAZINE
41310-1542 ARGLECIN
41310-4049 CYCLO-L-LEU-L-PRO
GANCIDIN-W
41310-5097 CYCLO-VAL-PRO
K-73
3-ISOPROPYL-2.5-DIOXO-1.4-DIAZABICYCLO-4.3.0-NONANE

41321 EPIDIKETOOLIGOTHIAPIPERAZINE, GLIOTOXIN-TYPE

41321-1543 ASPERGILIN
GLIOTOXIN
NSC-102866
S-82
13
41321-1544 GLIOTOXIN-MONOACETATE
41321-1546 GLIOTOXIN-B
41321-1547 DEHYDROGLIOTOXIN
41321-1549 VIROCYTIN
13
41321-1550 A-21101-III
ARANOTIN
ARIOTIN
41321-1551 ACETYL-ARANOTIN
LL-S-88-A"
41321-1552 A-21101-IV
APOARANOTIN
41321-1553 A-21101-II
ACETYLARANOTIN
LL-S-88-A"
41321-5295 EPICORAZINE-A

41322 EPIDIKETOOLIGOTHIAPIPERAZINE, CHAETOCIN-TYPE

41322-1554 CHAETOCIN
41322-1555 MELINACIDIN-IV
11.11-DIHYDROXYCHAETOCIN
41322-1556 VERTICILLIN-A
41322-1557 VERTICILLIN-B
11-HYDROXYVERTICILLIN-A
41322-1558 VERTICILLIN-C
41322-1559 MELINACIDIN
U-26362
41322-1560 MELINACIDIN-II
41322-1561 MELINACIDIN-III
41322-1562 MELINACIDIN-IV
11.11-DIHYDROXYCHAETOCIN
41322-1563 CHAETOMIN

41323 EPIDIKETOOLIGOTHIAPIPERAZINE, SPORIDESMIN-TYPE

41323-1564 SPORIDESMIN
SPORIDESMIN-A
41323-1565 SPORIDESMIN-B
41323-1566 SPORIDESMIN-C
41323-1567 SPORIDESMIN-D
41323-1568 SPORIDESMIN-E
41323-1569 SPORIDESMIN-F
41323-1570 SPORIDESMIN-G
41323-6495 SPORIDESMIN-H

41324 EPIDIKETOOLIGOTHIAPIPERAZINE, HYALODENDRIN-TYPE

41324-1571 HYALODENDRIN
41324-1572 HYALODENDRIN-II
41324-1573 A-26771-A
41324-1574 A-26771-C
41324-5679 HYALODENDRIN-III
3-BENZYL-6-HYDROXYMETHYL-1.4-DIMETHYL-3.6-EPITETRATHIOPIPERAZINE-2.6-DIONE

41325 EPIDIKETOOLIGOTHIAPIPERAZINE, SIRODESMIN-TYPE

41325-1575 SIRODESMIN-A
41325-1576 SIRODESMIN-B
41325-1577 SIRODESMIN-G
41325-1578 SIRODESMIN-J
41325-1579 SIRODESMIN-C
SIRODESMIN-F
41325-1580 SIRODESMIN-D
SIRODESMIN-F

41326 EPIDIKETOOLIGOTHIAPIPERAZINE

41326-1581 ORYZACHLORIN
41326-4785 A-30641
41326-5678 TRICHORIN-A

41330 ASPERGILLIC ACID-TYPE

41330-1582 ASPERGILLIC ACID
GRANEGILLIN
41330-1583 HYDROXYASPERGILLIC ACID
41330-1584 NEOASPERGILLIC ACID
41330-1585 MUTAASPERGILLIC ACID
41330-1586 NEOHYDROXYASPERGILLIC ACID
41330-1587 AO-3
41330-1588 PULCHERRIMINIC ACID
41330-1589 PULCHERRIMIN
PULCHERRIMINIC ACID-FE-SALT

42110 OLIGOPEPTIDE, NETROPSIN-LIKE

42110-1607 GRISEOCOCCIN
42110-1608 GRISEOCOCCIN-D

42111 OLIGOPEPTIDE, NETROPSIN-TYPE

42111-1590 CH-777-A
F-6
IA-887
K-117
NETROPSIN
SINANOMYCIN
T-1384
12782
2814-A
42111-1591 CONGOCIDIN
42111-1592 VIOLACETIN
42111-1593 EM-98
42111-1594 583
42111-1595 ANTHELVENCIN-A
42111-1596 ANTHELVENCIN-B
42111-1597 12782
42111-1598 DISTAMYCIN
DISTAMYCIN-A
STALLIMYCIN
42111-1599 S-685

42112 OLIGOPEPTIDE, NOFORMICIN-TYPE

42112-1600 MK-61
NOFORMICIN
42112-1601 AMIDINOMYCIN
M-141
MYXOVIROMYCIN

42113 OLIGOPEPTIDE, KIKUMYCIN-TYPE

42113-1602 KIKUMYCIN-A
R-719
42113-1603 KIKUMYCIN-B
42113-1604 A-4993-A
42113-1605 A-4993-B
42113-1606 AZOMULTIN
42113-3895 LL-BL-869-B"
42113-5681 LIA-0832-D

42120 OLIGOPEPTIDE

42120-1482 X-1092
1-S-HYDROXY-2.5.5-
VALYLAMIDO-CYCLOBUTANE-
1-ACETIC ACID
42120-1609 NEGAMYCIN
42120-1610 LEUCYLNEGAMYCIN
42120-1611 ACTINONIN
42120-1612 K-16
MALONOMYCIN
42120-1613 MSD-235-S2
STRAVIDIN-S2
42120-1614 MSD-235-S3
STRAVIDIN-S3
42120-1615 A-19009
FUMARYLCARBOXAMIDO-L-
2.3-DIAMINOPROIONYL-
L-ALANINE
42120-1617 BACILLIN
BACILYSIN
KM-208
TETAINE
42120-1618 BACILLIN
BACILYSIN
TETAINE
42120-1621 L-ARGINYL-D-ALLOTHREONYL-
L-PHENYLALANINE
42120-1622 FUMARYL-ALANINE
42120-1623 PHOSPHOTHRYCINYL-ALANYL-
ALANINE
SF-1293
42120-1624 PHOSPHOTHRYCINYL-ALANYL-
ALANINE
SF-1293
42120-1625 L-N5-PHOSPHONO-METHIONINE-
S-SULPHOXYMINYL-ALANYL-
ALANINE
42120-1631 MORIMYCIN
42120-2109 BACILLIN
BACILYSIN
KM-208
TETAINE
42120-3896 S-ALANYL-3-A"-S-CHLORO-3-
S-HYDROXY-2-OXO-3-
AZETIDINYLMETHYL-S-ALANINE
X-372-A
42120-3897 TABTOXIN
WILDFIRE TOXIN
42120-4940 E-64
42120-5112 FICELLOMYCIN
U-47929
42120-5188 BSA
42120-5249 FELDAMYCIN
U-48266
42120-5298 122110
42120-5417 102804
42120-5420 PLUMBEMYCIN-A
42120-5421 N-1409
PLUMBEMYCIN-B
42120-5984 3-EPIDEOXYNEGAMYCIN
42120-5985 LEUCYL-3-EPIDEOXYNEGAMYCIN
42120-5989 BESTATIN

42130 CYCLIC OLIGOPEPTIDE-LIKE, DIKETOPIPERAZINE DERIVATIVES

42130-1626 IKARUGAMYCIN
42130-1627 AIZUMYCIN
BICYCLOMYCIN
WS-4545
5879
42130-1628 AIZUMYCIN
BICYCLOMYCIN
5879
42130-5422 CAIROMYCIN-B

42210 PEPTIDE, GRAMICIDIN-TYPE

42210-1632 GRAMICIDIN-A
VALYL-GRAMICIDIN-A
42210-1633 GRAMICIDIN-B
VALYL-GRAMICIDIN-B
42210-1634 GRAMICIDIN-C

VALYL-GRAMICIDIN-C
42210-1635 GRAMICIDIN-D
42210-1636 GRAMICIDIN LIKE SUBST.
42210-1637 COLISAN
RB-103
42210-1638 ESEIN

42220 PEPTIDE, EDEIN-TYPE

42220-1639 EDEIN-A1
42220-1640 EDEIN-B1
GUANYL-EDEIN-A1
42220-1641 EDEIN-D
42220-6122 EDEIN-F

42230 PEPTIDE

42230-1642 CINNAMYCIN
NSC-71936
42230-1643 DURAMYCIN
F-17-B
NSC-71935

42240 PEPTIDE

42240-2101 STENOTHRICIN
STENOTHRICIN COMPLEX

42250 PEPTIDE, PEPTAIBOPHOL-TYPE

42250-1697 ALAMETHICIN
ALAMETHICIN-I
F-30
F-50
U-22324
42250-1701 TRICHOTOXIN-A
TRICHOTOXIN-A-40
42250-1747 ANTIAMOEBIN
STILBELLIN
42250-1748 ANTIAMOEBIN
ANTIAMOEBIN-I
STILBELLIN
42250-1869 EM-2
EMERIMICIN-II
U-40588
42250-1870 EM-3
EMERIMICIN-III
U-40589
42250-1871 EM-4
EMERIMICIN-IV
U-40590
42250-1872 ZERVACIN-1
ZERVAMICIN-I
42250-1873 ZERVACIN-2
ZERVAMICIN-II
42250-2081 SUZUKACILLIN-A
42250-2082 SUZUKACILLIN-B
42250-5193 SAMAROSPORIN
42250-5878 1037
42250-5986 ALAMETHICIN-II
42250-6071 ANTIAMOEBIN-II

42260 PEPTIDE, CEREXIN-TYPE

42260-3905 CEREXIN-A
60-6
42260-3906 CEREXIN-B
GP-3
42260-5424 CEREXIN-C
42260-5425 CEREXIN-D

42300 CYCLOPEPTIDE

42300-1661 B-344-A
42300-1662 B-344-B
42300-1696 MYCOBACILLIN
42300-1698 CHLAMYDOCIN
SL-3440
42300-1699 MALFORMIN-A1
42300-1700 MALFORMIN-B1
42300-1702 I-1
42300-1703 I-2
42300-1704 EPIDERMIDINS-A1
EPIDERMIDINS-A2
EPIDERMIDINS-B1
EPIDERMIDINS-B2
42300-1705 CEREIN-B2
42300-1707 ALBOVERTICILLIN
42300-1708 TRICULAMIN
42300-1709 A-287-A
42300-1710 A-287-B
42300-1711 300-A-B-C
42300-1712 REUMYCIN
42300-1713 ASPOCHRACIN
42300-5058 AS-N-136
42300-5191 MALFORMIN-C
42300-5445 MALFORMIN-B2
VALINE-MALFORMIN
42300-5446 GRACEILLIN
42300-6072 ISOTENTOXINE
42300-6123 CYL-2

42310 CYCLOPEPTIDE, TYROCIDINE-TYPE

42310-1664 GRAMINIC ACID
TYROCIDINE-A
42310-1665 TYROCIDINE-B
42310-1666 TYROCIDINE-C
42310-1667 TYROCIDINE-D
42310-1668 TYROCIDINE-E
42310-1669 GRAMICIDIN-J
GRAMICIDIN-S
42310-1670 GRAMICIDIN-J
GRAMICIDIN-S
42310-1671 B-456
42310-1672 BRESEIN
42310-1706 GRATIZIN

42320 CYCLOPEPTIDE, BACITRACIN-TYPE

42320-1673 AYFIVIN
BACITRACIN-A
42320-1674 BACITRACIN-B
42320-1675 BACITRACIN-C
42320-1676 BACITRACIN-F

BACITRACIN-G
BACITRACIN-X

42330 CYCLOPEPTIDE, VIOMYCIN-TYPE

42330-1677 FLORIMYCIN
KOLUOPTHISIN
PHTIOMYCIN
S-300
TUBERACTINOMYCIN-B
VINACTANE
VINACTIN
VIOCIN
VIOMYCIN
42330-1678 PHTIOMYCIN
VIOMYCIN
42330-1679 DESLYSIL-VIOMYCIN
LL-BM-547A"
42330-1680 A-250-II
CAPREOMYCIN-I-A
CAPROMYCIN
CAPSTAT
29275
42330-1681 CAPREOMYCIN-II-A
42330-1682 CAPREOMYCIN-I-B
42330-1683 CAPREOMYCIN-II-B
42330-1684 HYDROXYVIOMYCIN
TUBERACTIN
TUBERACTINOMYCIN-A
42330-1685 ENVIOMYCIN
TUBERACTINOMYCIN-N
42330-1686 TUBERACTINOMYCIN-O
42330-1687 XK-33-F-2
42330-5682 LL-BB-547-B"

42340 CYCLOPEPTIDE, ILAMYCIN-TYPE

42340-1688 ILAMYCIN
ILAMYCIN-A
RUFOMYCIN-A
42340-1689 ILAMYCIN-B
ILAMYCIN-B1+ILAMYCIN-B2
RUFOMYCIN-B
42340-1690 ILAMYCIN-C1
42340-1691 ILAMYCIN-C2
42340-1692 ILAMYCIN-A
RUFOMYCIN-A
RUFOMYCIN-III
42340-1693 RUFOMYCIN-B
RUFOMYCIN-I
42340-1694 ILAMYCIN-B1
RUFOMYCIN-B1
42340-1695 ILAMYCIN-B2
RUFOMYCIN-B2

42350 CYCLOPEPTIDE, CYCLOSPORIN-TYPE

42350-1879 RADICICOLIN
42350-4873 CYCLOSPORIN-A
S-7481-F1
42350-4874 CYCLOSPORIN-B
S-7481-F2
42350-5060 CYCLOSPORIN-C
42350-5575 CYCLOSPORIN-D
42350-5576 CYCLOSPORIN-E

43100 LIPOPEPTIDE

43100-2099 KUWAITIMYCIN
43100-2127 SAIHOCHIN-A
43100-2128 SAIHOCHIN-B
43100-5279 339-29
43100-5638 340-19-I
43100-5994 TRICHOPOLIN-A
43100-5995 TRICHOPOLIN-B
43110-1714 A-6786-52
AMPHOMYCIN
ASPARTOCIN
GLUMAMYCIN

43110 LIPOPEPTIDE, AMPHOMYCIN-TYPE

43110-1715 TSUSHIMYCIN
43110-1716 LASPARTOMYCIN
43110-1717 PARVULIN
PARVULIN-A
43110-1718 A-8999
AMPHOMYCIN
ASPARTOCIN
GLUMAMYCIN
T-3910
43110-1719 ZAOMYCIN
43110-1720 CRYSTALLOMYCIN
43110-1721 AMPHOMYCIN
ASPARTOCIN
GLUMAMYCIN
43110-5423 CP-41012
41012

43121 LIPOPEPTIDE, POLYMYXIN-TYPE

43121-1722 AEROSPORIN
POLYMYXIN-A
POLYMYXIN-M
43121-1723 POLYMYXIN-A
POLYMYXIN-M
43121-1724 POLYMYXIN-B1
43121-1725 POLYMYXIN-B2
43121-1726 POLYMYXIN-C
43121-1727 POLYMYXIN-D1
43121-1728 COLIMYCIN
COLISTIN
POLYMYXIN-E
43121-1729 POLYMYXIN-P1
43121-1730 POLYMYXIN-P2
43121-1731 BELCOMYCIN
COLIMYCIN
COLISTIN-A
COLISTINAT
POLYMYXIN-E1
43121-1732 COLISTIN-B
POLYMYXIN-E2
43121-1733 COLISTIN-C
43121-1734 CIRCULIN-A
43121-1735 CIRCULIN-B

43121-1740 THIANOSINE
43121-5683 POLYMYXIN-S1
43121-5684 POLYMYXIN-T1
43121-5991 POLYMYXIN-F1
43121-5992 POLYMYXIN-F2
43121-6073 POLYMYXIN-K
43121-6613 681-17

43122 LIPOPEPTIDE, OCTAPEPTIN-TYPE

43122-1742 E-49-A"
OCTAPEPTIN-A2
OCTAPEPTIN-A3
43122-1743 E-49-B"
OCTAPEPTIN-A1
43122-1744 E-49-G"
OCTAPEPTIN-B2
OCTAPEPTIN-B3
43122-1745 E-49-D"
OCTAPEPTIN-B1
43122-3904 BU-1880
BU-1975-B
OCTAPEPTIN
43122-4786 OCTAPEPTIN
Y-8495
43122-5061 TM-743
43122-5074 MX-A
43122-5192 OCTAPEPTIN-C1
333-25
43122-5427 AB-1

43123 LIPOPEPTIDE, POLYPEPTIN-TYPE

43123-1736 BACTERICID-4205-A
4204-A
4205-A
43123-1737 4205-C
43123-1738 4205-B
43123-1739 POLYPEPTIN-A
43123-1741 BN-7
43123-1746 JOLIPEPTIN
43123-5280 B-43
43123-5428 AB-2

43124 LIPOPEPTIDE, TRIDECAPTIN-TYPE

43124-3903 BN-109
43124-5426 AR-110
TRIDECAPTIN-A
43124-6229 TRIDECAPTIN-B
43124-6230 TRIDECAAPTIN-C

43130 PEPTIN, ECHINOCANDIN-TYPE

43130-1749 A-32204-B
ECHINOCANDIN-B
SF-7810-F
43130-2083 X-73
43130-3902 ACULEACIN COMPLEX
M-4214
43130-5017 ATHLESTAIN
43130-5063 ECHINOCANDIN-B
SL-7810-F
43130-5064 ECHINOCANDIN-C
SL-7810-FII
43130-5065 ECHINOCANDIN-D
SL-7810-FIII
43130-5066 ACULEACIN-A
43130-5067 ACULEACIN-B
43130-5068 ACULEACIN-C
43130-5069 ACULEACIN-D
43130-5070 ACULEACIN-E
43130-5071 ACULEACIN-F
43130-5072 ACULEACIN-G
43130-5075 A-32204-A
ECHINOCANDIN-A
43130-5429 S-31794-F-1
43130-5685 A-22082
A-30912-A
43130-5686 A-30912-B
43130-5687 A-30912-C
43130-5688 A-30912-D
43130-6231 ACULEACIN-A A"
43130-6232 ACULEACIN-D A"
43130-6233 ACULEACIN-A G"
43130-6234 ACULEACIN-D G"

43140 PEPTIDE, BACILLOMYCIN-TYPE

43140-1644 BACILLOMYCIN
BACILLOMYCIN-R
EUMYCIN
FUNGOCIN
ITURIN-A
43140-1645 BACILLOMYCIN-B
ITURIN-A
43140-1646 BACILLOMYCIN-C
43140-1647 TOXIMYCIN
43140-1649 BACILLOMYCIN-A
FUNGOCIN
ITURIN-A
43140-1650 "RAUBITSCHEK SUBSTANCE"
43140-1651 BACILLOCIN
43140-1652 AL-ANTIBIOTIC
43140-1653 "NANDY SUBSTANCE"
ASPERGILLUS FACTOR-II
43140-1654 POLCILLIN
43140-1655 B7-I
43140-1656 SUBSPORIN-A
43140-1657 SUBSPORIN-B
43140-1658 SUBSPORIN-C
43140-1659 A SUBST.
B7-II
43140-1660 B7-IV
43140-1663 MYCOSUBTILIN
43140-1750 BACILLOMYCIN
BACILLOMYCIN-B
BACILLOMYCIN-R
EUMYCIN
FUNGOCIN
ITURIN-A
43140-5639 "LANDY SUBSTANCE"
BACILLOMYCIN-L
43140-6074 ITURIN-C
43140-6076 BACILLOMYCIN-S

43150 PEPTIDE

43150-1751	LONGICATENAMYCIN
	S-520

43200 PEPTIDE

43200-1780	PEPTHIOMYCIN-A
43200-1781	PEPTHIOMYCIN-B
43200-1789	MICROPOLYSPORIN-AB
	55-AB
43200-1790	THERMOTHIOCIN
43200-1792	CHALCIDINES
	845
43200-5336	MC-902 COMPLEX
43200-5880	A-7413-B
43200-5881	A-7413-C
43200-5990	MC-902-I
43200-6079	L-13365
43200-6127	MC-902-I′

43211 THIAZOLYL-PEPTIDE, THIOSTREPTON-TYPE

43211-1752	A-8506
	BRYAMYCIN
	THIACTIN
	THIOSTREPTON
	X-146
	6761-31
43211-1753	BRYAMYCIN
	THIACTIN
	THIOSTREPTON
43211-1754	A-59-A
	MUTABILLICIN
	SIOMYCIN
	SIOMYCIN-A
	SPORANGIOMYCIN
	21-31
	6741-21
43211-1755	MUTABILLICIN
	SIOMYCIN-A
	SPORANGIOMYCIN
43211-1756	MUTABILLICIN
	SIOMYCIN-A
	SPORANGIOMYCIN
	21-31
	6741-21
43211-1757	SIOMYCIN-C
43211-1758	TATEMYCIN-A1
	THIOPEPTIN-A1
	THIOPEPTIN-A1A
43211-1759	THIOPEPTIN-A2
43211-1760	THIOPEPTIN-A3
	THIOPEPTIN-A3A
43211-1761	THIOPEPTIN-A4
	THIOPEPTIN-A4A
43211-1762	TATEMYCIN
	THIOPEPTIN-B
	THIOPEPTIN-BA
43211-1763	A-59-A
	SIOMYCIN-A
43211-1764	1456
	2337
43211-1765	SULFACTIN
43211-1982	MULTHIOMYCIN
	NOSIHEPTID
43211-5534	MULTHIOMYCIN
	NOSIHEPTID
	RP-9671
	TAITOMYCIN
43211-5572	SCH-18640
	68-1147-I
43211-5828	CP-41043
	41043
43211-5829	CP-41494
	41494
43211-5879	A-7413-A
43211-6075	SCH-18640-B
	68-1147-II
43211-6124	CP-46192
	46192
43211-6235	THIOPEPTIN-BB
43211-6236	THIOPEPTIN-A1B
43211-6237	THIOPEPTIN-A3B
43211-6238	THIOPEPTIN-A4B
43211-6614	S-53210-A-1
43211-6615	S-53210-A-II
43211-6616	S-53210-A-III
43211-6617	AB-97

43212 THIAZOLYL-PEPTIDE, ALTHIOMYCIN-TYPE

43212-1767	ALTHIOMYCIN
	MATAMYCIN
	116-A
43212-1768	ALTHIOMYCIN
	MATAMYCIN
43212-1769	RP-10206
43212-1770	GARLANDOSUS
	U-9279
43212-1771	ACTINOTHIOCIN

43213 THIAZOLYL-PEPTIDE

43213-1772	NSC-100844
	RO-2-7758
	SARAMYCETIN
	X-5079-C

43214 THIAZOLYL-PEPTIDE, MICROCOCCIN-TYPE

43214-1766	MICROCOCCIN
	MICROCOCCIN-P
	MICROCOCCIN-P1
43214-4872	MICROCOCCIN-M
	MICROCOCCIN-M1
43214-5194	G-15-II
	THIOCILLIN-I
43214-5195	G-15-I
	THIOCILLIN-II
43214-5196	THIOCILLIN-III
43214-6077	MICROCOCCIN-P2

43220 PEPTIDE, BOTTROMYCIN-TYPE

43220-1773 B-MYCIN
BOTTRO-MYCIN-A
BOTTROMYCIN
BOTTROMYCIN-A
METHOBOTTROMYCIN
1-337-C
43220-1774 BOTTROMYCIN-A2
43220-1775 AMETHOBOTTROMYCIN
BOTTROMYCIN-B1
43220-1776 BOTTROMYCIN-B2
43220-1777 BOTTROMYCIN-C2
43220-1778 AMETHOBOTTROMYCIN-B
BOTTROMYCIN-B1
43220-1779 BOTTROMYCIN-A1
METHOBOTTROMYCIN-C

43230 PEPTIDE, BERNINAMYCIN-TYPE

43230-1782 SULFOMYCIN-I
43230-1783 SULFOMYCIN-II
43230-1784 SULFOMYCIN-III
43230-1785 BERNINAMYCIN
BERNINAMYCIN-A
U-27810
43230-1786 THEIOMYCETIN
THERMOMYCETIN
43230-1791 PHALAMYCIN
43230-5073 BERNINAMYCIN-B

43240 PEPTIDE, LEUCINAMYCIN-TYPE

43240-1787 ARSIMYCIN
43240-1788 LEUCOPEPTIN
43240-1793 LEUCINAMYCIN
43240-1794 KOBENOMYCIN
43240-4787 NEGINAMYCIN
43240-4790 KM-8

43311 SIDEROMYCIN, ALBOMYCIN-TYPE

43311-1795 ALBOMYCIN
GRISEIN
X-2455
3510
43311-1796 ALBOMYCIN-A"
ALBOMYCIN-A4
GRISEIN-C
GRISEIN-4
43311-1797 ALBOMYCIN-A3
ALBOMYCIN-E"
GRISEIN-B
GRISEIN-3
RO-7-7731
43311-1798 ALBOMYCIN-A1
ALBOMYCIN-D"2
GRISEIN-1
RO-5-2667
43311-1799 ALBOMYCIN-A2
ALBOMYCIN-D"1
GRISEIN-A
GRISEIN-2
RO-7-7730
43311-1800 ALBOMYCIN-D"1
RO-7-7730
43311-1801 ALBOMYCIN-E"
RO-7-7731
43311-1802 ALBOMYCIN
GRISEIN
3510
43311-1803 LA-5352
43311-1804 A-418-Z4
43311-1805 ALVEOMYCIN
43311-1806 A-1787
43311-1807 1695
43311-1808 LA-5937
43311-1810 ALBOMYCIN-D"2
GRISEIN
RO-5-2667

43312 SIDEROMYCIN, FERRIMYCIN-TYPE

43312-1809 A-9578
FERRIMYCIN-A1
PILOSOMYCIN-A
43312-1811 FERRIMYCIN-A2
PILOSOMYCIN-B1
43312-1812 FERRIMYCIN-B
43312-1813 A-9578
FERRIMYCIN
PILOSOMYCIN
43312-1814 A-10073
GRISONOMYCIN

43313 SIDEROMYCIN, SUCCINIMYCIN-TYPE

43313-1815 A-22765
43313-1816 SUCCINIMYCIN
43313-1817 DANOMYCIN
425
43314-1818 GLUCONIMYCIN

43314 PSEUDOSIDEROMYCIN

43314-1819 FERRAMIDO-CHLOROMYCIN
43314-1820 ASK-753
43314-1821 NRCS-15
43314-5382 AS-N-7A

43315 SIDERAMINE

43315-1822 DESFERRI-FERRIOXAMIN-E
DESFERRI-FERRIOXAMIN-E
NOCARDAMIN
43315-1823 FERRICHROCIN
43315-1824 FERRICHRYSIN
43315-5448 TRIACETYLDESFERRIFUSIGEN
43315-5774 DESFERRIOXAMIN-B

43320 GLYCOPEPTIDE, BLEOMYCIN-TYPE

43320-1826 BLENOXANE
BLEO
BLEOMYCIN COMPLEX

43320-1827 BLEOMYCIN-A1
NSC-125066
43320-1828 BLEOMYCIN-A2
NSC-146842
43320-1829 BLEOMYCIN-A2′-B
43320-1830 BLEOMYCIN-A2′-A
43320-1831 BLEOMYCIN-A2′-C
43320-1832 DEMETHYLBLEOMYCIN-A2
43320-1833 BLEOMYCIN-A3
43320-1834 BLEOMYCIN-A4
43320-1835 BLEOMYCIN-A5
43320-1836 BLEOMYCIN-A6
43320-1837 BLEOMYCIN-B1
PHLEOMYCIN-D1
43320-1838 BLEOMYCIN-B2
DEHYDROPHLEOMYCIN-D1
PHLEOMYCIN-D2
43320-1839 BLEOMYCIN-B3
43320-1840 BLEOMYCIN-B4
DEHYDROPHLEOMYCIN-E
PHLEOMYCIN-F
43320-1841 BLEOMYCIN-B6
PHLEOMYCIN-G′
43320-1842 CU-PHLEOMYCIN COMPLEX
NSC-61586
PHLEOMYCIN
43320-1843 PHLEOMYCIN-C
43320-1844 DIHYDROBLEOMYCIN-B2
PHLEOMYCIN-D1
43320-1845 BLEOMYCIN-B2
PHLEOMYCIN-D2
43320-1846 DIHYDROBLEOMYCIN-B4
PHLEOMYCIN-E
43320-1847 BLEOMYCIN-B4
BLEOMYCIN-B5
CU-BT-5
PHLEOMYCIN-F
43320-1848 DIHYDROBLEOMYCIN-B6
PHLEOMYCIN-G
43320-1849 PHLEOMYCIN-H
43320-1850 PHLEOMYCIN-I
43320-1851 NSC-146208
U-30604
YA-56-X
ZORBAMYCIN
ZORBONAMYCIN
43320-1852 YA-56-X
ZORBAMYCIN
43320-1853 U-32166-E
ZORBAMYCIN-B
43320-1854 ZORBAMYCIN-C
43320-1855 PLATOMYCIN-A
XK-78-1
43320-1856 PLATOMYCIN-B
XK-78-2
43320-1857 YA-56-Y
43320-1858 VICTOMYCIN
XK-49-1-B-2
43320-5076 SS-70-A
43320-5077 SS-70-B
43320-5431 BU-2231-A
TALLYSOMYCIN-A
43320-5432 BU-2231-B
TALLYSOMYCIN-B
43320-5689 SF-1771
43320-5690 SF-1771-B
43320-5692 3-AMINOPROPYLAMINO-BLEOMYCIN
43320-5694 3-DIETILAMINOETILAMINO-BLEOMYCIN
43320-5693 3-BUTYL-3-AMINOPROPYL-BLEOMYCIN
43320-5695 3-CYCLOHEXYLAMINOPROPYL-AMINO-BLEOMYCIN
43320-5696 3-NN-DIMETILAMINOETIL-AMINO-BLEOMYCIN
43320-5697 3-1-METHYL-3-AMINOPROPYL-AMINOPROPYLAMINO-BLEOMYCIN
43320-6239 C-11924 F-1
43320-6353 PEP-BLEOMYCIN
43320-6618 SF-1961-A
43320-6619 SF-1961-B

43330 PEPTIDE-LIKE, CHELATE-FORMING

43330-1825 FERROVERDIN
43330-1859 MATCHAMYCIN
43330-1860 A-300-II
TRICHOSTATIN-B
43330-1861 A-300-I
TRICHOSTATIN-A
43330-1862 PROVIRIDOMYCIN
1876-1
43330-1863 VIRIDOMYCIN-A
43330-1864 IAQUIRIN-III
43330-1865 ACTINOMYCELLIN
43330-1866 168-"GREEN PIGMENT"
43330-1867 5066-"GREEN PIGMENT"
43330-1868 12428
15620
5505
7543-"GREEN PIGMENT"
43330-4788 VIRIDOMYCIN-B
43330-4789 VIRIDOMYCIN-C
43330-5698 FUSARININ
43330-6355 TRICHOSTATIN-C

INDEX OF PRODUCING ORGANISMS

ACREMONIUM CHRYSOGENUM, 41212-1513
ACREMONIUM CHRYSOGENUM+CARBOXYMETHYL-EYSTEIN, 41211-5418
ACROPHIALOPHORA LIMONISPORA, 43130-5429
ACROSTALAGMUS CINNABARINUS, 41322-1559
41322-1560
41322-1561
41322-1562
ACT.ATROOLIVACEUS, 43330-1868
ACT.BUCHANAN, 43315-1822
ACT.CHROMOGENES-GRAECUS, 42113-5681
ACT.CINEREORECTUS, 41211-1506
ACT.FULVOVIRIDIS-ACARBADICUS, 41125-6119
ACT.INTERMEDIUS, 43330-1868
ACT.MALACHITOFUSCUS, 43330-1867
ACT.MALACHITORECTUS, 43330-1867
ACT.MUTABILIS, 43211-1756
ACT.NETROPSIS, 42111-1597
ACT.ROSEOVIRIDIS, 43330-1868
ACT.ROSEUS, 43211-1765
ACT.SP., 41110-1457
42300-1712
43330-4788
ACT.STREPTOMYCINI, 43330-1866
ACT.VIRIDARIS, 43330-1862
43330-1863
43330-4788
43330-4789
ACTINOMADURA HELVATA-ANTIBIOTICA, 43211-6617
ACTINOMADURA PUSILLA, 43212-1771
ACTINOPLANES GARBADINENSIS, 40000-5059
ACTINOPLANES LIGURIAE, 40000-5059
ACTINOPLANES NIPPONENSIS, 43110-5423
ACTINOPLANES SARVEPARENSIS, 43200-6079
ACTINOPLANES SP., 43200-5880
43200-5881
43211-5879
ACTINOPLANES UTAHENSIS, 42300-1709
42300-1710
AEROBACILLUS COLISTINUS, 40000-1890
AEROBCILLUS COLISTINUS, 43123-1746
ALT.MALI, 42300-6072
ALTEROMONAS LUTEO-VIOLACEUS, 41214-4800
ANIXIOPSIS SP., 41212-1509
41212-1510
ARACHNIOTUS AUREUS, 41321-1550
41321-1552
41321-1553
ARACHNOMYCES SP., 41212-1509
ARTHRINIUM PHAEOSPERMUM, 41121-4781
ASP.ACULEATUS, 43130-3902
43130-5066
43130-5067
43130-5068
43130-5069
43130-5070
43130-5071
43130-5072
43130-6231
43130-6232
43130-6233
43130-6234
ASP.AWAMORI, 42300-1699
ASP.CHAVALLIERI, 41321-1543
41321-1548
ASP.DEFLECTUS, 43315-5448
ASP.FICUM, 42300-1699
ASP.FLAVUS, 41330-1582
41330-1583
41330-1584
41330-1586
ASP.FLAVUS-ORYZAE, 41130-1493
ASP.FUMIGATUS, 41321-1543
41321-1549
ASP.GIGANTEUS, 40000-5704
41211-1503
ASP.INDICUS, 42120-1622
ASP.JAPONICUS, 42120-4940
ASP.NIDULANS, 43130-1749
43130-5685
ASP.NIDULANS-ECHINULATUS, 43130-5075
ASP.NIGER, 41000-1495
42300-1699
42300-1700
42300-5191
42300-5445
43130-5017
ASP.OCHRACEUS, 41330-1584
41330-1587
42300-1713
ASP.ORYZAE, 41326-1581
41330-1583
41330-1585
ASP.RUGULOSUS, 43130-2083
43130-5063
43130-5064
43130-5065
43130-5685
43130-5686
43130-5687
43130-5688
ASP.SCLEROTIUM, 41330-1584
41330-1586
ASP.SOJAE, 41330-1582
41330-1583
ASP.SP., 41211-1498
41211-1500
41211-1504
43315-1823
43315-1824
ASP.TAMARII, 41326-4785
ASP.TERREUS, 41321-1551
ASP.WENTII, 41123-1479
B.AEROSPORUS, 43121-1727
B.BADIUS, 43214-5195
43214-5196

B.BREVIS, 40000-4393
42210-1633
42210-1634
42210-1635
42210-1636
42210-1638
42220-1639
42220-1640
42220-1641
42300-5446
42310-1664
42310-1665
42310-1666
42310-1668
42310-1669
42310-1670
42310-1672
42310-1706
43121-6613
B.BUNGOENSIS, 43122-4786
B.CEREUS, 40000-6125
41121-1472
41121-5297
41330-1589
42120-5417
42260-3905
42260-3906
42260-5424
42260-5425
42300-1705
43214-5194
43214-5195
B.CEREUS-MYCOIDES, 40000-4796
B.CIRCULANS, 43121-1734
43121-1735
43121-5991
43121-5992
43122-1742
43122-1744
43122-3904
43122-5061
43122-5074
43122-5192
43122-5427
43123-1739
43123-1741
43123-5280
43123-5428
B.COLISTINUS, 43121-1731
B.KRZEMIENIEWSKII, 43123-1739
B.LATEROSPORUS, 43100-5638
B.LICHENIFORMIS, 42320-1673
42320-1674
42320-1675
B.MEGATHERIUM, 43214-5194
43214-5195
B.NAGANO, 42310-1669
42310-1670
B.POLYMYXA, 43121-1722
43121-1723
43121-1724
43121-1725
43121-1726
43121-1727
43121-1728
43121-1729
43121-1730
43121-5683
43121-5684
43124-3903
43124-5426
43124-6229
43124-6230
B.POLYMYXA-COLISTINUS, 40000-1890
43121-1731
43121-1732
43123-1746
B.POLYMYXA-ROSS, 40000-5090
B.PULVIFACIENS, 40000-3898
40000-3899
B.PUMILUS, 42120-1617
43100-5279
43214-1766
B.SP., 40000-3920
40000-5573
41121-1472
41121-1475
42210-1637
42310-1664
42310-1665
42310-1666
42310-1667
42310-1669
43121-6073
43123-1736
43123-1737
43123-1738
B.SUBTILIS, 40000-5720
41123-1484
41330-1589
42120-1618
42120-2109
42120-5188
42300-1661
42300-1662
42300-1696
42310-1671
42320-1673
42320-1674
43140-1644
43140-1645
43140-1646
43140-1647
43140-1648
43140-1649
43140-1650
43140-1652
43140-1653
43140-1654
43140-1655
43140-1656
43140-1657
43140-1658
43140-1659
43140-1660
43140-1663

43140-5639
43140-6074
43140-6076
B.SUBTILIS-ANTIBLASTI, 43140-1651
B.SUBTILIS-ITURIENSIS, 43140-1750
B.SUBTILIS-NIGER, 43140-1663
B.THIAMINOLYTICUS, 43121-1740
B.VITELINUS, 43122-5074
BACTERIUM SP., 40000-1891
BOLETUS IXOCAMUS-NUDI, 41121-1467
CANDIDA PULCHERRIMA, 41330-1588
CEP.ACREMONIUM, 41211-1506
41212-1508
41212-1509
41212-1510
41212-4784
41212-5331
41212-5332
41212-5333
41212-5334
41212-5531
41212-5532
41212-5533
CEP.CHRYSOGENUM, 41212-1509
41212-5332
41212-5333
41212-5334
CEP.PIMPRINAE, 42250-1748
CEP.POLYALEURUM, 41212-5332
41212-5333
41212-5334
CEP.SALMOSYNNEMATUM, 41211-1506
CEP.SP., 41211-1506
41212-1508
41212-1509
41212-1510
41212-1521
CEPH.PIMPRINA, 42250-6071
CHAETOMIUM COCHLIODES, 41322-1563
CHAETOMIUM GLOBOSUM, 41322-1563
CHAETOMIUM MINUTUM, 41322-1554
CHAETOMIUM UMBONATUM, 41322-1563
CYLINDROCARPON LUCIDUM, 42350-4873
42350-4874
42350-5060
42350-5576
CYLINDROCARPON RADICICOLA, 42350-1879
CYLINDROCLADIUM SCOPARIUM, 42300-6123
DACTYLOSPORANGIUM VARIESPORUM,
42330-1680
42330-1681
42330-1682
42330-1683
DERMATOPHYTA, 41121-1473
DIHETEROSPORA CHLAMYDOSPORA,
42300-1698
DIHETEROSPORA SP., 41212-1509
EMERICELLOPSIS MICROSPORA, 42250-1869
42250-1870
42250-1871
EMERICELLOPSIS MINIMA, 41212-1522
EMERICELLOPSIS POONENSIS, 42250-1748
42250-6071
EMERICELLOPSIS SALMOSYNNEMATA,
42250-1748
42250-1872
42250-1873
EMERICELLOPSIS SP., 41212-1508
41212-1509
EMERICELLOPSIS SYNNEMINTICOLA,
42250-6071
EPICOCCUM NIGRUM, 41310-1541
41321-5295
FLAVOBACTERIUM ANTIBIOTICUM,
40000-6623
FUS.ARBENSE, 43330-5698
FUS.LYCOPERSICI, 41130-1494
FUS.ROSEUM, 43330-5698
FUS.SP., 40000-1875
GLIOCLADIUM FIMBRIATUM, 41321-1543
GLIOCLADIUM SP.+CEPHALOSPORIN,
41212-6070
GYLINDROCARPON LUCIDUM, 42350-5575
GYMNOASAUS SP., 41211-1497
HYALODENDRON SP., 41324-1571
41324-1572
41324-5679
KERATINOPHYTON TERREUM, 42120-1621
KITASATOA KANAENSIS, 43220-1773
MALBRANCHELLA SP., 41211-1497
MIC.ARBORENSIS, 43211-5572
43211-6075
MIC.CHALCEA, 43200-1792
MIC.SP., 40000-6078
40000-6218
MICROCOCCUS SP., 43214-1766
43214-6077
MICROELLOBOSPORIA BRUNEA, 43211-6614
43211-6615
43211-6616
MICROPOLYSPORA CAESIA, 43200-1789
MIROTHECIUM RORIDUM-MINUS, 40000-1876
MORAXELLA SP., 40000-4380
MYCOBACTERIUM TUBERCULOSIS, 41124-1489
NANIZZIA GYPSEA, 41121-1473
NOC.FORMICA, 42112-1600
NOC.FUKAYAE, 41130-1463
NOC.HISTIDANS, 40000-1882
40000-1883
NOC.MADURAE, 43200-1790
NOC.SP., 42330-1679
42330-5682
43315-1822
NOC.UNIFORMIS, 41213-5675
NOC.UNIFORMIS-TSUYAMAENSIS, 41213-5980
NOC.UNIFORMIS-TSUYAMANENSIS,
41213-4025
41213-5186
41213-5187
41213-5676
41213-5875
41213-5876
P.CHRYSOGENUM, 41211-1497
41211-1498
41211-1507
P.CINERASCENS, 41321-1543

P.FREQUENTANS, 41130-1462
P.GRISEOFULVUM, 41310-1538
P.LILACINUM, 40000-1874
40000-1877
40000-1878
P.NIGRICANS, 41310-1538
P.NOTATUM, 41211-1498
P.OBSCURUM, 41321-1543
41321-1544
41321-1545
P.OMANTIV-VIOLACEUM, 41130-1462
P.PATULUM, 41310-1538
P.PURPURESCENS, 41130-1462
P.RESTICULOSUM, 42120-1622
P.SP, 41211-1501
P.SP., 41211-1498
41211-1500
41211-1502
41211-1503
41211-1504
P.SP.+ALLYMERCAPTOACETIC ACID,
41211-1505
P.SP.+PHENOXYACETIC ACID, 41211-1499
P.TERLIKOWSKII, 41321-1543
41321-1544
41321-1546
41321-1547
P.TUBERATUM, 41324-1573
41324-1574
PAECYLOMYCES ABRUPTUS, 40000-6620
PAECYLOMYCES CARNEUS, 41211-5330
41212-1508
41212-1509
41212-1510
PAECYLOMYCES PERSICINUS, 41211-5330
41212-1509
41212-1510
PAECYLOMYCES SP., 40000-2100
41212-1509
PITHOMYCES CHARTARUM, 41323-1564
41323-1565
41323-1566
41323-1567
41323-1568
41323-1569
41323-1570
41323-6495
PLANOMONOSPORA PARONTOSPORA,

POLYPAECILIUM SP., 41211-1497
PS.AERUGINOSA, 41121-1474
PS.FLUORESCENS, 41124-1491
PS.SP., 40000-5877
41121-1490
42120-3897
43100-2127
43100-2128
PS.SYRINGAE, 40000-6219
PS.TABACI, 42120-3897
PSEUDONOCARDIA FASTIDIOSA, 43211-5828
43211-5829
RHIZOBIUM JAPONICUM, 41122-1476
S.ABIKOENSIS, 42330-1677
S.ACIDOMYCETICUS, 41230-1533
S.ACTUOSUS, 43211-5534
S.ADAINENSIS, 40000-5197
S.AIZUENSIS, 42130-1628
S.AKIYOSHIENSIS, 41121-1468
S.ALANOSINICUS, 41121-1460
S.ALBADUNCUS, 43313-1817
S.ALBOGRISEOLUS, 41212-1513
S.ALBOVERTICILLATUS, 42300-1707
S.ALBULUS, 41310-1537
S.ALBUS, 40000-1881
40000-1885
41220-1525
S.ALBUS-FUNGATUS, 41310-1537
S.ALTHIOTICUS, 43212-1767
43212-1770
S.AMAGASAKAENSIS, 43330-1859
S.AMBOFACIENS, 41110-1455
41110-1456
41110-1457
41110-1458
42111-1591
S.ANTIBIOTICUS, 41123-1480
43211-1982
S.ARENAE, 41123-1483
S.ARMENTOSUS, 41121-1464
S.ARSITIENSIS, 43240-1787
S.ATRATUS, 42340-1692
42340-1693
S.AUREOFACIENS, 43313-1815
S.AUREUS, 41124-1487
S.AVIDINII, 42120-1613
42120-1614
S.AZUREUS, 43211-1752
S.BELLUS, 43212-1768
S.BERNIENSIS, 43230-1785
43230-5073
S.BIKINIENSIS, 43320-1851
43320-1853
43320-1854
S.BIKINIENSIS-ZORBONENSIS, 43320-5691
S.BOBILAE-SPORIFICANS, 43311-1808
S.BOTTROPENSIS, 43220-1773
43220-1775
43220-1777
S.CALIFORNICUS, 42330-1677
S.CANADENSIS, 43220-1778
43220-1779
S.CANDIDUS-AZOTICUS, 41110-1458
41110-1459
41110-1461
S.CANUS, 43110-1714
S.CAPREOLUS, 42330-1680
42330-1681
42330-1682
42330-1683
S.CARNOSUS, 40000-5996
S.CATTLEYA, 41214-5056
41214-5677
41214-6265
41214-6568
S.CELLULOFLAVUS, 41220-1523
41220-1525

S.CHARTREUSIS, 41122-1477
41212-4783
41212-5278
S.CHIBAENSIS, 41124-4057
S.CHROMOGENES, 42111-1590
S.CHROMOGENES-GRAECUS, 42113-5681
S.CINEROVIRIDIS, 43230-1782
43230-1783
43230-1784
S.CINNAMONENSIS, 41230-1533
S.CINNAMONEUS, 42230-1642
43240-1793
S.CINNAMONEUS-AZACOLUTA, 42230-1643
S.CLAVULIGERUS, 41212-1515
41212-1516
41215-5057
41215-5081
41215-6213
41215-6610
41215-6611
S.COLLINUS, 42120-1615
S.CYANOFLAVUS, 41220-1523
S.DIASTATICUS, 43150-1751
S.DIASTATOCHROMOGENES, 41123-1483
S.DIASTATOCHROMOGENES-LUTEUS,
42120-1631
S.DISTALLICUS, 42111-1598
S.DOKKI, 40000-5091
S.ERYTHROCHROMOGENES, 41122-1477
43314-5382
S.FARCINICUS, 41220-1523
S.FELIS, 42120-1611
S.FICELLUS, 42120-5112
42120-5249
S.FILAMENTOSUS, 43320-6618
43320-6619
S.FILIPINENSIS-CEPHAMICINI,
41212-1513
S.FIMBRIATUS, 41212-1511
41212-1512
41212-1513
S.FLAVOCHROMOGENES, 42112-1601
S.FLAVOCHROMOGENES-IMAYAENSIS,
41220-6222
S.FLAVOGRISEUS, 41214-4902
41214-5982
41214-5983
41214-6120
41214-6121
41214-6265
S.FLORIDAE, 42330-1677
S.FRADIAE, 41121-1490
S.FRAGILIS, 41110-1454
S.FULVOVIRIDIS, 41214-6227
41214-6228
S.FULVOVIRIDUS, 41214-4253
S.FUNGICIDICUS, 41214-5677
41214-6265
S.GALILAEUS, 43312-1809
S.GANCIDICUS, 41310-4049
S.GARYPHALUS, 41124-1491
S.GOSHIKIENSIS, 42120-5984
42120-5985
S.GRAMINOFACIENS, 40000-5335
S.GRISEOFLAVUS, 43312-1809
43312-1811
43312-1812
S.GRISEOLUS-SULFOANTIBIOTICUS,
41220-1531
S.GRISEOLUTEUS, 41310-1540
S.GRISEOPLANUS, 41110-1459
41123-1484
S.GRISEOVERTICILLATUS-TUBERACTICUS,
42330-1684
42330-1685
42330-1686
S.GRISEUS, 41124-1489
41212-1511
41212-1512
41212-1513
41220-1524
42110-1607
42110-1608
43311-1795
43311-1800
43311-1801
43311-1802
43311-1810
43312-1814
S.GRISEUS-PSYCHROPHYLUS, 40000-2111
S.GRISEUS-PURPUREUS, 42330-1677
S.GRISEUS-SPIRALIS, 43110-1718
S.HACHIJOENSIS-TAKAHAZIENSIS,
43240-1788
S.HALSTEDII, 41212-1511
41212-1512
41212-1513
S.HAWAIIENSIS, 43211-1753
S.HETEROMORPHUS, 41212-1511
41212-1512
41212-3894
S.HUMIDUS-ANTITUMORIS, 43320-1852
43320-1857
S.HYGROSCOPICUS, 41121-5004
42120-1624
43330-1860
43330-1861
43330-6355
S.HYGROSCOPICUS-GELDANUS, 43315-1822
S.IAKYRUS, 43330-1864
S.INSUBTUS, 42340-1688
42340-1690
42340-1691
S.IRABENSIS, 42130-1627
S.ISLANDICUS, 42340-1688
42340-1689
42340-1690
42340-1691
42340-1695
S.JUMONJINENSIS, 41212-1520
41215-5057
41215-5369
S.KASUGAENSIS, 42112-1601
S.KENTUCKENSIS, 42113-1604
42113-1605
S.KOBENENSIS, 43240-1794

S.KUWAITINENSIS, 43100-2099
S.LACTAMDURANS, 41212-1509
41212-1513
41212-1515
S.LAURENTII, 43211-1752
S.LAVENDULAE, 40000-1884
40000-6126
41123-1481
41124-1491
41230-1533
42120-1613
42120-1614
43312-1809
S.LAVENDULAE-AMYCLENOMYCINT, 41230-1536
S.LEMENSIS, 41123-1483
S.LIPMANII, 41212-1514
41220-1527
S.LONGISPORUS-GRISEUS, 40000-1888
S.LUTEOGRISEUS, 41121-5981
41123-1483
S.LUTEORETICULI, 41220-1525
41220-1532
S.LYDICUS, 41230-1533
41230-1534
41230-1535
41230-1536
S.MATENSIS, 43212-1768
S.MEDIOLANI, 40000-1882
S.MUTABILIS, 43211-1756
S.NAGASAKIENSIS, 41124-1491
41310-1539
S.NEOCALIBERIS, 41121-1465
S.NETROPSIS, 42111-1590
42111-1597
S.NOBORITOENSIS, 42113-1606
S.NOURSEI, 41121-3728
41310-1537
43230-1791
S.NOVOVERTICILLUS, 40000-1889
S.OGANAENSIS+NA2S2O3, 41212-5874
S.OGANOENSIS, 41212-5054
S.OGANOENSIS+MERCAPTO-5-METHYL-1-1H-TETRAZOLE, 41212-5672
S.OGANOENSIS+5-MERCAPTO-1.3.4-THIADIAZOL-2-ACETYC ACID, 41212-5671
S.OGANOENSIS+5-MERCAPTO-1.3.4-THIADIAZOLE, 41212-5674
S.OGANOENSIS+5-MERCAPTO-2-METHYL-1.3.4-THIADIAZOLE, 41212-5673
S.OLIVACEUS, 41214-2262
41214-4800
41214-5370
41214-6223
41214-6224
41214-6225
41214-6226
41214-6227
41214-6228
S.OLIVOCHROMOGENES, 43313-1816
S.OLIVOGRISEUS, 43320-5076
43320-5077
S.OLIVORETICULI, 42120-5989
42330-1677
S.OLIVORETICULI-CELLULOPHYLUS, 42330-1687
S.OLIVOVIRIDIS, 43330-1862
43330-1863
S.ORCHIDACEUS, 41124-1491
S.ORIENTALIS, 42111-1594
S.PANAYENSIS, 41212-1511
41212-1512
41212-3894
S.PARVULUS, 43110-1717
S.PHAEOCHROMOGENES, 41110-1455
41220-1526
42113-1602
42113-1603
42130-1626
S.PIMPRINA, 41220-1525
41220-1528
S.PLATENSIS, 43200-5336
43200-6127
S.PLUMBEUS, 42120-5420
42120-5421
S.POLYCHROMOGENES, 41121-1490
S.PSEUDOGRISEOLUS, 43110-1715
43110-1717
S.PUNICEUS, 42330-1677
S.PURPEOCHROMOGENES, 42111-1592
S.PURPEOFUSCUS, 42120-1609
42120-1610
S.RETICULI, 42111-1590
S.RIMOSUS, 41130-1496
S.RIMOSUS-PAROMOMYCETICUS, 42120-1612
S.ROSEOCHROMOGENES, 41124-1491
41230-1533
S.ROSEOPALLIDUS, 42120-1611
S.ROSEOSPINUS, 43200-1780
43200-1781
S.ROSEOVIRIDIS, 43330-1862
43330-1863
S.ROSEUS, 43211-1765
43240-1787
S.SAPPOROENSIS, 42130-1627
S.SARACETICUS, 43213-1772
S.SCIVEUS, 41124-1488
41124-3893
S.SIOYAENSIS, 43211-1754
43211-1757
S.SP., 40000-1886
40000-1887
40000-2084
40000-4143
40000-5198
40000-5455
40000-5536
40000-5574
40000-5680
40000-5703
40000-5993
41000-4005
41000-4006
41110-1455
41121-1467
41121-1469
41121-1470
41121-1471

41121-4781
41121-5053
41122-1466
41123-1483
41124-1491
41124-1492
41124-4782
41211-1506
41212-1513
41214-6080
41220-1528
41220-1529
41220-1530
41220-5419
41310-1542
41310-4049
42111-1590
42111-1599
42112-1601
42113-3895
42120-1482
42120-1609
42120-1610
42120-1613
42120-1614
42120-1625
42130-5422
42240-2101
42300-1711
42300-1712
42300-5058
42330-1678
42330-1679
42340-1692
42340-1694
42340-1695
43110-1714
43200-5990
43211-1752
43211-1763
43211-1764
43212-1769
43220-1774
43220-1775
43220-1776
43220-1777
43230-1786
43311-1798
43311-1803
43311-1804
43311-1805
43311-1806
43311-1807
43312-1809
43312-1813
43314-1818
43314-1819
43314-1820
43314-1821
43315-1822
43315-5774
43330-1825
43330-1865

S.SP.+PARAFFIN, 40000-4875

S.STREPTOMYCINI, 43330-1866

S.SUBTROPICUS, 43311-1796
43311-1797
43311-1798
43311-1799

S.TANASHIENSIS, 41310-5097

S.TATEYAMAENSIS, 43211-6235
43211-6236
43211-6237
43211-6238

S.TATEYAMENSIS, 43211-1759
43211-1760
43211-1761
43211-1762

S.TATEYAMENSIS+N-ACETYL-METHIONINE, 43211-1758

S.TENDAE, 41123-5055

S.THIOLUTEUS, 41220-1523
41220-1525

S.TOXYTHRICINI, 41310-1542

S.TOYOCAENSIS, 43320-5689
43320-5690

S.TRICULAMINICUS, 42300-1708

S.TUMEMACERANS, 41310-1537

S.VENEZUELAE, 42111-1593
42111-1595
42111-1596

S.VERTICILLUS, 43320-1826
43320-1827
43320-1828
43320-1829
43320-1830
43320-1831
43320-1832
43320-1833
43320-1834
43320-1835
43320-1836
43320-1837
43320-1838
43320-1839
43320-1840
43320-1841
43320-1842
43320-1843
43320-1844
43320-1845
43320-1846
43320-1847
43320-1848
43320-1849
43320-1850

S.VERTICILLUS+BUTYL-AMINOPROPANE, 43320-5693

S.VERTICILLUS+CYCLOHEXYLAMINOPROPYL-AMINE, 43320-5695

S.VERTICILLUS+N-2-B"-PYRIDYL-ETHYL-1.3-DIAMINOPROPANE, 43320-6353

S.VERTICILLUS+N-3-AMINO-1-METHYLPROPYL-1.3-DIAMINOPROPAN, 43320-5697

S.VERTICILLUS+NN-DIETIL-1.2-DIAMINO-ETAN, 43320-5694

S.VERTICILLUS+NN-DIMETHYL-1.2-DI-AMINOETHAN, 43320-5696

S.VERTICILLUS+1.3-DIAMINOPROPANE,
43320-5692
S.VINACEUS, 42330-1677
S.VIOLACEAE-NIGER, 43110-1720
S.VIOLACEUS, 43110-1714
43110-1718
S.VIRGINIAE, 41230-1533
S.VIRIDARIS, 43330-1862
43330-1863
S.VIRIDOCHROMOGENES, 41212-1511
41212-1512
41212-4783
42120-1623
43110-1716
43230-1782
43230-1783
43230-1784
S.WADAYAMENSIS, 41212-1509
41212-1513
41212-1517
41212-1518
41212-1519
S.ZAOMYCELICUS, 41124-6221
S.ZAOMYCETICUS, 43110-1719
43110-1721
SACCHAROMYCES CEREVISIAE, 40000-6217
42300-1702
42300-1703
SAMAROSPORA SP., 42250-5193
SIRODESMIUM DIVERSUM, 41325-1575
41325-1576
41325-1577
41325-1578
41325-1579
41325-1580
SPIRIDONIUM SP., 41212-1509
SPOROCYTOPHAGA CAULIFORMIS,
40000-1880
STAPHYLOCOCCUS AUREUS, 43214-4872
STAPHYLOCOCCUS EPIDERMIDIS, 42300-1704
43214-4872
STAPHYLOCOCCUS SP., 40000-5337
STILBELLA SP., 42250-1747
STREPTOALLOTEICHUS HINDUSTANUS,
43320-5431
43320-5432
STREPTOSPORANGIUM ROSEUM-INCARNATUM,
43211-6124
STREPTOSPORANGIUM VIOLACEOCHROMOGENES,
43320-1858
STREPTOSPORANGIUM VIOLACEOCHROMOGENES-
GLOBOPHILUM, 43320-1855
43320-1856
STV.CINNAMONEUM, 40000-6220
43240-4787
43320-6239
STV.SP., 42330-1684
42330-1684
STV.TAITOENSIS, 43240-4790
THERMOACTINOPOLYSPORA COREMIALIS,
43200-1790
THERMOMONOSPORA VIRIDIS, 43200-1789
TILACLADIUM SP., 41211-1506
TORULA SP., 41324-1571
TRICHODERMA POLYSPORUM, 42350-4873
42350-4874
42350-5060
42350-5575
42350-5576
43100-5994
43100-5995
TRICHODERMA SP., 41326-5678
42250-6612
TRICHODERMA VIRIDAE, 41321-1543
42250-1697
42250-1701
42250-2081
42250-2082
42250-5878
42250-5986
TRICHOPHYTON INDICUM, 42120-1621
TRICHOPHYTON SP., 41211-1498
VERTICILLIUM SP., 41322-1556
41322-1557
41322-1558
VERTICILLIUM TERERUM, 41322-1555